28 a

32 / .

D1493183

A Short Course of Physical Chemistry

By the Same Author

THE KINETICS OF REACTIONS IN SOLUTIONS
Oxford University Press: 1933
Second edition: 1947

PHYSICAL CHEMISTRY: AN INTRODUCTION
Cambridge University Press: 1940   ·
Reprinted: 1947
Reprinted with corrections: 1951

PHYSICAL CHEMISTRY
Pergamon Press: 1957
Second edition: 1961
Reprinted: 1964

STATES OF MATTER
Oliver and Boyd: 1961

A Short Course of Physical Chemistry

E. A. MOELWYN-HUGHES

D.Sc. (*Liverpool*), D.Phil. (*Oxon.*), Sc.D. (*Cantab.*), F.R.I.C.

Fellow of Darwin College and University Lecturer, Cambridge

 LONGMANS

LONGMANS GREEN AND CO. LTD
48 Grosvenor Street, London, W.1

*Associated companies, branches and representatives
throughout the world*

© *E. A. Moelwyn-Hughes 1966*
First published 1966

*Set in 10 on 12 point Times New Roman
and printed by J. W. Arrowsmith Ltd., Bristol, England*

Contents

Acknowledgements

We are indebted to the following for permission to make use of copyright illustrations from the sources mentioned:

Blackie & Son Ltd., from *Atomic Physics* (1962 edition) by M. Born; Professor M. Born, from *Proc. Roy. Soc.*, A. 1934, 658 (1932); McGraw-Hill Book Company, from *Introduction to Atomic Spectra* by White and *Quantum Mechanics* by Condon and Morse; Oliver & Boyd Ltd., from *States of Matter* by A. E. Moelwyn-Hughes; Dr. A. W. Chapman and The Chemical Society, from *Journal of the Chemical Society*, 1550, 1934; and The American Chemical Society, from *J. Amer. Chem. Soc.*, 74, 4445 (1952) by Busey and Giaque, and *J. Phys. Chem.*, **61**, 518, 1957 by Moelwyn-Hughes and Missen.

Preface

Lecture courses in most branches of science are currently being modified in scope and content. The present regulations governing the natural sciences tripos at this university have been so amended as to require the candidate to sit examinations at the end of his first, second and third years. This book is an attempt to meet the needs of students reading physical chemistry in their second year. It is naturally briefer and less advanced than the text books I wrote under this title in 1940 and 1957 from both of which I have drawn freely. To these the reader may be referred for more complete versions and for detailed references to the literature.

E. A. M.-H.

The Department of Physical Chemistry,
Lensfield Road,
Cambridge.

January 1966.

I The atomic theory

Belief in the essential simplicity of things is one of the chemist's articles of faith. True, if one is to accept the recent claims of mathematicians, physicists, engineers and technologists concerning nuclear processes, doubts may arise in his mind, but these 'amongst thoughts are like bats amongst birds; they ever fly by twilight'. When more light appears, the laws yet to be established by them on nuclear reactions may prove to be as simple as those established by chemists on atomic processes. In the meantime, physical chemistry is conventionally limited to the study of material changes that can be brought about in ordinary laboratories, with temperatures reaching to a few thousand degrees, pressures to a few thousand atmospheres, and electricity to a few thousand volts. Even thus restricted, there is much to learn.

In the first place, the multitudinous things that come our way are not as multitudinous as they seem, for most of them are mixtures. Brine, for example, can easily be separated into water and a mixture of crystalline salts, which can further be separated into a small number of pure salts. By a pure substance is meant anything which cannot be further separated by such simple operations as distillation and crystallisation. Pure substances – henceforth to be called compounds – melt and freeze at the same temperature. With certain exceptions, which are easily detected, it is equally true to say that any substance which melts and freezes at the same temperature is pure. Solvents and centrifuges provide other means of resolving mixtures into their component compounds. The number of things to be examined is thus greatly reduced, but is still very large.

Pure compounds; the laws of constant and multiple proportions

Pure compounds can, by chemical rather than mechanical artifices, be further analysed into their constituents. Water, for example, can be split up by electrolysis into hydrogen and oxygen, which appear in the constant proportion (by weight) of approximately 1 to 8. Hydrogen peroxide is found to be formed of the same constituents, in the constant proportion of 1 to 16. Neither hydrogen nor oxygen can be further split up by any of the simple operations previously mentioned. They are examples of matter in elementary forms. All the pure compounds known can be broken up into elements, of which there are about 100 different kinds. Conversely, all known compounds can, at least in principle, be built up from the elements, although with complicated compounds synthesis proves to be more difficult than analysis. The law of constant proportions states that when two elements combine to form a pure compound they do so in a constant weight ratio. When two elements can unite to form more than one pure compound, the weights of one of the elements which combine with a fixed weight of the other stand in an integral ratio: this is the law of multiple proportions. The two laws form the basis of the atomic theory of matter.

The atomic theory was known to Leukippos in the sixth century B.C., and formed the subject of a celebrated ode by Lucretius; it was adopted by Boyle and used by Newton, 'but the merit of having independently elaborated a chemical atomic theory capable of co-ordinating all the known facts, and of being modified and extended with the progress of science, belongs unquestionably to John Dalton (1766–1844)' (Partington, 1933). Dalton assumed the chemical elements to be minute particles of matter – atoms – which preserve their individuality during chemical change. All atoms of the same element he regarded as identical in all respects, particularly in weight. Atoms of different elements have different weights. The absolute weight of any atom being extremely small, and in Dalton's time immeasurably small, he contented himself with finding the relative weights of the various chemical elements, taking the weight of the lightest atom (hydrogen) as unity. The atomic weight of an element is thus the ratio of the weight of an atom of that element to the weight of an atom of hydrogen. Values internationally accepted in 1961 as the atomic weights of the commoner elements are given in Table 1.1. They will be discussed later. Dalton's atomic theory is so simple that, as Lothar Meyer observed, it seems at first to be unilluminating.

The term molecule has been given to the smallest unit of a chemical compound that can have an independent existence. Molecules are thus formed by the union of atoms, in integral ratios, such as $1:1$, $1:2$, $2:3$, and so on.

Footnote to Table 1.1 on page 3.

* *Report of Commission on Atomic Weights*, Comptes rendus (1961). Those labelled † not given in this report.

Table I.1 *Atomic weights and atomic numbers of the common elements**

	Sym-bol	At. no.	At. wt.		Sym-bol	At. no.	At. wt.
Aluminium	Al	13	26·9815	Neodymium	Nd	60	144·24
Antimony	Sb	51	121·75	Neon	Ne	10	20·183
Argon	A	18	39·948	Nickel	Ni	28	58·71
Arsenic	As	33	74·9216	Niobium	Nb	41	92·906
Barium	Ba	56	137·34	Nitrogen	N	7	14·0067
Beryllium	Be	4	9·0122	Osmium	Os	76	190·2
Bismuth	Bi	83	208·980	Oxygen	O	8	15·9994
Boron	B	5	10·811	Palladium	Pd	46	106·4
Bromine	Br	35	79·909	Phosphorus	P	15	30·9738
Cadmium	Cd	48	112·40	Platinum	Pt	78	195·09
Caesium	Cs	55	132·905	Potassium	K	19	39·102
Calcium	Ca	20	40·08	Praseodymium	Pr	59	140·907
Carbon	C	6	12·01115	Protoactinium	Pa	91	231†
Cerium	Ce	58	140·12	Radium	Ra	88	226·05†
Chlorine	Cl	17	35·453	Radon	Rn	86	222†
Chromium	Cr	24	51·996	Rhenium	Re	75	186·2
Cobalt	Co	27	58·9332	Rhodium	Rh	45	102·905
Copper	Cu	29	63·54	Rubidium	Rb	37	85·47
Dysprosium	Dy	66	162·50	Ruthenium	Ru	44	101·07
Erbium	Er	68	167·26	Samarium	Sm	62	150·35
Europium	Eu	63	151·96	Scandium	Sc	21	44·956
Fluorine	F	9	18·9984	Selenium	Se	34	78·96
Gadolinium	Gd	64	157·25	Silicon	Si	14	28·086
Gallium	Ga	31	69·72	Silver	Ag	47	107·870
Germanium	Ge	32	72·59	Sodium	Na	11	22·9898
Gold	Au	79	196·967	Strontium	Sr	38	87·62
Hafnium	Hf	72	178·49	Sulphur	S	16	32·064
Helium	He	2	4·0026	Tantalum	Ta	73	180·948
Holmium	Ho	67	164·930	Tellurium	Te	52	127·60
Hydrogen	H	1	1·00797	Terbium	Tb	65	158·924
Indium	In	49	114·82	Thallium	Tl	81	204·37
Iodine	I	53	126·9044	Thorium	Th	90	232·038
Iridium	Ir	77	192·2	Thulium	Tm	69	168·934
Iron	Fe	26	55·847	Tin	Sn	50	118·69
Krypton	Kr	36	83·80	Titanium	Ti	22	47·90
Lanthanum	La	57	138·91	Tungsten	W	74	183·85
Lead	Pb	82	207·19	Uranium	U	92	238·03
Lithium	Li	3	6·939	Vanadium	V	23	50·942
Lutecium	Lu	71	174·97	Xenon	Xe	54	131·30
Magnesium	Mg	12	24·312	Ytterbium	Yb	70	173·04
Manganese	Mn	25	54·9380	Yttrium	Y	39	88·905
Mercury	Hg	80	200·59	Zinc	Zn	30	65·37
Molybdenum	Mo	42	95·94	Zirconium	Zr	40	91·22

The equivalent weight of an element is that weight which can combine with an atomic weight of hydrogen or with one-half an atomic weight of oxygen. The ratio of the atomic weight of an element to its equivalent weight is termed the valency. Atoms, therefore, have integral valencies, which experiment shows can be as high as 7, but not higher.

There is an alternative definition of atomic weight, based on Avogadro's observation that, at a common temperature and pressure, the volumes of different gases are proportional to the number of molecules in the system. The molar weight, M, of a pure compound can be defined as the weight of that compound which, in the gaseous state, exerts a pressure of one atmosphere when contained in a vessel of volume 22,415 cm^3 at the temperature of melting ice. The atomic weight of an element is then the smallest weight of it found by analysis in one molar weight of any of its compounds. The molar weights of some of the elements, notably hydrogen, nitrogen, oxygen, and the halogens – fluorine, chlorine, bromine and iodine – are found to be twice their atomic weights. Molecules of these elements in the gaseous state must therefore consist of two atoms each. For that reason, their usual symbols are H_2, N_2, O_2, F_2, Cl_2, Br_2, and I_2. This definition of molar weight is based on the assumption, which is not in fact absolutely sound, that the gases under the conditions stipulated obey the ideal gas laws, now to be discussed.

The ideal gas laws

The relation between the pressure, P, volume, V, and absolute temperature, T, of a system consisting of v molar weights of an ideal gas is

$$PV = vRT, \qquad \text{I.1}$$

where R is a universal constant, known as the gas constant. This equation summarises the laws of Boyle (product of pressure and volume of a given mass of gas is constant at a constant temperature), Charles (volume of a given mass of gas at constant pressure varies as the temperature) and Avogadro (different gases at the same pressure, volume and temperature contain the same number of molecules). The most common mistake made by beginners in physical chemistry is to omit the integer v from this equation, and thus to restrict the laws to systems containing one molar weight of gas. In the general form of the law given here

$$v = W/M$$

where W is the weight of gas in any system, and M is its molar weight. In terms of the density ($\rho = W/V$), we can clearly write

$$P = (RT/M)\rho \qquad \text{I.2}$$

showing that the pressure of an ideal gas is directly proportional to its density. In terms of the concentration ($C = v/V$), we can also write

$$P = RTC \qquad \text{I.3}$$

showing that the pressure is proportional to the concentration, i.e. to the number of molar weights per unit volume.

These laws are called the ideal gas laws because they are found to be obeyed by gases under conditions which have been regarded as ideal, i.e. at low pressures and high temperatures.

The fractional increase in the volume of any system when its temperature is raised by one degree at constant pressure is termed the coefficient of isobaric expansion, and is defined as

$$\alpha = \frac{1}{V}\left(\frac{dV}{dT}\right)_P \qquad \text{I.4}$$

The fractional decrease in volume per unit increase in pressure at a constant temperature is known as the isothermal compressibility and is defined as

$$\beta = -\frac{1}{V}\left(\frac{dV}{dP}\right)_T \qquad \text{I.5}$$

Equation I.1 makes it clear that, for ideal gases,

$$\alpha = 1/T \qquad \text{I.6}$$

$$\beta = 1/P \qquad \text{I.7}$$

Numerical values of the gas constant

Since $R = PV/vT$, and P is one atmosphere when V is 22·415 litres, when v is unity and when T is 273·16°, we have

$$R = 22{\cdot}415/273{\cdot}16 = 0{\cdot}08205 \text{ atmosphere-litre per mole-degree} \qquad \text{I.8}$$

To obtain R in absolute units, V must be expressed in cm^3, and the

5

atmospheric pressure as $1 \cdot 0132 \times 10^6$ dynes per cm^2. Then

$$R = 8 \cdot 314 \times 10^7 \text{ ergs per mole-degree.} \qquad \text{I.9}$$

On dividing by the mechanical equivalent of heat ($4 \cdot 184 \times 10^7$ ergs equal 1 calorie), we have

$$R = 1 \cdot 987 \text{ calories per mole-degree.} \qquad \text{I.10}$$

We shall find that heat capacities and molar entropies have the same dimensions as R, and may thus be expressed in the same units. The term 'entropy unit' and the abbreviation e.u. should never be used.

Experimental determinations of Avogadro's number, N_0

In order to obtain the mass, m, of one molecule from the molar weight, M, of the compound, we must know the number of molecules in one gram-mole, which is the same as the number of atoms in an atomic weight of any of the elements. This number, known as Avogadro's number or Loschmidt's number, has been found by many different methods, two of which we shall here describe.

1. *Evaluation of N_0 from the analysis of crystals by X-rays.* X-rays, which are like light rays except that their wavelengths are shorter, are reflected from the surfaces of crystals in such a way as to show that the atoms in the crystal are regularly spaced. If, for example, the crystal be divided mentally into identical cubes, it is found that, with some of the elements, such as tungsten, the centre of each cube and its eight corners are occupied by atoms. With aluminium, on the other hand, the centres of the cubes are found to be empty, but the eight corner atoms are again occupied, as are the centres of the six faces. There are many other patterns of great beauty and simplicity into which atoms arrange themselves in crystals. Such discoveries have been made possible by the application of Bragg's law to the reflection of X-rays from their surfaces.

When a ray, starting from A (Fig. I.1) reaches an atom B on the crystal surface, it is scattered in all directions. B, in other words, becomes a new centre for the propagation of the rays. The same is true of the parallel ray starting from A', which is scattered by an atom deeper down in the crystal, at the point B'. The rays emanating from the points B and B' reinforce each other in the direction of BC when the difference in their paths is an integral multiple of their

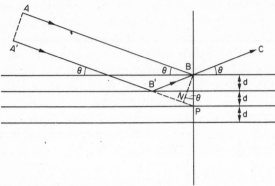

Fig. I.1 *Bragg's law of reflection*

wavelength, λ. Now the difference in path is $B'B - B'N = B'P - B'N = NP = 2d \sin \theta$, where d is the distance apart of the planes bearing the atoms, and θ is the glancing angle. The condition for reflection is thus

$$2d \sin \theta = n\lambda, \qquad \qquad \text{I.11}$$

where n is an integer. The intensest reflection occurs when θ is such an angle that $n = 1$. Less intense reflections correspond to angles θ_2, θ_3, etc., such that $2d \sin \theta_2 = 2\lambda$, $2d \sin \theta_3 = 3\lambda$, and so on. Experiments on sodium chloride yield only one value of d. In this crystal, each of the identical cubes into which it is mentally divided has all its eight corners occupied, and the centre and face-sides empty. Since only one-eighth of an atom at the corner of a cube is inside it, each unitary cube contains the substance of one atom. For this type of crystal, therefore, the molecular volume, v_m, is $2d^3$. The molar volume, V_m, is known from the density to be M/ρ. Avogadro's number is clearly V_m/v_m. Some examples are given in Table I.2.

Table I.2 *Avogadro's number from the densities and interionic distances in crystals at 20°C*

Crystal	ρ (g/cm^3)	V_m (cm^3/mole)	$d \times 10^8$ (cm)	$(N_0 = V_m/2d^3) \times 10^{-23}$
LiCl	2·068	20·50	2·572	6·207
LiBr	3·464	25·08	2·745	6·058
LiI	4·061	32·96	3·020	5·984
			Mean	6·023 ± 0·039

Since the wavelength of X-rays can be accurately measured by means of fine diffraction gratings, the method yields an absolute result. It has been found, however, that different crystals, though thoroughly pure, lead to slightly different values of N_0. The explanation is that, though the method is perfect, the crystal may not be. Experiments on diffusion in metals and on the electrical conductivity of salts indicate that the lattices in many crystals are slightly imperfect, due to the presence of a small number of holes. With the diamond and a few minerals like calcite, their number is negligible, and consistent values of Avogadro's number emerge.

2. *Evaluation of N_0 from the measurement of the electronic charge.* Faraday found that the weight of any metal deposited on a cathode during the electrolysis of any of its salts is proportional to the time of flow of the current and to the chemical equivalent weight of the metal. The quantity of electricity, $\mathfrak{F}$, required to liberate 1·008 grams of hydrogen, 31·77 grams of copper, or, in short, one gram-equivalent of any element is found to be 96 493 coulombs, or 1 faraday of electricity. These laws rank among the most accurate generalisations of science, and it may be some encouragement to young physicochemists to reflect that they were established by a man who was unfamiliar with mathematics. They indicate that electricity is made up of units, such that one unit of it will react with a sodium atom, two units with a calcium atom, three with an aluminium atom, and so on.

Classical researches on the conduction of electricity through gases proved that gaseous molecules are broken up by the discharge into positively charged particles, which retain most of the mass and travel in one direction, and into light negative particles which, in the same electrical field, naturally move in the opposite direction. The negative particles are identical in all gases, and must therefore be some substance common to all types of atoms. By studying their motion in a combined electric and magnetic field, J. J. Thomson was able to measure the ratio of the charge to the mass, e/m. This proved to be 1 837 times as great as for the smallest particle of electrically charged matter until then known, which is the positively charged hydrogen atom, i.e. the hydrogen ion. The negatively charged particles which can be obtained by the ionisation of atoms of all kind are called electrons. The charge on an electron has the same magnitude as that on the ionised hydrogen atom, but is of opposite sign. Obviously, if the magnitude of this charge can be measured, another method presents itself for determining Avogadro's number, since

$$N_0 = \mathfrak{F}/e = 96{,}493 \times (1/10) \times 2{\cdot}9979 \times 10^{10}/e$$

The factor 1/10 in the numerator converts coulombs into electromagnetic units. The velocity of light, which is the next term, converts electromagnetic into electrostatic units.

Millikan, modifying an earlier experimental method, found that minute droplets of different liquids, such as oil, glycerine and mercury, acquired the same unit charge in the process of spraying. A single charged droplet of mass m, observed through a microscope, was allowed to enter a chamber containing air, through which its rate of fall in the gravitational field was measured. An electrical field of strength E was then applied, to work with or against gravity, and the new rate of fall was measured. From the ratio of the two velocities, the electronic charge can be found. The principle of the method is simple. The external force, F, acting on the droplet is assumed to be opposed by a retarding force Cu, where C is a constant, and u is the velocity. According to Newton's second law, the equation of motion is

$$m(du/dt) = F - Cu \qquad \text{I.12}$$

The acceleration, however, soon vanishes, and a uniform terminal velocity

$$u = F/C \qquad \text{I.13}$$

is observed. In the absence of an electric field, the driving force is $F_1 = mg$, where g is the acceleration due to gravity. In the presence of an electric field acting against gravity, the driving force is $F_2 = mg - Ee$. Using the same subscripts to denote the steady velocities attained in both cases, we have, after eliminating C,

$$e = \frac{mg}{E}\left(1 - \frac{u_2}{u_1}\right) \qquad \text{I.14}$$

The mass of the droplet is measured from a knowledge of its radius and of the density of the liquid. In fields of a few thousands of volts/cm, the velocities of many of the drops are found to have the order of magnitude of 1 mm/sec.* Numerous measurements with about a

---

* It is wrong to say 'of the order of 1 millimetre per second'. The order of magnitude denotes, in powers of 10, the number of units (in this case of velocity) best suited to convey the results. The phrase 'of the order of' 11·3 electron-volts means about 11·3 electron volts. The order of magnitude in this instance is 10 electron volts, but it is pointless to say so because the result is given, with an implied precision of 1 part in 100.

thousand different drops enabled Millikan to determine the electronic charge with precision. The magnitude now accepted, after a slight revision, is

$$e = -4{\cdot}802 \times 10^{-10} \text{ e.s.u.} \qquad \text{I.15}$$

On combining with Faraday's constant, we find for the Avogadro number:

$$N_0 = 6{\cdot}024 \times 10^{23} \qquad \text{I.16}$$

This value agrees with that given by the X-ray method already described, and has been confirmed in many other ways, two of which, due to Perrin, are to be described in Chapter II.

Avogadro's number enables us to deal with the actual rather than the relative weights of atoms and molecules. The weight of a hydrogen atom, for example, is seen to be $1{\cdot}0080/N_0 = 1{\cdot}673 \times 10^{-24}$ g, and that of an electron is $9{\cdot}109 \times 10^{-28}$ g. One should note that this is the mass of the electron when at rest; its mass when moving is somewhat larger according to the theory of relativity.

The Boltzmann constant

Let us return to the ideal gas laws, $PV = vRT$, and substitute for the number of gram-moles, v, the ratio N/N_0, where N is the number of molecules in the system. Then $PV = N(R/N_0)T$, or

$$PV = NkT \qquad \text{I.17}$$

where

$$k = R/N_0 \qquad \text{I.18}$$

This important constant of nature is known as Boltzmann's constant. From the numerical value of R already derived, it is seen that

$$k = 1{\cdot}3803 \times 10^{-16} \text{ erg per molecule-degree} \qquad \text{I.19}$$

Since the molecular concentration, expressed as the number of molecules in 1 cm^3 is

$$n = N/V$$

the ideal gas laws may be written as follows:

$$P = nkT \qquad \text{I.20}$$

which is the analogue of equation I.3.

Isotopes

We have seen that the particles that travel towards the cathode in a discharge tube are the negatively charged electrons which are common to all kinds of atoms. The particles that travel towards the anode are positively charged; they move more slowly, exhibit properties peculiar to the atoms or molecules from which they are formed, and on colliding with the anode, are discharged. If, however, the anode is perforated, they penetrate it to the other side, where their movements may be studied under the combined influence of magnetic and electric fields of strength M and E respectively. Electromagnetic theory then predicts that they will hit a screen placed in their path at a point x, y on the parabola

$$\frac{y^2}{x} = K\left(\frac{H^2}{E}\right)\left(\frac{e}{m}\right) \qquad \text{I.21}$$

where K is an apparatus constant, and e/m is the charge-mass ratio. The origin of the parabola is the point on the screen which would be hit in the absence of either field. This method of analysis, perfected by Aston, is now in common use under the name of mass spectroscopy.

Experiments with chemically pure gases show that, taking the electronic charge as -1, the charges on most of the particles in the positive rays are $+1$, $+2$, and so on, in the order of diminishing intensity of the parabolic stain on the screen. Taking the mass of the hydrogen atom as 1, the values of m are found to be roughly those of the atoms or molecules forming the gas. If this were all, mass spectroscopy would merely confirm chemical analysis; but it is not all. With a gas like argon, for example, the parabola anticipated, with $m = 40$, indubitably appears, but is accompanied by two other parabolas indicating atomic weights (in these units) of 36 and 38. There are but few gases that do not behave in a similar way, and the conclusion is inevitable that elements which are chemically pure are, in fact, mixtures of atoms of two or more different kinds. Atomic chlorine, for example, with its awkward atomic weight of 35·475, proves to be a mixture of two different types of chlorine atoms, with atomic weights of 35 and 37. Atoms with identical chemical properties and different atomic weights are said to be isotopic.

Because most of the elements are isotopic mixtures, the compounds formed from them must also be mixtures. Silver chloride, for example,

11

contains four kinds of molecules, namely $Ag^{107}Cl^{35}$, $Ag^{107}Cl^{37}$, $Ag^{109}Cl^{35}$ and $Ag^{109}Cl^{37}$.

The most effective method of separating gaseous isotopes is that due to Clusius (1938). The gas is passed slowly up a number of vertical glass tubes, the walls of which are at room temperatures. Down the axis of each tube is fixed an electrically heated platinum wire. Because of the temperature gradient between the centre and the wall of each tube, thermal diffusion sets in horizontally, effecting a partial separation at all heights, since the rate of diffusion varies inversely as $m^{1/2}$. Superimposed on the thermal diffusion is the convection caused by the hot gas rising at the centre, and the cold gas descending near the wall. The joint effect is to favour the appearance of the heavy isotope at the top of each tube. With several scores of tubes running slowly for weeks, complete separation can be effected.

The usual way of denoting an isotope is to use the conventional chemical symbol of the element, with a superscript giving the atomic weight, as instanced above. With the isotope of hydrogen, however, the symbol D is commonly used to denote the heavy isotope H^2. This was discovered spectroscopically by Urey, Brickwedde and Murphy (1931), and can be prepared from heavy water (D_2O or H_2^2O) obtained by the prolonged electrolysis of ordinary water.

Isotopes have had a number of important applications, not least of which is the determination of the mechanism of chemical reactions.

Prout's hypothesis

A glance at Table I.1 reveals that many of the elements have atomic weights which are integers, or nearly integers. This fact led Prout (1815) to surmise that all elements are made, one way or another, out of hydrogen. The hypothesis seemed to lose its appeal as increasingly accurate determinations of atomic weights were made, but it can now once again be substantiated, for, when we allow for the isotopic nature of the elements, the true atomic weights are in fact very nearly integral multiples of the atomic weight of hydrogen. The key words here are 'very nearly'. If, for example, an atom of helium were to be formed by the fusion of four atoms of the light isotope of hydrogen (atomic weight 1.008 g), its atomic weight would be 4.032. Its actual atomic weight is 4·003. According to Einstein, the matter lost in the process, which amounts to 0·029 g, has been converted into energy;

and the proportionality factor relating the mass lost to the energy produced is the square of the velocity of light. Herein lies the secret of solar energy and the enormous energy exchanges attending nuclear processes.

II The kinetic theory

The kinetic theory of gases, like the atomic theory of matter, was known to the ancients, but it is chiefly to Waterston (1845), Clausius (1857) and Maxwell (1859) that we owe its quantitative formulation. According to it, gases consist of negligibly small, incompressible, perfectly elastic spheres in perpetual motion, exerting no forces on one another, and possessing an energy which is entirely kinetic. The pressure of a gas is attributed to the bombardment of the walls of the containing vessel by what Newton called the 'massy, hard, impenetrable, moveable particles'. The picture thus drawn, though now known to be incomplete, is admirably clear, and continues after a century of use to be of great service. It provides, among other things, a ready explanation of the ideal gas laws.

Let us consider N identical gas particles, either atoms or molecules, to occupy a rectangular box of length x, breadth y and height z (Fig. II.1). The velocity c of a particle at any instant can be resolved into components u, v and w resolved in the direction of the x, y and z axes, according to the equation $c^2 = u^2 + v^2 + w^2$. To compute the

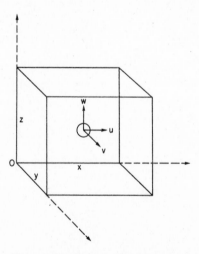

Fig. II.1 *Resolution of the velocity of a gas molecule into three components*

number of bombardments made against the right hand wall of the box, we need consider only the component u. Each of the N particles hits this wall $u/2x$ times per second, and since its momentum is in each case reversed from mu to $-mu$ the total rate of change of momentum is $N(u/2x)(2mu) = Nmu^2/x$. According to Newton's second law, this is the force exerted on the right hand side wall. Pressure is force per unit area. Hence $P = (Nmu^2/x)/yz = Nmu^2/xyz = Nmu^2/V$, where V is the volume of the box. Because we generally deal with a very large number of gas molecules, we may confidently assume that, on an average, u, v and w have all the same value. Hence

$$PV = \tfrac{1}{3}Nmc^2 \qquad \text{II.1}$$

We have seen that the ideal gas laws can be expressed as $PV = NkT$. If the kinetic theory is right, it follows that the average kinetic energy of a gas molecule is

$$\bar{\varepsilon} = \overline{\tfrac{1}{2}mc^2} = \tfrac{3}{2}kT \qquad \text{II.2}$$

The actual kinetic energy of any given gas molecule at any instant is $\tfrac{1}{2}m(u^2 + v^2 + w^2)$, which is seen to be the sum of three quadratic terms. It can be proved that, quite generally, if the total energy of a molecule can be expressed as the sum of $2s$ quadratic terms, the average energy per molecule is

$$\bar{\varepsilon} = skT \qquad \text{II.3}$$

On multiplying both sides of this equation by the Avogadro number, we see that the kinetic energy of one gram-mole of an ideal gas is

$$E = \tfrac{1}{2}Mc^2 = \tfrac{3}{2}RT \qquad \text{II.4}$$

Average velocities

The velocity of a gas molecule, which, according to these relationships, is $(3kT/m)^{1/2}$ or $(3RT/M)^{1/2}$, depends only on the temperature of the system and the molar weight of the gas. Oxygen molecules at 25°C thus travel with a velocity of 48,375 cm/sec, or approximately 1,079 miles per hour, and hydrogen molecules at the same temperature travel nearly four times as fast. Now gas molecules collide not only with the walls of their container but with one another, and due to this the velocity of any given molecule changes in magnitude and direction several times in one second. A molecule may emerge from collision

15

with its velocity enhanced or diminished, and if an instantaneous picture could be taken of the system one would find some molecules to be moving very fast and others to be momentarily at rest. A rigorous method of averaging can be applied to the problem on the assumption that the momenta of the molecules are distributed among them in a completely random fashion. It can then be shown (Appendix 3) that the mean velocity of all the molecules is

$$\bar{c} = (8kT/\pi m)^{1/2} = (8RT/\pi M)^{1/2} \qquad \text{II.5}$$

This expression gives an average velocity which is only 8·5 per cent lower than that derived in the preceding section above, but since it is exact it is the expression which we shall consistently use. Another equation of great physicochemical interest is that giving the average velocity of a gas molecule in a selected direction, say, for example, the direction of the x axis. It is

$$\bar{u} = (kT/2\pi m)^{1/2} = (RT/2\pi M)^{1/2} \qquad \text{II.6}$$

In deriving it (Appendix 3), the components of the velocity in directions at right angles to the x axis are irrelevant, and can therefore be allowed all possible values. The component of the velocity in the selected direction, however, is allowed to have positive values only, i.e. to range from zero to infinity. Clearly it is this average velocity in a particular direction that is required when dealing with the escape of particles through an orifice in the wall of the container. The ratio of the average velocities is

$$\bar{c}/\bar{u} = 4 \qquad \text{II.7}$$

The frequency of molecular collisions with a surface; the Hertz–Knudsen equation

The number of gas molecules which collide in one second with a surface of area O cm^2 can be calculated as follows. Consider a specimen of a pure gas, containing n molecules per cm^3 to occupy a parallelepiped standing on an area O cm^2 in the plane yz (Fig. II.2). Let the height of the box be $\bar{u}$ cm, where $\bar{u}$ is the magnitude of the average velocity in a direction perpendicular to the plane yz. All the molecules contained in this parallelepiped clearly reach the base in one second. Their number is evidently the product of the volume $O\bar{u}$ and the

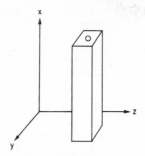

Fig. II.2 *Molecular collisions on a plane surface*

concentration n. The number of collisions made per second on an area O is thus

$$Z = On\bar{u} \qquad \text{II.8}$$

We can substitute for n the ideal gas expression $n = P/kT$ and use equation II.6 for $\bar{u}$, so that

$$Z = \frac{OP}{(2\pi mkT)^{1/2}} \qquad \text{II.9}$$

This equation, derived by Hertz (1882) and verified by Knudsen (1915), can be applied to determine the vapour pressure of a solid or a relatively involatile liquid. The validity of the method is restricted to systems where the linear dimensions of the orifice (roughly $O^{1/2}$) are at least ten times as small as the mean free path of the molecules. Since Z is the number of molecules escaping per second, the rate of loss of weight, W, of the system is Zm, so that

$$-\frac{dW}{dt} = OP(m/2\pi kT)^{1/2} \qquad \text{II.10}$$

The equilibrium pressure of the gas escaping into a vacuum is, under the conditions stipulated, the vapour pressure of the system, and is

$$P = \left(\frac{2\pi kT}{m}\right)^{1/2} \left(-\frac{1}{O}\frac{dW}{dt}\right) \qquad \text{II.10a}$$

The term in the second bracket is the rate of loss of weight scaled up to what it would be from an orifice of unit area, and can be readily determined experimentally.

There is another important application of equation II.8. Suppose the particles in the system possessed on an average an energy $\bar{\varepsilon}$ each; then the energy density is $E = n\bar{\varepsilon}$, and the rate of loss of energy from the system is $Z\bar{\varepsilon} = OE\bar{u} = \frac{1}{4}OE\bar{c}$. This is the starting point of the study of the escape of radiation from a heated body.

The frequency of binary molecular collisions

Molecules cannot react without coming into contact, and for this reason the frequency of molecular collisions is one of the factors which determine the velocity of chemical change. We shall need to know how many collisions are made, in 1 cm^3 in 1 sec, between spherical molecules of types A and B in a gaseous system where their concentrations are n_A and n_B, and their radii are r_A and r_B respectively. Let us first find the number of molecules of type B that collide in one second with one molecule of type A. From Fig. II.3, we see that it is

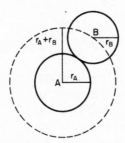

Fig. II.3 *Binary collision between spherical particles*

the number of B molecules the centres of which reach the surface of area $4\pi(r_A + r_B)^2$ in 1 second. According to equation II.8, the number is

$$_1Z_B = 4\pi(r_A + r_B)^2 n_B \left(\frac{kT}{2\pi\mu}\right)^{1/2}$$

II.11

where μ, the reduced mass of the colliding pair, is defined as follows;

$$\mu = \frac{m_A m_B}{m_A + m_B}$$

II.12

The reason for using this mass rather than that of molecule B for the

18

average velocity in a given direction (that of the line of centres) is that we are not interested in the absolute value of the velocity of molecule B in this direction, but only in its value relative to the velocity of molecule A in the same direction. The total number of collisions between molecules of type A and those of type B per cm^3 per second is the product of $_1Z_B$ and n_B. We see that it is

$$_AZ_B = n_A n_B (r_A + r_B)^2 \left[8\pi k T \left(\frac{1}{m_A} + \frac{1}{m_B} \right) \right]^{1/2} \qquad \text{II.13}$$

If molecules of type A were incomparably larger than those of type B, we could ignore $1/m_A$ in comparison with $1/m_B$, and r_B in comparison with r_A. In that case $_AZ_B$ reduces to $n_A n_B r_A^2 (8\pi k T/m_B)^{1/2}$ or $n_B . 4\pi r_A^2 n_A .$ $(kT/2\pi m_A)^{1/2}$, in agreement with the simple expression nOu. The area under these circumstances is furnished by the large molecules and the velocity determined by the small ones.

The frequency of ternary molecular collisions

Ternary collisions are naturally less frequent than binary ones, and require the instantaneous appearance of the centres of three molecules within a given volume. Such a contingency can arise when the three molecules reach the given volume independently from different directions or when one molecule encounters a pair of molecules already in contact. Most physicochemical problems dependent on ternary collisions are those in which two of the colliding molecules are identical. Various approximate expressions, such as

$$Z = n_A^2 n_B (2r_A + r_B)^2 (2r_A)^3 \left[8\pi k T \left(\frac{2}{m_A} + \frac{1}{m_B} \right) \right]^{1/2} \qquad \text{II.14}$$

can be derived for the frequency of ternary collisions. The dimensions of the frequencies of both binary and ternary collisions are those of $(\text{cm}^3\text{-sec})^{-1}$.

The mean free path

We have seen that one molecule of type A collides every second with

$$n_B \sigma_{AB}^2 \left[8\pi k T \left(\frac{1}{m_A} + \frac{1}{m_B} \right) \right]^{1/2}$$

molecules of type B. Here σ_{AB} has been written for the sum of the radii

19

$r_A + r_B$. If the molecules are identical, the number of collisions which one molecule makes per second is then $n\sigma^2[8\pi kT(2/m)]^{1/2}$ or $4n\sigma^2(\pi kT/m)^{1/2}$. This is the number of times that the free motion of a molecule is interrupted in one second. Now the mean free path can be defined as the distance gone by a molecule in a given time divided by the number of interruptions to its motion during that time. We can then write

$$\lambda = \frac{\text{Average distance travelled in one second}}{\text{Number of collisions suffered in one second}}$$

$$= \frac{(8kT/\pi m)^{1/2}}{4n\sigma^2(\pi kT/m)^{1/2}} \qquad \text{II.15}$$

$$= \frac{1}{\sqrt{2}\pi\sigma^2 n}$$

The mean free path of a molecule in an ideal gas is thus completely determined by its diameter and concentration. Now the average volume occupied by a single gas molecule is $v = V/N = 1/n$, so that

$$v = V/N = \sqrt{2}\pi\sigma^2\lambda \qquad \text{II.16}$$

We may thus regard the average volume occupied by a gas molecule as a cylinder, on a base of area πr^2 and of length $4\sqrt{2}\lambda$.

In gases under ordinary conditions, λ is several thousands of times greater than σ. On the other hand, λ in solids is less than, and in liquids is comparable with, σ.

Viscosity, thermal conductivity and diffusion

Let us suppose that the magnitude, G, of some property possessed by molecules in a gaseous system depends on the distance of the molecules from the plane xy, i.e. depends on their z coordinates. The gradient, $\partial G/\partial z$, which would be zero if the property G were uniformly distributed, now has a real value. The problem facing us is the determination of the rate at which the property G is transported through the system. To solve it, we draw, as in Fig. II.4, an imaginary plane $ABCD$ perpendicular to the z axis, and two other planes of the same area, O, above and below it and at the same distance λ away from it. If G be the magnitude of the property possessed by each molecule in the plane $ABCD$, its magnitude at a vertical distance λ below the

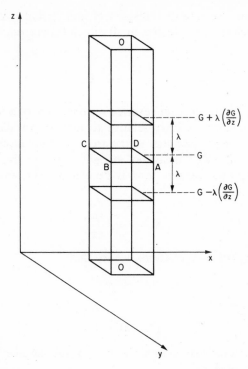

Fig. II.4 *Transport phenomena*

plane is $G - \lambda(\partial G/\partial z)$. The number of molecules reaching the plane per second from above is $nO\bar{w}$, where n is the concentration, and $\bar{w}$ is the average velocity in a selected direction, which here is the direction perpendicular to the plane. The same number of molecules reach the plane from below in the same time. The rate at which molecules transport the property from below upwards is then $nO\bar{w}\,[G - \lambda(\partial G/\partial z)]$, and the rate at which molecules transport it from above downwards is $nO\bar{w}\,[G + \lambda(\partial G/\partial z)]$. Hence the net rate of transport upwards is

$$\Gamma = -2nO\bar{w}\lambda\frac{\partial G}{\partial z} \qquad\qquad \text{II.17}$$

Let G, in the first instance, be the component of the molecular momentum mu in all directions perpendicular to the z axis. The differential coefficient $\partial G/\partial z$ now becomes $m\partial u/\partial z$, and Γ becomes the net rate of transport of this momentum. But, according to Newton's second

21

law of motion, the rate of transport of momentum is equal to the force, X, which in this case acts in all directions perpendicular to the z axis. Then

$$X = -2mnO\bar{w}\lambda \frac{\partial u}{\partial z}$$

The tangential force, or drag, exerted on one layer of a fluid when it moves with uniform velocity relative to another parallel layer has been found to be proportional to the area, O, of the layer and to the velocity gradient, $\partial u/\partial z$, measured at right angles to the direction of motion. The proportionality term is denoted by $-\eta$, and η is called the viscosity:

$$X = -\eta O \frac{\partial u}{\partial z}$$

On comparing the two equations, we see that

$$\eta = 2mn\bar{w}\lambda \qquad \text{II.18}$$

or, using equation II.7

$$\eta = (\tfrac{1}{2})mn\bar{c}\lambda \qquad \text{II.19}$$

We may substitute expressions (5) and (15) for the average velocity and free path, obtaining

$$\eta = \frac{1}{\pi\sigma^2}\left(\frac{kTm}{\pi}\right)^{1/2} \qquad \text{II.20}$$

In first deriving an expression for the viscosity of an ideal gas in terms of its temperature and of the molecular mass and diameter, Maxwell (1890) slipped by a factor of $\tfrac{2}{3}$. S. Chapman (1917) has shown that the present expression is the more exact one, but is still to be multiplied by the factor 0·998.

Let G next be the average energy of the gas molecule, which we have seen to be proportional to the temperature, so that $G = c_v T$, where the proportionality term is the heat capacity per molecule. Then $\partial G/\partial z$ is $c_v(\partial T/\partial z)$, and Γ becomes the net rate of transport of energy, so that

$$\frac{dE}{dt} = -(\tfrac{1}{2})nO\bar{c}\lambda c_v \frac{\partial T}{\partial z}$$

But thermal conductivity, κ, is defined as the amount of thermal

22

energy transported in unit time across unit area under unit (negative) temperature gradient;

$$\frac{dE}{dt} = -\kappa O \frac{\partial T}{\partial z}$$

Hence

$$\kappa = (\tfrac{1}{2})n\bar{c}\lambda c_v \qquad\qquad \text{II.21}$$

Let us finally consider an ideal gas system in which the property which depends on the z coordinates is the molecular concentration, n. At a distance λ above the reference plane it is $n + \lambda(\partial n/\partial z)$, and the rate at which molecules are transported downwards through this plane is evidently $\tfrac{1}{2}\bar{c}O[n + \lambda(\partial n/\partial z)]$. Following the same line of reasoning as before, we find that the net rate at which molecules move upwards through the plane is

$$\frac{dN}{dt} = -\tfrac{1}{2}\bar{c}O\lambda\frac{\partial n}{\partial z}$$

The coefficient of diffusion, D, is defined by Fick's first law as the number of molecules carried across unit area in unit time under unit (negative) concentration gradient, i.e.

$$\frac{dN}{dt} = -DO\frac{\partial n}{\partial z}$$

Hence

$$D = \tfrac{1}{2}\bar{c}\lambda \qquad\qquad \text{II.22}$$

The coefficients of viscosity, thermal conductivity and diffusion are closely related to one another. All three can be measured, and their approximate consonance was at one time hailed as a triumph of the kinetic theory of gases. Later developments, both experimental and theoretical, have brought out many of its inadequacies. In order to reveal and assess some of them, we shall briefly describe the kinetic theory method of determining molecular diameters, and some of the results obtained.

Determination of molecular diameters from the viscosity of gases

The Maxwell–Chapman equation II.20 enables us to determine the diameter of a gas molecule at any temperature in terms of the viscosity, η. The viscosity of a fluid, unless it is flowing very fast, can be measured by means of Poiseuille's equation, which relates the volume V of fluid expressed in t seconds through a capillary of length L and radius R with the excess pressure P on the reservoir end of the tube

$$V = \pi P R^4 t / 8 \eta L \qquad \text{II.23}$$

The rate of flow, V/t, is seen to be directly proportional to the excess pressure and to the fourth power of the radius, and inversely proportional to the length. This unusual relationship was established experimentally by Poiseuille from his clinical observations on human blood, and was later derived theoretically by Wiedemann (1856). The viscosities of some gases at the ice point are given in Table II.1, along with the diameters derived from them.

Table II.1 *Molecular diameters from the viscosity of gases at* $273 \cdot 16°K$

Gas	$\eta \times 10^4$ (g/cm-sec)	$\sigma \times 10^8$ (cm)
He	1.887	2.174
A	2.104	3·664
H_2	0·850	2·730
N_2	1·674	3.756
H_2O	0·904	4·32
CO_2	1·380	4·630
NH_3	0·944	4·416
CH_4	1·033	4·158
CH_3Cl	0·9886	5·662

These molecular diameters are internally consistent and of the correct order of magnitude. Fuller tables show that pairs of simple molecules containing the same number of electrons (the so-called isoelectronic molecules) like nitrogen and carbon monoxide, or nitrous oxide and carbon dioxide, have the same molecular diameters. In the light of knowledge gained since these figures were derived, however, we cannot but regard them as unsatisfactory. The 'diameter' of the water molecule at the ice point, for example, is much greater than the distance apart of the centres of neighbouring molecules in water or ice at the same temperature. Moreover, diameters found from diffusion coefficients differ slightly, and diameters from thermal conductivities considerably, from those derived from viscosities. More disconcerting still is the experimental conclusion that, if we accept the kinetic theory as here formulated, and regard molecules as incompressible spheres, the molecular diameters ascribed to them have different values at different temperatures. This rather detracts from the idea of a diameter.

Simple and satisfactory formulae have yet to be found to reproduce the variation, with respect to temperature, of the diameters computed on the present basis. One empirical attempt is due to W. Sutherland (1893):

$$\sigma^2 = \sigma_\infty^2 \left(1 + \frac{S}{T}\right) \qquad \text{II.24}$$

Here S is a specific constant which Rankine (1915) found to be not very different from the critical temperature, T_c. For the gases listed in Table II.1, omitting helium and hydrogen, S is 0·94 T_c to within about 10 per cent. We can regard σ_∞ as the 'diameter' at an infinite temperature. The drawbacks to this equation are its empiricism, and the implication of an infinite diameter at the absolute zero of temperature.

By and large, one must conclude that the kinetic theory of gases not only as here formulated, but with quite elaborate mathematical refinements, is in some important respects deficient.

The variation of molecular concentration with respect to height

That the air at the top of a mountain is more rarified than at its base is a fact which the kinetic theory of gases can readily explain. Let us redraw Fig. II.2, and consider a gaseous system at constant temperature in a parallelepiped of height H and in a slice of the same cross-sectional area, O, and of thickness dH, above it (Fig. II.5). If n is the number of molecules per cm^3 of gas, the number contained in this slice is $OdH.n$. These constitute a system, which can, like a massive particle, be regarded as in a state of equilibrium when the sum of all the forces acting on it is zero. The forces here are those due to the bombardment of the lower and upper faces of the slice by molecules below and above it, and the force of gravity. The pressure exerted on the bottom face is $P = nkT$, and the force exerted is therefore $OP = OnkT$. The force exerted downwards on the top face is $O(n+dn)kT$. The net kinetic force acting upwards on all the molecules in the slab is thus $-OkTdn$, and the average kinetic force acting in the positive

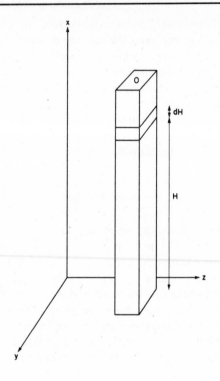

Fig. II.5

direction on a single molecule is consequently $-OkTdn/OndH = -(kT/n)(dn/dH)$. It is to be noted that the net kinetic force acting on a gas molecule is proportional to the concentration gradient, and is exerted in a direction counter to it. Now if y represents a variable, $(1/y)\,dy$ is $d\ln_e y$, where $\ln_e$ stands for the natural logarithm. We shall usually drop the subscript e, and write $\ln y$ for the natural logarithm of y. The average kinetic force on one molecule is thus $-kT(d\ln n)/dH$. The other force acting on a single molecule, again reckoned in the positive direction, is clearly $-mg$, where g is the gravitational constant. When equilibrium is established, the sum of these forces must be zero. Then

$$-kT(d\ln n/dH) - mg = 0$$

or

$$\frac{d\ln n}{dH} = -\frac{mg}{kT}$$

26

which is the required equation. On integrating it, we see that

$$\ln n = C - mgH/kT \qquad \text{II.25}$$

It is not necessary to determine the integration constant, C, for we can apply the equation to concentrations at different heights, H_1 and H_2, obtaining

$$\ln n_1 = C - mgH_1/kT$$

and

$$\ln n_2 = C - mgH_2/kT$$

from which C can be eliminated. In doing so, we recall that $\ln a - \ln b = \ln (a/b)$, and arrive at the result:

$$\ln (n_2/n_1) = (mg/kT)(H_1 - H_2) \qquad \text{II.25a}$$

This equation has been used by Perrin to determine Boltzmann's constant, k, and thence the Avogadro number, $N_0 = R/k$. Every gas molecule is invisible, even under the most powerful microscope, but a colloid particle, which is an aggregate of molecules, behaves in many respects as if it were a single molecule with a molecular weight equal to its particular weight. Perrin observed colloidal particles of mastic and of gamboge suspended in water, and counted, by means of a microscope, the numbers visible in a given area at two heights differing by 0·01 cm. The effective mass, m, of each particle is $\frac{4}{3}\pi r^3(\rho - \rho_0)$, where r is its radius, ρ its density, and ρ_0 the density of the medium. On substituting in this equation, he obtained a value for Avogadro's number which is within 12 per cent of that more securely established by later methods.

Let us replace the constant C of equation (II.25) by $\ln K$, where K is another constant, so that

$$n = K \cdot e^{-mgH/kT} \qquad \text{II.26}$$

We have here derived a particular form of a general law due to Boltzmann, according to which the concentration of molecules possessing an energy ε each is proportional to $\exp. (-\varepsilon/kT)$.

The Brownian movement

Very small particles suspended in a liquid, like the colloids studied by Perrin, are in constant and random motion. The projection of the

27

trajectories of three such particles, observed at intervals of 30 seconds, is shown in Fig. II.6. Such continual motion in haphazard directions was first recorded by R. Brown (1827) in an investigation of pollen

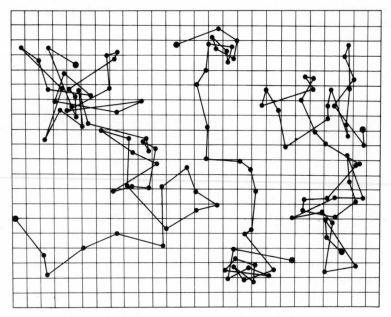

Fig. II.6   *Displacements of the Brownian movement, observed by Perrin*

grain. From the fact that this irregular and perpetual movement seems to characterise all kinds of small particles, irrespective of their weight and composition, it was argued by C. Wiener (1863) that the same type of motion is executed by molecules, although it cannot be directly observed. The so-called Brownian movement he thus attributed to the jostling of the colloid particles by repeated and chaotically oriented collisions with molecules of the solvent.

The basic law of the Brownian movement is that the average distance covered by each particle in a given time is proportional to the square-root of the time. This is an unusual feature, as the distance travelled in unimpeded motion is proportional to the time.

The first theoretical interpretation was given by Einstein (1905), as a corollary to a general theory of fluctuations. Because of the difficulty felt by many of his contemporaries in following his mathematics, he

28

obligingly provided a simple version of the same theory; and this admirably suits our purpose. Let Δ denote the magnitude of the average linear displacement suffered by a particle in time t, irrespective of its direction. The average rate of movement, to the right or the left, is thus Δ/t. The essence of the solution to the problem is to be found in the randomness of the motion. In a horizontal cylinder of unit cross section, let us imagine two adjacent compartments, each of length Δ (Fig. II.7). Let the concentrations in the left-hand and right-hand compartments be n_1 and n_2 particles per cm^3 respectively. The

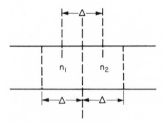

Fig. II.7 *Einstein's elementary description of linear diffusion*

number of particles crossing the central partition from left to right in one second is $\frac{1}{2}n_1(\Delta/t)$. The factor $\frac{1}{2}$ appears because the particles are as likely to move to the left as to the right. The number of particles crossing the same partition from right to left is $\frac{1}{2}n_2(\Delta/t)$. The total number of particles crossing from left to right in one second is thus

$$\frac{dN}{dt} = \frac{1}{2}\frac{(n_1-n_2)\Delta}{t}$$

But, since the centres of the two compartments are at a distance Δ apart, the concentration gradient is

$$\frac{dn}{dx} = \frac{(n_2-n_1)}{\Delta}$$

and consequently

$$\frac{dN}{dt} = -\frac{1}{2}\frac{\Delta^2}{t}\frac{dn}{dx}$$

On recalling the definition of the coefficient of diffusion, (equation

29

II.22), and remembering that the cylinder is of unit cross-section, we see that

$$D = \Delta^2/2t \qquad \text{II.27}$$

which is Einstein's law of diffusion.

Another expression for the coefficient of diffusion may be derived by considering the equation of motion of a particle of mass m under the influence of a driving force F and a force of resistance assumed to be proportional to the velocity u:

$$m(du/dt) = F - Cu$$

where C is a constant. When steady conditions have been reached, there is no acceleration, i.e. du/dt is zero, and the terminal velocity is

$$u = F/C$$

Now we have seen that, on an average, the driving force on a single molecule in a dilute system is $-kT(d \ln n/dx)$. Hence

$$u = -\frac{kT}{nC}\frac{dn}{dx}$$

The number of molecules crossing unit area in one second is $dN/dt = nu$:

$$\frac{dN}{dt} = -\frac{kT}{C}\frac{dn}{dx}$$

Hence

$$D = kT/C$$

G. G. Stokes (1856) has shown that C for spheres of radius r in a medium of viscosity η is $6\pi\eta r$. This leads to the Stokes–Einstein expression:

$$D = kT/6\pi\eta r \qquad \text{II.28}$$

On equating the two different equations derived for D, we find that

$$kT = 3\pi\eta r\Delta^2/t \qquad \text{II.29}$$

This provided Perrin with his second method of measuring k, and thence Avogadro's number, $N_0 = R/k$. Reasonable agreement was found with the results of his first method. Both his values are now regarded as of historical interest.

Other treatments of the Brownian movement

M. von Smoluchowski (1906) solved the same problem in a different way, by applying the theory of probability to the movement of a molecule subjected to successive collisions by other molecules coming at it from random directions. The linear component of the resultant motion resembles that of a man walking in a straight line but undecided, when his right foot is on the ground, whether his left is going to be placed before or after it. The problem is often referred to as that of the random walk. The theory of probability then makes it clear that the distance traversed by the man in a given time is as likely to be to the right as to the left, and in either case is proportional to the square-root of the time he has been spending in this singular way. The equation $\Delta^2 = 2Dt$ again emerges.

Langevin (1908) arrived at the same result by solving the equation of linear motion of a particle when, on an average, its kinetic energy is constant and the product of the driving force and the displacement is zero. A slight extension of his treatment leads to the solution:

$$\Delta^2 = \frac{2kTt}{C}\left[1 - \frac{m}{Ct}(1 - e^{-Ct/m})\right] \qquad \text{II.30}$$

which has the advantage that it reduces to the Einstein–Smoluchowski relationship $\Delta^2 = 2kT/C$ for long time intervals, and to the kinetic theory result $\Delta^2 = (kT/m)t^2$ for short time intervals.

Boltzmann's exponential law

We now know sufficient to realise that the simplest of physicochemical systems, such as a single crystal, a drop of liquid, or a few cubic centimetres of gas under ordinary conditions, contains an enormous number of molecules. Those in the gaseous state suffer such frequent and random collisions that their individual properties must differ widely and vary rapidly; and the problem of applying Newton's laws of motion simultaneously to each particle is inconceivably difficult. We are, however, less concerned with the properties of individual molecules than with their average properties, for these are what we generally measure. In deriving expressions for these average properties, the very enormity of the molecular population simplifies the task, for the laws of probability may be the more confidently applied; and these, as the prosperity of insurance firms proves, are the more

31

rigorous the greater the number of individuals concerned. It was Ludwig Boltzmann who first successfully applied these laws to gaseous systems. He considered a chemically pure gas consisting of a fixed number of molecules at a constant volume and temperature, and argued that its equilibrium state is that which corresponds to the most probable distribution of the total energy among all the molecules. In a simple logical argument, to be outlined in Chapter VI, Boltzmann showed that in a system at equilibrium, the number of molecules possessing an energy ε each is proportional to the factor $e^{-\varepsilon/kT}$. The particular form of this equation when $\varepsilon = mgH$ we have already derived (equation II.26). We can thus write for the number of molecules with a particular energy ε_i each

$$N_i = Ke^{-\varepsilon_i/kT}$$ II.31

where K is a constant for the system, and is usually a function of temperature. This is Boltzmann's exponential law – one of the securest generalisations of physical science.

It readily explains why so many physical and chemical properties are such that their logarithms decrease linearly with respect to the reciprocal of the absolute temperature. On taking the logarithms of both sides, we may write the equation as follows

$$\ln N_i = \ln K - \varepsilon_i/kT$$

This is the form of the laws governing the variation, with respect to temperature, of the electrical current issuing from heated metals, the vapour pressure of monatomic solids and the velocity of simple chemical change, where ε_i represents the energy required, respectively, to release an electron from the metal, to transfer an atom from the solid to the gaseous phase, and to rearrange chemical bonds.

Boltzmann's law may be expressed in another way. If a system contains N_1 molecules with energy ε_1 each, N_2 molecules with energy ε_2 each, and so on, we may write

$$N_1 = Ke^{-\varepsilon_1/kT}$$

$$N_2 = Ke^{-\varepsilon_2/kT}$$

and generally

$$N_i = Ke^{-\varepsilon_i/kT}$$

On adding all the numbers written on the left, we obtain the total number N of molecules in the system. If we then denote by Σ 'the sum of all such terms as', we may write

$$N = K\sum e^{-\varepsilon_i/kT}$$

The constant K can now be eliminated, and we arrive at the alternative form of the exponential law:

$$\frac{N_i}{N} = \frac{e^{-\varepsilon_i/kT}}{\sum e^{-\varepsilon_i/kT}} \qquad \text{II.32}$$

The ratio N_i/N may be thought of in two ways. It is, in the first place, the fraction of the total number of molecules which, in a system at equilibrium, possesses an energy of ε_i per molecule. It is also the probability that any molecule in the system, taken at random, shall possess an energy ε_i. If, for example, the fraction of Englishmen with good singing voices is 1/100, then the probability that any Englishman encountered at random shall be found to have a good singing voice is also 1/100.

Let us apply this law to obtain an equation for the average energy of a molecule. The total energy of the system is clearly

$$E = N_1\varepsilon_1 + N_2\varepsilon_2 + \cdots = \sum N_i\varepsilon_i$$

and the average energy of a molecule is

$$\bar{\varepsilon} = \frac{E}{N} = \frac{N_1}{N}\varepsilon_1 + \frac{N_2}{N}\varepsilon_2 + \cdots = \frac{\sum N_i\varepsilon_i}{N}$$

On substituting Boltzmann's expression for the various number ratios, we see that

$$\bar{\varepsilon} = \frac{\sum e^{-\varepsilon_i/kT}\varepsilon_i}{\sum e^{-\varepsilon_i/kT}} \qquad \text{II.33}$$

The Maxwell–Boltzmann distribution law

Maxwell in England and Boltzmann in Germany independently and simultaneously examined the distribution of properties among ideal gas molecules, assuming the energy to be entirely kinetic, so that

$$\varepsilon = \tfrac{1}{2}mc^2 = \tfrac{1}{2}m(u^2 + v^2 + w^2) \doteq \left(\frac{1}{2m}\right)(p_x^2 + p_y^2 + p_z^2) \qquad \text{II.34}$$

where u, v and w are the components of the velocity resolved in the x, y and z directions (Fig. II.1), and p_x, p_y and p_z are the components of the corresponding momenta. The fraction of the total number of

B*

33

molecules with energy ε each is, according to the exponential law, proportional to $\exp(-\varepsilon/kT)$. We now, however, want to know how many molecules possess this energy apiece, while having components of momenta lying within the region between p_x and $p_x + dp_x$, between p_y and $p_y + dp_y$ and between p_z and $p_z + dp_z$. This fraction is naturally smaller than N_i/N, and will be denoted by dN/N. It must also be proportional to the volume-like element $dp_x dp_y dp_z$. The argument underlying this step is the very simple one that the chance of finding a man roaming freely within a given area is proportional to the extent of that area. Denoting the proportionality factor by C, we then have

$$dN/N = Ce^{-\varepsilon/kT} dp_x \, dp_y \, dp_z$$

Both sides of this equation are now to be integrated. The left-hand side, integrated over all the molecules in the system, is clearly unity. The right hand side must be integrated over all values of the momenta from minus infinity to plus infinity. Then

$$C = \frac{1}{\iiint_{-\infty}^{\infty} e^{-\varepsilon/kT} \, dp_x \, dp_y \, dp_z}$$

After eliminating C, we obtain the distribution law in the form

$$\frac{dN}{N} = \frac{e^{-\varepsilon/kT} \, dp_x \, dp_y \, dp_z}{\iiint_{-\infty}^{\infty} e^{-\varepsilon/kT} \, dp_x \, dp_y \, dp_z}$$

On changing the variables and performing the integrations (Appendix 3), we obtain, for the fraction of the molecules with energies lying between ε and $\varepsilon + d\varepsilon$,

$$\frac{dN}{N} = \frac{2e^{-\varepsilon/kT} \varepsilon^{1/2} \, d\varepsilon}{\pi^{1/2}(kT)^{3/2}} \qquad \text{II.35}$$

and for the fraction of the molecules with velocities lying between c and $c + dc$,

$$\frac{dN}{N} = \left(\frac{2}{\pi}\right)^{1/2} \left(\frac{m}{kT}\right)^{3/2} e^{-(\frac{1}{2})(mc^2/kT)} c^2 \, dc \qquad \text{II.36}$$

which are the laws of the distribution of energy and velocity derived respectively by Boltzmann and Maxwell.

34

Statistical averaging

To specify the position of the centre of gravity of a molecule, we must state the values of the positional coordinates x, y and z. To define its energy and the direction of motion of its centre of gravity, we must know the values of the momental coordinates p_x, p_y and p_z. When the magnitude of these six variables is known the state of an atom is completely defined. The complete definition of the state of a molecule calls for further information on the magnitude of variables in terms of which the relative position and motion of the atoms within the molecule may be described. Let the total number of positional variables necessary be s. Connected with each is a momentum variable. On generalising the argument of the preceding section, we may now express the distribution law as follows;

$$\frac{dN}{N} = \frac{e^{-\varepsilon/kT} \, dq_1 \, dq_2 \, dq_3 \ldots dq_s . \, dp_1 \, dp_2 \, dp_3 \ldots dp_s}{\iint_{-\infty}^{\infty} e^{-\varepsilon/kT} \, dq_1 \, dq_2 \, dq_3 \ldots dq_s . \, dp_1 \, dp_2 \, dp_3 \ldots dp_s} \qquad \text{II.37}$$

where q is a positional coordinate, p the conjugated momental coordinate, and s is the total number of either kind required completely to specify the state of the molecule.

Now the average value, $\bar{P}$, of any property, P, which is governed by the coordinates of position and momentum, may be obtained by multiplying the number of molecules in each energy group by the extent to which each molecule in that group possesses the property, by adding together all such products, and by dividing the sum by the total number of molecules:

$$\bar{P} = \frac{\int P \, dN}{N} = \int P \frac{dN}{N} \qquad \text{II.38}$$

Hence

$$\bar{P} = \frac{\int \ldots \int_{-\infty}^{\infty} e^{-\varepsilon/kT} . P . dq_1 \ldots dp_s}{\int \ldots \int_{-\infty}^{\infty} e^{-\varepsilon/kT} . dq_1 \ldots dp_s} \qquad \text{II.39}$$

This general equation is applied in Appendix 3 to ideal gas molecules, for which s is 3, with the following results:

Property, P	Symbol	Range	Average value, $\bar{P}$
Velocity in a given direction	u	0 to ∞	$(kT/2\pi m)^{1/2}$
Velocity in space	c	0 to ∞	$(8kT/\pi m)^{1/2}$
Component of kinetic energy in one dimension	$(\tfrac{1}{2})mu^2$	0 to ∞	$(\tfrac{1}{2})kT$
Total kinetic energy	$(\tfrac{1}{2})m(u^2+v^2+w^2)$	0 to ∞	$(3/2)kT$

The last two expressions are special cases of the general equation 3, according to which the average energy per molecule is skT, provided the energy of a single molecule can be expressed as the sum of $2s$ quadratic terms. It will be shown later that this conclusion is valid only when molecular motions obey the laws of classical, as distinct from those of quantal, mechanics.

Simple molecular models

Molecules are not point particles. They are not even incompressible spheres although with monatomic molecules like those of the inert elements this model is a fair approximation to the truth. Organic chemistry has proved that molecules have definite structures, built of atoms held together by chemical bonds. Each type of molecule has its own architecture. The determination of molecular structure is one of the main tasks of organic chemistry. The determination of molecular stability is one of the main tasks of physical chemistry. We shall here consider diatomic molecules only, and those motions which, in addition to the translation of the mass centre, they can execute.

The rigid planar diatomic rotator

Let the atoms in a diatomic molecule have masses m_1 and m_2, and let their centres be separated by a constant distance, a, which is the sum of their separate distances, r_1 and r_2, from the centre of gravity, O, of the molecule (Fig. II.8). Then $a = r_1 + r_2$. On taking moments about O, we have $m_1 r_1 = m_2 r_2$, so that

$$r_1 = \frac{m_2}{m_1 + m_2} a$$

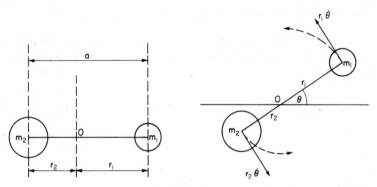

Fig. II.8 *The rigid diatomic rotator, (1) at rest, (2) rotating about its centre of gravity and in the plane of the paper*

and

$$r_2 = \frac{m_1}{m_1+m_2}a$$

The moment of inertia about any axis passing through the centre of gravity at right angles to the molecular axis is, by definition,

$$I = m_1 r_1^2 + m_2 r_2^2$$

On eliminating r_1 and r_2, we see that

$$I = \left(\frac{m_1 m_2}{m_1+m_2}\right)a^2 = \mu a^2 \qquad \text{II.40}$$

where μ is the reduced mass of the molecule (equation II.12). If the atoms in the molecule are at a constant distance apart, and the molecule itself is not subject to external forces, the only energy it can possess (in addition to the energy associated with the movement of its centre of gravity) is that due to the rotation of the atoms about the centre of gravity, which is

$$\varepsilon = \tfrac{1}{2}m_1 v_1^2 + \tfrac{1}{2}m_2 v_2^2$$

where v_1 and v_2 are the velocities of the atoms in the circles which they describe about O. In terms of the angular velocity ω, $v_1 = r_1\omega$ and $v_2 = r_2\omega$, so that

$$\varepsilon = \tfrac{1}{2}I\omega^2 \qquad \text{II.41}$$

37

The rigid diatomic rotator in space

In treating the motion of the diatomic rotator in space, the position
of each atom is best expressed in terms of the polar coordinates r,
θ and ϕ, rather than in terms of the Cartesian coordinates, x, y and z.
We shall again consider rotation about the centre of gravity of the
molecule, which may conveniently be taken as the origin (Fig. II.9).

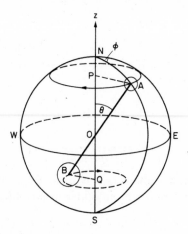

Fig. II.9   *The rigid diatomic rotator in space*

θ is the angle subtended between the molecular axis, AB, and the z
axis, which passes through the north and south poles, N and S. ϕ is
the angle subtended between the plane $NASB$, in which the molecule
lies, and the reference plane NES. The distance OA of the centre of
gravity of the first atom from the centre of gravity of the molecule
may again be denoted by r_1, and the corresponding distance OB of the
second molecule by r_2.

To derive an expression for the kinetic energy, let us first regard ϕ
as constant, and allow θ to vary. The smaller atom may then move
from the position A along the great circle NAS, and the larger atom
in a smaller circle in the same plane and in the same direction. As in
the preceding section, the moment of inertia is

$$I = m_1 r_1^2 + m_2 r_2^2$$

$$= \left(\frac{m_1 m_2}{m_1 + m_2} \right) a^2 \qquad \text{II.42}$$

and the kinetic energy associated with this motion is

$$T_\theta = \tfrac{1}{2}m_1(r_1\dot\theta)^2 + \tfrac{1}{2}m_2(r_2\dot\theta)^2$$
$$= \tfrac{1}{2}I\dot\theta^2 \qquad\qquad \text{II.43}$$

where $\dot\theta = d\theta/dt$.

Secondly, we regard θ as constant, and allow ϕ to vary. Both atoms now transcribe circles about the z axis, i.e. in planes which are parallel to the plane of the equator, moving in the same direction but in different hemispheres. The moment of inertia about the z axis is

$$I' = m_1\overline{AP}^2 + m_2\overline{BQ}^2$$
$$= m_1(r_1 \sin\theta)^2 + m_2(r_2 \sin\theta)^2$$
$$= I \sin^2\theta$$

and the kinetic energy associated with this motion is

$$T_\phi = \tfrac{1}{2}m_1(\overline{AP}\,\dot\phi)^2 + \tfrac{1}{2}m_2(\overline{BQ}\,\dot\phi)^2$$
$$= \tfrac{1}{2}[m_1(r_1 \sin\theta)^2 + m_2(r_2 \sin\theta)^2]\dot\phi^2$$
$$= \tfrac{1}{2}I\,\dot\phi^2 \sin^2\theta$$

where $\dot\phi = d\phi/dt$.

Adding to these kinetic energies a potential energy, V, we obtain for the total energy of the rotating molecule:

$$\varepsilon = T_\theta + T_\phi + V$$
$$= \tfrac{1}{2}I(\dot\theta^2 + \dot\phi^2 \sin^2\theta) + V$$

When the total energy remains constant, the angular momenta are

$$p_\theta = \frac{\partial\varepsilon}{\partial\dot\theta} = I\dot\theta$$

and

$$p_\phi = \frac{\partial\varepsilon}{\partial\dot\phi} = I\dot\phi\sin^2\theta.$$

The total energy may thus be expressed in the form

$$\varepsilon = \frac{1}{2I}\left(p_\theta^2 + \frac{p_\phi^2}{\sin^2\theta}\right) + V \qquad\qquad \text{II.44}$$

The linear harmonic oscillator

When the gain in potential energy of a particle of mass m (or more generally a system of particles of reduced mass μ) on being displaced by a distance x from its equilibrium is $\frac{1}{2}fx^2$, where f is a constant, the particle executes simple harmonic motion, the principal feature of which is that the energy, though constant, periodically changes from the kinetic to the potential form. The potential energy, as stated, is

$$V = \tfrac{1}{2}fx^2 \qquad\qquad \text{II.45}$$

and the force acting on the particle is

$$X = -(dV/dx) = -fx$$

The equation of motion is consequently

$$\mu\frac{d^2x}{dt^2} = -fx$$

the solution of which is

$$x = a\cos(2\pi vt + \eta) \qquad\qquad \text{II.46}$$

where a, v and η are constants representing the amplitude, frequency and initial phase of the motion. Since the cosine of an angle can vary only from $+1$ to -1, x must lie between a and $-a$. Moreover, since the cosine of an angle is the same as the cosine of 2π plus that angle, the motion must repeat itself v times per second. The total energy of the oscillator is the sum of its kinetic and potential energies, and is

$$\varepsilon = \frac{1}{2}\mu\left(\frac{dx}{dt}\right)^2 + \frac{1}{2}fx^2 \qquad\qquad \text{II.47}$$

On substituting in this equation the general expression for x, and for dx/dt, it is found that

$$\varepsilon = 2(\pi va)^2\mu \qquad\qquad \text{II.48}$$

which is constant, and independent of the phase. During the period of oscillation, $T = 1/v$, the energy on two occasions is wholly potential, i.e. when $x = a$ and when $x = -a$. In the same time interval, it also becomes twice wholly kinetic, i.e. when the particle passes through the origin, from the left and from the right.

40

The particular expression for the energy when the particle is momentarily at rest is $\varepsilon = \frac{1}{2} f a^2$. On comparing this with equation II.48, we obtain the following familiar equation for the frequency of vibration of a simple harmonic oscillator:

$$v = \frac{1}{2\pi} \sqrt{\frac{f}{\mu}}$$

II.49

Many particles of physicochemical interest are found to vibrate harmonically when slightly displaced from their positions of minimum energy. This is true, for example, of an electron vibrating with respect to the remainder of an atom, of an atom in a crystal vibrating with respect to its surroundings, and of two atoms vibrating with respect to each other within a molecule.

Since, according to equation 3, the total energy of a linear harmonic oscillator consists of two squared terms, its average energy, in classical mechanics, is kT.

III The quantum theory

At the turn of the century, new laws of nature were discovered, of such a character as to demand a complete reorientation of scientific enquiry. The revolution began with Max Planck's theoretical analysis of the distribution of energy among the various spectral regions of thermal radiation. Its consequences, first felt in the fields of physics and chemistry, have since spread to many regions of natural, and even of pure, philosophy. One of Planck's basic ideas is that energy does not vary continuously, as one had imagined it to do in classical theory, but only by definite increments, or quanta. According to classical theory, the kinetic energy (for example) of a particle of mass m moving with a velocity v is expressed as $\frac{1}{2}mv^2$, with the implication that the energy can have any value from zero to infinity. According to quantal theory the energy of such a particle can have only certain definite, discrete values. This idea, though novel, somehow strikes a natural chord, for so many familiar human actions are of this type. When we move from one place to another, for example, we usually walk, that is, we cover the distance in increments called steps, and our movement is essentially quantal; it is only when we slide that it becomes classical. A corollary to the quantisation of kinetic energy states that the lowest allowed value is not zero, so that inanimate particles, like human beings, know no rest except that of perfect motion.

It is reasonable to ask, if these new laws of quantal theory are in fact the true laws of nature, how is it that the old laws of classical theory had ever emerged and had been, within their province, so well sustained? The answer is that they were based on facts established for systems so conditioned that the quantum of energy separating one allowed level from its neighbour was imperceptibly small. We must therefore henceforth regard the laws of quantal theory as general, and those of classical theory as special cases to which quantal laws reduce under particular conditions.

We shall first recount briefly some of the facts which rendered the quantum theory necessary.

The distribution of energy in thermal radiation

If a small hole is bored into the wall of a hot, evacuated and perfectly blackened cylinder, radiation escapes through it, of a character which, after resolution through a fluorite prism, is found to depend on the temperature only. Denoting by E the energy density inside the cylinder, and by c the velocity of light, the rate of escape of radiant energy from unit area is, as shown in equations II.7 and II.8,

$$S = \tfrac{1}{4}cE \qquad\qquad \text{III.1}$$

Stefan found S to be proportional to the fourth power of the absolute temperature:

$$S = \sigma T^4 \qquad\qquad \text{III.2}$$

His experimental value of the constant of total radiation, ($\sigma = 5 \cdot 72 \times 10^{-5}$ erg cm^{-2} sec^{-1} degree^{-4}) has been used in estimating the temperature of celestial bodies.

The problem is to explain how the quantity E_λ, defined by the equation

$$dE = -E_\lambda \, d\lambda \qquad\qquad \text{III.3}$$

varies with respect to the temperature of the oven and the wave length of the thermal radiation issuing from it. dE is that part of the energy density which is associated with radiations having wavelengths lying between λ and $\lambda + d\lambda$. We begin by finding the number of ways, Z, that an elastic body of volume V can be set vibrating with frequency ν, or c/λ. Roughly, it is the quotient of its volume V and an elementary volume $(\lambda/2)^3$. More exactly, the quotient must be multiplied by $\pi/3$ and Z is therefore $8\pi V/3\lambda^3$. The number of modes of vibration in a system of unit volume, and restricted to wave lengths within a strip of breadth $d\lambda$ is consequently $dZ = -(8\pi/\lambda^4) \, d\lambda$. If the average energy associated with one mode of vibration is denoted by $\bar{\varepsilon}$, it follows that

$$dE = -(8\pi/\lambda^4)\bar{\varepsilon} \, d\lambda \qquad\qquad \text{III.4}$$

Hence

$$E_\lambda = \frac{8\pi}{\lambda^4}\bar{\varepsilon} \qquad\qquad \text{III.5}$$

So far, we have merely formulated the problem in the general terms of

43

electromagnetic theory. What remains is to find the right expression for $\mathcal{E}$.

The energy of a linear harmonic oscillator consists of two quadratic terms (equation II.47) and its average value according to classical kinetic theory is kT. This was adopted by Rayleigh and Jeans, whose equation thus becomes

$$E_\lambda = \frac{8\pi k T}{\lambda^4} \qquad \text{III.6}$$

For high values of λ and T, it is in moderate agreement with the facts. Otherwise, it is inadequate. In particular, it predicts values of E_λ which increase rapidly as the wave length is diminished, and gives no indication of the maxima in the $E_\lambda - \lambda$ curves which are found at all temperatures (Fig. III.1). A way out of the difficulty is to assume that space is granular rather than continuous, the grains being of atomic dimensions. Theoretical maxima then emerge, but in the wrong parts of the spectra. A better equation was derived thermodynamically by Wien, in terms of two empirical constants, α and β. It runs

$$E_\lambda = \frac{\alpha}{\lambda^5} \cdot e^{-\beta/\lambda T} \qquad \text{III.7}$$

On differentiation, we see that the value of λ at any of the maxima is $\beta/5T$, and that the corresponding value of E is $\alpha(5T/\beta e)^5$. The former conclusion is consistent with the observation that bodies become red-hot before they become blue-hot. Both conditions are well confirmed by experiment. The constants α and β, however, are empirical, and Wien's equation does not fit the facts when λ and T are large.

Planck's treatment begins with the acceptance of the general electromagnetic equation and of Boltzmann's expression (II.33) for the average energy;

$$E_\lambda = \frac{8\pi}{\lambda^4}\bar{\mathcal{E}} = \frac{8\pi}{\lambda^4} \frac{\sum e^{-\varepsilon_i/kT}\varepsilon_i}{\sum e^{-\varepsilon_i/kT}} \qquad \text{III.8}$$

In order, however, to arrive at a radiation equation which reproduces the facts, Planck found it necessary to make two postulates for which there was no warrant except their necessity. They were that the energy of an electromagnetic oscillator of frequency v is proportional

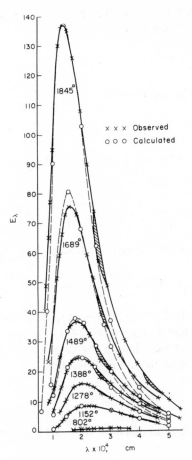

Fig. III.1 *The density of temperature radiation* (after Lummer and Pringsheim, 1899)

to the frequency and to an integer, n, i.e.

$$\varepsilon = nhv; \qquad n = 0, 1, 2, 3, \ldots \qquad \text{III.9}$$

so that the permissible energies of the oscillators are

$$\varepsilon_i = 0, hv, 2hv, 3hv \ldots$$

The proportionality factor h thus introduced has since become universally known as Planck's constant. It ranks in importance with the constants of Faraday and Boltzmann. To evaluate the average

45

energy, let x stand for $e^{-\varepsilon_i/kT}$, so that the summation in the denominator of equation III.8 becomes

$$\sum e^{-\varepsilon_i/kT} = \sum_0^\infty e^{-nh\nu/kT} = 1+x+x^2+x^3+\ldots = 1/(1-x)$$

The summation in the numerator is

$$\sum e^{-\varepsilon_i/kT}\varepsilon_i = \sum_0^\infty e^{-nh\nu/kT}nh\nu = 0+h\nu.x+2h\nu.x^2+3h\nu.x^3+\ldots$$

$$= h\nu.x(1+2x+3x^2+\ldots) = h\nu.x/(1-x)^2$$

The average energy is thus

$$\bar\varepsilon = h\nu\frac{x}{1-x} = h\nu\frac{e^{-h\nu/kT}}{1-e^{-h\nu/kT}} = \frac{h\nu}{e^{h\nu/kT}-1} \qquad \text{III.10}$$

Recalling that $\nu = c/\lambda$, the radiation law becomes

$$E_\lambda = \frac{8\pi hc}{\lambda^5}\frac{1}{e^{hc/\lambda kT}-1} \qquad \text{III.11}$$

At high values of λ and T, we may expand the exponential expression, retaining only two terms. Equation III.6 is thus recovered. At low values of λ and T, we may ignore the term unity appearing in the denominator, and obtain the approximation

$$E_\lambda = \frac{8\pi hc}{\lambda^5}e^{-hc/\lambda kT} \qquad \text{III.12}$$

which has the same form as equation III.7, and becomes identical with it if

$$\alpha = 8\pi hc; \qquad \beta = hc/k \qquad \text{III.13}$$

Finally, the total energy density, obtained by integrating equation III.3 over all wave-lengths, is

$$E = -\int_0^\infty E_\lambda\,d\lambda = -8\pi\int_0^\infty \frac{\bar\varepsilon}{\lambda^4}\,d\lambda = \frac{8\pi^5(kT)^4}{15(hc)^3} \qquad \text{III.14}$$

which coincides with equations III.1 and III.2, provided

$$\sigma = 2\pi^5 k^4/15h^3c^2 \qquad \text{III.15}$$

The experimental values of α, β and σ independently yield the same value of Planck's constant:

$$h = 6 \cdot 624 \times 10^{-27} \text{ erg-second} \qquad \text{III.16}$$

It remains to point out that, since the total number of modes of vibrations possible in unit volume is $Z = 8\pi/3\lambda^3 = 8\pi v^3/3c^3$, the average energy associated with a single mode of vibration is

$$\bar{\varepsilon} = \frac{E}{Z} = \frac{(\pi k T)^4}{5(hv)^3} \qquad \text{III.17}$$

The heat capacity of monatomic solids

The fact established by Dulong and Petit, that the heat capacity of monatomic solids approximates to $3R$ calories per gram-atom-degree at relatively high temperatures is one that can be readily understood in terms of classical kinetic theory. For if each atom in the solid vibrates harmonically in three dimensions, its energy can be represented as a sum of six quadratic terms, namely $\frac{1}{2}m(u^2+v^2+w^2)+\frac{1}{2}f(x^2+y^2+z^2)$, where m is the atomic mass, u, v and w are the atomic velocities, f is the restoring force constant, and x, y and z denote the displacements of the centre of gravity of an atom from its position of minimum potential energy (cf. equation II.47). On an average, the energy associated with each quadratic term is $\frac{1}{2}kT$. The vibrational energy of N_0 atoms is thus $3N_0kT = 3RT$, and the heat capacity at constant volume is $C_V = (dE/dT)_V = 3R$. Classical kinetic theory, however, cannot explain the falling off of C_V which is observed at low temperatures. The quantum theory, as Einstein showed, offers a prompt explanation. If, for the average energy of a linear harmonic oscillator, we accept Planck's expression III.10, the energy of a system of N_0 identical oscillators, each vibrating in three dimensions with a frequency v, is

$$E = \frac{3N_0hv}{e^{hv/kT}-1} \qquad \text{III.18}$$

On differentiating with respect to temperature, remembering that $N_0k = R$, we obtain the following expression for the heat capacity;

$$C_V = 3R\left(\frac{hv}{2kT} \text{ cosech } \frac{hv}{2kT}\right)^2 \qquad \text{III.19}$$

To test it, Einstein accepted the heat capacity measured by Weber for the diamond at 331·3°K, and, solving for v, found it to be $2·79 \times 10^{13}$ sec^{-1}. With this value of v, the theoretical equation reproduces in a satisfactory way the results obtained by Weber at other temperatures (see Fig. III.2). It leads to a zero value of C_V at the absolute zero of temperature, and approximates to $3R$ at high temperatures when cosech $(hv/2kT)$ is nearly $2kT/hv$. Other methods of determining v have confirmed Einstein's original estimate.

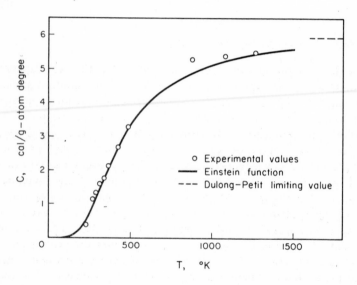

Fig. III.2   *The heat capacity of diamond as a function of temperature*

In a modification of Einstein's treatment due to Debye, the monatomic solid is regarded as capable of vibrating with a whole spectrum of frequencies, from zero to a maximum, v_m, which is greater by one third than Einstein's average frequency. At high temperatures, the revised theory is indistinguishable from the original one. At low temperatures, however, it predicts that the total energy of a system of N_0 atoms is

$$E = \frac{3N_0}{5} \frac{(\pi k T)^4}{(hv_m)^3} \qquad \text{III.20}$$

This result is seen to be Planck's expression III.17 for the average energy associated with a single mode of oscillation, necessarily multiplied by $3N_0$. The heat capacity at low temperatures is thus

$$C_V = \frac{12\pi^4}{5} R \left(\frac{kT}{hv_m}\right)^3 \qquad \text{III.21}$$

or, if we replace the characteristic frequency v_m by a characteristic temperature θ, defined as hv_m/k, and express C_V in calories per gram-atom-degree

$$C_V = 464 \cdot 4(T/\theta)^3 \qquad \text{III.22}$$

This equation has been frequently employed to determine v_m from experimental values of C_V at low temperatures.

The photoelectric effect

When the scrupulously clean surface of a pure metal is irradiated *in vacuo* with light having a frequency beyond a certain lower limit, electrons are instantly emitted, in numbers proportional to the intensity of the radiation and with velocities which are independent of the intensity but vary directly as the square-root of the frequency. Einstein recognised in this phenomenon, which, like the heat capacity of monatomic solids, was difficult to understand in classical terms, another manifestation of quantum laws. He ascribed the effect to collisions between light quanta and electrons in the metal, during which all the energy hv of a light quantum, or photon, is transferred to an electron at or near the metal surface. The electron utilises a part, W, of this energy to overcome the attraction of the metal, and the remaining part to move away from it after its release. Then, by the law of the conservation of energy,

$$hv = W + \tfrac{1}{2}mv^2 \qquad \text{III.23}$$

where h is Planck's constant, v the frequency of the radiation, m is the mass of an electron, and v its velocity. The release energy, W, coincides with that of the lowest quantum, hv^0, which can effect electronic emission. Light of frequency lower than the threshold value v^0 is photoelectrically ineffective. The velocity of the released electrons can be determined by measuring the stopping voltage V, since $\tfrac{1}{2}mv^2 = Ve$, where e is the charge on the electron. Einstein's photochemical law can thus be written as follows:

$$v = v^0 + \left(\frac{e}{h}\right)V \qquad \text{III.24}$$

49

Millikan's results on the photoelectric effect in the case of caesium have been plotted in Fig. III.3. The linear relationship between the frequency and the stopping voltage is seen to be obeyed. The gradient e/h provides yet another, and completely independent, experimental method of determining Planck's constant. The value found for h agrees with that afforded by the many other methods already described.

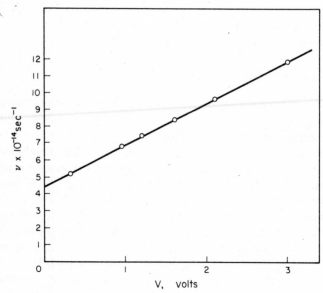

Fig. III.3   *The photoelectric effect in the case of caesium*

Experiment shows that the work, W, required to liberate an electron from a metal is less than that required to liberate it from an isolated atom of the same metal in the vapour phase. Its magnitude can be independently found in experiments designed to release electrons from hot metals in the dark (the thermionic effect). The photoelectric work term and the thermionic work term are identical, and vary periodically among the elements, being low for the alkali and alkaline-earth metals, and high for carbon, platinum and the coinage metals.

There exists between two different metals in dry contact a potential difference, known as the Volta potential. By considering the separate response of the two metals to irradiation of the same frequency, it can readily be deduced that the Volta potential is determined by the difference in the threshold frequencies:

$$V = \left(\frac{h}{e}\right)(v_2^0 - v_1^0) \qquad \text{III.25}$$

The spectrum of atomic hydrogen

When an electrical discharge is passed through hydrogen gas sealed in a tube at a low pressure, the molecules are dissociated into atoms, and the atoms become excited, emitting radiations which, after passage through a prism, are resolved into lines of varying frequencies and intensities. To find a relationship between these frequencies long remained a puzzling problem in pure empiricism. The form of the most successful equations was found by Ritz, and the numerical value of the dominant constant by Rydberg. Between them, they showed that the observed wave numbers could be accurately reproduced by a set of equations of the form

$$\frac{1}{\lambda} = R\left(\frac{1}{n_1^2} - \frac{1}{n_2^2}\right) \qquad \text{III.26}$$

where the empirical constant R is 109,678·2 cm^{-1}, and n_1 and n_2 are integers of which n_1 is naturally the smaller. When n_1 is given, successively, the values 1, 2 and 3, this empirical equation reproduces the series of lines found, respectively, by Lyman, Balmer and Paschen, in the ultra-violet, visible and infra-red regions of the spectrum. Other series are reproduced with still higher values of n_1.

The fact that the spectrum of atomic hydrogen, which may reasonably be assumed to be the simplest of the atomic spectra, consists of lines rather than a continuous spectrum like the rainbow raises a problem of fundamental importance. Another problem besets the success of the Ritz-Rydberg equations, for it implies that the frequencies of all the radiations can be represented as differences between pairs of terms, or implied frequencies, which do not in themselves appear.

Concerning the dynamics of an electron (mass m_e, charge $-e$) revolving in a circular orbit of radius a about a proton (mass m_H, charge $+e$), classical theory has something to say, but, as we shall see, not enough. The total energy of such a system is the sum of its

51

kinetic and potential energies:

$$\varepsilon = \frac{1}{2}I\omega^2 - \frac{e^2}{a} \qquad \text{III.27}$$

where ω is the angular velocity and the moment of inertia I is $[m_H m_e/(m_H + m_e)]a^2$, or μa^2. The electrostatic force $-e^2/a^2$ exerted between the particles must equal the rate of change of momentum, which, for a circular orbit is $-I\omega^2/a$. There are thus two alternative expressions for the total energy:

$$\varepsilon = -\tfrac{1}{2}I\omega^2 = -\tfrac{1}{2}e^2/a \qquad \text{III.28}$$

The angular momentum,

$$I\omega = \pm e(\mu a)^{1/2} \qquad \text{III.29}$$

can have any value from minus to plus infinity, depending on the direction of motion and the radius of the orbit. If orbits of all conceivable radii are permissible, any increase or decrease in the energy of the system, which corresponds to the absorption or emission of radiation, would be continuous. This is contrary to the facts.

In applying the quantum theory to the problem, Bohr realised that consistency with its earlier applications could be retained if the product of the momentum variable p and the conjugated positional variable q, integrated over a complete revolution, were restricted to values which are integral multiples of Planck's constant, h. This condition he expressed in the form

$$\oint p \, dq = nh \qquad \text{III.30}$$

where the circular sign denotes integration over a complete revolution, and n is an integer. Because the angular momentum $p(= I\omega)$ of a particle moving in a circle is independent of the phase, the integration gives directly $I\omega \cdot 2\pi$, so that

$$I\omega = n\frac{h}{2\pi} \qquad \text{III.31}$$

The allowed angular momenta are $(h/2\pi)$ and integral multiples thereof. The total energy of the system thus becomes

$$\varepsilon = -\frac{1}{2}I\omega^2 = -\frac{1}{2I}(I\omega)^2 = -\frac{1}{2I}\frac{n^2 h^2}{4\pi^2} = -\frac{n^2 h^2}{8\pi^2 \mu a^2} \qquad \text{III.32}$$

But ε may also be expressed as $-\frac{1}{2}e^2/a$, so that the radii of the permitted orbits are given by the equation

$$a = \frac{n^2h^2}{4\pi^2\mu e^2} \qquad \text{III.33}$$

The smallest radius of the hydrogen atom, found by putting $n = 1$, is 0·5291 Å. The other radii are greater than this by factors of 4, 9, 16 and so on (Fig. III.4). On substituting this expression for a into that for the energy, we have

$$\varepsilon = -\frac{2\pi^2\mu e^4}{n^2h^2} \qquad \text{III.34}$$

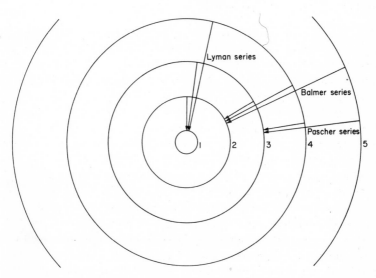

Fig. III.4 *Circular orbits of the electron in a hydrogen atom; origin of emission spectra*

The total energy of the hydrogen atom consequently increases as the quantum number n increases. According to a second postulate due to Bohr, the transition of the hydrogen atom from a state characterised by a quantum number n_2 to a state characterised by a lower quantum number n_1 is attended by the instantaneous emission of a photon, or quantum of radiation, of frequency v and energy hv:

$$hv = \varepsilon_2 - \varepsilon_1 \qquad \text{III.35}$$

Transitions in the opposite direction are attended by the instantaneous absorption of photons. The wave numbers of the lines in the emission spectrum of hydrogen are therefore given by the theoretical expression

$$\frac{1}{\lambda} = \frac{2\pi^2 \mu e^4}{ch^3} \left(\frac{1}{n_1^2} - \frac{1}{n_2^2} \right)$$
III.36

This is clearly of the form required to explain the Ritz equations. Moreover, on using the accepted values of the constants μ, e, c and h the term preceding the brackets is found to be 109,677·8 cm^{-1}, in satisfactory agreement with Rydberg's constant.

Ionisation and resonance potentials

The basic idea that atoms can exist only in certain states of definite energy has been independently confirmed in experiments where the atoms are excited by collisions with electrons, generated photochemically, and accelerated in an electrical field of known strength. When the kinetic energy of the electrons exceeds a certain value, characteristic of the atoms with which they collide, the collisions become inelastic, and most of the kinetic energy is converted into internal energy of the atom which is subsequently emitted as radiation. The critical potential at which this occurs is known as the first resonance potential of the atom, and is accompanied by a monochromatic glow, and by a sharp decrease in the electrical conductivity of the system. Vapours of the alkali metals reveal many maxima and minima in the curve relating conductance to accelerating potential, and the weighted mean resonance potential in each case corresponds with the energy required to excite the atoms to levels known spectroscopically. The critical potential required to produce the complete emission spectrum is termed the ionisation potential. In the case of hydrogen, it is 13·603 volts, in agreement with the predicted difference between the energy of the atom when n is infinite and its energy when $n = 1$. From equation III.34, this difference is seen to be $\varepsilon_{n=\infty} - \varepsilon_{n=1} = 2\pi^2 \mu e^4/h^2$.

The correspondence principle

Let us compare the frequency of electronic motion in a hydrogen atom with the frequency of the light it absorbs or emits when transitions occur only between neighbouring orbits of high quantum number. The angular velocity, according to equation III.31, is

$$\omega = \frac{nh}{2\pi I} = \frac{nh}{2\pi \mu a^2}$$

On substituting the expression for a given by equation III.33, the frequency with which the electron completes its orbit is seen to be

$$\nu_V = \frac{\omega}{2\pi} = \frac{4\pi^2 \mu e^4}{n^3 h^3} \qquad \text{III.37}$$

The frequency of the radiation emitted when the electron descends from a state characterised by the quantum number n to the state immediately beneath it is

$$\nu = \frac{c}{\lambda} = \frac{2\pi^2 \mu e^4}{h^3} \left[\frac{1}{(n-1)^2} - \frac{1}{n^2} \right]$$

When n is a high number, the term in the square brackets approximates to $2/n^3$, and the frequency of the radiation becomes

$$\nu = \frac{4\pi^2 \mu e^4}{n^3 h^3} \qquad \text{III.38}$$

which is the same as the frequency of vibration of the electron. This is the conclusion anticipated by classical electromagnetic theory. Here, as with the heat capacity of monatomic solids, the predictions of the quantum theory merge into and become identical with those of classical theory in systems of high quantum numbers.

Elliptical electronic orbits; the azimuthal quantum number

Despite its success, Bohr's treatment of the hydrogen atom, which forms the basis of the modern theory of atomic spectra, is incomplete in several respects. It provides no explanation for the fact, not hitherto mentioned, that many of the lines in the spectrum of atomic hydrogen are not single lines, but pairs, lying close together like the well known doublet in the visible spectrum of atomic sodium. Furthermore, Bohr's theory overlooks one of Kepler's laws, i.e. that the general path of a particle subject to the inverse square law of force is an ellipse. Sommerfeld extended Bohr's theory by applying to the dynamical problem of elliptical motion two independent quantisations, namely:

$$\oint p_r \, dr = k_k h; \qquad k_r = 1, 2, 3, \ldots$$

$$\oint p_\theta \, d\theta = k_\theta h; \qquad k_\theta = 1, 2, 3, \ldots \qquad \text{III.39}$$

Here r is the distance, at any instant, between the electron and the proton, which is at one of the foci, and θ is the angle subtended, at the same instant, between the radius and the major axis of the ellipse. p_r is the momentum resolved along the direction of the radius, and p_θ the angular momentum. The solution of the problem affords the following expressions for the major semi-axis, a, and the minor semi-axis, b:

$$a = \frac{(k_\theta + k_r)^2 h^2}{4\pi^2 m_e e^2}; \qquad b = \frac{k_\theta (k_\theta + k_r) h^2}{4\pi^2 m_e e^2} \qquad \text{III.40}$$

The major semi-axis, therefore, has the same value as the radius in Bohr's theory, for we may replace the sum of the integers k_θ and k_r by n. The axial ratio becomes.

$$\frac{b}{a} = \frac{k_\theta}{k_\theta + k_r} = \frac{k_\theta}{n} \qquad \text{III.41}$$

Now the maximum value of the axial ratio is clearly unity, corresponding to a circle. The maximum value that k can assume is thus n. With values of k other than n, the permissible orbits are ellipses of varying eccentricities (Fig. III.5). In this diagram the large numerals are the values of the total quantum number n. The numerical subscripts are the values of the azimuthal quantum number k_θ. The letters s, p, d and f are alternative ways of denoting, respectively, that k_θ is 1, 2, 3, and 4. The total energy of the hydrogen atom is found to be given by Bohr's expression, with the sum of the azimuthal quantum number k_θ and the radial quantum number k_r replacing the total quantum number n. The wave numbers of the spectral lines are consequently given by the equation

$$\frac{1}{\lambda} = \frac{2\pi^2 m_e e^4}{h^3 c} \left[\frac{1}{(k_\theta + k_r)^2} - \frac{1}{(k'_\theta + k'_r)^2} \right] \qquad \text{III.42}$$

The theory still provides no explanation for the doublets, although it allows for the generation of a given line in a number of ways. Thus, for example, when the principal quantum number is 3, there are three sub-states, corresponding to values of 1, 2 and 3 for k_θ; and when n

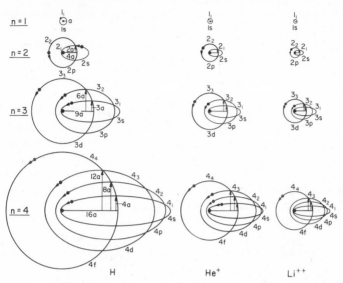

Fig. III.5 *Permissible elliptic electronic orbits for hydrogen-like atoms* (after H. E. White, *Introduction to Atomic Spectra*, McGraw-Hill, 1934)

is 2, there are two sub-states ($k = 1$ or 2); but all six transitions give rise to the same line.

A further amendment to Bohr's treatment is necessitated by the fact that the velocity with which the electron moves in its orbit is a sufficiently high fraction of the velocity of light to justify a relativity correction. The velocity is $v = a\omega$. On substituting the expressions given by equations III.33 and III.37 for a and ω, v is found to be $2\pi e^2/nh$. The ratio of the electronic velocity in the innermost orbit ($n = 1$) to the velocity of light is therefore $2\pi e^2/hc = 1/137$. Instead of the rest mass, m_0, of the electron, the proper mass, m_e, must now be used, where $m_e = m_0 137(136 \times 138)^{-1/2}$. Sommerfeld showed that the correction, though small, has slightly different values for orbits of varying eccentricities, and is capable of explaining the spectral separation of $0 \cdot 365$ cm^{-1} observed in the multiplets due to the six transitions discussed above.

The Zeeman effect; the magnetic quantum number

In dealing with the circular model of the hydrogen atom, one spatial variable θ and its conjugated momentum variable p_θ, and one quantum number n sufficed. The elliptical model requires two spatial variables, r and θ, the two conjugated momenta p_r and p_θ, and two quantum numbers k_r and k_θ. The product of each pair of variables, integrated over a complete revolution, was allowed the single value h or integral multiples thereof. In order to specify the position of any particle in space, three variables are needed, such as the Cartesian coordinates x, y and z, or the polar coordinates r, θ and ϕ. Retaining r and θ to define the position of the electron in its elliptical orbit, ϕ may be used to denote the angle of inclination of the plane of this orbit to some reference plane. Logic demands that the motion of the plane of the orbit be quantised, i.e. that the component of the angular momentum resolved along the reference plane, which is $p_\phi = p_\theta \cos \phi$, shall have integral values of $h/2\pi$. Then

$$p_\phi = m(h/2\pi) \tag{III.43}$$

where the integer m is a third quantum number. Now p_θ is already restricted to the values $k_\theta(h/2\pi)$, so that

$$\cos \phi = m/k \tag{III.44}$$

Because the cosine of an angle can vary only from -1 to $+1$, m can have only the values $-k$, $-k+1$, $-k+2, \ldots 0, 1, 2, \ldots k-1, k$, that is $(2k+1)$ values in all. When the azimuthal quantum number is 2, for example, there are five settings for the plane of the orbit. This argument has provided an explanation of how the lines in the spectrum of atomic hydrogen are resolved in a magnetic field.

A current i flowing in a small closed circuit of area dS is equivalent, as Faraday showed, to a magnet of moment idS placed at the centre and standing perpendicular to the plane of the circuit. When the angular velocity of the electron in a circular orbit of radius a is ω the current is $(\omega/2\pi)e$. Hence, on dividing by c to convert into electromagnetic units, the magnetic moment is

$$M = i \, dS = (\omega/2\pi)e \cdot \pi a^2/c = e\omega a^2/2c \cdot = eI\omega/2m_ec. \tag{III.45}$$

But the angular momentum $I\omega$ is allowed only the quantised values $k_\theta(h/2\pi)$. Hence

$$M = \left(\frac{he}{4\pi m_ec}\right)k_\theta \tag{III.46}$$

The quantisation of angular momentum thus implies the quantisation of magnetic moment, the smallest value of which (the Bohr magneton) is seen to be $he/4\pi m_e c = 9\cdot1 \times 10^{-21}$ e.m.u. Direct experiments by Stern and Gerlach have confirmed this theoretical estimate. Though the choice of the reference plane is arbitrary, it is convenient to let ϕ stand for the angle subtended between the directions of the magnetic axis and the magnetic field. The potential energy possessed by a magnet of moment M in a field of strength H, when its axis is inclined at an angle ϕ to the direction of the field is

$$u = -MH \cos \phi \qquad \text{III.47}$$

On substituting for M the expression given by equation III.46, and recalling that $\cos \phi$ is m/k, we see that

$$u = -\frac{he}{4\pi m_e c} . Hm \qquad \text{III.48}$$

When dealing with transitions in a magnetic field, a term of this form is to be added to the energy term obtaining in the absence of the field. The emission spectrum in a magnetic field consequently consists of lines with wave numbers given by the equation

$$\frac{1}{\lambda} = \frac{2\pi^2 m_e e^4}{ch^3} \left(\frac{1}{n_1^2} - \frac{1}{n_2^2}\right) + \frac{eH}{4\pi m_e c^2}(m_1 - m_2) \qquad \text{III.49}$$

Since m_1 and m_2 can have positive and negative values, the original line should appear in the presence of the magnetic field, attended by a number of other lines separated from one another by multiples (in terms of wave numbers) of an elementary separation $eH/4\pi m_e c^2$ which is proportional to the strength of the field. These facts were discovered by Zeeman and interpreted on classical grounds by Larmor. Classical theory, however, cannot explain the number of lines into which the original one is split; nor can the quantum theory without postulating that the only transitions permitted are those in which m remains constant or changes by unity:

$$\Delta m = 0 \text{ or } \pm 1 \qquad \text{III.50}$$

The operation of this selection rule greatly reduces the number of actual lines from the total number $(2k_1^\theta + 1)(2k_2^\theta + 1)$ which would otherwise appear.

The spectra of the alkali metals; the spin quantum number

To explain why fewer lines appear in the spectrum of atomic hydrogen than would result from the indiscriminate combination of terms, it has been found necessary to postulate a second selection rule according to which the only transitions permitted are those in which the azimuthal quantum number changes by unity:

$$\Delta k = \pm 1 \qquad \text{III.51}$$

The familiar doublet (5,896 Å and 5,890 Å) appearing in the spectrum of atomic sodium is resolved, by magnetic fields of moderate intensity, in a complicated way. Both original lines are deleted, one being replaced by four new lines and the other by six, with an elementary separation less than that of $eH/4\pi m_e c^2$ found in the Zeeman effect. Landé argued on empirical, and Uhlenbeck and Goudsmit on theoretical grounds that the electron is capable of spinning about its own axis, and that a third selection rule was required, namely

$$\Delta j = 0 \text{ or } \pm 1 \qquad \text{III.52}$$

where j is an inner quantum number, compounded vectorially from the azimuthal and spin quantum numbers:

$$j = k \pm s \qquad \text{III.53}$$

By analogy with the argument which led to $(2k+1)$ for the number of planes in which an electron with an azimuthal quantum number k could move, we expect $(2s+1)$ settings for the spin motion. Now the terms, or inferred wave numbers, in the spectrum of atomic sodium are mostly doublets, suggesting that $(2s+1) = 2$, or that $s = \frac{1}{2}$. Since the addition of s to k in the selection rule is vectorial, it follows that s can also have the value $-\frac{1}{2}$. The deduction that the electron is capable of spinning on its own axis in either of two directions has proved to be of direct chemical interest, for, as later developments have shown, the univalent homopolar bond, such as that which unites the two atoms of hydrogen in the hydrogen molecule, consists of a pair of electrons with opposite spins.

De Broglie's law

According to Einstein's theory of relativity, the energy ε of a particle of mass m is mc^2. On combining this with Planck's expression ($\varepsilon = h\nu$) for the energy of a photon, we see that its momentum is $h(1/\lambda)$. De Broglie suggested that such a relationship holds for all particles, i.e. that generally

$$mv = h/\lambda \qquad \text{III.54}$$

The consequences of such a suggestion were so important that scientists promptly sought to test it in the only satisfactory way, i.e. by experiment with particles other than photons. G. P. Thomson applied the equation to electrons moving with velocities which could be measured in terms of the stopping voltage V, where $\frac{1}{2}mv^2 = Ve$. De Broglie's equation in this case becomes

$$\lambda = h/(2m_e eV)^{1/2} \qquad \text{III.55}$$

A narrow beam of electrons, after passage through thin foils of gold or aluminium, were found to produce diffraction rings just like those generated by the interference of light waves. From the diameters of the rings and the distance of the screen from the foil, the wave length could be estimated. It proved to be the same as that predicted by de Broglie's equation. A magnetic field distorted the pattern, showing the effect to be in fact due to the electrons, and not to X-rays generated by them in the metals. An equally convincing experimental verification of de Broglie's law was given in quite another way and almost simultaneously by Davisson and Germer.

The wave-corpuscle parallelism

J. J. Thomson made out a convincing case for regarding electrons as corpuscles, and his son G. P. Thomson an equally convincing case for regarding them as waves. What electrons are we shall never know. How they behave is becoming increasingly clear. Sometimes they behave as corpuscles, and sometimes as waves. Newton, faced with the same dilemma concerning light, concluded that its corpuscles had fits. The truth of de Broglie's law endows all matter with the same idiosyncrasy. The way of dealing with it forms the subject of the next chapter.

IV Wave mechanics

According to classical theory, the propagation of a system of plane harmonic waves in the direction of the x axis is described by the equation

$$\psi = Ae^{2\pi i(\pm kx - vt)} \qquad\qquad \text{IV.1}$$

where $i = (-1)^{1/2}$, x is the distance, t the time, k the wave number and v the frequency. Partial differentiation with respect to x and t shows that

$$\frac{\partial^2 \psi}{\partial x^2} = -4\pi^2 k^2 \psi \qquad\qquad \text{IV.2}$$

and

$$\frac{\partial^2 \psi}{\partial t^2} = -4\pi^2 v^2 \psi \qquad\qquad \text{IV.3}$$

At any given instant, therefore, ψ vibrates harmonically with respect to x, and at any given position harmonically with respect to t. It resumes its value of A whenever $kx = vt$. The velocity of propagation is $x/t = v/k = v\lambda = c$. The fundamental assumption of wave mechanics is that the measurable properties of all particles, be they photons, electrons, atoms or molecules, are governed by a function ψ, the form of which can be derived in simple cases, and inferred or conjectured in others. De Broglie's relationship between the momentum of the particle and the wave-length of the function which determines its properties is accepted as valid for all particles, on the strength of its experimental verification with photons and electrons. Then, since $k = 1/\lambda = mv/h$, equation IV.2 may be cast in the form

$$\frac{\partial^2 \psi}{\partial x^2} = -\frac{4\pi^2 m^2 v^2}{h^2} \psi$$

or, if the kinetic energy $\frac{1}{2}mv^2$ be replaced by the difference between the total energy E and the potential energy V,

$$\frac{\partial^2 \psi}{\partial x^2} = -\frac{8\pi^2 m}{h^2}(E - V)\psi \qquad\qquad \text{IV.4}$$

For propagation in three dimensions, we have

$$\frac{\partial^2 \psi}{\partial x^2} + \frac{\partial^2 \psi}{\partial y^2} + \frac{\partial^2 \psi}{\partial z^2} = -\frac{8\pi^2 m}{h^2}(E - V)\psi \qquad \text{IV.5}$$

This is Schrödinger's equation. Like all differential equations, it has an infinite number of solutions. Those of interest are picked out by imposing on ψ and its first derivatives the conditions that they must be finite and continuous everywhere, i.e. in all phases and at all boundaries between phases. With some supplementary limitations of a formal nature, these suffice to yield values for ψ which are solutions of the original differential equation. They are termed proper functions (*Eigenfunktionen*). It is found that each proper function corresponds to a stationary energy level as the term is understood in the earlier quantum theory. The complete solution of Schrödinger's equation yields expressions for ψ as a function of the four independent variables, and explains not only why particles are confined to certain states of constant energy but what the probabilities are which govern the transit from one level to another. Such probabilities may be great, as when an electron in an atom changes from the p to the s state, or small, as when a molecule of orthohydrogen changes to parahydrogen in the absence of a magnetic field. We shall first be concerned with determining stationary energy levels, and shall later refer to the more difficult problem of transition probabilities.

The connexion between ψ and the particle whose behaviour it governs has been clearly explained by Born. ψ is a variable such that $|\psi|^2$ at any particular point x, y, z is proportional to the probability of finding the particle at that point. If ψ is real, $|\psi|^2$ is simply ψ^2. If, on the other hand, ψ is imaginary, $|\psi|^2$ stands for the product of ψ and its complex variable, ψ, which is identical with ψ except that all the i terms are replaced by $-i$. In this way it is ensured that $|\psi|^2$ is never negative.

As in classical theory, the probability of finding a particle within the region lying between x and $x+dx$, y and $y+dy$, z and $z+dz$, is proportional to the volume element $dv = dx\, dy\, dz$. Hence the probability of finding the particle possessing the properties determined by ψ within the volume element is

$$dP = K|\psi|^2 \, dv$$

where K is a proportionality constant. Since the particle must be somewhere, the integral of dP over all possible values of $|\psi|^2$ and v

must be unity:

$$\int_0^\infty dP = K \int_0^\infty |\psi|^2 \, dv = 1 \qquad \text{IV.6}$$

This step is termed normalisation. On eliminating K, we have

$$dP = \frac{|\psi|^2 \, dv}{\int_0^\infty |\psi|^2 \, dv} \qquad \text{IV.7}$$

The freely moving point particle

The potential energy, V, of a free particle is zero, and equation IV.4 which governs its behaviour in one dimension becomes

$$\frac{\partial^2 \psi}{\partial x^2} = -\frac{8\pi^2 mE}{h^2} \psi \qquad \text{IV.8}$$

The general solution is

$$\psi = A \cos (2\pi/\lambda)x + B \sin (2\pi/\lambda)x \qquad \text{IV.9}$$

where A and B are constants, and

$$\lambda = h/(2mE)^{1/2} \qquad \text{IV.10}$$

The reader should satisfy himself, by differentiating ψ of equation IV.9 twice with respect to x, that this solution is correct, irrespective of the values of A and B. The probability of finding the particle at any point x is proportional to ψ^2, which is evidently

$$\psi^2 = A^2 \cos^2(2\pi/\lambda)x + 2AB \cos(2\pi/\lambda)x \,.\, \sin(2\pi/\lambda)x + B^2 \sin^2(2\pi/\lambda)x$$

Now if motion is limited between the origin ($x = 0$) and some extremity at a distance $x = l$ away from the origin, ψ^2 must be zero when x has either of these values. The first condition can be true only when A is zero. Hence, on using a well known trigonometrical theorem,

$$\psi^2 = B^2 \sin^2(2\pi/\lambda)x = \frac{B^2}{2}[1 - \cos(4\pi/\lambda)x] \qquad \text{IV.11}$$

The second condition is that ψ^2 shall be zero for all values of x which make $1 - \cos(4\pi/\lambda)x$ zero. Let these particular values of x be denoted by l. The second condition is thus equivalent to $\cos(4\pi/\lambda)l = 1$. Now the cosine of an angle is unity when the angle is zero, or 2π, or $4\pi, \ldots$, or, in short $2n\pi$, where n is an integer. Hence $(4\pi/\lambda)l = 2n\pi$, or

$$l = n(\lambda/2); \qquad n = 1, 2, 3, \ldots \qquad \text{IV.12}$$

Stationary states of the freely moving point particle are therefore those in which the particle moves along distances which are integral multiples of one-half of the wave length of the function ψ. After eliminating λ from equations IV.10 and IV.12, the total energy of the particle is seen to be

$$E = \frac{n^2 h^2}{8ml^2}; \qquad n = 1, 2, 3, \ldots \qquad \text{IV.13}$$

The forms of ψ and ψ^2 for a freely moving particle in the quantum state $n = 2$ are shown in Figs. IV.1 and IV.2.

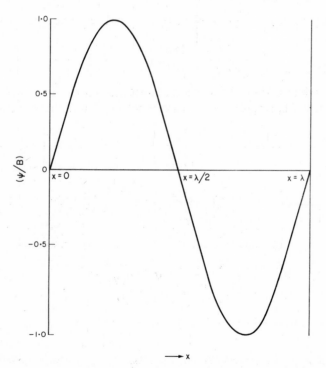

Fig. IV.1 *Wave function for the freely moving point particle in the second quantum state* ($n = 2$)

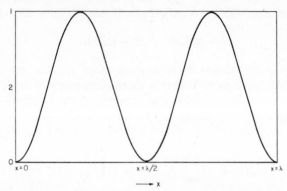

Fig. IV.2 *Probability function for the freely moving point particle in the second quantum state* ($n = 2$)

The linear harmonic oscillator

The potential energy V is now $\frac{1}{2}fx^2$, and Schrödinger's equation becomes

$$\frac{\partial^2 \psi}{\partial x^2} = -\frac{8\pi^2 m}{h^2} \left(E - \frac{1}{2}fx^2\right)\psi \qquad \text{IV.14}$$

The solution shows ψ to be a complicated function of x and of an integer, v, having the forms shown in Fig. IV.3, and that the allowed

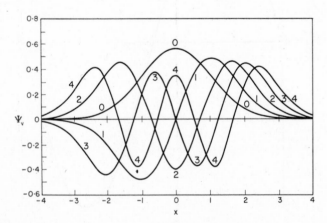

Fig. IV.3 *Normalised wave functions for the linear harmonic oscillator in the lower quantum states* (after Condon and Morse, *Quantum Mechanics*, McGraw-Hill, 1929)

66

energy levels of the oscillator are given by the equation

$$E = (v + \tfrac{1}{2})h\nu; \qquad v = 0, 1, 2, 3, \ldots \qquad \text{IV.15}$$

where ν is the frequency of vibration.

The probability, at any instant, of finding the centre of gravity of the oscillator within a distance lying between x and $x + dx$ from the origin is proportional to ψ^2, and is shown as a function of x/a_0 by the wavy curves (A) in Fig. IV.4. The B curves are the corresponding

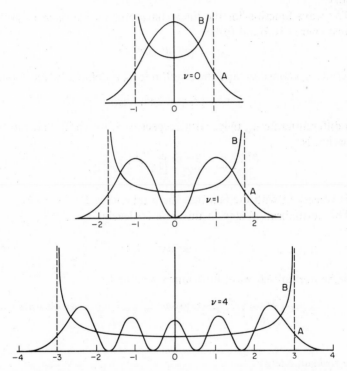

Fig. IV.4 $\Psi_v^2 \, dx$ *for the linear harmonic oscillator, according to quantal theory (curves A) and classical theory (curves B), plotted as a function of the relative displacement,* (× 90)

probabilities predicted by classical theory. The contrast is great, particularly for the linear oscillator in its ground vibrational state $(v = 0)$. The most probable region, according to classical theory, is near the extremities of its swing, when $x = \pm a_0$; the least probable position is at the origin; and there is no likelihood whatsoever that the particle shall be found at distances greater than a_0 away from the origin. The most probable region, according to quantal theory, is at the origin; and, it is important to note, there is a small but finite probability that the particle may be found at distances away from the origin which exceed the classical amplitude, a_0. From the remaining graphs reproduced in Fig. IV.4 it can be inferred that the probability curve in a state characterised by a high quantum number is a very wavy one, inclined to drape itself around the simpler curve of classical theory.

The wave function for the linear harmonic oscillator in its state of lowest energy is found to be

$$\psi_0 = C e^{-[(1/2)(x/a_0)^2]} \qquad \text{IV.16}$$

where C is a constant, and the amplitude a_0 is defined by the equation

$$\tfrac{1}{2}hv = \tfrac{1}{2}fa_0^2 = 2\pi^2 v^2 m a_0^2 \qquad \text{IV.17}$$

On differentiating ψ_0 twice with respect to x, we verify that the wave equation is

$$\frac{\partial^2 \psi_0}{\partial x^2} = -\frac{8\pi^2 m}{h^2}\left(\tfrac{1}{2}hv - \tfrac{1}{2}fx^2\right)\psi_0 \qquad \text{IV.18}$$

as is consistent with the fact that the total energy E is now $\tfrac{1}{2}hv$.

The normalisation step in this case is clearly

$$\int_{-\infty}^{\infty} \psi_0^2\, dx = 1 \qquad \text{IV.19}$$

and the normalised wave function is seen to be

$$\psi_0 = \left(\frac{4\pi vm}{h}\right)^{1/4}\! . \, e^{-(2\pi^2 vm/h)x^2} = \frac{1}{(\pi a_0)^{1/2}} . \, e^{-[(1/2)(x/a_0)]^2} \qquad \text{IV.20}$$

The residual energy

The lowest permissible energy of a linear harmonic oscillator according to the quantum theory is given by equation IV.15 with $v = 0$. It is

$$E_0 = \tfrac{1}{2}hv \qquad \text{IV.21}$$

The lowest permissible energy of a particle of mass m moving freely along a length l is, according to the same theory, given by equation

IV.13 with $n = 1$. It is

$$E_0 = h^2/8ml^2 \qquad\qquad \text{IV.22}$$

These expressions, which we shall presently show to be equivalent, are fundamentally different from the expressions of classical theory, according to which an oscillator and a translator may have zero energy, when the particle is at rest. The quantum theory does not countenance a state of rest; even in their state of lowest energy, all particles must be in motion. At the absolute zero of temperature, when thermal energy has been completely drained from the system, each linear oscillator retains an energy $\frac{1}{2}hv$. For that reason, E_0 is known as the residual energy.* Its existence has been independently proved by spectroscopy and low temperature calorimetry.

The equivalence of the two expressions for E_0 can be directly shown by using de Broglie's law ($\lambda = h/mu$), and remembering that $l = \lambda/2$ in the ground state. Then

$$E_0 = \frac{h^2}{8ml^2} = \frac{h^2}{2m\lambda^2} = \frac{hu}{2\lambda} = \frac{1}{2}h\left(\frac{u}{2l}\right) = \frac{1}{2}hv$$

since $u/2l$ is the frequency with which the linear motion is repeated.

The hydrogen atom

In terms of the charge, e, on the proton and its distance, r, from the electron, the potential energy of the hydrogen atom is $V = -e^2/r$. Equation IV.5 for the system thus becomes

$$\frac{\partial^2\psi}{\partial x^2} + \frac{\partial^2\psi}{\partial y^2} + \frac{\partial^2\psi}{\partial z^2} = -\frac{8\pi^2 m}{h^2}\left(E + \frac{e^2}{r}\right)\psi \qquad\qquad \text{IV.23}$$

The solution to the problem shows that the energy and momenta can have only the quantised values

$$E = -\frac{2\pi^2 me^4}{n^2 h^2}; \qquad n = 1, 2, 3, \ldots \infty \qquad\qquad \text{IV.24}$$

---

* The German name for $\frac{1}{2}hv$ is *Nullpunktsenergie*, a characteristically logical term, for *Nullpunkt* to the German scientist means the absolute zero of temperature. 'Zero point', on the other hand, does not connote the absolute zero of temperature to the monoglot English scientist or technician. For that reason the term 'zero point energy' is poor English for *Nullpunktsenergie*, as C. G. Darwin long ago pointed out. Nevertheless, it is often used.

$$p_\theta = \frac{h}{2\pi}\sqrt{[l(l+1)]}; \qquad 1 = 0, 1, 2, \ldots (n-1) \qquad \text{IV.25}$$

$$p_\phi = \frac{h}{2\pi}m; \qquad m = 0, \pm 1, \pm 2, \ldots \pm 1 \qquad \text{IV.26}$$

The expression for the total energy is the same as that derived by Bohr and Sommerfeld. That for the angular momentum, however, is different, in that the former azimuthal quantum number, k, is replaced by $\sqrt{l(l+1)}$. Moreover, energy states with no angular momentum are now permissible.

The *Eigenfunktionen* for the hydrogen atom, from which these generalities have been derived, depend in a complicated way on the Cartesian coordinates x, y and z, which it is convenient to replace by the polar ordinates r, θ and ϕ. The relation between them is seen from Fig. IV.5 to be

$$x = r \sin\theta \sin\phi \qquad \text{IV.27}$$

$$y = r \sin\theta \cos\phi \qquad \text{IV.28}$$

$$z = r \cos\theta \qquad \text{IV.29}$$

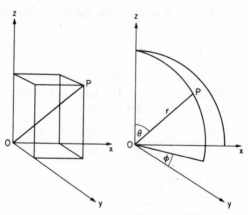

Fig. IV.5 *The relation between Cartesian and polar coordinates*

Each *Eigenfunktion* can then be resolved into the product of three proper functions which depend solely on r, θ and ϕ;

$$\psi_{n,l,m}(r, \theta, \phi) = R_{n,l}(r) \cdot \Theta_{l,m}(\theta) \cdot \Phi_m(\phi) \qquad \text{IV.30}$$

Each of the component functions depends on the integers denoted here by subscripts, and can be normalised separately.

The ground state of the hydrogen atom

The ground state of a system is its state of lowest energy. For the hydrogen atom it corresponds, according to equation IV.24, to unit value of the principal quantum number n. The energy in the ground state is seen to be $E = -2\pi^2me^4/h^2$. On substituting the values of the constants, we find $E = -13{\cdot}603$ electron-volts, or $-2{\cdot}179 \times 10^{-11}$ erg per atom or $-313{\cdot}71$ kilocalories per gram-atom. Since the maximum value of l is $n-1$, l in this instance must be zero; m also can have only a zero value. The quantum numbers which characterise the hydrogen atom in the ground state are therefore

$$n = 1; \qquad l = 0; \qquad m = 0$$

The normalised wave function of the atom in this state is found to be

$$\psi_{100} = \frac{1}{(\pi a_1^3)^{1/2}} e^{-r/a_1} \qquad \qquad \text{IV.31}$$

where a_1 is the smallest orbit $(h^2/4\pi^2me^2 = 0{\cdot}5291$ Å$)$ appearing in Bohr's theory. This function is seen to be independent of the angles θ and ϕ, i.e. the value of ψ_{100} depends entirely on the distance r of the electron from the proton. Such functions are said to be spherically symmetrical. This is a property possessed by the hydrogen atom in the ground state, and by the same atom in all other quantum states for which l is zero. These states are known as s states. They are non-degenerate. The function ψ_{100} is shown in Fig. IV.6. Its maximum value is at the origin; at a distance of $1{\cdot}2$ Å it has fallen to about one tenth of this value. A similar curve, falling off more steeply with increasing values of r is found for ψ_{100}^2. The chance that the electron shall be in a volume element dv is $\psi_{100}^2\, dv$. Hence, for a volume element of fixed extension, the probability distribution function is greatest at the origin. The same conclusion can be expressed by saying that the density of negative electricity is greatest at the origin. It decreases rapidly as r increases, and is only one per cent of the maximum value when r is $1{\cdot}2$ Å. This spherical symmetry of the electron cloud was not a consequence of Bohr's theory, according to which the electron was thought of as moving in a plane. The general expression for dv in polar coordinates is $r^2\, dr \sin\theta\, d\theta\, d\phi$. Since here ψ is independent of the angles, we may integrate over all values of θ from 0 to π and over all values of ϕ from 0 to 2π, obtaining $dv = 4\pi r^2\, dr$. The probability that the electron shall be in this volume element is $\psi^2 4\pi r^2\, dr$. On using

71

the expression given above for the wave function, it is easily verified that

$$\int_0^\infty \psi_{100}^2 4\pi r^2 \, dr = 1$$

By reasoning as in Chapter III when deriving a general expression for the average value of a property, P, in classical mechanics, we obtain

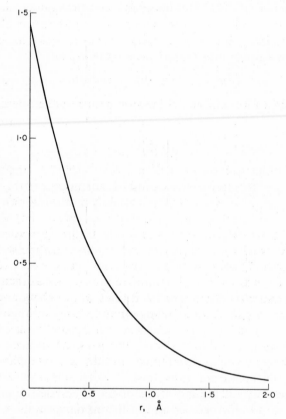

Fig. IV.6   *The normalised wave function* Ψ_{100} *for the hydrogen atom in the ground state*

the following general expression in wave mechanics:

$$\bar{P} = \int_0^\infty \psi^2 \cdot P \cdot dv$$

This equation is a direct consequence of equation IV.7. When applied to determine the average value of r in the present problem, we find

$$\bar{r} = \int_0^\infty \psi_{100}^2 \cdot r \cdot 4\pi r^2 \, dr = \tfrac{3}{2}a_1 \qquad \text{IV.32}$$

The average value of the reciprocal of r is

$$\overline{\left(\frac{1}{r}\right)} = \int_0^\infty \psi_{100}^2 \cdot \frac{1}{r} \cdot 4\pi r^2 \, dr = \frac{1}{a_1} \qquad \text{IV.33}$$

Hence the average potential energy is the same as in Bohr's theory.

The term $D = \psi^2 4\pi r^2$ is known as the radial distribution function. It represents the probability, reckoned per unit radial length, that the electron shall be at a distance r from the nucleus. In the present example,

$$D = \frac{4r^2}{a_1^3} e^{-2r/a_1} \qquad \text{IV.34}$$

By inspection of the plot shown in Fig. IV.7, or by differentiation, we

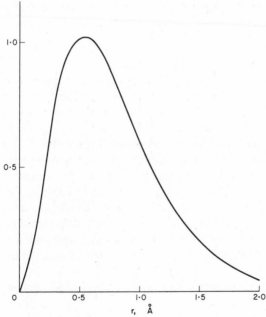

Fig. IV.7 *The radial distribution function* $(D = \Psi_{100}^2 4\pi r^2)$ *for the hydrogen atom in the ground state*

see that D is zero at the origin and has a maximum value when r equals a_1. Thus although the electron does not revolve on the surface of a sphere of radius a_1, but has, in fact, no angular momentum, its most probable position is on such a surface.

Radial solutions of the wave function for the hydrogen atom in higher quantum states

When the principal quantum number, n, is 2, the second quantum number, l, may be either 0 or 1. Corresponding to these two permissible states of the hydrogen atom there are two radial components of the total wave function. They are

$$R_{2,0} = \frac{1}{(2a_1^3)^{1/2}} \left(1 - \frac{r}{2a_1}\right) e^{-r/2a_1} \qquad \text{IV.35}$$

and

$$R_{2,1} = \frac{1}{(6a_1^3)^{1/2}} \left(\frac{r}{2a_1}\right) e^{-r/2a_1} \qquad \text{IV.36}$$

where a_1 retains its former significance. Both these radial parts of the wave function have been normalised by means of the relation

$$\int_0^\infty R_{2,l}^2 \cdot r^2 \, dr = 1$$

as may be easily verified. This particular normalisation procedure is being here followed in order to allow the angular components of the total wave function to be, like the radial components, separately normalised. It is to be noted that when r is zero, $R_{2,0}$ is real and $R_{2,1}$ is zero. This is a general distinction between the atom in s states ($l = 0$) and in p states ($l = 1$). By the method of averaging described above, it can be shown that the average value of r for the 2s election ($n = 2$; $l = 0$) is $6a_1$, and for the 2p electron ($n = 2$; $l = 1$) is $5a_1$, and that the average value of $1/r$ for each is $1/4a_1$. Here also, the average potential energy is the same as in Bohr's theory, according to which the radius of the circular orbit with $n = 2$ is four times the radius of the innermost orbit ($n = 1$). The same conclusion holds for all states of the hydrogen atom.

The radial distribution function for the 2s electron is seen from equation IV.35 to be

$$D_{2,0} = R_{2,0}^2 r^2 = \frac{1}{2a_1^3} \left(r - \frac{r^2}{2a_1}\right)^2 e^{-r/a_1} \qquad \text{IV.37}$$

Its value is zero at the origin and when $r = 2a_1$, and it has two maximum values, the higher when $r/a_1 = 3+5^{1/2} = 5\cdot24$, and the lower when $r/a = 3-5^{1/2} = 0\cdot76$.

From the radial distribution function of the $2p$ electron (equation IV.36),

$$D_{2,1} = R_{2,1}^2 r^2 = \frac{r^4}{24a_1^5} e^{-r/a_1} \qquad \text{IV.38}$$

we see that its value can be zero only at the origin, and that it exhibits only one maximum, when $r = 4a_1$. The remarks concerning the $1s$ electron thus apply to the $2p$ electron. They hold also for the $3d$ and $4f$ electrons, and generally when the quantum number l is one less than the total quantum number, n.

Radial distribution functions for the hydrogen atom in some of its low quantum states are shown in Fig. IV.8, where the numerals give the values of the principal quantum number, n, and the letters s, p and d respectively refer to azimuthal quantum numbers, l, of 0, 1 and 2.

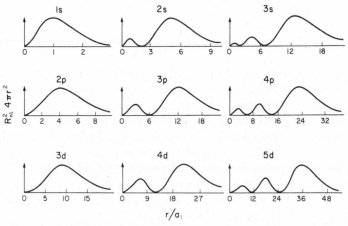

Fig. IV.8   *Radial distribution functions for the hydrogen atoms in certain low quantum states*

Angular solutions of the wave function for the hydrogen atom

The part of the wave function which depends solely on the angle ϕ is

$$\frac{\partial^2 \Phi}{\partial \phi^2} = -m^2 \Phi \qquad \text{IV.39}$$

75

the solution of which is

$$\Phi = Ae^{im\phi}; \qquad m = 0, \pm 1, \pm 2, \pm 3, \ldots \qquad \text{IV.40}$$

The complex conjugate of Φ is $Ae^{-im\phi}$, so that normalisation gives us

$$\int_0^{2\pi} \Phi\Phi^* \, d\phi = A^2 \int_0^{2\pi} d\phi = A^2 2\pi = 1$$

Then A is $(2\pi)^{-1/2}$, and the normalised function is

$$\Phi = \frac{1}{\sqrt{(2\pi)}} e^{im\phi}; \qquad m = 0, \pm 1, \pm 2, \pm 3, \ldots \qquad \text{IV.41}$$

The three lowest members of this series are consequently

$$\Phi_{m=0} = \frac{1}{\sqrt{(2\pi)}}$$

$$\Phi_{m=1} = \frac{1}{\sqrt{(2\pi)}} \cdot e^{i\phi} = \frac{1}{\sqrt{(2\pi)}} (\cos\phi + i\sin\phi)$$

and

$$\Phi_{m=-1} = \frac{1}{\sqrt{(2\pi)}} \cdot e^{-i\phi} = \frac{1}{\sqrt{(2\pi)}} (\cos\phi - i\sin\phi) \qquad \text{IV.42}$$

The first member is real; the others are imaginary*. If, however, ψ_1 and ψ_2 are separate solutions of Schrödinger's equation, it follows that any linear combination of ψ_1 and ψ_2 is also a solution. Thus, for example, Φ $(m = 1)$ plus Φ $(m = -1)$, divided by $\sqrt{2}$ is $(1/\sqrt{\pi})\cos\phi$; and Φ $(m = 1)$ minus Φ $(m = -1)$, divided by $i\sqrt{2}$ is $(1/\sqrt{\pi})\sin\phi$. Both these values are real, and are used in later sections.

A general expression is readily derived for the other angular component Θ of the total wave function. We shall here merely give the solutions for the electron in the s and p states (Table IV.1). These have been normalised by means of the equation

$$\int_{\theta=0}^{\theta=\pi} \Theta^2 \, d\cos\theta = 1$$

The angular wave functions for electrons in s states are independent of the angles θ and ϕ. For the p electron with zero magnetic quantum number m the angular part of the wave function depends on θ only, and is shown in the polar graph (Fig. IV.9). Since this function is

---

* $e^{im\phi} = \cos m\phi + i\sin m\phi$. $\quad e^{-im\phi} = \cos m\phi - i\sin m\phi$.

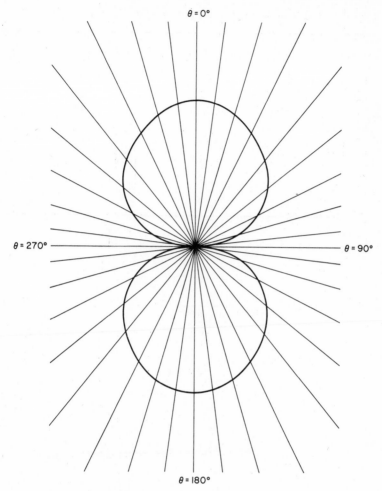

$\theta = 0°$

$\theta = 270°$

$\theta = 90°$

$\theta = 180°$

Fig. IV.9   *The wave function* $\Psi_{210} = R_{21}\frac{1}{2}\sqrt{(3/\pi)}\cos\theta$, *plotted to show the dependence on* θ. *The magnitude of the function for any value of* θ *is proportional to the distance between the origin of the curve at this angle.*

independent of ϕ, we would obtain figures of the same shape for all values of ϕ. A solid model of the function is thus obtained by revolving the figure about the line corresponding to $\theta = 0$, which is the z axis. The solid models similarly obtained in the remaining cases ($m = \pm 1$) are shown in Fig. IV.10.

Table IV.1 *Normalised angular wave functions for the hydrogen atom in low states*

Electron	n	l	m	Φ	Θ	$\Phi\Theta$
s	1	0	0	$\dfrac{1}{\sqrt{(2\pi)}}$	$\dfrac{1}{\sqrt{2}}$	$\dfrac{1}{2\sqrt{\pi}}$
s	2	0	0	$\dfrac{1}{\sqrt{(2\pi)}}$	$\dfrac{1}{\sqrt{2}}$	$\dfrac{1}{2\sqrt{\pi}}$
p	2	1	0	$\dfrac{1}{\sqrt{(2\pi)}}$	$\sqrt{\tfrac{3}{2}}\cos\theta$	$\dfrac{1}{2}\sqrt{\dfrac{3}{\pi}}\cos\theta$
p	2	1	1	$\dfrac{1}{\sqrt{(2\pi)}}\cdot e^{i\phi}$	$\tfrac{1}{2}\sqrt{3}\sin\theta$	$\dfrac{1}{2}\sqrt{\dfrac{3}{2\pi}}\sin\theta\cdot e^{i\phi}$
p	2	1	-1	$\dfrac{1}{\sqrt{(2\pi)}}\cdot e^{-i\phi}$	$\tfrac{1}{2}\sqrt{3}\sin\theta$	$\dfrac{1}{2}\sqrt{\dfrac{3}{2\pi}}\sin\theta\cdot e^{-i\phi}$

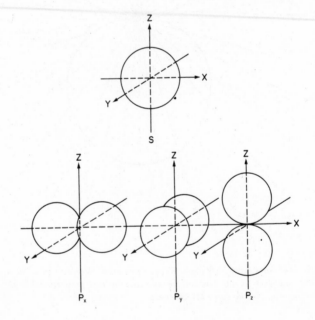

Fig. IV.10

The probability density distribution function for the electron in the 210 state is

$$\Theta^2 = \tfrac{3}{2}\cos^2\theta \qquad \text{IV.43}$$

which is shown graphically in Fig. IV.11. This, like the wave function itself, is naturally independent of the angle ϕ, and a solid model representing (in polar form) the probable position of the electron in this state is obtained by revolving the figure about the z axis. The least probable position is at the origin; significantly probable positions are on the surface of the dumbbell formed round the z axis; and the most probable positions are on the z axis (i.e. at the top or bottom of the dumbbell) at a distance which is determined by the radial part

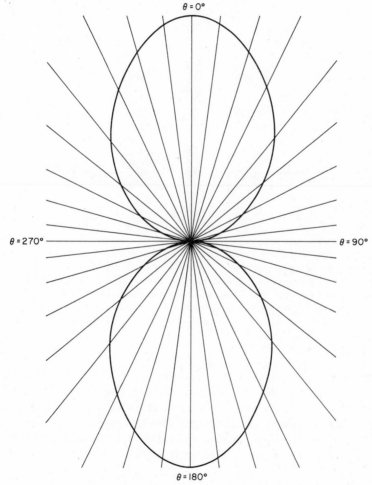

Fig. IV.11 *The probability density distribution function $\theta_{21}^2 = (\frac{3}{2})\cos^2\theta$*

of the total wave function. Solid models similarly drawn for other states of the hydrogen atom are shown in Fig. IV.12. Because of the similarity of these models to the planar orbits envisaged in the earlier theory, the name orbital has been given to the wave function governing the behaviour of a single electron. It will be observed that there are fewer orbitals than there were orbits, because the new azimuthal quantum number l is less than the old quantum number k.

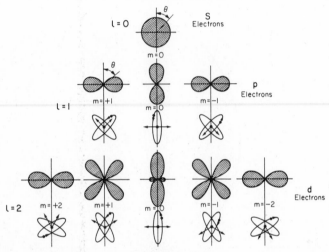

Fig. IV.12 *The probability-density distribution factor plotted as a function of the angle for s, p, and d electrons. The classical oriented orbit for each state is given below each figure, tilted slightly out of the normal plane to show an orbit rather than a straight line* (after White, *Introduction to Atomic Spectra*, p. 63, 1934)

The rigid diatomic rotator

The energy of the rigid diatomic rotator, as derived in Chapter II is $\frac{1}{2}I\omega^2$. Bjerrum, in the early days of the quantum theory, suggested that the angular momentum, $I\omega$, should be restricted to the quantised values $J(h/2\pi)$, where J is an integer. This assumption is the same as Bohr's in his treatment of the hydrogen atom, and historically precedes it. Bjerrum's expression for the energy is thus

$$E = \tfrac{1}{2}I\omega^2 = \left(\frac{1}{2I}\right)(I\omega)^2 = \left(\frac{1}{2I}\right)\left(\frac{Jh}{2\pi}\right)^2 = J^2\left(\frac{h^2}{8\pi^2 I}\right)$$

Bjerrum's quantisation, however, refers to rotation in a plane, whereas a diatomic molecule free to rotate does so in space (See Fig. II.9), and its total kinetic energy consists of two quadratic terms,

$$E = \frac{1}{2I}\left(p_\theta^2 + \frac{p_\phi^2}{\sin^2\theta}\right). \qquad \text{II.44}$$

On substituting this expression into Schrödinger's equation, with a constant value of the potential energy, V, we obtain a differential equation identical with the θ part of the wave equation of the hydrogen atom, and find that the allowed energy levels are

$$E = J(J+1)\frac{h^2}{8\pi^2 I}\,; \qquad J = 0, 1, 2, \ldots \qquad \text{IV.44}$$

This equation differs from Bjerrum's in that his J^2 is replaced by $J(J+1)$. It provides, as previously stated, the basis of the theory of infra-red spectroscopy.

The linear anharmonic oscillator

It is only when the atoms in a diatomic molecule are displaced by a very small distance, x, from their equilibrium positions that the restoring force is proportional to x, and the motion is, as proved in Chapter II, a simple harmonic one. Generally, the restoring force becomes less as x increases, allowing the atoms eventually to break apart. A successful empirical relationship between the potential energy, V, of such an anharmonic oscillator and the internuclear distance, r, has been proposed by Morse, in terms of an empirical constant, κ:

$$V = D[1 - e^{-\kappa(r - r_e)}]^2 \qquad \text{IV.45}$$

When r is equal to the equilibrium separation, r_e, V is zero; when r is infinite, $V = D$, the energy of dissociation. When the displacement, $r - r_e$, is very small, we may expand the exponential, omitting all terms beyond the second, when we find that

$$V = D\kappa^2(r - r_e)^2 \qquad \text{IV.46}$$

which implies harmonic vibration of frequency v, where

$$v = \frac{\kappa}{\pi}\sqrt{\frac{D}{2\mu}} \qquad \text{IV.47}$$

81

On substituting this expression into Schrödinger's equation, the allowed energy levels of the anharmonic oscillator are found to be

$$E = (v+\tfrac{1}{2})hv - \frac{(hv)^2}{4D}(v+\tfrac{1}{2})^2 \qquad \text{IV.48}$$

where v is an integer. According to this equation, which is to be compared with equation IV.15 for the harmonic oscillator, the difference between the energies of two neighbouring quantum states decreases as the quantum number, v, increases, and vanishes when v reaches the limiting value given by $v_{\text{lim}}+\tfrac{1}{2} = 2D/hv$. This equation provides the basis for the theory of the absorption spectra of molecules in the visible region.

Coupled electronic oscillators

Let us consider two atoms or non-polar molecules, each containing an electron (charge $-e$) and a nucleus (charge $+e$), when the nuclei are at a distance r apart, and the electrons have been displaced, one to the left by a distance x_1, and one to the right by a distance x_2 from their positions of minimum energy. Provided the displacements x_1 and x_2 are small, the potential energy of the system (shown in Fig. IV.13) is

$$V = \tfrac{1}{2}fx_1^2 + \tfrac{1}{2}fx_2^2 + \frac{e^2}{r} + \frac{e^2}{r+x_1+x_2} - \frac{e^2}{r+x_1} - \frac{e^2}{r+x_2}$$

Fig. IV.13 *Linear coulombic interaction energy of static dipoles*

The first two terms are the displacement energies; the next two the Coulombic repulsions; and the last two the Coulombic attractions. On expanding these expressions by means of the binomial theorem (Appendix 4), retaining only the first three terms, we find that

$$V = \tfrac{1}{2}f(x_1^2 + x_2^2) + \frac{2e^2 x_1 x_2}{r^3} \qquad \text{IV.49}$$

After substituting this expression for the potential energy into Schrödinger's equation, London (1931) showed that the allowed energy levels of the system were

$$E = (n_s + \tfrac{1}{2})hv_s + (n_a + \tfrac{1}{2})hv_a \qquad \text{IV.50}$$

where n_s and n_a are integers, and v_s and v_a are related as follows to the vibration frequency, v, of the isolated electronic oscillator, and to the polarisability, α, of the atom or molecule of which the electron forms a part:

$$v_s = v\left(1 + \frac{2\alpha}{r^3}\right)^{1/2}; \qquad v_a = v\left(1 - \frac{2\alpha}{r^3}\right)^{1/2}$$

Now the lowest energy which the system can have is that when n_a and n_s are zero:

$$E_{00} = \tfrac{1}{2}hv_s + \tfrac{1}{2}hv_a$$

and the lowest energy which the two isolated oscillators can have is $\tfrac{1}{2}hv + \tfrac{1}{2}hv = hv$. The difference between the two energies is the potential energy due to the coupling of the oscillators, and is seen, after expansion by means of the binomial theorem, to be approximately

$$\phi = -\frac{1}{2}\frac{hv\alpha^2}{r^6}$$

The interaction energy of a pair of identical non-polar molecules of polarisability α containing one oscillating electron each, when at a distance r apart is thus proportional to the electronic vibration frequency and to the square of the polarisability of the isolated molecule, and varies inversely as the sixth power of their distance, r, apart. The interaction energy of two such atoms or non-polar molecules in space is

$$\phi = -\frac{3}{4}\frac{hv\alpha^2}{r^6} \qquad \text{IV.51}$$

The constants v and α can be readily found from the way in which the refractive index of gases varies with respect to the wave length of the light refracted, i.e. from dispersion constants. For that reason, London's energy is sometimes referred to as a dispersion energy. It is the modern version of the vague van der Waals energy, which was an empirical term, implying that the attractive energy of a pair of molecules varies inversely at the fourth power of the intermolecular separation.

83

London's theory offers the only satisfactory explanation of why uncharged, non-polar molecules attract one another. From independently determined values of v and α he successfully computed the heats of condensation of the inert elements, and of non-polar molecules like hydrogen and oxygen. In such molecules, the number of electrons exceeds 1, and more elaborate forms of London's theory have been advanced by Slater and Kirkwood, and by Hellmann.

Heisenberg's principle of indeterminacy

In order to derive a special form of a general theorem due to Heisenberg – sometimes called the uncertainty principle – we shall again consider the linear harmonic oscillator in its ground state. The average value of the square of the linear displacement is

$$\overline{x^2} = \frac{\int_{-\infty}^{\infty} \psi_0^2 x^2 \, dx}{\int_{-\infty}^{\infty} \psi_0^2 \, dx} \qquad \text{IV.52}$$

As we are using the normalised wave function, the denominator becomes unity. Integration of the numerator, using equation IV.16, yields the result

$$\overline{x^2} = h/8\pi^2 vm$$

Since the energy of the oscillator is $\varepsilon = \frac{1}{2}fx^2 + \left(\dfrac{1}{2m}\right)p^2$, its average value is

$$\bar{\varepsilon} = \frac{1}{2}f\overline{x^2} + \left(\frac{1}{2m}\right)\overline{p^2}$$

On substituting $\frac{1}{2}hv$ for $\bar{\varepsilon}$ and the value derived here for $\overline{x^2}$, we find that $\overline{p^2} = \frac{1}{2}hvm$. Hence

$$\overline{x^2} \cdot \overline{p^2} = \frac{h^2}{16\pi^2}$$

so that, if we denote $\sqrt{\overline{x^2}}$ by Δx and $\sqrt{\overline{p^2}}$ by Δp, we arrive at the equation

$$\Delta x \Delta p = \frac{h}{4\pi} \qquad \text{IV.53}$$

Here Δx stands for the magnitude of the displacement x, irrespective of whether it is to the left or to the right of the origin, and Δp stands for the magnitude of the momentum, irrespective of whether it is positive or negative. We see that, on an average, neither of these variables can be zero, and that their product is Planck's constant, divided by a relatively small numerical factor. This is the exact formulation of the principle of indeterminacy as applied (by Born) to the linear harmonic oscillator. In looser terms we may say that, since neither Δx nor Δp can be zero, the exact and simultaneous specification of the position and momentum of any particle is impossible. Precision in the spatial variable is possible by making Δx extremely small, but this precision is obtainable only at the expense of making Δp relatively large, i.e. by losing precision in the momentum variable. The law applies to any two variables into which h can be resolved, so that $\Delta\varepsilon\Delta t$ must also be approximately equal to h. Then the

exact determination of position implies an uncertainty in the momentum

exact determination of momentum implies an uncertainty in the position

exact determination of energy implies an uncertainty in the time

exact determination of time implies an uncertainty in the energy.

There is another way in which the principle can be expressed; h represents the limit to the simultaneous measurement of position and momentum. A chlorine molecule, for example, restricted to move along a length of one cm could, according to classical theory, have any momentum from $-\infty$ to $+\infty$, including a zero value. According to the quantum theory, the minimum value of its momentum would be $6 \cdot 624 \times 10^{-27}/4\pi$ g-cm/sec, and its minimum velocity would thus be about $0 \cdot 17$ cm/sec. Compared with the average velocity of gas molecules under ordinary conditions, this value can be ignored.

According to classical theory, as developed in Chapter II, the probability that a molecule shall possess an energy ε while having components of position and momentum lying in the range between x and $x + dx$, and between p and $p + dp$, is proportional to the Boltzmann factor $\exp(-\varepsilon/kT)$ and to the product $dx\,dp$. It can be shown that the proportionality factor is $1/h$, or, if s positional coordinates and s conjugated momentum coordinates are required to define the energy, $1/h^s$. When the product $dx\,dp$ is greater than h, we retain it and the proportionality factor $1/h$, recognising that we are then dealing with

expressions in classical statistics, which are ultimately to be integrated as in equation II.39. When, however, the product $dxdp$ has
reached its lowest limit of h, $dxdp/h$ becomes unity; the differentials
vanish, and our expressions are those of quantal statistics, which have
ultimately to be summed, as in equation II.33.

The reflexion and refraction of light

When a ray of light in air falls on a glass surface, it is in part reflected
and in part refracted according to well known laws; the angle of
incidence equals the angle of reflection; and the sine of the angle of
incidence bears a constant ratio to the sine of the angle of refraction.

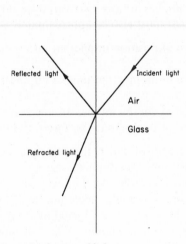

Fig. IV.14   *The reflexion and refraction of light*

Simultaneous reflection and transmission are difficult to understand
on the corpuscular theory of light, for, if the kinetic energy of the light
corpuscles in air, resolved along the normal to the interface, is insufficient to permit penetration, they should all be reflected. On the
other hand, if this component of the kinetic energy exceeds the energy
required to pass from air into glass, all the light should be transmitted.
Wave mechanics can account compactly for the phenomenon. The
behaviour of the incident light in air is governed by a wave function
of the form

$$\psi_a = A \exp^{2\pi i k_a x} = A \exp^{(2\pi i/h)[2m(E-V_a)]^{1/2}x} \qquad \text{IV.54}$$

where E is the total energy of one photon, and V_a is its potential energy in air. The behaviour of the light reflected in the same medium is governed by a similar equation with $-x$ written for x. In the dense medium, the potential energy, V_g, exceeds the kinetic energy, and the wave function is accordingly

$$\psi_g = A \exp^{2\pi i k_g x} = A \exp^{(2\pi i/h)[2m(E-V_g)]^{1/2}x} = A \exp^{-(2\pi/h)[2m(V_g-E)]^{1/2}x}$$

IV.55

The intensity of the refracted light, which is proportional to ψ_g^2, is thus seen to diminish exponentially with respect to its penetration in the dense medium. ψ_a^2, on the other hand, varies with respect to x as in Fig. IV.2, and has an average value of $\frac{1}{2}A^2$, which is independent of x. It must not be overlooked that ψ for the photon in the system considered (air plus glass) is one and indivisible, although its form is different in the two media. At the boundary separating them, $\psi_a = \psi_g$, and $\partial\psi_a/\partial x = \partial\psi_g/\partial x$.

The tunnel effect

Another important phenomenon, bearing, at first sight, no connexion with the reflection and refraction of light, has been interpreted in much the same way. It is radioactivity – the spontaneous conversion of atomic nuclei into smaller ones, at measurable rates, with the emission of γ-rays, electrons, protons, helium nuclei and other subatomic particles. Most of these conversions obey the unimolecular law, according to which a constant fraction of reactant breaks down in unit time. The unimolecular law can be stated in another way, i.e. there is a definite probability per second that any atom of reactant shall break down. This probability may be very low (5×10^{-18} sec^{-1} for uranium I) or very high (7×10^5 for polonium). The problem is to understand why these atoms break down at measurable rates, or, in other words, why atoms have only a qualified stability. The particles contained within an atomic nucleus have, like all particles, kinetic and potential energy. If the kinetic energy exceeds the amount necessary for escape, all the atoms should, on classical grounds, break up; and if the kinetic energy is insufficient, all the atoms should be permanently stable.

Let us suppose that a subatomic unit inside the nucleus has a potential energy of the form shown in Fig. IV.15, and let the origin coincide with the centre of the nucleus. If the subatomic unit has energy E, it

87

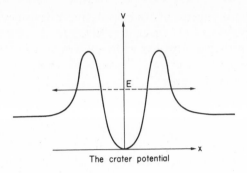

The crater potential

Fig. IV.15

will, according to classical mechanics, always remain inside it, performing, in fact, a periodic motion. It will never escape, because, though it were to expend all its energy in the effort, it is unable to surmount the barrier surrounding the crater. According to wave mechanics, the probability that the subatomic unit shall be at a position x is proportional to ψ^2 at that point, and this, as with the corresponding functions for the harmonic oscillator and the photon, has a real value at distances from the centre which are much greater than those allowed by classical theory. The subatomic unit has thus a chance of appearing outside the crater, though it has, classically speaking, insufficient energy to surmount it. It is as if it were able to tunnel through the wall.

The fractional number of incident particles which penetrate the barrier is known as its transparency, or coefficient of transmission, κ_t. It can, in principle, be evaluated for any particle of mass m and total energy E, provided the form of the potential energy V is known. A plausible expression of V for a crater has been used by Eckart (1930) to calculate κ_t. With the artificial barriers shown in Fig. IV.16, somewhat similar expressions for the transparency emerge. They can be written collectively as

$$\kappa_t = \exp\{-(\gamma\pi l/h)[2m(V_0 - E)]^{1/2}\} \qquad \text{IV.56}$$

where l is the thickness of the barrier at the point of penetration, and V_0 is the height of the barrier. The small numerical factor γ is 4 for the rectangular barrier (Frenkel, 1932), 8/3 for the triangular barrier (Mott and Sneddon, 1948), and π for the parabolic barrier. The coefficient of transmission is thus not very sensitive to the exact shape of the barrier, and is governed chiefly by its height and depth. Other

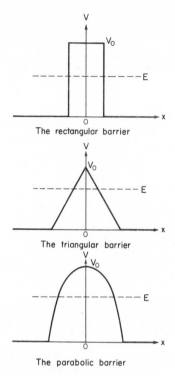

The rectangular barrier

The triangular barrier

The parabolic barrier

Fig. IV.16 *Some hypothetical energy barriers*

things being equal, light particles are transmitted more freely than heavy particles. Thus, for example, for a parabolic barrier of thickness 2 Å and height 20 kilocalories per mole, the coefficient of transmission for an electron is 0·15, and for a hydrogen atom 0·028. It is probably by the tunnel effect that electrons pass from one metal to another, and from an electrode into solution. The rate of a chemical reaction involving a hydrogen atom may, particularly at low temperatures, be increased by the tunnel effect, and approximate expressions to allow for the correction have been derived by Wigner (1932) and Bell (1959).

The hydrogen molecule; covalent bonds

A wide variety of attractive forces can come into play between atoms, ions and molecules, and these, in conjunction with repulsive forces, result in the formation of a wide variety of bonds. A simple

D

type of bond is that in which the attractive force is due to the Coulombic interaction of a positive and negative ion, supplemented by forces of electrostatic induction. The general behaviour of highly polar molecules like KCl in the gaseous and crystalline states can be derived in terms of the electrostatic properties of the constituent ions; the bonds formed between the ions are said to be ionic or electrovalent. At the other end of the scale is the type of bond formed between two hydrogen atoms in the hydrogen molecule. Here, polar properties are absent, and the bond consists of 2 electrons one contributed by each atom. Such bonds have been appropriately termed covalent by Langmuir. If we represent the electrons in the outer shells by dots, the electronic descriptions of three typical homonuclear diatomic molecules are:

$$\text{H} : \text{H} \qquad \overset{\cdot\cdot}{\underset{\cdot\cdot}{\text{O}}} : : \overset{\cdot\cdot}{\underset{\cdot\cdot}{\text{O}}} \qquad : \text{N} \overset{\cdot\cdot}{\cdot\cdot} \text{N} :$$

The letters stand for the kernel of the atom, i.e. the whole atom minus the electrons in its outer shell. The bonding electrons, which optical studies reveal to be 2, 4 and 6 in number must be appropriated equally by both nuclei. When we count the number of electrons 'around' each atom, we thus find 2 for each of the atoms in the hydrogen molecule, and 8 for each of the atoms in the oxygen and nitrogen molecules. Stable molecular structures, like stable atomic structures, thus seem to correspond to symmetrical or closed arrangements of 2, 8, 18 and 32 electrons, as G. N. Lewis first pointed out (the 'octet' rule). Moreover, if we apply Pauli's exclusion principle to molecular as to atomic structures, we must ascribe different quantum numbers to the two electrons in the hydrogen molecule when in the ground state. The only number that can be different is the spin quantum number; one of the bonding electrons has $s = +\frac{1}{2}$, and the other $s = -\frac{1}{2}$. We thus approach the study of the covalent link by noting the experimental facts that, in homonuclear diatomic molecules, the single covalent link consists of a pair of electrons, with opposite spins, one deriving from each atom; that double and triple covalent bonds consist, respectively, of 2 and 3 pairs of electrons; and that, whatever their motion, they do not render the molecules polar.

The first wave-mechanical interpretation of the stability of the hydrogen molecule was given by Heitler and London (1927), using a method now referred to as that of atomic orbitals. The primary assumption of their theory, and, in fact of all wave-mechanical theories of molecular structure, is that the atomic nuclei may be regarded as at rest. The error thus introduced has been shown by van Vleck (1936) to be negligible. From Fig. IV.17, the potential energy

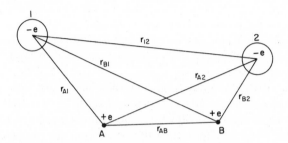

Fig. IV.17 *Coulombic interactions of the hydrogen molecule*

of the system is seen to consist of six Coulombic interactions,

$$V = \frac{e^2}{r_{AB}} + \frac{e^2}{r_{12}} - \frac{e^2}{r_{A1}} - \frac{e^2}{r_{A2}} - \frac{e^2}{r_{B1}} - \frac{e^2}{r_{B2}}$$ IV.57

The reference state of zero potential energy is seen to be that of the two electrons and the two hydrogen ions when they are all infinitely far apart. The total energy of the molecule is the sum of V and the kinetic energy of the electrons. The wave equation to be solved is

$$\nabla_1^2 \Psi + \nabla_2^2 \Psi + \frac{8\pi^2 m}{h^2}(E - V)\Psi = 0$$ IV.58

where Ψ is the wave function for the whole molecule, m is the mass of one electron, and E is the total energy of the molecule. ∇_1^2 stands for the Laplacian operator

$$\frac{\partial^2}{\partial x_1^2} + \frac{\partial^2}{\partial y_1^2} + \frac{\partial^2}{\partial z_1^2}$$

where x_1, y_1, z_1 are the coordinates of the first electron. ∇_2^2 is the corresponding operator relating to electron 2. The task now is to construct a reasonable form of the wave function. We start with that for an isolated atom of hydrogen in the ground state, for which we have already derived the normalised wave function (equation IV.31): $\psi_1 = (\pi a_1^3)^{-1/2} \cdot \exp(-r/a_1)$, where a_1 is the smallest Bohr orbit.

A similar wave function, ψ_2, governs the behaviour of the second hydrogen atom, when it, likewise, is isolated. For the pair of hydrogen atoms at an infinite distance apart, therefore, the wave function for the system is $\Psi = \psi_1 \psi_2$, since it is necessary, when the two atoms are without influence on each other, that the energy, E, of the system is $2E_H$, where E_H is the energy of an isolated atom. This expression for Ψ holds when the electron labelled 1 is attached to the nucleus labelled A, and electron 2 is attached to nucleus B, and it can be written more precisely as $\Psi_1 = \psi_A(1)\psi_B(2)$. Let the atoms now unite to form a hydrogen molecule, and then dissociate into atoms in such a way that the electrons have exchanged their nuclei. For the pair of isolated atoms now the total wave function is $\Psi_2 = \psi_A(2)\psi_B(1)$. Both these wave functions are valid to account for the behaviour of the hydrogen system when the atoms are infinitely far apart: they are special solutions which hold in the limit. It is next assumed that Ψ for the real system, when the atoms influence each other, has the same form as Ψ_1 and Ψ_2, to either of which it must reduce in the limit. Now it is an easily verified property of Schrödinger's equation that, if Ψ_1 and Ψ_2 are separate solutions of it, then any linear combination of the two must also be solutions of it, so that

$$\Psi = a\psi_A(1)\psi_B(2) + b\psi_A(2)\psi_B(1) \qquad \text{IV.59}$$

where a and b are constants which, mathematically, can have any value, but which, physically, are chosen so that the energy of the system to which Ψ refers has its minimum value. On substituting this expression in Schrödinger's equation and solving for those values of Ψ which conform to this condition, the allowed energy levels of the system are found to be given by the equation

$$E = 2E_H + \frac{(K \pm J)}{(1 \pm T^2)} \qquad \text{IV.60}$$

where E_H is the energy of an isolated hydrogen atom. The common reference state of energy for the free atoms as for the molecule is that of zero energy when the two protons and the two electrons are infinitely separated. Clearly $E - 2E_H$ is the bond energy. K, J and T involve integrals, conveniently referred to as Coulombic, exchange and overlapping:

$$K = \frac{e^2}{r_{AB}} - 2e^2 \iiint \frac{\Psi_A^2(1)}{r_{B1}} \, dv_1 + e^2 \int \cdots \int \frac{\psi_A^2(1)\psi_B^2(1)}{r_{12}} \, dv_1 \, dv_2$$

$$J = \frac{e^2 T^2}{r_{AB}} - 2Te^2 \iiint \frac{\psi_A(1)\psi_B(1)}{r_{B1}} \, dv$$

$$+ e^2 \int \cdots \int \frac{\psi_A(1)\psi_B(2)\psi_A(2)\psi_B(1)}{r_{12}} \, dv_1 \, dv_2$$

$$T = \iiint \psi_A(1)\psi_B(1) \, dv_1 \qquad\qquad \text{IV.61}$$

These integrals can be evaluated in closed form except those involving r_{12}, for which a series expansion is used. J has a negative value. The two expressions for the energy of the hydrogen molecule, relative to that of the isolated atoms, are

$$E_\alpha = E - 2E_H = \frac{K + J}{1 + T^2} \qquad\qquad \text{IV.62}$$

and

$$E_\beta = E - 2E_H = \frac{K - J}{1 - T^2} \qquad\qquad \text{IV.63}$$

These equations, showing E_α and E_β as functions of r/a_1, are shown in Fig. IV.18. The upper curve, marked E_β, shows a hydrogen molecule for which the energy is positive at all internuclear distances. Such a molecule is inherently unstable. The energy of the stable hydrogen

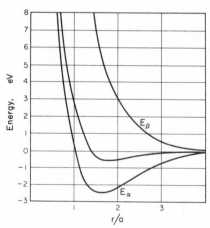

Fig. IV.18 *The potential energy of two neutral hydrogen atoms (after W. Heiter and F. London).* $E_\alpha = $ *homopolar attraction;* $E_\beta = $ *elastic repulsion*

93

molecule is shown as a function of r/a_1 in the bottom curve (E_a), the form of which is precisely that required to explain its principal properties. The minimum energy is found to correspond to $r/a_1 = 3/2$, so that the calculated value of r is 0.792 Å, which agrees well with the observed interatomic distance of 0.749 Å. The depth of the trough, however, is only about 2.4 electron-volts, or 55 kilocals/mole, which is about one-half of the experimental value. The middle curve in Fig. IV.18 shows the energy calculated for the system of two hydrogen atoms when either Ψ_1 or Ψ_2 is used alone in Schrödinger's equation, and the idea of a linear combination has not been incorporated. This curve is far too shallow to correspond to the true behaviour, and has been included by Heitler and London specifically to reveal its inadequacy.

The treatment of Heitler and London, has been improved and extended by many investigators, notably Pauling and Slater. The essence of their work is to show that, according to wave mechanics, the very fact that each electron is shared equally by the two atoms confers a stability on the molecule. 'Heitler and London's work must be considered as the greatest single contribution to the clarification of the chemist's conception of valence which has been made since G. N. Lewis's suggestion in 1916 that the chemical bond between two atoms consists of a pair of electrons held jointly by the two atoms.' (Pauling and Wilson, 1935.)

Another procedure, developed independently by Lennard-Jones, Hund, Herzberg and Mulliken, is known as the method of molecular orbitals. Its basis is Hartree's treatment of electronic motion in atoms containing many electrons. Its fundamental assumption is that the wave function which governs the behaviour of a molecule containing n electrons can be constructed as the product of n wave functions, or molecular orbitals, each of which governs the behaviour of one of its constituent electrons, so that

$$\Psi = \psi_1(x_1, y_1, z_1)\psi_2(x_2, y_2, z_2)\dots\psi_n(x_n, y_n, z_n) \qquad \text{IV.64}$$

Applied to two significant electrons in a diatomic molecule, AB, the wave function has the form

$$\Psi = [a\psi_A(x_1, y_1, z_1) + b\psi_B(x_1, y_1, z_1)] \times [a\psi_A(x_2, y_2, z_2) + b\psi_B(x_2, y_2, z_2)].$$

On normalising both atomic orbitals to unity,

$$\iiint_{-\infty}^{\infty} \psi_A^2 \, dv = \iiint_{-\infty}^{\infty} \psi_B^2 \, dv = 1$$

94

and on similarly normalising the two molecular orbitals, it is found that

$$a^2 + b^2 + 2abT = 1 \qquad \text{IV.65}$$

where T is defined by equation IV.63. When there is little overlapping of the wave functions of the two atoms, T is nearly zero, and the wave function governing the behaviour of the whole molecule can be written as follows:

$$\Psi = a^2\psi_A(1)\psi_A(2) + b^2\psi_B(1)\psi_B(2) + ab[\psi_A(1)\psi_B(2) + \psi_A(2)\psi_B(1)]$$

The first term in this equation covers the case of the two electrons being both on atom A; the second term, the case when both electrons are on atom B; the third term, the case when electron 1 is on atom A, and electron 2 is on atom B; the fourth term is self-explanatory. When $a^2 = b^2$, the two first terms, which are clearly ionic, represent an equal probability of the existence of the molecule A^+B^- and A^-B^+; the net behaviour of the molecule is then non-polar. All grades of polarity are possible by allowing a^2 to differ from b^2.

The wave-mechanical theory of directed valency

The wave function of an s electron is spherically symmetrical (Fig. IV.12). So also must be the density of negative electricity in the cloud to which it gives rise. If the stable union of two atoms, each containing an s electron, is to be attributed to the fusing or interpenetration of such clouds, the bond formed can have no preference for any particular direction. The wave functions ψ of a p electron, on the other hand, are functions of the angles θ and ϕ. If the stable union of two atoms depends on the interpenetration of the clouds of electricity due to an s electron in one atom and a p electron in a second atom, we expect the exchange integrals and, consequently, the exchange energy, to have their highest values when the wave functions overlap as much as possible, i.e. when the centre of the cloud of electricity due to the s electron of one atom lies on the particular axis about which the cloud of electricity due to the p electron of the second atom is centred and concentrated. We shall now show that the cloud of electricity due to a p electron is, in fact, centred round the Cartesian axes, x, y and z: it follows that the valency forces which they exert must be mutually at right angles.

From the normalised angular wave functions of a p electron given in Table IV.1, the total wave functions are obtained on multiplying each by the radial wave function $R(r)$. Of the three resulting total wave functions, one is seen to be real and two are seen to be imaginary. Since all three are solutions of Schrödinger's equations, we know that linear combinations of them are also solutions. Let us, therefore, use instead of the two imaginary values of ψ their sum and their difference, which multiplied by a constant are both real. The three normalised total wave functions of the p electron are

$$\psi(l = 1, m = 0) = R(r)\frac{1}{2}\sqrt{\frac{3}{\pi}}\ \cos\theta$$

$$= f(r)\cos\theta$$

$$\psi(l = 1, m = 1) = R(r)\frac{1}{2}\sqrt{\frac{3}{2\pi}}\ \sin\theta\cdot e^{i\phi}$$

$$= f(r)\sin\theta(\cos\phi + i\sin\phi)$$

$$\psi(l = 1, m = -1) = R(r)\frac{1}{2}\sqrt{\frac{3}{2\pi}}\ \sin\theta\cdot e^{-i\phi}$$

$$= f(r)\sin\theta(\cos\phi) - i\sin\phi)$$

and we work with linear combinations of the second and third functions, $(1/\sqrt{2})(\psi_{1,1} + \psi_{1,-1})$ and $(1/i\sqrt{2})(\psi_{1,1} - \psi_{1,-1})$. Reference to equations IV.27–29 makes it clear that these functions are directly proportional to z, y and x, since

$$\psi_{1,0} = \frac{f(r)}{r}z = \psi(p_z)$$

$$\psi_{1,1} = \frac{f(r)}{r}y = \psi(p_y)$$

and

$$\psi_{1,-1} = \frac{f(r)}{r}x = \psi(p_x) \hspace{2cm} \text{IV.66}$$

Thus, for example, $\psi(p_x)$ is zero in the plane $x = 0$. Above and below this plane it is real, and symmetrical about the z axis. The three wave functions of the p electron are represented in Fig. IV.10, which is reproduced from Pauling and Wilson's monograph. The density of negative electricity, or the probability of the presence of the electron is proportional to ψ^2, and the surfaces formed are similar in shape. This probability is seen to be zero at the origin, and elsewhere to vary symmetrically around the three Cartesian axes. ψ^2 forms surfaces on which the electron is most probably found. On account of the shape of these surfaces, the p electron orbitals are sometimes referred to as dumbbell orbitals. A solid figure which more nearly presents their actual surfaces, however, is the old fashioned sand-in-glass instrument used to time the boiling of eggs. Which of the three orbitals we label p_x or p_y or p_z is, of course, immaterial; the fundamental conclusion is that the three orbitals are mutually at right angles. This important deduction was made independently and almost simultaneously by J. C. Slater and L. Pauling in 1931.

If the stable union of two atoms of hydrogen with one atom of oxygen is due to the interpenetration of the clouds of electricity due to the two s electrons in the hydrogen atoms and those due to two electrons in the p state in the oxygen atom, we would expect the water molecule to be right-angled. The valency angle is, in fact, 105° (Chapter X). If the ammonia molecule is formed in a similar way, then, since the p_x, p_y and p_z orbitals of the nitrogen atom determine the valency angles, we would expect the angle of inclination of any two neighbouring N—H bonds to be 90°, so that the molecule NH_3 should be a pyramid, the direction of each N—H bond being inclined at an angle of 54° 42′ to the principal axis of the molecule. The ammonia molecule is, in fact, a pyramid, but the inclination angle is about 67° (Chapter X). In both these, and in numerous other instances, the Slater-Pauling theory explains their principal features. That the valency angles are somewhat wider than anticipated is thought to be due to the fact that the binding is not entirely covalent, but in part ionic: the hydrogen atoms in the molecules formed retain something of their protonic character, and thus repel one another. Had we imagined the molecules to be formed from the oxygen ion, O^{--} and the nitrogen ion, N^{---} and 2 (respectively 3) protons, H^+, while each ion exerted a spherically symmetrical field of force, we would have concluded that the water molecule was straight and the ammonia molecule flat.

Let us finally consider the carbon atom. In the free atomic state its electronic configuration is $1s^2 2s^2 2p^2$. The two $1s$ electrons in the first or K shell mutually satisfy each other, as do the two $2s$ electrons in the second or L shell. Only the two $2p$ electrons are left to form valency bonds with other atoms. If this electronic arrangement were correct, carbon would be divalent. It is well known that it is tetra-valent. To explain this fact, we imagine one of the $2s$ electrons to be promoted to the $2p$ level, giving the electronic arrangement $1s^2 2s^1 2p^3$. In this state the carbon atom could certainly form four univalent bonds, three of which, due to the p electrons, being mutually at right angles, and the fourth, due to the $2s$ electron, being indifferent as to direction. This model, though an improvement on the first one, is still inadequate, as the absolute equivalence of the four valency bonds in methane is the cardinal fact of aliphatic organic chemistry. Its interpretation in terms of wave mechanics has been given by Pauling. We first disregard the difference in energy between the $2s$ and the three $2p$ electrons, and next recall that, if $\psi(2s)$, $\psi(2p_x)$, $\psi(2p_y)$ and $\psi(2p_z)$ are wave functions for the four electrons, any linear combina-tion of them is a legitimate solution of ψ for the carbon atom. On solving for the coefficients, which correspond to a and b of equation IV.67, and making use of the condition that the energy of the molecule must be a minimum, it follows by a fairly direct theorem that the four valencies must be identical, and must have directions inclined to one another at an angle α given by $\cos \alpha = -\frac{1}{3}$. This is the angle re-quired to build a regular tetrahedron.

V The chemical elements

The systematic description of the chemical elements and their properties constitutes almost the whole province of inorganic chemistry. Those parts of it which can be quantitatively formulated are essential also to physical chemistry. Evidence accumulated from various branches of science now provides a fairly complete picture of the structures of the various kinds of atoms. Starting with the hydrogen atom, with its nucleus bearing a unit positive charge, we can pass successively through all the elements until we reach mendelevium with its nuclear charge of 101. Since all atoms in their natural states are electrically neutral, there must surround the atomic nuclei a number of electrons, ranging from 1 in the hydrogen atom to 101 in the mendelevium atom. It is convenient, despite the probability interpretation recommended by wave mechanics, to think of the electrons in this connexion as discrete particles, forming concentric shells around the nucleus, as shown in Fig. v.1 for the cadmium atom. It must be emphasised that the electrons in all atoms do not move on the surfaces of spheres, and that the representation is schematic. The shells labelled K, L, M, ... correspond to electrons having principal quantum numbers of 1, 2, 3, ... Let us focus attention first on the two electrons in the O shell ($n = 5$), for it is to these that the cadmium atom owes its valency of 2, and its visible spectrum, produced when one of the electrons, having been temporarily removed to larger spheres, returns to the O shell, emitting radiation of varying frequencies, depending on how far away it has been. These two electrons may be called valency electrons or optical electrons. The representation of the atoms of zinc and mercury are similar, except that in zinc, the two valency electrons occupy shell N ($n = 4$) and in mercury shell P ($n = 6$). Such similarity as these three elements of group IIB in the periodic table (Table v.1) possess is due to the similarity in their electronic structure. The same may be said of the elements in group O (He, Ne, A, Kr, Xe, Rn). The atoms of the elements in this group are surrounded by closed shells of electrons, which render them chemically inert. The similarity in the chemical behaviour of the elements in group IA (H, Li, Na, K, Rb, Cs, Fr) and their relatively large atomic

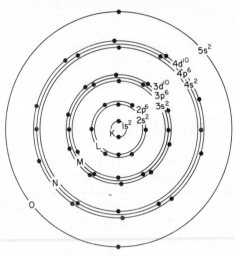

Fig. v.1 *Schematic representation of the orbits of the electrons in the cadmium atom* (after White *Introduction to Atomic Spectra*, p. 309)

volumes are attributed to the single valency electron in the outermost shell. So also is the similarity in their spectra, the analysis of which is a sufficient indication of when a shell can be regarded as closed, and therefore incapable of accommodating more electrons. Experiment shows that the highest terms in the principal series of the spectra of lithium and sodium correspond, respectively, with terms in the hydrogen spectrum with $n = 2$ and 3. This can only mean that, in the lithium atom, two electrons form a closed shell, prohibiting further additions, and that in the sodium atom, ten electrons form between them two closed shells. In ways like this, electronic theory has furnished a fascinating explanation of the periodic table of the elements as drawn up by Mendeleeff and Newlands.

Two sets of quite different investigations have enabled the nuclear charge, or atomic number, of the elements to be measured.

X-ray spectra of the elements; Moseley's law

When the electrons in a cathode-ray tube hit an elementary anti-cathode, they generate X-rays. Moseley (1913) measured their wavelengths by using a potassium ferrocyanide grating and applying Bragg's law. He found that, for any given element, the lines in the

100

Table v.1 *Periodic classification of the elements**

Group / Period	I A	I B	II A	II B	III A	III B	IV A	IV B	V A	V B	VI A	VI B	VII A	VII B	VIII	0
1	1 H 1·0080															2 He 4·003
2	3 Li 6·940		4 Be 9·013			5 B 10·82		6 C 12·011		7 N 14·008		8 O 16·0000		9 F 19·00		10 Ne 20·183
3	11 Na 22·991		12 Mg 24·32			13 Al 26·98		14 Si 28·09		15 P 30·975		16 S 32·066		17 Cl 35·457		18 A 39·944
4	19 K 39·110	29 Cu 63·54	20 Ca 40·08	30 Zn 65·38	21 Sc 44·96	31 Ga 69·72	22 Ti 47·90	32 Ge 72·60	23 V 50·95	33 As 74·91	24 Cr 52·01	34 Se 78·96	25 Mn 54·94	35 Br 79·916	26 Fe 55·85 27 Co 58·94 28 Ni 58·69	36 Kr 83·80
5	37 Rb 85·48	47 Ag 107·880	38 Sr 87·63	48 Cd 112·41	39 Y 88·92	49 In 114·76	40 Zr 91·22	50 Sn 118·70	41 Nb 92·91	51 Sb 121·76	42 Mo 95·95	52 Te 127·61	43 Tc [99]	53 I 126·91	44 Ru 101·1 45 Rh 102·91 46 Pd 106·7	54 Xe 131·3
6	55 Cs 132·91	79 Au 196·0	56 Ba 137·36	80 Hg 200·61	57 La 138·92	81 Tl 204·39	72 Hf 178·6	82 Pb 207·21	73 Ta 180·95	83 Bi 209·00	74 W 183·92	84 Po 210	75 Re 186·31	85 At [210]	76 Os 190·2 77 Ir 192·2 78 Pt 195·23	86 Rn 222
7	87 Fr [223]		88 Ra 226·05		89 Ac 227		90 Th 232·05		91 Pa 231		92 U 238·07		93 Np 237		94 Pu 242 95 Am 243 96 Cm 245	

The *lanthanide series* (to be placed between 57 La and 72 Hf):

58 Ce 140·13	59 Pr 140·92	60 Nd 144·27	61 Pm [145]	62 Sm 150·43	63 Eu 152·0	64 Gd 156·9	65 Tb 158·93	66 Dy 162·46	67 Ho 164·94	68 Er 167·2	69 Tm 168·94	70 Yb 173·04	71 Lu 174·99

The *actinide series* (to be placed after 90 Th):

91 Pa 231	92 U 238·07	93 Np [237]	94 Pu [242]	95 Am [243]	96 Cm [245]	97 Bk [245]	98 Cf [248]	99 [253]	100 [254]	101 Mv [256]

* A value given in brackets denotes the mass number of the isotope of longest known half-life.

101

spectrum could be classified into series, labelled K, L and M, in the order of decreasing hardness or penetrability. When the first line in the K series for this element was compared with the first lines in the K series for other elements, it was found that the square-root of the frequency of the various lines varied linearly with respect to integers (3 for Li; 11 for Na, and so on). In fact, all the frequencies of the lines in the X-ray spectra of all the elements could be expressed by means of the general equation

$$v/c = R(Z-\sigma)^2\rho \qquad\qquad \text{v.1}$$

where R is Rydberg's constant, σ and ρ are empirical constants, and Z is an integer. The K series, for example, are reproduced by the equation

$$v/c = R(Z-1)^2 \; \tfrac{3}{4} \; = R(Z-1)^2\left(\frac{1}{1^2}-\frac{1}{2^2}\right) \qquad\qquad \text{v.2}$$

and the L series by the equation

$$v/c = R(Z-7\cdot4)^2 \; \tfrac{5}{36} = R(Z-7\cdot4)^2\left(\frac{1}{2^2}-\frac{1}{3^2}\right) \qquad\qquad \text{v.3}$$

These laws may be understood by supposing that an electron in the cathode rays, penetrating an atom in the anti-cathode, collides with and ejects an electron from the K or L shell. The return of this electron to the vacant place in the K or L shell is attended by the emission or K or L radiation (Fig. v.2). Now the energy of an atom of the hydrogen type, consisting of one electron (charge $-e$) and a nucleus possessing a positive charge Ze is $\varepsilon = -2\pi^2 Z^2 e^4 m_e/n^2 h^2$. By applying Bohr's frequency relation ($hv = \varepsilon_2 - \varepsilon_1$), the theoretical expression for the wave numbers of the radiation emitted is seen to be

$$\frac{v}{c} = \frac{2\pi^2 Z^2 e^4 m_e}{h^3 c}\left(\frac{1}{n_1^2}-\frac{1}{n_2^2}\right) = RZ^2\left(\frac{1}{n_1^2}-\frac{1}{n_2^2}\right) \qquad\qquad \text{v.4}$$

where R is Rydberg's constant. Moseley's experiments indicate that the electron awaiting its return to the K shell responds to the nucleus as if it had a positive charge of $(Z-1)e$. The explanation is that the total charge of Ze on the nucleus is screened by the other electron still occupying the K shell. The screening constant σ is greater for the L radiation, and shows that the total nuclear charge of Ze is now screened by all the electrons (seven in number) still occupying this shell.

The number (Z) of units of positive charge possessed by the nucleus of an atom is termed its atomic number (see Table 1.1). It is a more significant property than the atomic weight, and has made possible the construction of a periodic table of the elements which is free from chemical inconsistencies.

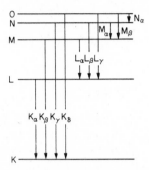

Fig. v.2 *Term scheme, illustrating the origin of the X-ray spectra of the elements* (after Born, *Atomic Physics*, p. 127, seventh edition, Blackie, 1962)

The scattering of α-particles; Rutherford's law

Helium atoms deprived of two electrons are known as alpha particles – a name given them before their nature had been established. They are produced at varying rates in the natural decay of unstable atoms, and possess enormous kinetic energies. Rutherford argued that, if the nucleus of another atom does in fact possess a positive charge Ze, then the path of an alpha particle (charge E; mass M; velocity v) under its influence should be a hyperbola with a deviation angle ϕ given by the equation

$$\frac{n}{n^0} = \left[\frac{ZeE}{2Mv^2R} \operatorname{cosec}^2\left(\frac{\phi}{2}\right) \right]^2 \qquad \text{v.5}$$

where R is the distance between the scatterer (i.e. the atomic nucleus) and a screen on unit area of which n alpha particles arrive per unit time. n^0 is the corresponding rate of arrival per unit area when there is no scatterer, and is a measure of the intensity of the incident beam. The presence of an alpha particle can be detected by various means, e.g. by observing the scintillation produced by it when it hits a screen

103

coated with zinc sulphide (Crookes's method), or by noting the kick of a galvanometer needle connected to a chamber containing an ionisable gas (Geiger's method). Rutherford's equation has been verified in every particular. For example, the number of particles (n) reaching unit area of the screen per second is proportional to the fourth power of the cosecant of one half of the angle through which they have been scattered, and inversely proportional to the fourth power of their velocity. The nuclear charges found experimentally are Ze, where Z is the same number as appears in Moseley's equations.

Optical spectra of the elements

The analysis of the optica spectra of the elements is based on the Ritz–Rydberg principle of combination, according to which, as already shown in the case of hydrogen, the wave numbers of the lines in the spectrum of any given element can be reproduced as differences between certain inferred wave numbers, called terms. Each term, T, is directly proportional to the energy, ε, of a given state of the atom, since, by Bohr's frequency relation, $T = -\varepsilon/hc$. The terms for any given element divide themselves, chiefly on the basis of intensities, into four series, called sharp, principal, diffuse and fundamental, and denoted by the letters S, P, D and F. The terms found for the spectrum of atomic lithium are shown in Table v.2. It is to be observed that the highest term in the principal series ($28581 \cdot 4 \, \text{cm}^{-1}$) lies near to the second term in the spectrum of atomic hydrogen, which is $R/4 = 27419 \cdot 4$. We may therefore reasonably assume that the principal quantum number of the lithium atom in its ground state is 2. The

Table v.2 *Terms in the optical spectrum of atomic lithium*

Term	Electron	$n = 2$	$n = 3$	$n = 4$	$n = 5$	$n = 6$	$n = 7$	l
S	s	43484·4	16280·5	8474·1	5186·9	3499·6	2535·3	0
P	p	28581·4	12559·9	7017·0	4472·8	3094·4	2268·9	1
D	d	—	12202·5	6862·5	4389·2	3046·9	2239·4	2
F	f	—	—	6855·5	4381·2	3031·0	—	3
Hydrogen		27419·4	12186·4	6854·8	4387·1	3046·6	2238·3	

smaller terms in the spectrum of lithium, counting on this basis, come closer and closer to the corresponding terms in the spectrum of hydrogen. For example, when n is 7, the difference between the terms for Li and H is only $1\cdot1$ cm^{-1}, which corresponds to a difference about 3 calories per gram-atom. The optical electron in the lithium atom particularly in states of high quantum numbers thus closely resembles the electron in the hydrogen atom, and responds to the remainder of the lithium atom as if it were a single positive charge. The total charge on the nucleus ($+3$) has thus been effectively reduced to 1 by the remaining two electrons. The spectrum of sodium similarly shows that the electron responsible for its spectrum is attracted, especially in high quantum states, to the remainder of the atom as if the total positive charge were 1.

The restrictions imposed on the combination of terms are those summarised by the selection rules enunciated in Chapter III, and their application to the spectrum of lithium is shown schematically in Fig. v.3. Theoretical terms for atomic hydrogen are shown, in the same units (cm^{-1}), on the ruler. In the symbols denoting the energy levels, the large numeral means the principal quantum number, the letters S, P, D and F indicate, consecutively, values of 0, 1, 2 and 3 for the azimuthal quantum number, 1, and the superscript gives the multiplicity of the energy state, that is, the number of energy states lying very close together. All states of the lithium atom are seen to be doublets from the diagram, though the doublet separation is not included in the data of Table v.2. There, for example, the difference between the 2^2P and 2^2S terms is given as $14\,903\cdot0$ cm^{-1}, corresponding to a wavelength of $6\,710\cdot06$ Å. In fact, there are two very similar transitions between these states, giving a pair of lines differing in wave numbers by $0\cdot338$ cm^{-1}, and in wavelengths by $0\cdot152$ Å. In the spectrum of sodium the familiar pair of lines at $5\,890$ and $5\,896$ Å are due to the transitions

$$3^2P_{1/2} \searrow$$
$$3^2S_{1/2}$$
$$3^2P_{3/2} \nearrow$$

Subscripts denote inner quantum numbers. The analysis of the various atomic spectra shows that, in their state of lowest energy, atoms of the elements in groups O and II exist in singlet states; those of groups I, III and VII in doublet states: those of groups IV and VI as triplets; and those of group V as quartets (Table v.3).

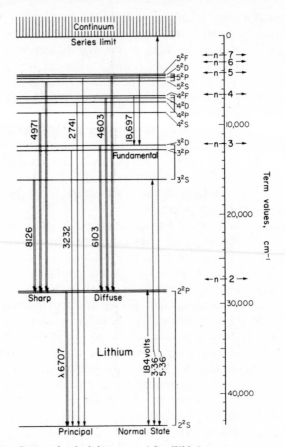

Fig. v.3 *Term diagram for the lithium atom* (after White)

The arrangement of electrons in the chemical atoms

Optical spectra provide, as we have shown, information concerning the state of the valency electrons, i.e. those electrons which occupy the outermost shell. X-ray spectra provide information on the state of electrons in the innermost shells. With supplementary knowledge in the fields of magnetism and general chemistry, it is possible to give a description of the state of most of the electrons in the various atoms, and of all the electrons in atoms of low atomic weights. Following Bohr and Stoner (1924), let us mentally build up the various types of

106

Table v.3 *Ground electronic states of the commoner elements*

Periodic group	Elements	Normal state	Multiplicity
I	H, Li, Na, K, Rb, Cs; Cu, Ag, Au	$^2S_{\frac{1}{2}}$	2
II	Be, Mg, Ca, Sr, Ba; Zn, Cd, Hg	$^1S_0$	1
III	B, Al, Ga, In, Tl	$^2P_{\frac{1}{2}}$	2
IV	C, Si, Ge, Sn, Pb	$^3P_0$	3
V	N, P, As, Sb, Bi	$^4S_{1\frac{1}{2}}$	4
VI	O, S, Se, Te, Po	$^3P_2$	3
VII	F, Cl, Br, I	$^2P_{1\frac{1}{2}}$	2
O	He, Ne, A, Kr, X, Rn	$^1S_0$	1

atoms by starting with their bare nuclei and adding electrons one at a time until each atom is electrically neutral. We are interested in constructing only the most stable atoms, i.e. those in the states of lowest energy, so that, if there are two possible configurations of the electrons around a given nucleus, we accept that with the lower energy. This is our first guiding principle. The second is the exclusion principle of Pauli, which states that no two electrons in an atom can have all their quantum numbers the same. To describe completely the state of any electron we require, as shown in Chapter IV, four quantum numbers, namely

n, the total quantum number, which can have any value from $1, 2, 3 \ldots$ to ∞,

l, the azimuthal quantum number, which can have any value from 0 to $n-1$,

m, the magnetic quantum number, which can have any value from $-l$ to $+l$, that is, $2l+1$ values in all, and

s, the spin quantum number, which can be either $+\frac{1}{2}$ or $-\frac{1}{2}$.

Let us start with the hydrogen nucleus and add one electron. The energy principle determines that n is 1. The only possible values of l and m are 0. s, however, may be either $+\frac{1}{2}$ or $-\frac{1}{2}$. Let us suppose it is $+\frac{1}{2}$. Next we start with the helium nucleus: the same remarks apply to the addition of the first electron. The second electron can have the same values of n, l and m $(1, 0, 0)$ but not the same value of s; it can, however, have $s = -\frac{1}{2}$. There can be no further addition of electrons with n still equal to 1. This means the first shell is closed, and in building an atom of lithium on the same principles, the third electron must have $n = 2$, i.e. it is the first occupant of the second shell. With $n = 2$, we can consistently label eight electrons and no more; thus

$$
n = 2
\begin{cases}
l = 0 \begin{cases} m = 0 & \begin{cases} s = +\frac{1}{2} \\ s = -\frac{1}{2} \end{cases} \end{cases} \\[2ex]
l = 1 \begin{cases}
m = +1 & \begin{cases} s = +\frac{1}{2} \\ s = -\frac{1}{2} \end{cases} \\[1.5ex]
m = 0 & \begin{cases} s = +\frac{1}{2} \\ s = -\frac{1}{2} \end{cases} \\[1.5ex]
m = -1 & \begin{cases} s = +\frac{1}{2} \\ s = -\frac{1}{2} \end{cases}
\end{cases}
\end{cases}
$$

Now the spectrum of lithium shows that the ground state is an S state. Carrying over the notation, we may describe the valency electron in the lithium atom as an s electron. The complete electronic arrangement of the lithium atom in the ground state is then written as $1s^2 2s$, where the numerals give the total quantum number. The letters s, p and d denote azimuthal quantum numbers $l = 0$, $l = 1$ and $l = 2$, respectively. The superscripts are the numbers of electrons. The remaining elements in the second period of the periodic table are built up as shown in Table v.4 by the addition of electrons to the L shells, filling up first the sub-shell of two s electrons, and then the sub-shell of six p electrons. Neon has therefore the electronic structure $1s^2 2s^2 2p^6$. The building of the remaining atoms now proceeds uninterruptedly until we reach potassium with nuclear charge 19. According to the exclusion principle there is room for ten electrons in the third sub-shell of M, but the electron added to make the potassium atom is known from the spectrum to be not a d electron but an s electron. It must therefore be concluded that the minimum-energy principle is here a determining factor; to the structure of argon $(1s^2 2s^2 2p^6 3s^2 3p^6)$ with one extra unit of nuclear charge, a $4s$ electron is more firmly held than a $3d$ electron. Not until we reach scandium $(Z = 21)$ is the third sub-shell of M occupied; it is somewhat irregularly supplied with electrons

108

Table v.4 *Electronic configuration of the chemical elements*

Shells — K (n = 1): 1s; L (n = 2): 2s, 2p; M (n = 3): 3s, 3p, 3d; N (n = 4): 4s, 4p, 4d, 4f; O (n = 5): 5s, 5p, 5d.

	1s	2s	2p	3s	3p	3d	4s	4p	4d	4f	5s	5p	5d	Ionisation Potential	Normal State
1 H	1													13·59	$^2S_{\frac12}$
2 He	2													24·45	$^1S_0$
3 Li	2	1												5·37	$^2S_{\frac12}$
4 Be	2	2												9·48	$^1S_0$
5 B	2	2	1											8·25	$^2P_{\frac12}$
6 C	2	2	2											11·22	$^3P_0$
7 N	2	2	3											14·47	$^4S_{1\frac12}$
8 O	2	2	4											13·56	$^3P_2$
9 F	2	2	5											18·6	$^2P_{1\frac12}$
10 Ne	2	2	6											21·46	$^1S_0$
11 Na	2	2	6	1										5·12	$^2S_{\frac12}$
12 Mg				2										7·61	$^1S_0$
13 Al		Neon	Core	2	1									5·96	$^2P_{\frac12}$
14 Si				2	2									7·39	$^3P_0$
15 P				2	3									10·3	$^4S_{1\frac12}$
16 S				2	4									10·31	$^3P_2$
17 Cl				2	5									12·96	$^2P_{1\frac12}$
18 A				2	6									15·96	$^1S_0$
19 K	2	2	6	2	6		1							4·32	$^2S_{\frac12}$
20 Ca							2							6·09	$^1S_0$
21 Sc						1	2							6·59	$^2D_{1\frac12}$
22 Ti						2	2							6·80	$^3F_2$
23 V						3	2							6·76	$^4F_{1\frac12}$
24 Cr		Argon	Core			5	1							6·74	$^7S_3$
25 Mn						5	2							7·40	$^6S_{2\frac12}$
26 Fe						6	2							7·83	$^5D_4$
27 Co						7	2							7·81	$^4F_{4\frac12}$
28 Ni						8	2							7·61	$^3F_4$
29 Cu	2	2	6	2	6	10	1							7·69	$^2S_{\frac12}$
30 Zn							2							9·35	$^1S_0$
31 Ga							2	1						5·97	$^2P_{\frac12}$
32 Ge							2	2						7·85	$^3P_0$
33 As		Copper	Core				2	3						9·4	$^4S_{1\frac12}$
34 Se							2	4						9·70	$^3P_2$
35 Br							2	5						11·80	$^2P_{1\frac12}$
36 Kr							2	6						13·94	$^1S_0$
37 Rb	2	2	6	2	6	10	2	6			1			4·16	$^2S_{\frac12}$
38 Sr											2			5·67	$^1S_0$
39 Y									1		2			6·5	$^2D_{1\frac12}$
40 Zr									2		2			6·92	$^3F_2$
41 Nb									4		1				$^6D_{\frac12}$
42 Mo		Krypton	Core						5		1			7·35	$^7S_3$
43 Tc									6		1				$^6D_{4\frac12}$
44 Ru									7		1			7·7	$^5F_5$
45 Rh									8		1			7·7	$^4F_{4\frac12}$
46 Pd									10					8·5	$^1S_0$

Table v.4—*continued*

Shell groupings: **K** $n = 1$ (1s); **L** $n = 2$ (2s, 2p); **M** $n = 3$ (3s, 3p, 3d); **N** $n = 4$ (4s, 4p, 4d, 4f); **O** $n = 5$ (5s, 5p, 5d, 5f); **P** $n = 7$ (6s, 6p, 6d); **Q** $n = 7$ (7s).

	1s	2s	2p	3s	3p	3d	4s	4p	4d	4f	5s	5p	5d	5f	6s	6p	6d	7s	Ionisation potential	Normal state
47 Ag	2	2	6	2	6	10	2	6	10		1								7.54	$^2S_{1/2}$
48 Cd											2								8.95	$^1S_0$
49 In											2	1							5.76	$^2P_{1/2}$
50 Sn											2	2							7.37	$^3P_0$
51 Sb						Silver Core					2	3							8.35	$^4S_{1\frac12}$
52 Te											2	4							8.96	$^3P_2$
53 I											2	5							10.44	$^2P_{1\frac12}$
54 Xe											2	6							12.08	$^1S_0$
55 Cs	2	2	6	2	6	10	2	6	10		2	6			1				3.88	$^2S_{1/2}$
56 Ba															2				5.19	$^1S_0$
57 La						Xenon Core							1		2					$^2D_{1\frac12}$
58 Ce	2	2	6	2	6	10	2	6	10	1	2	6	1		2					$^3H_4$
59 Pr										2			1		2					$^4K_{5\frac12}$
60 Nd										3			1		2					$^5L_6$
61 Pm										4			1		2					$^6L_{4\frac12}$
62 Sm										5			1		2					$^7K_4$
63 Eu										6			1		2					$^8H_{1\frac12}$
64 Gd										7			1		2					$^9D_2$
65 Tb										8			1		2					$^8H_{8\frac12}$
66 Dy										9			1		2					$^7K_{10}$
67 Ho										10			1		2					$^6K_{9\frac12}$
68 Er										11			1		2					$^5L_{10}$
69 Tm										12			1		2					$^4K_{8\frac12}$
70 Yd										13			1		2					$^3H_6$
71 Lu										14			1		2					$^2D_{1\frac12}$
72 Hf	2	2	6	2	6	10	2	6	10	14	2	6	2		2					$^3F_2$
73 Ta													3		2					$^4F_{1\frac12}$
74 W													4		2					$^5D_0$
75 Re						Hafnium Core							5		2					$^6S_{2\frac12}$
76 Os													6		2					$^5D_4$
77 Ir													9							$^2D_{2\frac12}$
78 Pt													9		1					$^3D_3$
79 Au	2	2	6	2	6	10	2	6	10	14	2	6	10		1				9.20	$^2S_{1/2}$
80 Hg															2				10.39	$^1S_0$
81 Tl															2	1			6.08	$^2P_{1/2}$
82 Pb															2	2			7.39	$^3P_0$
83 Bi						Gold Core									2	3			8.0	$^4S_{1\frac12}$
84 Po															2	4				$^3P_2$
85 At															2	5				$^2P_{1\frac12}$
86 Rn															2	6			10.69	$^1S_0$
87 Fr	2	2	6	2	6	10	2	6	10	14	2	6	10		2	6		1		
88 Ra																		2		
89 Ac						Radon Core											1	2		
90 Th														1			1	2		
91 Pa														2			1	2		
92 U														3			1	2		
93 Np														4			1	2		
94 Pu														5			1	2		
95 Am														6			1	2		
96 Cm														7			1	2		

as we ascend the series of elements, and is first completed in the case of copper ($Z = 29$). An exactly similar state of affairs is encountered in later periods of the table. Thus there is no attempt at occupying the fourth sub-shell of N until cerium ($Z = 58$) appears, after which a perfectly regular addition occurs, covering the whole group of rare earth elements (cerium to lutecium; $Z = 58$ to $Z = 71$). These are all characterised by an identical electronic configuration of the 11 electrons in shells O and P, and differ only in the number of electrons in the fourth sub-shell of N.

Many of the basic facts of chemistry have gained a new significance in the light of this table. Chemical inertness, manifesting itself at its best in the elements of Group O and to a considerable extent by palladium and platinum, is occasioned by the completeness and symmetry of the electronic configuration. Chemical reactivity and valency are due to the electrons in the outermost shells. Chemical periodicity is due to the repetitive electronic pattern of the atoms, and is well illustrated by the ionisation potentials (Fig. v.4). Chemical

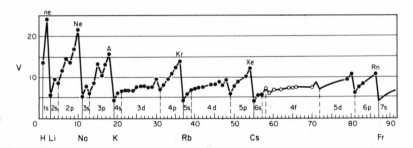

Fig. v.4 *Ionisation potentials of the chemical elements as a function of their atomic numbers*

affinity is governed largely by the anxiety of atoms with incomplete shells to attain the completeness of the inert gas structures; thus the union of fluorine and sodium atoms takes place readily by the gift of the 3s electron from the metal to the halogen:

F $1s^2 2s^2 2p^5$ NaF

Ne $1s^2 2s^2 2p^6$ $[1s^2 2s^2 2p^6]^+ [1s^2 2s^2 2p^6]^-$

Na $1s^2 2s^2 2p^6 3s$

111

The molecule of sodium fluoride formed has thus two complete electronic structures of the neon type, and differs from a close pair of neon atoms only in that one-half of the molecule has now a positive charge, and the other half a negative charge.

Elements of the transition groups

The transitional elements have characteristics which differentiate them sharply from the other elements. Chief among these is the ability of their cations to form stable complexes with anions, such as F^-, CN^- and OH^-, and with polar molecules, such as H_2O and NH_3. The anions and the polar molecules are collectively termed ligands, and the number of attachments to the cation is the co-ordination number. Optical and X-ray studies have revealed the structures of most of these complex ions. They may be linear, with coordination number 2, as in $Ag(CN)_2^-$ and I_3^-, planar, with coordination number 4, as in $CoCl_4^{2-}$, or octahedral, with coordination number 6, as in $Co(NH_3)_6^{3+}$. When, in the last category, the ligands are dissimilar, distorted octahedra result, such as

Ethylene diamine ($NH_2CH_2CH_2NH_2$, abbreviated as *en*) and the carbonate ion $O = C \big\langle{}^{O-}_{O^-}$ are examples of polar and ionic bidentate ligands, each of which can attach itself at two positions round the central ion.

The type of bond joining the ligand to the central ion varies widely, from the four covalent bonds in the ammonium ion NH_4^+ to the 6 electrostatic bonds in $[FeF_6]^{3-}$ and $[CoF_6]^{3-}$. Before dealing with the bond type, we must first recount some of the properties of the elements and their ions, confining attention to the three elements of the first transition period, the element immediately preceding them and the two elements immediately following them. Table v.5 lists, in order, the atomic number, the standard electrode potentials of the ions, the specific conductivity of the metals, the increase in heat content attending the escape of one gram ion from an infinitely dilute aqueous solution, the sum of the first and second ionisation potentials, and the standard decrease in free energy, $-\Delta G^0 = RT \ln K$, associated with the replacement of two molecules of water by one molecule of ethylenediamine in aqueous solution:

$$[M, 6H_2O]^{2+} + en \rightleftarrows [M, 4H_2O, en]^{2+} + 2H_2O: \quad K$$

It will be observed, as Irvine and R. J. P. Williams (1948) have pointed out, that the magnitude of all these properties increases steadily as we go from manganese to copper, and thereafter falls. The entries in the last three lines are quantitative indications of the affinities of the bivalent cations for water molecules, electrons and the bidentate ligand, and are naturally related to one another. The problem is to explain their maxima at the cupric ion.

Table v.5 *Numerical constants relating to elements and ions of the first transitional period (all energies in kilocals)*

Element	Mn	Fe	Co	Ni	Cu	Zn
Atomic number, Z	25	26	27	28	29	30
E^0(volts), $M \rightarrow M^{2+}(aq)$	$-1{\cdot}10$	$-0{\cdot}441$	$-0{\cdot}283$	$-0{\cdot}236$	$+0{\cdot}339$	$-0{\cdot}761$
$\kappa \times 10^{-4}$(ohm^{-1} cm^{-1})	$1{\cdot}10$	$9{\cdot}36$	$10{\cdot}3$	$14{\cdot}42$	$64{\cdot}0$	$17{\cdot}8$
ΔH_{escape}; $M^{2+}(aq) \rightarrow M^{2+}(gas)$	407	447	469	496	496	482
ΣV_i	505	547	583	613	646	633
$-\Delta G^0 = RT \ln K$	$3{\cdot}73$	$5{\cdot}84$	$8{\cdot}04$	$10{\cdot}25$	$14{\cdot}40$	$7{\cdot}79$

Electronic structure of complex ions of the first transition period

The chemical, magnetic and optical properties of elements in the first transition period derive chiefly from the number and state of electrons in the $3d$ and $4s$ shells. Starting with manganese, which has five d electrons, the occupancy of the $4s$ shell remains at two electrons, except for copper, where there is only one electron in the $4s$ shell. The maxima which occur as the properties of these elements are plotted as functions of the atomic number occur at this point.

The electronic states of the atoms, as revealed by their spectra, are shown in Table v.6. The number, n, of unpaired electrons in the d shell of the ions M^{2+} is obtained from Langevin's equation relating the total magnetic moment, M, with the magnetic susceptibility,

$$\kappa = \kappa_0 + \tfrac{1}{3}\frac{M^2}{kT} \qquad \text{v.6}$$

Table v.6 *Electronic structure and certain properties of transition metal atoms*

Atomic number	Atom	Electronic structure, excluding argon core	Number of unpaired electrons in a shell of ion M^{2+}	Energy of escape of ion M^{2+} from water (kilocals/gram-ion)		
				Observed	Ligand field correction	Difference
20	Ca	— $4s^2$	0	358	0	358
25	Mn	$3d^5$ $4s^2$	5	407	0	407
26	Fe	$3d^6$ $4s^2$	4	447	10	437
27	Co	$3d^7$ $4s^2$	3	469	20	449
28	Ni	$3d^8$ $4s^2$	2	496	25	471
29	Cu	$3d^{10}$ $4s^1$	1	496	20	476
30	Zn	$3d^{10}$ $4s^2$	0	482	0	482

where M is a multiple of the Bohr magneton, $he/4\pi m_e c$ (equation III.46);

$$M = \left(\frac{he}{4\pi m_e c}\right)[n(n+2)]^{1/2} \qquad \text{v.7}$$

It is found that this number, for a given ion, is not always the same for the free ion as for the complex ion, and the change gives an indication of the nature of the bond uniting the ion and the ligands. The magnetic moment of the cobaltic ion, for example, indicates that four out of the six d electrons are unpaired. This fact, and the emptiness of the $4s$ and $4p$ shells can be represented as follows:

Co^{3+} ⟶ $3d$ ⟵ $4s$ $4p$
    ↑↓ ↑ ↑ ↑ ↑

The magnetic moment of the complex ion $[CoF_6]^{3-}$ is the same as that of the elementary ion. None of the d electrons has therefore

114

changed its state or entered into combination with ligand electrons to form covalent bonds. That is the reason that the properties of this complex ion can be almost wholly understood in terms of electrostatic interactions between the central cobaltic ion Co^{3+} and the six F^- fluoride ions surrounding it. The magnetic moments of the ferric ion Fe^{3+} and the hexacyanoferric ion $[Fe(CN)_6]^{3-}$, on the other hand, are different, indicating that in the elementary ion, the five d electrons are unpaired, whereas in the complex ion only one d electron remains unpaired. Their states may be represented schematically as follows:

Fe^{3+} 3d   4s   4p

↑   ↑   ↑   ↑   ↑

$[Fe(CN)_6]^{3-}$ 3d   4s   4p

↑↓   ↑↓   ↑ | ↑↓   ↑↓   ↑↓   ↑↓   ↑↓   ↑↓ |

Each of the CN^- ions has two paired electrons, so that the six ligands bring twelve electrons to the system. Optical evidence shows that the highest level occupied by them in the complex ion is the $4p$ level, i.e. no electrons appear in $4d$ levels or above. This can be explained by supposing that four of the previously unpaired d electrons of the elementary ion have coupled up, leaving one unpaired d electron and two empty d orbitals. In terms of Pauling's theory of atomic orbitals, these two d orbitals can hybridise with one s and three p orbitals to give six equivalent orbitals, denoted by the symbol d^2sp^3, whose directions are those of the six lines joining the centre of a regular octahedron to its corners. Such a complex is termed a six-covalent spin paired complex. When the energy difference between a d electron and an s electron is greater than the small value assumed in this example, planar and tetrahedral structures can, according to this theory, be more stable than the octahedral structures.

Ligand field theory

When hydrogen atoms are placed in a strong electric field, their energy levels are split, i.e. new energy levels, above and below the original ones, become available (Stark effect). The difference between any two successive levels is proportional to the field strength. Penny and

115

Schlapp (1932) and van Vleck (1932) have shown that the electric field exerted by the ligands around a central ion of the transition metals produces a similar effect. In particular, the cubic field due to six water molecules at the corners of a regular octahedron surrounding the Co^{2+} ion split its original single energy level into three levels, the separation between successive levels being about $10^4 cm^{-1}$ or 28 kilocalories. The effect of a slight distortion in the regular octahedron can be allowed for by superimposing a rhombic field on the perfect cubic field. There results a further splitting on the two lower levels into triplets, with a much smaller separation, as shown schematically below:

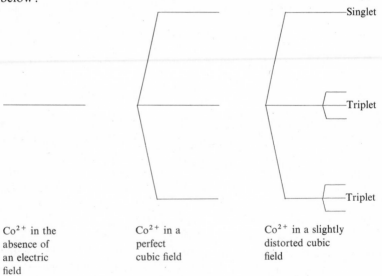

Singlet

Triplet

Triplet

Co²⁺ in the absence of an electric field

Co²⁺ in a perfect cubic field

Co²⁺ in a slightly distorted cubic field

As the occupancy of the seven levels is determined by Boltzmann's law, most of the ions in a system at equilibrium are found in the lowest levels. The net effect of the ligand field, therefore, is to lower the total energy of the complex ion and thus to confer on it a greater stability than it would have in the absence of the field. Similar results are found in fields of different symmetry.

Originally advanced to account for certain anomalous magnetic properties of transition metal ions in crystals, the ligand field theory has found numerous other applications. The absorption of light by salts of the transition metals is due to the excitation of a d electron from a low energy level E_2 to a higher energy level, E_1. For example, the first two maxima in the absorption spectrum of $[Co(H_2O)_6]^{2+}$ are at 8 100 and 11 300 cm^{-1}. With the ion $[Co(NH_3)_6]^{2+}$ the positions are 9 000 and 18 500 cm^{-1}. Nyholm (1956) on analysing the complete spectra, finds that $E_1 - E_2$ is 9 700 cm^{-1} for the aquo complex, and 10 500 cm^{-1} for the ammine complex, both of which lie near to Penny and Schlapp's theoretical estimate of the split.

Orgel (1952) has examined certain properties of transition metal ion complexes in terms of both the molecular orbital and the ligand field theories. We shall here be concerned chiefly with his application of ligand field theory to the determination of the energy of escape of the bivalent ions from aqueous solution. The decrease in energy of the complex ion due to the ligand field is determined by the symmetry and strength of the field (i.e. the arrangement and kind of ligand) and by the number and state of the d electrons. The theory predicts that there is no ligand field effect when the d shell is full, as in Zn^{2+}, or when it is exactly half full, as in Mn^{2+}. For the intervening ions, the decrease in energy due to the ligand field is, to a first approximation, proportional to $(v-5)$, where v is the number of d electrons. After making allowance for certain complicating factors, especially in the case of the Cu^{2+} ion, Orgel has estimated the energy decreases shown, to the nearest 5 kilocalories, in Table v.6. When these are deducted from the observed energies of escape, corrected energies are found which increase with the atomic number. When, from the sum of the first two ionisation potentials of the cupric ion Cu^{2+} the energy required to raise an electron from the d to the s state is deducted, the maximum in the curve found by plotting ionisation potentials against atomic numbers also vanishes. It is thus concluded that the erratic variation of the heats of escape with respect to atomic number is due to the ligand field effect. Its magnitude, it may be noted, may amount to as much as 5 per cent of the total heat of escape. Orgel's conclusion in no way conflicts with that of Irving and Williams, whose correlation of ionisation potentials, heats of escape and standard free energy changes is based firmly on experiments.

The stability of complex ions is discussed later (Chapter XII) in terms of electrostatic theory.

Radioactive elements: spontaneous nuclear transformations

The early history of radioactivity (Becquerel, 1896; Madame Curie, 1898; Rutherford and Soddy, 1902) is known to all cultured

117

individuals, whether scientists or not. Certain ores, containing compounds of which one constituent possessed a high atomic weight, were found to emit radiations of three kinds, labelled α, β and γ. The α rays have been shown to consist of helium nuclei, the β rays of electrons, and the γ rays of electromagnetic radiation, like X-rays, but with smaller wavelengths. The frequencies with which the rays are emitted obey the first order equation of chemical kinetics. Unlike ordinary chemical decompositions which obey the same law, however, the rates of radioactive changes are not affected by temperature or pressure, or even by the physical state of the decomposing compound. The velocity of spontaneous disintegration is beyond control by ordinary means. The particles emitted possess high energies, and their paths can be fairly easily traced in various ways. One of the first methods used was that of C. T. R. Wilson, who passed the rays through dust-free supersaturated water vapour, and photographed the cloud produced by the condensation of water on the air molecules ionised by the rays. Fig. v.6 is one such photograph. The lower track shows the determined

Fig. v.6

course of an alpha particle, and the upper one the less certain and more frequently interrupted course of a β-particle. Photographic emulsions have latterly been used, with striking results (C. F. Powell and G. P. S. Occhialini 1947). Uranium and radium were among the first of the elements detected as responsible for radioactivity. Apart from its radioactivity, radium is a metal that fits comfortably into group IIA of the periodic table: its atomic weight is 226·05; its valency, determined electrometrically is 2; and the properties of its halides resemble those of the halides of Ca, Sr and Ba. All compounds containing radium, however, disintegrate spontaneously at the same rate, showing the effect to be due to the radium atom, and to be as independent of its chemical commitments as it is of its physical state. Moreover, the breakdown must be in the nucleus, since this is the only possible source of alpha particles. Now if a nucleus of atomic number Z shoots off an alpha particle, its atomic number must be reduced to $Z - 2$, and it must therefore move up two places in the periodic Table. Experiment shows that the emission of alpha particles is always accompanied or followed by the emission of two electrons from the same nucleus. This restores the atomic number to Z, but the two processes have reduced the atomic weight by four. It is in this way that Fajans and Soddy discovered the group displacement law and established the existence of isotopes – elements with different atomic weights but identical atomic numbers.

One of the sequences of changes in the uranium series is shown in Table v.7, which begins with RaA. In chemical properties it resembles selenium, tellurium and polonium. After losing an alpha particle, it changes its chemical character, and shows a family likeness to germanium, tin and lead. The subsequent loss of a nuclear electron endows it with properties like those of arsenic, antimony and bismuth. With the loss of a second nuclear electron, it reverts to its original group VIB. RaC can be converted into RaD by another route, not shown here. It can first emit an alpha particle and then an electron. All four processes take place, but 99·96 per cent of the change from RaC to RaD takes place by the route shown in the table.

When all the known natural radioactive changes are considered, it is found that the unimolecular constants governing the emission of α-particles differ, from one element to another, by a factor of 10^{24}, and that the range in the values of k_1 for the emission of nuclear electrons is about 10^{14}. Comparable ranges are found in ordinary chemical changes.

119

Table v.7 *A sequence of radioactive changes in the uranium series*

Element	Atomic weight	Atomic number	First order velocity constant k_1 (sec^{-1})	Group in the periodic table
RaA	218	84		VIB
$\downarrow\alpha$			$3{\cdot}79 \times 10^{-3}$	
RaB	214	82		IVB
$\downarrow\beta$			$4{\cdot}33 \times 10^{-4}$	
RaC	214	83		VB
$\downarrow\beta$			$5{\cdot}86 \times 10^{-4}$	
RaC'	214	84		VIB
$\downarrow\alpha$			$4{\cdot}6 \times 10^{3}$	
RaD	210	82		IVB
$\downarrow\beta$			$1{\cdot}0 \times 10^{-9}$	
RaE	210	83		VB
$\downarrow\beta$			$1{\cdot}60 \times 10^{-6}$	
Po	210	84		VIB
$\downarrow\alpha$			$5{\cdot}73 \times 10^{-8}$	
RaG	206	82		IVB

Induced nuclear transformations

The velocity of the slowest α-particle emitted in natural radio-activity is $1{\cdot}45 \times 10^9$ cm/sec. This corresponds to a kinetic energy of 7×10^{-6} ergs per particle, or $4{\cdot}4 \times 10^6$ electron volts, or about 10^8 kilocalories per gram-ion. If the particle travels through air under ordinary conditions, it generates about 2×10^5 ions, thus expending, on an average, the equivalent of 500 kilocalories for each gram-ion produced. The energies required for the processes $O_2 \rightarrow O + O^+ + \ominus$ and $N_2 \rightarrow N + N^+ \ominus$ are 430 and 558 kilocalories per mole. Rutherford found that the enormous kinetic energies of these α-particles could be used, not only to explore the electrical field around the nucleus, but to bombard the nucleus itself, and disrupt it. The kinetic energy possessed by the naturally produced helium nuclei can be increased by driving them through powerful electric fields where their initial energy may be more than doubled. Among the particles resulting from the break-down of ordinarily stable nuclei are found new primary particles, such as the neutron (mass 1, compared with hydrogen; zero charge) and the positron (mass 1 compared with the electron; unit positive charge). Controlled transmutation of the elements is thus possible, provided energy sources reckoned in millions of electron-volts (MeV) are available. A few examples of changes brought about by bombarding atoms with neutrons ($_0n^1$), protons ($_1H^1$), deuterons ($_1H^2$) and α-particles ($_2He^4$) may be written as follows, using a pre-subscript to denote the charge and a post-superscript to denote the mass:

$$_0n^1 + {}_1H^1 \rightarrow {}_1H^2$$

$$_0n^1 + {}_7N^{14} \rightarrow {}_2He^4 + {}_5B^{11}$$

$$_1H^1 + {}_6C^{12} \rightarrow {}_6C^{13} + \oplus$$

$$_1H^1 + {}_{11}Na^{23} \rightarrow {}_2He^4 + {}_{10}Ne^{20}$$

$$_1H^2 + {}_1H^2 \rightarrow {}_1H^3 + {}_1H^1$$

$$_1H^2 + {}_7N^{14} \rightarrow {}_6C^{12} + {}_2He^4$$

$$_2He^4 + {}_7N^{14} \rightarrow {}_9F^{17} + {}_0n^1$$

$$_2He^4 + {}_{12}Mg^{25} \rightarrow {}_1H^1 + {}_{14}Si^{28} + \ominus$$

Among the products will be discerned not only the nuclei of the elements boron, carbon, fluorine, neon and silicon in their common form, but rudimentary particles such as the neutron, electron and positron, and the nuclei of the high isotope of carbon and the highest isotope of hydrogen, called the tritron.

As stated above, large energy changes, positive or negative, attend all nuclear transformations. The energy released in induced nuclear changes has already found belligerent and pacific applications. The computation of the energy changes is based on the first law of thermodynamics (Chapter VI), with the relativity corollary due to Einstein, according to which a loss of mass, m, is attended by the generation of energy mc^2, where c is the velocity of light. Bethe's list of nuclear masses (Table v.8) agrees well with Aston's earlier estimates, and allows of an evaluation of the energy change in any reaction involving only the substances cited. For example, in the production of a deuteron from a proton and a neutron

$$_1H^1 + {}_0n^1 \rightarrow {}_1H^2,$$

the loss in mass is

$$1 \cdot 0081 + 1 \cdot 0085 - 2 \cdot 0142 = 0 \cdot 0024 \text{ g}$$

E

Table v.8 *Nuclear masses based on transmutation data*

Particle	Mass	Particle	Mass
$_0n^1$	1·0085	$_5B^{10}$	10·0146
$_1H^1$	1·0081	$_5B^{11}$	11·0111
$_1H^2$	2·0142	$_6C^{12}$	12·0037
$_1H^3$	3·0161	$_6C^{13}$	13·0069
$_2He^4$	4·0034	$_7N^{14}$	14·0076
$_3Li^6$	6·0161	$_7N^{15}$	15·0053
$_3Li^7$	7·0169	$_8O^{16}$	16·0000
$_4Be^9$	9·0135	$_8O^{17}$	17·0040

This corresponds to an energy of $3·56 \times 10^{-6}$ erg per nucleus, and manifests itself as a quantum of radiation $h\nu$, where ν is $5·43 \times 10^{20}$ sec^{-1}. The wavelength of the γ-radiation is thus $5·52X$, where $X = 10^{-3}$ Å.

VI Chemical thermodynamics

Thermodynamics deals with the conversion of one kind of energy into another. Some of the energies which we shall discuss are thermal, mechanical, electrical, gravitational, centrifugal, superficial and chemical. Thermodynamics rests on three laws of nature and is in no way dependent on the atomic theory. From one point of view, this is an advantage, for its conclusions must be of general applicability. From another point of view, it is a disadvantage, because no insight is afforded into the mechanism of molecular processes, which is a major concern of physical chemistry. In a science which claims generality, formalism is inevitable, but physical chemists must not be deterred by it. A system, for example, is defined in thermodynamics as that portion of the objective world which is the subject of discourse. Humbler terms often serve just as well; to say that we have five grams of copper turnings in a dry test tube open to the atmosphere at the temperature of boiling water is to provide a perfectly satisfactory specification of this particular system. A homogeneous system is defined as one with uniform properties, i.e. properties which are the same in all its parts, and a heterogeneous system as one which consists of two or more physically distinct and mechanically separable homogeneous systems.

The first law

The first law of thermodynamics is the law of the conservation of energy. Energy cannot be created or destroyed – merely changed. One calorie of heat, for example, if wholly converted into work, provides $4 \cdot 184 \times 10^7$ ergs of mechanical energy (Joule's mechanical equivalent of heat). To express the first law mathematically, we consider any system of constant mass, homogeneous or heterogeneous, to undergo any change whatsoever. Associated with the change in state of the system there are generally associated the following energy changes; (1) The energy, E, of the system may increase by an amount dE, which may be positive or negative. (2) A quantity of heat, q, may be absorbed by the system. If q turns out to be negative, it

123

means that heat is evolved by the system. When q is zero, heat is neither absorbed nor evolved, and the change is said to be adiabatic. (3) A quantity of work, w, may be done by the system on its surroundings. This term also may prove to be negative, in which case work will have been expended by the surroundings on the system. The first law, then, is

$$dE = q - w \qquad \qquad \text{VI.1}$$

The work term may consist of many components. To begin with, we shall consider only the mechanical work term $P \, dV$ which a system at pressure P exerts on its surroundings when the system expands by the volume element dV. For such changes

$$dE = q - P \, dV \qquad \qquad \text{VI.2}$$

The second law

This law, unlike the first, applies to reversible changes only. It states that, if a quantity of heat, q, is absorbed in a reversible change at a temperature, T, the entropy, S, of the system is increased by the amount

$$dS = q/T \qquad \qquad \text{VI.3}$$

A reversible change may be defined as one which, at all stages, departs only infinitesimally from equilibrium conditions.

The third law

The entropy of each pure crystalline substance at the absolute zero of temperature is itself zero:

$$S_0 = 0 \qquad \qquad \text{VI.4}$$

Were it not for the existence of a few anomalous substances like helium, which can remain liquid at extremely low temperatures, it would have been superfluous to insert the adjective 'crystalline', for, with very few exceptions, pure substances at the absolute zero of temperature are naturally crystalline. It follows that the entropy change attending all reactions between solids at the absolute zero of temperature must be zero. It was by showing that this is in fact true that Nernst discovered the third law. Its present formulation is due to Planck. Entropy, as will be shown later, is a measure of disorderliness. Zero entropy means no disorderliness, i.e. complete order. The atoms and molecules which constitute crystals at the absolute zero of temperature are all at their posts, like well-drilled soldiers in a crack regiment. Disorderliness increases as the temperature is raised and other states of matter emerge. It is marked in liquids, and amounts to chaos in gases.

The thermodynamic definition of temperature

On combining the first and second laws, we have

$$dE = T\,dS - P\,dV \qquad \text{VI.5}$$

Contrary to what may be expected, this equation is not limited to reversible changes. The reason is that dE, dS and dV are complete differentials. The energy, entropy and volume of a system depend only on its state, and not on how that state was reached. By letting each differential be zero, we obtain three equations. For example, when dV is zero,

$$\left(\frac{dE}{dS}\right)_V = T \qquad \text{VI.6}$$

The subscript V is to remind us that the volume is kept constant. This equation defines temperature on the thermodynamic basis (Kelvin).

Heat content and heat capacities

Because measurements are more frequently made at constant pressure than at constant volume, it is convenient to define a new variable, called the heat content, H, as follows:

$$H = E + PV \qquad \text{VI.7}$$

H is sometimes referred to as enthalpy. An infinitesimal change in H consists of three parts:

$$dH = dE + P\,dV + V\,dP \qquad \text{VI.8}$$

But, according to the first law, $dE + P\,dV = q$; hence

$$dH = q + V\,dP \qquad \text{VI.9}$$

If heat is absorbed at constant pressure, clearly

$$dH_P = q_P \qquad \text{VI.10}$$

In any change at constant pressure, therefore, the heat absorbed by a system is a direct measure of its increase in heat content. An analogous equation results from the first law, since

$$dE_V = q_V \qquad \text{VI.11}$$

In any change at constant volume, the heat absorbed by a system is a direct measure of its increase in energy.

Two heat capacities are defined by the equations

$$C_P = \frac{dq_P}{dT} = \left(\frac{dH}{dT}\right)_P; \qquad H = H_0 + \int_0^T C_P \, dT \qquad \text{VI.12}$$

and

$$C_V = \frac{dq_V}{dT} = \left(\frac{dE}{dT}\right)_V; \qquad E = E_0 + \int_0^T C_V \, dT \qquad \text{VI.13}$$

It may readily be shown that the two heat capacities are related as follows:

$$C_P - C_V = \frac{\alpha^2 V T}{\beta} \qquad \text{VI.14}$$

where α is the coefficient of isobaric (i.e. constant pressure) expansion

$$\alpha = \frac{1}{V}\left(\frac{dV}{dT}\right)_P$$

and β is the coefficient of isothermal (i.e. constant temperature) compression

$$\beta = -\frac{1}{V}\left(\frac{dV}{dP}\right)_T \qquad \text{VI.16}$$

When C_P or C_V refer to one gram, they are known as specific heats. In physical chemistry, C_P and C_V generally refer to one gram-mole.

The Helmholtz free energy

E is the total energy of a system, and TS its bound energy. The difference between them has been termed by Helmholtz the free energy. In this work it is denoted by the letter A. Thus

$$A = E - TS \qquad \text{VI.17}$$

An infinitesimal change in A consists of three parts, namely

$$dA = dE - T\,dS - S\,dT \qquad \text{VI.18}$$

On combining with equation VI.5, we see that

$$dA = -P\,dV - S\,dT \qquad \text{VI.19}$$

A general definition of pressure and a further definition of entropy are thus provided, since

$$P = -(dA/dV)_T \qquad \text{VI.20}$$

and

$$S = -(dA/dT)_V \qquad \text{VI.21}$$

By eliminating S from equations VI.17 and VI.21, we obtain a convenient relationship between the total energy, E, and the Helmholtz free energy, A:

$$E = A - T(dA/dT)_V = -T^2\left[\frac{d(A/T)}{dT}\right]_V \qquad \text{VI.22}$$

The Gibbs free energy

Gibbs defined a free energy by the equation

$$G = H - TS \qquad \text{VI.23}$$

Proceeding as before, we now have

$$\begin{aligned}
dG &= dH - T\,dS - S\,dT \\
&= dE + P\,dV + V\,dP - T\,dS - S\,dT \\
&= V\,dP - S\,dT \qquad \text{VI.24}
\end{aligned}$$

A general definition of volume and a further definition of entropy emerge from this equation, since

$$V = (dG/dP)_T \qquad \text{VI.25}$$

and

$$S = -(dG/dT)_P \qquad \text{VI.26}$$

By eliminating S from equations VI.23 and VI.26, we obtain a convenient relationship between the heat content and the Gibbs free energy:

$$H = G - T(dG/dT)_P = -T^2 \left[\frac{d(G/T)}{dT} \right]_P \qquad \text{VI.27}$$

Equations VI.22 and VI.27 are indiscriminately known as the Kelvin–Helmholtz relations. The application of equation VI.27 to electrode processes is due to Gibbs.

Maxwell's equations

Many equations, of which Maxwell's celebrated set are the best known, can be derived from the basic equations of thermodynamics. If, for example, we differentiate both sides of equation VI.21 with respect to volume at constant temperature, we obtain

$$\left(\frac{dS}{dV} \right)_T = -\frac{d}{dV_T} \left(\frac{dA}{dT} \right)_V = -\frac{\partial^2 A}{\partial V \partial T}$$

Now A is a function of V and T only, and the order of differentiation is immaterial, so that we may write

$$\left(\frac{dS}{dV} \right)_T = -\frac{\partial^2 A}{\partial T \partial V} = \frac{d}{dT_V} \left(-\frac{dA}{dV} \right)_T$$

From the definition of pressure (equation VI.20), it follows that

$$\left(\frac{dS}{dV} \right)_T = \left(\frac{dP}{dT} \right)_V \qquad \text{VI.28}$$

which is the first of Maxwell's relationships which we shall need. Starting from equation VI.26, we similarly find that

$$\left(\frac{dS}{dP} \right)_T = \left(\frac{dV}{dT} \right)_P \qquad \text{VI.29}$$

The Clausius–Clapeyron equation

Let us apply equation VI.28 to a system containing two phases of a pure substance in equilibrium, such as a solid and a liquid, or a liquid and a vapour. It is an experimental fact that the pressure of such a system is independent of its total volume, so that we may drop the subscript attached to dP/dT. The changes of state contemplated in these systems are reversible: according to the second law, we then have $dS = q/T = dH/T$, so that

$$\frac{dP}{dT} = \frac{1}{T}\left(\frac{dH}{dV}\right)_T$$

Since both H and V are extensive properties, we may replace $(dH/dV)_T$ by the incremental quotient $\Delta H_T/\Delta V_T$, where ΔH_T is the increase in heat content and ΔV_T the increase in volume attending the reversible process of fusion or vaporisation:

$$\frac{dP}{dT} = \frac{\Delta H_T}{T\Delta V_T} \qquad\qquad \text{VI.30}$$

This is the Clausius–Clapeyron equation, which can be applied to a variety of physicochemical problems.

Pressure and compressibility at the absolute zero of temperature

Let us divide each term in equation VI.5 by dV, and restrict its use to changes taking place at constant temperature. We then have

$$\left(\frac{dE}{dV}\right)_T = T\left(\frac{dS}{dV}\right)_T - P \qquad\qquad \text{VI.31}$$

On combining with equation VI.28, we obtain the following general expression for the pressure:

$$P = T\left(\frac{dP}{dT}\right)_V - \left(\frac{dE}{dV}\right)_T \qquad\qquad \text{VI.32}$$

The two terms on the right-hand side of this equation denote the kinetic and static pressures respectively. The former is seen to be zero at the absolute zero of temperature, leaving

$$P_{T=0} = -(dE/dV)_{T=0} \qquad\qquad \text{VI.33}$$

It follows from equations VI.16 that the reciprocal of the compressibility of a system at the absolute zero of temperature is given by the relation

$$1/\beta_{T=0} = V_{T=0}(d_2E/dV^2)_{T=0} \qquad\qquad \text{VI.34}$$

E*

This equation has been applied (Born, 1919; Landé, 1921) to determine the nature of the repulsive forces in ionic crystals.

As the term $(dP/dT)_V$ of equation VI.32 is not always known, we replace it by other terms obtained by recalling that the volume is a function of pressure and temperature:

$$V = f(P, T).$$

We are thus regarding V as the dependent variable. If the system now changes from a state at a temperature T and pressure P to a state at temperature $T+dT$ and pressure $P+dP$, the infinitesimal change in volume consists of two parts, namely,

$$dV = \left(\frac{\partial V}{\partial T}\right)_P dT + \left(\frac{\partial V}{\partial P}\right)_T dP$$

When the volume change is zero ($dV = 0$),

$$\left(\frac{\partial P}{\partial T}\right)_V = -\left(\frac{\partial V}{\partial T}\right)_P \bigg/ \left(\frac{\partial V}{\partial P}\right)_T$$

On combining with equations VI.15 and VI.16, we see that the kinetic pressure $T(dP/dT)_V$ is $T\alpha/\beta$, and that the total pressure is

$$P = T\frac{\alpha}{\beta} - \left(\frac{dE}{dV}\right)_T \qquad \text{VI.32a}$$

The chemical potential

Equation VI.19 shows that, in the absence of electrical, gravitational, centrifugal and superficial forces, the two ways in which a system can increase its free energy is by suffering a contraction, and a depression in temperature. This is true for so-called closed systems, i.e. those in which the amount of matter is constant. Another way of increasing the free energy of a system is available if a further supply of molecules is added to it. If, for example, dN_i molecules of a given species were added to it, each bringing a contribution of μ_i, the increment in the free energy would be $\mu_i dN_i$. When the number dN_i is small compared with the total number of molecules originally in the system, its composition is not varied by the new addition. A more general expression for dA, therefore, is

$$dA = -P\,dV - S\,dT + \sum \mu_i\,dN_i \qquad \text{VI.35}$$

where the last term covers all the various types of molecules concerned. The chemical potential of a molecule of the first type may now be defined as

$$\mu_1 = (dA/dN_1)_{V,T,N_2,N_3,\dots}$$

Similarly

$$\mu_2 = (dA/dN_2)_{V,T,N_1,N_3,\dots}$$

and generally

$$\mu_i = (dA/dN_i)_{V,T,N_j,\dots}$$

In words, the chemical potential of a molecule of type i is defined as the increase in the (Helmholtz) free energy of a system containing a very large number of molecules when, at constant volume and temperature, one molecule of the type i is added to it. On using equations VI.24, VI.5 and VI.8, we find that the chemical potential may be defined in three further ways:

$$\mu_i = (dA/dN_i)_{T,V,N_j,\dots} = (dG/dN_i)_{T,P,N_j,\dots} = (dE/dN_i)_{S,V,N_j,\dots}$$
$$= (dH/dN_i)_{S,P,N_j,\dots} \qquad \text{VI.36}$$

The corresponding gain when one mole of a pure substance is added to a system containing a very large number of moles we shall denote by G_i, which is the molar chemical potential, as distinct from μ_i which is the molecular chemical potential. The relationship between them is evidently $G_i = N_0\mu_i$, where N_0 is Avogadro's number. Expressions for μ_i generally contain the term kT, where k is Boltzmann's constant, and those for G_i contain the term RT, where R is the gas constant.

Equilibria

By comparing equations VI.19, VI.24 and VI.35 we see that, provided electrical, gravitational and surface effects are omitted, the gain in the Helmholtz free energy attending any reversible change at constant temperature and volume is the same as the gain in the Gibbs free energy attending the same reversible change in the system at constant temperature and pressure, since

$$(dA)_{T,V} = \sum \mu_i \, dN_i = (dG)_{T,P}$$

Now the free energy in thermodynamics corresponds to the potential energy, U, in ordinary dynamics, where we learn that the condition of

131

equilibrium of a particle free to move in one dimension, say along the x axis, is that dU/dx is zero. Other ways of expressing the truth are to say that the force $(-dU/dx)$ acting on the particle is zero, that the potential energy has a minimum value, and that small virtual displacements of the particle about the position of minimum energy result in no gain in potential energy. In thermodynamic systems, equilibrium is said to have been reached when the free energy of the system has reached its minimum value, or when small virtual displacements of the system about the position of equilibrium are attended by no increase in free energy. We consequently arrive at the following equivalent conditions of equilibrium:

$$(dA)_{T,V} = (dG)_{T,P} = (dE)_{S,V} = (dH)_{S,P} = 0 \qquad \text{VI.37}$$

They all lead to the same fundamental equation of thermodynamic equilibrium, namely

$$\sum \mu_i \, dN_i = 0 \qquad \text{VI.38}$$

Equilibria in homogeneous systems

Let us consider a homogeneous system containing three chemical species at equilibrium, as represented by the stoichiometric equation

$$xX \rightleftarrows yY + zZ$$

According to equation VI.38, the condition of equilibrium is

$$\mu_X \, dN_X + \mu_Y \, dN_Y + \mu_Z \, dN_Z = 0$$

where dN represents the number of molecules formed or destroyed during a slight virtual displacement of the system under equilibrium conditions. If, however, dN_X molecules of reactant undergo chemical change, the number of molecules of the Y type generated is, from the chemistry of the change, $(y/x) \, dN_X$, and the number of molecules of the Z type formed is $(z/x) \, dN_X$. Thus

$$+ dN_Y = -(y/x)dN_X \quad \text{and} \quad + dN_Z = -(z/x) \, dN_X$$

It follows that

$$x\mu_X = y\mu_Y + z\mu_Z$$

or, more generally,

$$\sum v_i \mu_i = \sum v_j \mu_j \qquad \text{VI.39}$$

where the summation of the left hand side is over all the reactants, that on the right hand side over all the resultants, and the v's are stoichiometric integers of the chemical equation.

Equilibria in heterogeneous systems

Let us next consider an equilibrated system containing one chemical species, denoted by W, in two phases, such as a solid and a liquid, or a liquid and its saturated vapour. The physical change contemplated is

$$W(\text{phase 1}) \rightleftarrows W(\text{phase 2})$$

Equation VI.38 now gives the condition of equilibrium as

$$\mu_1 \, dN_1 + \mu_2 dN_2 = 0$$

where μ_1 is the chemical potential in the first phase, and μ_2 that in the second. Such equilibria are always studied in closed systems, in which the total number of molecules is constant. It follows that $dN_1 + dN_2 = 0$, and therefore that

$$\mu_1 = \mu_2 \qquad\qquad \text{VI.40}$$

A pure substance can thus exist in two phases at equilibrium when its chemical potential is the same in both.

The phase rule

The state of a homogeneous phase in a system at equilibrium is completely specified when the values ascribable to its temperature, T, and pressure, P, and to the numbers $N_1, N_2, \ldots N_c$ of the molecules of all the chemical species in it are known. If c denote the number of components, the number of variables required to specify the state of the one-phase system is thus $2 + c$. Now the composition of a phase containing c components is determined when $c - 1$ data are given. In a two-component system, for example, its composition is known when the molar fraction or the weight percentage of one component is known. The number of independent variables governing the state of a system of c components is thus $2 + (c - 1)$. Let the number of phases in a heterogeneous system be denoted by p. Since the system is at equilibrium, P and T must have common values for all the phases. The number of variables available is therefore $2 + (c - 1)p$. Not all these are independent variables, because the chemical potential of

133

each component must be the same in all phases. For example μ_i(phase α) = μ_i(phase β) = μ_i(phase γ) = ... This equilibrium law reduces the number of independent variables by $p-1$ for each component, and by $c(p-1)$ for the whole system. The number of independent variables, or degrees of freedom, left is

$$f = c - p + 2 \qquad \text{VI.41}$$

This is the phase rule of Gibbs.

A more general formulation of the first and second laws

According to the first and second laws of thermodynamics (equations VI.1 and VI.3) the increase in energy attending any change undergone by a closed system is $dE = T dS - w$, and for an open system

$$dE = T dS - w + \sum \mu_i dN_i \qquad \text{VI.42}$$

Hitherto, the only component of the work done by the system that has been considered is the mechanical component $P dV$. If, during the change contemplated, each molecule of type i is raised a distance L_i in the gravitational field, the work done on the system includes the contribution $\sum m_i g L_i dN_i$, and w therefore includes the term $-\sum m_i g L_i dN_i$. Similarly, if the change contemplated involves transporting a quantity de of electricity through an electrostatic potential ψ, the work done on the system is $\psi\, de$, and w thus contains terms of the form $-\sum \psi\, de$. Finally, the change may be attended by the creation of a surface, of extension dO, against a surface tension γ. The work done on the system is now $\sum \gamma\, dO$, and w contains terms of the form $-\sum \gamma\, dO$. Other forms of work are possible, but will not be considered here. Then

$$w = P dV - \sum m_i g L_i\, dN_i - \sum \psi\, de - \sum \gamma\, dO \qquad \text{VI.43}$$

The first and second laws may thus be more generally expressed as follows:

$$\left.\begin{aligned} dE &= \quad T dS - P dV \\ dH &= \quad T dS + V dP \\ dA &= -S dT - P dV \\ dG &= -S dT + V dP \end{aligned}\right\} + \sum(\mu_i + m_i g L_i)dN_i + \sum \psi\, de + \sum \gamma\, dO \qquad \text{VI.44}$$

Convention regarding signs

In any chemical or physical change denoted by the equation $A \rightarrow B$, the corresponding changes in volume, heat capacity, enthalpy, total energy and entropy are denoted by the symbols ΔV, ΔC_P, ΔH, ΔE and ΔS, where the sign Δ stands for the increase in the value of the property measured when one gram mole of A is converted into B, or changes its state. The following examples illustrate the convention:

$$Pb(cr.) \rightarrow Pb(liq.) \qquad \begin{aligned} \Delta V_{600°K} &= V(liq.) - V(cr.) \\ &= 0.871 \text{ cc/mole} \end{aligned}$$

$$H_2O(cr.) \rightarrow H_2O(liq.) \qquad \begin{aligned} \Delta C_{P(273.16°K)} &= C_P(liq.) - C_P(cr.) \\ &= 9.222 \text{ cal/mole-degree} \end{aligned}$$

$$KCl(cr.) \rightarrow KCl(vap.) \qquad \begin{aligned} \Delta H_{900°K} &= H(vap.) - H(cr.) \\ &= 51.72 \text{ kilocal/mole} \end{aligned}$$

$$HD(g.) \rightarrow \tfrac{1}{2}H_2(g.) + \tfrac{1}{2}D_2(g.) \qquad \begin{aligned} \Delta E_{376°K} &= E(\tfrac{1}{2}H_2) + E(\tfrac{1}{2}D_2) - E(HD) \\ &= -79 \text{ cal/mole} \end{aligned}$$

$$CO(cr., \alpha) \rightarrow CO(cr., \beta) \qquad \begin{aligned} \Delta S_{61.55°K} &= S(\beta) - S(\alpha) \\ &= 2.457 \text{ cal/mole-degree} \end{aligned}$$

Cyclic processes

A sequence of processes of any number and complexity which carries a system through a number of states but finally brings it back to its original state is termed a cycle. Since the initial and final states are identical, the sum $\Sigma(\Delta E)$ of all the separate internal energy increases (ΔE) associated with the different steps must be zero, if the cycle of operations is carried out at constant volume. Similarly, if the cycle is conducted at constant pressure, $\Sigma(\Delta H)$ must be zero. The steps in the cycle may be real or imaginary, reversible or irreversible. For example, in the following cycle of changes at constant temperature and pressure,

$$B \rightarrow Y \qquad \Delta H_1$$
$$Y \rightarrow Z \qquad \Delta H_2$$

and

$$Z \rightarrow B \qquad \Delta H_3$$

we have

$$\Delta H_1 + \Delta H_2 + \Delta H_3 = 0$$

The value of this extremely simple corollary to the first law of thermodynamics is that it provides an indirect means of estimating the increase in heat content of reactions which elude direct investigation. If a cycle consists of s steps, it is sufficient to measure ΔH values for $s-1$ steps. The principle is generally applied by treating the chemical equations and the ΔH values as additive, e.g.

$$
\begin{array}{ll}
B \rightarrow Y & \Delta H_1 \\
Y \rightarrow Z & \Delta H_2 \\
\hline
\therefore \ B \rightarrow Z & \Delta H_1 + \Delta H_2
\end{array}
$$

The relation between thermodynamic variables and the partition function

The properties with which we have dealt in this brief account of thermodynamics, such as energy and entropy, are bulk properties for the whole system. They are often called macroscopic properties, to distinguish them from the microscopic properties such as moments of inertia and discrete energy levels of the molecules forming the system. The bridge between the two sets of properties is provided by the partition function. This is a dimensionless quantity, as its name implies, and it conveniently summarises the way in which the total energy of a system of molecules is partitioned among the molecular inhabitants. If, in a system at equilibrium, there are N_1 molecules with energy ε_1 each, N_2 molecules with energy ε_2 each, and so on, the total number of molecules is

$$ N = N_1 + N_2 + N_3 + \cdots \qquad = \sum N_i \qquad \text{VI.45} $$

and the total energy of the system is

$$ E = N_1\varepsilon_1 + N_2\varepsilon_2 + N_3\varepsilon_3 + \cdots = \sum N_i\varepsilon_i \qquad \text{VI.46} $$

The partition function is simply the sum of all the Boltzmann factors:

$$ f = e^{-\varepsilon_1/kT} + e^{-\varepsilon_2/kT} + e^{-\varepsilon_3/kT} + \cdots \qquad \text{VI.47} $$

As the molecular energy increases, the Boltzmann factor decreases. Energy among molecules is like money among men: the poor are numerous, the rich few. The series represented by equation VI.47 rapidly converges, and, although in principle we should always sum to infinity, in practice it is sometimes sufficient to count only the first ten terms or so. For generality, equation VI.47 is therefore summarised as follows:

$$f = \sum_{i=0}^{i=\infty} e^{-\varepsilon_i/kT}, \qquad \text{VI.48}$$

where ε_i is the energy possessed by a molecule in the ith state. We have already shown that the Boltzmann law, as applied to a system of chemically identical molecules, may be expressed as follows:

$$\frac{N_1}{N} = \frac{e^{-\varepsilon_1/kT}}{\sum e^{-\varepsilon_i/kT}}; \qquad \frac{N_2}{N} = \frac{e^{-\varepsilon_2/kT}}{\sum e^{-\varepsilon_i/kT}}; \qquad \cdots \frac{N_i}{N} = \frac{e^{-\varepsilon_i/kT}}{\sum e^{-\varepsilon_i/kT}} \qquad \text{II.32}$$

The denominator in these expressions is the partition function. Hence

$$\frac{N_1}{N} = \frac{e^{-\varepsilon_1/kT}}{f}; \qquad \frac{N_2}{N} = \frac{e^{-\varepsilon_2/kT}}{f}; \qquad \cdots \frac{N_i}{N} = \frac{e^{-\varepsilon_i/kT}}{f} \qquad \text{VI.49}$$

From this equation we note that the partition function, f, bears the same relation to the total number of molecules, N, as the Boltzmann factor bears to the number, N_i, of molecules in the specified energy level, ε_i. The partition function is thus simply a generalised Boltzmann factor. The system partition function, F, for an assembly of N identical molecules is the product of the N molecular partition functions:

$$F = f^N \qquad \text{VI.50}$$

Let us differentiate equation VI.47 with respect to temperature at constant volume. We have

$$\left(\frac{df}{dT}\right)_V = \frac{\varepsilon_1}{kT^2}e^{-\varepsilon_1/kT} + \frac{\varepsilon_2}{kT^2}e^{-\varepsilon_2/kT} + \ldots = \frac{1}{kT^2}\sum_0^\infty \varepsilon_i e^{-\varepsilon_i/kT}$$

Multiplying throughout by kT^2, dividing throughout by f, and remembering that dx/x equals $d \ln x$, we obtain

$$kT^2\left(\frac{d\ln f}{dT}\right)_V = \frac{e^{-\varepsilon_1/kT}}{f}\varepsilon_1 + \frac{e^{-\varepsilon_2/kT}}{f}\varepsilon_2 + \ldots = \frac{1}{f}\sum_0^\infty e^{-\varepsilon_i/kT}\varepsilon_i$$

For the various ratios in this equation, let us substitute the number ratios to which, according to equation VI.49, they are equal. We then see that

$$NkT^2\left(\frac{d\ln f}{dT}\right)_V = N_1\varepsilon_1 + N_2\varepsilon_2 + N_3\varepsilon_3 + \ldots = \sum_0^\infty N_i\varepsilon_i$$

By combining with equation VI.46, we deduce that

$$E = NkT^2 \left(\frac{d \ln f}{dT}\right)_V \qquad \text{VI.51}$$

which is the general relation between the total energy, E, of a system of N identical molecules at constant temperature, T, and the molecular partition function, f.

When a system is at equilibrium, the mathematical probability, W, of its existence, and its entropy, S, have maximum values. That there is a relation between W and S is obvious, but it was Boltzmann who first concluded that S is solely a function of W and that the relation must be a logarithmic one. By virtue of the third law of thermodynamics, established during this century, Boltzmann's relation may now be expressed in the simple form

$$S = k \ln W \qquad \text{VI.52}$$

The mathematical probability of a system is defined as the number of distinguishable ways in which that system can be realized. N molecules may be arranged in $N!$ ways, but not all these arrangements are distinguishable. If N_1 molecules have all the same energy, ε_1, arrangements within this group will lead to indistinguishable configurations. Similarly, swopping around the N_2 molecules in the group having energy ε_2 per molecule leads to no new distinguishable arrangements. The total number, $N!$, of conceivable arrangements must thus be reduced by the product $N_1! \, N_2! \, N_3!\ldots$, since each of these numbers represents the number of ways in which molecules in a given energy group can be arranged. We thus have

$$W = \frac{N!}{N_1! \, N_2! \, N_3!\ldots} = N!(\overset{i}{\Pi}N_i!)^{-1} \qquad \text{VI.53}$$

Combining equations VI.52 and VI.53, and making use of Stirling's approximation, $\ln x! = x \ln x - x$, which is valid when x is large, we cast equation VI.52 into the following form:

$$\frac{S}{k} = \ln W = N \ln N - N$$

$$- \left\{ \begin{array}{l} N_1 \ln N_1 - N_1 \\ N_2 \ln N_2 - N_2 \\ N_3 \ln N_3 - N_3 \\ \ldots \end{array} \right\}$$

According to equation VI.45, however, the numbers in the last column cancel out, leaving

$$\frac{S}{k} = N \ln N - \sum N_i \ln N_i$$

By writing equation VI.49 in logarithmic form, we see that

$$\ln N_i = \ln N - \frac{\varepsilon_i}{kT} - \ln f$$

and, consequently, that

$$N_i \ln N_i = N_i \ln N - \frac{N_i \varepsilon_i}{kT} - N_i \ln f$$

The sum of all such terms is

$$\sum N_i \ln N_i = N_1 \ln N - \frac{N_1 \varepsilon_1}{kT} - N_1 \ln f$$

$$+ N_2 \ln N - \frac{N_2 \varepsilon_2}{kT} - N_2 \ln f$$

$$+ N_3 \ln N - \frac{N_3 \varepsilon_3}{kT} - N_3 \ln f$$

$$+ \cdot \quad \cdot \quad \cdot \quad \cdot \quad \cdot \quad \cdot$$

$$= N \ln N - \sum \frac{N_i \varepsilon_i}{kT} - N \ln f$$

By means of equation VI.46, we therefore have

$$\frac{S}{k} = \frac{E}{kT} + N \ln f$$

Substituting for E the expression already derived (equation VI.51), we arrive at the general relation between the entropy, S, and the partition function, f:

$$S = Nk \left[\ln f + T \left(\frac{d \ln f}{dT} \right)_V \right] \qquad \text{VI.54}$$

By inserting the general expressions derived above for E and S, we have the following expression for the Helmholtz free energy (equation VI.17):

$$A = -NkT \ln f. \qquad \text{VI.55}$$

Equations VI.51, VI.54 and VI.55 may be regarded as key equations, from which the relationship between f and thermodynamic functions other than E, S, and A may readily be derived.

The general thermodynamic expression for the pressure, for example, is $P = -(dA/dV)_T$ (equation VI.20) so that, in terms of the partition function,

$$P = NkT\left(\frac{d \ln f}{dV}\right)_T \qquad \text{VI.56}$$

Similarly, the heat capacity at constant volume, which is defined as, $C_V = (dE/dT)_V$ (equation VI.13) becomes

$$C_V = N_0 k\left[T^2\left(\frac{d^2 \ln f}{dT^2}\right)_V + 2T\left(\frac{d \ln f}{dT}\right)_V\right] \qquad \text{VI.57}$$

The reciprocal of the isothermal compressibility, (equation VI.16), becomes

$$\frac{1}{\beta} = -NkTV\left(\frac{d^2 \ln f}{dV^2}\right)_T \qquad \text{VI.58}$$

Finally, the chemical potential, $\mu = (dA/dN)_{T,V}$, is seen to be

$$\mu = -kT\left[\ln f + \left(\frac{d \ln f}{d \ln N}\right)_{T,V}\right] \qquad \text{VI.59}$$

If we wish to use the system partition function, F, instead of the molecular partition function, f, we may, according to equation VI.50 write the three key expressions as follows:

$$\text{total energy:} \quad E = kT^2\left(\frac{d \ln F}{dT}\right)_V \qquad \text{VI.60}$$

$$\text{free energy:} \quad A = -kT \ln F, \qquad \text{VI.61}$$

$$\text{entropy:} \quad S = k\left[\ln F + T\left(\frac{d \ln F}{dT}\right)_V\right] \qquad \text{VI.62}$$

These are general relations which may be applied to systems of any number of components.

Degeneracy

Let us write the partition function in the expanded form

$$f = e^{-\varepsilon_a/kT} + e^{-\varepsilon_b/kT} + e^{-\varepsilon_c/kT} + e^{-\varepsilon_d/kT} + e^{-\varepsilon_e/kT} +$$

and consider the particular case where the energy levels ε_a and ε_b are so close together that they may be taken to coincide. The first two terms in the expansion may then be replaced by the expression $2e^{-\varepsilon_0/kT}$, where $\varepsilon_0 = \varepsilon_a = \varepsilon_b$. Similarly, suppose that the energy levels ε_c, ε_d and ε_e coalesce. The next three terms may then be replaced by the expression $3e^{-\varepsilon_1/kT}$, where $\varepsilon_1 = \varepsilon_c = \varepsilon_d = \varepsilon_e$. The partition function may accordingly be rewritten with a smaller number of terms, but with each term multiplied by an integer, g, which is said to be a measure of degeneracy;

$$f = g_0 e^{-\varepsilon_0/kT} + g_1 e^{-\varepsilon_1/kT} + \cdots = \sum g_i e^{-\varepsilon_i/kT} \qquad \text{VI.63}$$

The degeneracy of an atom is equal to the multiplicity of the terms required to reproduce its spectral lines. Thus, for the inert gas atoms in the ground electronic state, $g_0 = g_1 = g_2 = \cdots = g_i = 1$. For the alkali metal atoms, $g_0 = g_1 = g_2 = \cdots = g_i = 2$. For diatomic molecules, the factor g may be complicated. In a ground electronic state of unit multiplicity (i.e. in a non-degenerate electronic level), the degeneracy is $2J + 1$, where J is the number of units of rotational quanta possessed by the molecule. Thus only the ground level in such a molecule is non-degenerate, the other energy levels having a degeneracy of 3, 5, 7, ... The vibrational levels of all diatomic molecules may be taken as non-degenerate ($g = 1$).

VII Crystals

A striking property of crystals, evident on even a casual inspection, is the beauty of their form. Their perfect planar surfaces intersect at well-defined angles, and suggest that the units from which the crystals are built are arranged in an orderly manner. The exact arrangement of the crystalline units has been revealed by the application of Bragg's law (equation I.11) to the reflexion of X-rays from the crystal surfaces. Experiment shows that the atoms or ions forming the crystal occupy parallel planes at fixed distances, d, apart. Reflexions from different crystallographic facets of the same crystal show that not all the planes are identical. Helpful guides in exploring the internal structure of crystals are provided by their chemical composition, their densities and the intensities of the reflected X-rays, which are stronger from those planes which contain the heavier elements. The structure of crystals as revealed by X-ray analysis has in many instances been confirmed by experiments on the diffraction of electrons. We shall first consider some of the results obtained with some very simple crystals possessing cubic symmetry.

Some simple crystals with cubic symmetry

With the exception of the chloride, bromide and iodide of caesium, the alkali halides crystallise as shown in Fig. VII.1. Each point marks

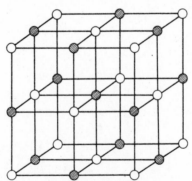

Fig. VII.1 *Unit cell in the simple cubic or rock-salt lattice*

the intersection of three mutually perpendicular planes, and is occupied by an ion. Shaded spheres represent (say) the cations, and unshaded spheres the anions. If the length of the edge of the unit cube shown is denoted by l, we see that the distance of an ion from its nearest neighbour is $a = l/2$. The lattice points are alternately occupied by cations and ions, each ion of a given kind being surrounded by 6 ions of the other kind. We thus say that the coordination number of either ion in the rock salt lattice is 6. The unit cell contains, in all, the substance of 8 ions, contributed as follows:

1 whole ion at the centre of the unit cell	= 1
6 halves at the centres of the faces	= 3
12 quarters at the centres of the edges	= 3
8 eighths at the corners of the unit cell	= 1

The average volume per ion is thus $l^3/8 = a^3$, and the average volume per molecule is $2a^3$. The interionic distances cited in Table VII.1 are the averages of the closely agreeing results of X-ray reflexion and electron diffraction. The oxides and sulphides of magnesium, calcium, strontium and barium form similar crystals, with smaller interionic distances.

Table VII.1 *Cation-anion distance* (Å) *in certain crystals of the rock-salt type*

Element	F	Cl	Br	I
Li	2·014	2·570	2·746	3·010
Na	2·330	2·849	2·982	3·236
K	2·679	3·149	3·304	3·538
Rb	2·815	3·286	3·434	3·663
Cs	3·005	—	—	—

The body-centred cubic lattice (Fig. VII.2) is a more open structure. The unit cell contains the substance of two atoms only, i.e. one at the centre and 8 eighths at the corners. The coordination number is 8, and the average volume per atom $l^3/2$. The nearest interatomic distance is one-half of the cube diagonal. If we denote it, as before, by a, then $(2a)^2 = 3l^2$. The average volume per atom is thus $4a^3/3\sqrt{3}$. Cell lengths and interatomic distances of the alkali metals, which crystallise

143

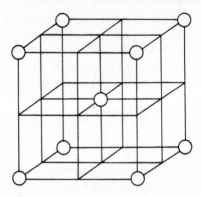

Fig. VII.2   *Unit cell in the body-centred cubic lattice*

in body-centred cubes, are given in Table VII.2. A few metallic elements of higher valency, such as barium, tungsten and molybdenum, also crystallise in body-centred cubic lattices.

Table VII.2 *Lattice constants and internuclear distances (Å) in certain metal crystals of the body-centred cubic type*

Element	Cell length, l	Internuclear distance, a
Li	3·50	3·03
Na	4·30	3·72
K	5·20	4·50
Rb	5·62	4·87
Cs	6·05	5·24

The inert elements (excepting helium) and numerous metallic elements crystallise in face-centred cubic lattices (Fig. VII.3). The distance, a, between nearest neighbours is one-half of the face diagonal. Hence, denoting the cell length by l, $(2a)^2 = 2l^2$, so that $a = l/\sqrt{2}$. Numerical results are given in Table VII.3. The unit cell contains the substance of four atoms, i.e. one-half of each of the six atoms at the centres of the faces, and one-eighth of each atom at the corners. The average atomic volume is thus $a^3/\sqrt{2}$. Each atom is surrounded by

Table VII.3 *Lattice constants and internuclear distances*
(Å) *for certain elements crystallising in face-centred cubic lattices*

Element	Cell length, l	Internuclear distance, a
Ne	4·52	3·20
A	5·43	3·84
Kr	5·59	3·95
Xe	6·18	4·37
Cu	3·597	2·544
Ag	4·078	2·884
Au	4·070	2·878
Al	4·041	2·864
Ca	5·66	4·00
Sr	6·05	4·28
Pd	3·882	2·745
Ir	3·831	2·709
Pt	3·916	2·770
Pb	4·940	3·493

twelve equidistant neighbours, i.e. four in each of the mutually perpendicular planes ($c = 12$).

There are several variants based on the face-centred cubic lattice. If, for example, in the unit cell of Fig. VII.3, the centre of each alternate

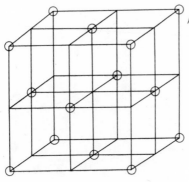

Fig. VII.3 *Unit cell in the face-centred cubic lattice*

small cube is occupied by an atom, then each atom in the crystal is symmetrically surrounded, as in Fig. VII.4, by four equidistant neighbours at a separation $a = (l\sqrt{3})/4$. Now when the alternate corners of a cube are joined, there appears a regular tetrahedron. The structure formed is thus one in which each atom occupies the centre of a

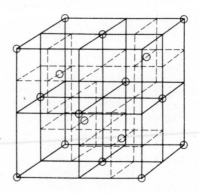

Fig. VII.4   *Unit cell in the diamond lattice*

regular tetrahedron, and is surrounded by four atoms, one at each of its corners. This is the diamond lattice, (Fig. VII.4) as revealed by X-ray analysis (W. H. and W. L. Bragg). It substantiates a basic law of aliphatic organic chemistry, according to which the four equivalent valencies of the saturated carbon atom are directed in space as from

Fig. VII.4a   *The diamond structure*

the centre to the four corners of a regular tetrahedron (Le Bel; van't Hoff). The other elements in group IV B of the periodic table, with the exception of lead, crystallise in the same pattern.

When the centres of alternate small cubes in the unit cell of the face-centred cubic lattice are occupied by atoms differing from those at the corners, there results a pattern in which many salts crystallise, particularly those like zinc blende (ZnS) with cations and anions of the same electrovalencies (Table VII.4).

Table VII.4 *Lattice constants of crystals of the zinc blende type* (Å)

Compound	Cell length	Compound	Cell length	Compound	Cell length
AgI	6·491	CdTe	6·41	CSi	4·348
BeS	4·85	ZnS	5·43	HgS	5·84
BeSe	5·07	ZnSe	5·65	HgSe	6·07
BeTe	5·54	ZnTe	6·07	HgTe	6·36
AlP	5·42	GaP	5·436	CuCl	5·407
AlAs	5·62	GaAs	5·635	CuBr	5·681
AlSb	6·13	GaSb	6·118	CuI	6·047

Finally, when the centres of the small cubes in the unit cell of the face-centred cubic lattice are all occupied by atoms differing from those at the corners, there results a structure assumed by fluorspar (CaF_2) and other salts such as lithium oxide (Li_2O), cuprous selenide (Cu_2Se), strontium chloride ($SrCl_2$) and thorium oxide (ThO_2) with electro-valent ratios of 1 : 2 or 2 : 1 (Table VII.5).

Table VII.5 *Lattice constants of crystals of the fluorspar type* (Å)

Compound	Cell length	Compound	Cell length	Compound	Cell length
Li_2O	4·61	CaF_2	5·46	CeO_2	5·41
Li_2S	5·70	SrF_2	5·86	ThO_2	5·59
Cu_2S	5·59	$SrCl_2$	7·00	ZrO_2	5·07
Cu_2Se	5·75	CdF_2	5·40	PrO_2	5·36
Mg_2Si	6·39	PbF_2	5·93	UO_2	5·47

Dimorphism

Many elements, such as phosphorus, iron and tin, are dimorphous, i.e. they exist in two distinct crystalline forms. The most striking instance is carbon, which occurs not only in the form of the diamond, as described above, but more abundantly as graphite. In contrast to the diamond, which is colourless, very hard, and a non-conductor of electricity, graphite is black, very soft, and conducts electricity well. Its crystalline structure is wholly different from that of the diamond. The atoms are bound firmly together in parallel planes formed of regular hexagons (Fig. VII.5; Hassel and Mark; Bernal). The interatomic

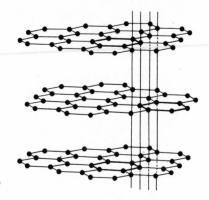

Fig. VII.5   *Graphite*

distance in the hexagons (1.42 Å) is less than in the diamond (1·542 Å), and only slightly greater than in benzene (1·397 Å). The perpendicular distance between neighbouring planes, however, is relatively large (3·40 Å), and the forces between them correspondingly weak. Bragg has likened the graphitic structure to a pack of slippery cards. It is to the weakness of the interplanar bonds that graphite owes its lubricating properties, and to the six mobile electrons in each of the benzene-like rings that it owes its electrical conductivity.

Molecular crystals may also exhibit dimorphism. Calcite and aragonite are two different crystalline forms of calcium carbonate, the former being the more stable under ordinary conditions.

The vapour pressure of a monatomic crystal

According to Einstein, each atom in a monatomic crystal vibrates harmonically in three dimensions about its mean position. We have seen (equation III.19) that such a conception explains the change of the heat capacity with respect to temperature. We shall now show how the same simple model accounts for the vapour pressure of the crystal. The easiest way to do so is to equate the chemical potentials of an atom in the crystal and an atom in the vapour phase with which the crystal is in equilibrium (equation VI.40).

The allowed energy levels of a harmonic oscillator vibrating with a frequency v is $(v+\frac{1}{2})hv$ (equation IV.15), and the partition function (equation VI.47) for a linear oscillator is consequently

$$f = \sum_0^\infty e^{-(v+\frac{1}{2})hv/kT} = e^{-hv/2kT} \sum_0^\infty e^{-vhv/kT}$$

The summation is readily carried out by substituting x for $e^{-hv/kT}$. The sum is then seen to be $1+x+x^2+x^3+\ldots$, which is known to be $1/(1-x)$. Hence

$$f = e^{-hv/2kT}(1-e^{-hv/kT})^{-1} \qquad \text{VII.1}$$

For a three-dimensional oscillator in the crystal, we have

$$f_c = e^{-3hv/2kT}(1-e^{-hv/kT})^{-3} \cdot e^{-u_c/kT} \qquad \text{VII.2}$$

where u_c is the potential energy of an atom at rest in the crystal. In deriving the chemical potential from the general equation VI.59, we note that, in this instance, $(d\ln f/d\ln N)_{T,V}$ is zero, so that

$$\mu_c = 3kT\ln(1-e^{-hv/kT})+\tfrac{3}{2}hv+u_c \qquad \text{VII.3}$$

The partition function for a monatomic gas molecule (to be derived later), is

$$f_g = \frac{(2\pi mkT)^{3/2}Ve}{h^3N} \cdot e^{-u_g/kT} \qquad \text{IX.46}$$

In deriving the chemical potential, we note that $(d\ln f/d\ln N)_{T,V}$ is now -1, and, since $\ln_e e$ is 1, we find

$$\mu_g = -kT\ln\left[\frac{(2\pi mkT)^{3/2}V}{h^3N}\right]+u_g \qquad \text{VII.4}$$

Here u_g is the potential energy of the monatomic gas molecule. On equating the chemical potentials, and noting that $V/N = kT/p$, we obtain the vapour pressure equation

$$p = \frac{(2\pi mkT)^{3/2}kT}{h^3}(1-e^{-hv/kT})^3 \cdot e^{-\lambda_0/kT} \qquad \text{VII.5}$$

149

where λ_0, the observed heat of sublimation at the absolute zero of temperature, is given (as explained in Fig. VII.6), by the relation

$$\lambda_0 = u_g - u_c - \tfrac{3}{2}hv \qquad \text{VII.6}$$

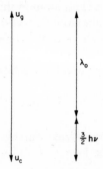

Fig. VII.6 *Actual energy gain, λ_0, and gain in static energy $(u_g - u_c)$*

At relatively high temperatures, the equation simplifies to

$$p = (2\pi m)^{3/2} v^3 (kT)^{-1/2} . e^{-\lambda_0/kT} \qquad \text{VII.7}$$

For a given crystal, therefore,

$$\ln_e(pT^{1/2}) = \text{constant} - \frac{\lambda_0}{kT} \qquad \text{VII.8}$$

and λ_0 may be found by plotting $\ln_e(pT^{1/2})$ as a function of $1/T$. The value thus found, by the static measurement of pressure, is 445 cal/mole for neon. The value found for graphite, using the effusion method (equation II.10), is 170 400 cal/mole. The vibration frequencies, v, are 1.01×10^{12} and 29.99×10^{12} sec^{-1} respectively. These two monatomic solids roughly represent the range of vapour pressures and heats of sublimation met with in practice. At a temperature of 20°K, we find, from equation VII.7, using these numerical constants, that p(neon)/p(graphite) is 10^{1850}.

Mie's equation

A convenient expression for the interaction energy, ϕ, of a pair of molecules at a distance, a, apart when the forces exerted between the molecules are spherically symmetrical has been proposed by Mie

150

(1903):

$$\phi = Aa^{-n} - Ba^{-m} \qquad \text{VII.9}$$

A and B are constants, and n and m are integers $(n > m)$. The stability condition $(d\phi/da = 0$ when $a = a_e)$ becomes

$$a_e^{n-m} = nA/mB \qquad \text{VII.8}$$

and the following alternative expressions emerge for the minimum potential energy of the pair;

$$-\phi_e = Ba_e^{-m}\left(1 - \frac{m}{n}\right) = Aa_e^{-n}\left(\frac{n}{m} - 1\right) \qquad \text{VII.9}$$

Eliminating A and B, the general equation of Mie can now be re-written in the following way:

$$\phi = \phi_e \frac{1}{(m-n)}\left[m\left(\frac{a_e}{a}\right)^n - n\left(\frac{a_e}{a}\right)^m\right] \qquad \text{VII.10}$$

Its application to a pair of mercury atoms, for which $m = 6$ and $n = 9$, is shown in Fig. VII.7. The displacement energy $\phi - \phi_e$, on being expanded in power series of the displacement $a - a_e$, yields the

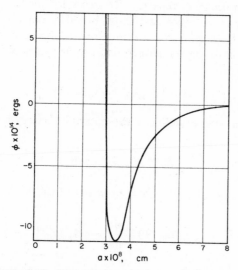

Fig. VII.7   *Potential energy of a pair of mercury atoms as a function of their distance apart*

following equation for the harmonic vibration frequency:

$$v_e = \frac{1}{2\pi a_e}\left(\frac{mnD_e}{\mu}\right)^{1/2} \qquad \text{VII.11}$$

where D_e is $-\phi_e$, the energy of dissociation of the stable pair, and μ is its reduced mass (Sutherland, 1938; See Appendix 5).

Mie's equation has found numerous applications in various branches of physical chemistry. One of these we shall now discuss.

Application of Mie's equation to monatomic crystals

The avalent atoms of chemistry are those of the inert elements. Examples of symmetrical, non-polar molecules are methane and carbon tetrachloride. The only forces of attraction to be considered are the dispersion forces, for which values of B are provided by London's theory, and m is 6. In applying Mie's equation to crystals formed from such entities, we must first sum the interaction energies over the whole crystal. The interaction energy of one atom or molecule with its c equidistant neighbours is $c\phi$. The total near-neighbour interaction energy of N identical molecules is $\frac{1}{2}Nc\phi$, the $\frac{1}{2}$ being introduced to avoid counting each interaction twice. The average potential energy per atom or molecule is thus $\frac{1}{2}c\phi$. To allow for the additional interactions between any atom and those in shells outside the first coordination shell, we introduce summation constants, s, whose magnitude depends on the crystal pattern and on the values of the integers n and m. Then

$$u = \tfrac{1}{2}c(s_n A a^{-n} - s_m B a^{-m}) \qquad \text{VII.12}$$

The separation corresponding to the minimum energy is given by the equation

$$a_0^{n-m} = s_n nA/s_m mB \qquad \text{VII.13}$$

and the minimum energy is given by either of the equations

$$-u_0 = \tfrac{1}{2}cs_m Ba_0^{-m}\left(1-\frac{m}{n}\right) = \tfrac{1}{2}cs_n Aa_0^{-n}\left(\frac{n}{m}-1\right) \qquad \text{VII.14}$$

On eliminating A and B, we obtain for the average potential energy of one atom or molecule in a system of atoms or molecules subject to

152

these laws of force:

$$u = \frac{u_0}{m-n}\left[m\left(\frac{a_0}{a}\right)^n - n\left(\frac{a_0}{a}\right)^m\right] \qquad \text{VII.15}$$

It can be shown that the average vibration frequency of the atom or molecule in the crystal when a is not very different from a_0 is

$$v_0 = \frac{1}{2\pi a}\left(\frac{2mn|-u_0|}{3\mu}\right)^{1/2} \qquad \text{VII.16}$$

These five expressions are analogous with those given in the preceding section. The potential energy of a free gas atom or molecule in an infinitely dilute system is taken as zero. u_0 is the lowest value of the potential energy of an atom in the crystal, when all atoms are assumed to be at rest. Hence, as shown in Fig. VII.6,

$$-u_0 = \lambda_0 + \tfrac{3}{2}hv_0 \qquad \text{VII.17}$$

where λ_0 is the observed latent heat of sublimation at the absolute zero of temperature, and $\tfrac{3}{2}hv_0$ is the residual energy.

Let us apply some of these expressions to argon, which crystallises in a face centred cubic lattice ($c = 12$) with an interatomic distance of 3.74 A at $T = 0$. We have $m = 6$, and, as shown later, $n = 9$. Moreover, since $s_6 = 1.2045$ and $s_9 = 1.0410$ for this lattice, $(a_e/a_0) = (s_m/s_n)^{1/(n-m)} = 1.050$, and a_e becomes 3.93 A. We may estimate the value of B from the equation $B = \tfrac{3}{4}Z^{1/2}hv_v\alpha_0^2$ (cf. equation IV.51), where the number Z of valency electrons is 8, the average electronic vibration frequency v_v is $4.124 \times 10^{15}\text{sec}^{-1}$, and the polarisability α_0 towards light of infinite wave length is 1.6264×10^{-24} cm^3. Then $B = 1.533 \times 10^{-58}$, and, since $A = (m/n)Ba_e^{n-m}$, we derive the inter-molecular energy equation

$$\phi = \frac{6.20 \times 10^{-81}}{a^9} - \frac{1.533 \times 10^{-58}}{a^6}$$

The values of $-u_0$ and v_0 calculated by means of equations VII.14 and VII.16 are 1.94 kilocalories per mole and 1.15×10^{12} sec^{-1}, in reasonable agreement with the observed values of 2.03 and 1.32 in the corresponding units.

It will be observed that the equilibrium separation of a pair of argon atoms in the gas phase is about 50 per cent greater than that of the ions in a KCl molecule in the gas phase, and that the ratio of

F

the dissociation energy of the atomic pair to that of the ionic pair is roughly 1 : 60. Moreover, the residual energy is an important fraction of $-u_0$ for the atomic pair, but is small enough to be ignored in the ionic pair.

Table VII.6 *Intermolecular energy constants of the equation* $\phi = Aa^{-n} - Ba^{-6}$

Molecule	n	A (erg-cm^n)	$B \times 10^{60}$ (erg-cm^6)	$a_e \times 10^8$ (cm)	$D_e \times 10^{14}$ (erg/pair)
A	9	$6 \cdot 20 \times 10^{-81}$	$153 \cdot 3$	$3 \cdot 93$	$1 \cdot 386$
Hg	9	$7 \cdot 71 \times 10^{-81}$	337	$3 \cdot 25$	$9 \cdot 53$
Xe	11	$5 \cdot 07 \times 10^{-95}$	527	$4 \cdot 46$	$3 \cdot 045$
H_2	12	$9 \cdot 13 \times 10^{-105}$	$13 \cdot 6$	$3 \cdot 32$	$0 \cdot 5066$
N_2	12	$3 \cdot 70 \times 10^{-103}$	140	$4 \cdot 174$	$1 \cdot 324$
CH_4	12	$6 \cdot 20 \times 10^{-103}$	226	$4 \cdot 20$	$2 \cdot 06$
CS_2	15	$8 \cdot 36 \times 10^{-124}$	$1 \, 490$	$4 \cdot 82$	$7 \cdot 14$
CCl_4	15	$1 \cdot 45 \times 10^{-122}$	$5 \, 540$	$5 \cdot 72$	$9 \cdot 49$

The experimental determination of the lattice energy of alkali halides

The energy required to transform one gram-mole of a pure crystalline salt at the absolute zero of temperature into gaseous ions at infinite dilution, also at $T = 0$, is known as the lattice energy of the crystal. It cannot be measured directly, but can be found by means of a cycle of operations devised by Born and Haber, for each of which an experimental value can be given to the increase in heat content. The six steps in the cycle may be described as follows:

$$
\begin{array}{ll}
MX(cr.) \rightarrow M(cr.) + \tfrac{1}{2}X_2(s) & \Delta H_1 = Q_f \\
M(cr.) \rightarrow M(g) & \Delta H_2 = L_M \\
\tfrac{1}{2}X_2(s) \rightarrow \tfrac{1}{2}X_2(g) & \Delta H_3 = \tfrac{1}{2}L_{X_2} \\
M(g) \rightarrow M^+(g) + \ominus(g) & \Delta H_4 = V_i \varepsilon \\
\tfrac{1}{2}X_2(g) \rightarrow X(g) & \Delta H_5 = \tfrac{1}{2}D \\
X(g) + \ominus(g) \rightarrow X^-(g) & \Delta H_6 = -E_X \\
\hline
MX(cr) \rightarrow M^+(g) + X^-(g) & \Delta H = \sum_{}^{6} \Delta H
\end{array}
$$

The first step is the reverse of the formation of the crystalline compound from its elements in the states (s) which they normally exist in; the increase in heat content equals the heat evolved, Q_f, in forming the compound, and can be measured calorimetrically. In the second step, L_M represents the molar heat of sublimation of the metal crystal; this can be determined from the variation of its vapour pressure with respect to temperature. The gain in heat content attending step three is one-half of the molar latent heat of sublimation of the solid or of vaporisation of the liquid halogen, and can be similarly found, or measured by direct calorimetry. The fourth step represents the ionisation of one gram-atom of the monatomic metal vapour into ions and electrons; V_i, the ionisation potential of the metal atom, is known from its spectrum. In step five, one-half of a gram-mole of diatomic halogen in the gas phase is dissociated into free atoms in their ground electronic state: D is the dissociation energy, and can be found from the vibrational spectrum of the molecular gas, and in other ways. E_X in the sixth step is the electron affinity of the halogen

Table VII.7 *Experimental determination of the lattice energy of certain alkali halides at* 298·16°K (kilocals.)

Salt	L_M	V_i	$\frac{1}{2}L_{x_2}$	$\frac{1}{2}D_{x_2}$	E_x	Q_f	$-U_0$
LiF	37·07	125·79	0	18·86	82·1	146·3	245·9
NaF	25·98	120·04	0	18·86	82·1	136·0	218·8
KF	21·51	101·56	0	18·86	82·1	134·5	194·3
RbF	20·51	97·79	0	18·86	82·1	131·3	186·3
LiCl	37·07	125·79	0	28·97	86·6	97·7	202·9
NaCl	25·98	120·04	0	28·97	86·6	98·2	186·6
KCl	21·51	101·56	0	28·97	86·6	104·2	169·6
RbCl	20·51	97·79	0	28·97	86·6	102·9	163·6
LiBr	37·07	125·79	3·76	22·74	80·9	83·7	192·2
NaBr	25·98	120·04	3·76	22·74	80·9	86·0	177·7
KBr	21·51	101·56	3·76	22·74	80·9	93·7	162·4
RbBr	20·51	97·79	3·76	22·74	80·9	93·0	156·9
LiI	37·07	125·79	7·42	18·05	73·2	64·8	179·9
NaI	25·98	120·04	7·42	18·05	73·2	68·8	167·1
KI	21·51	101·56	7·42	18·05	73·2	78·3	153·7
RbI	20·51	97·79	7·42	18·05	73·2	78·5	149·1

atom, i.e. the energy evolved when a gaseous atom and an electron unite to form a stable anion in the dilute gaseous state. The magnitude of this energy term has been determined by the mass-spectrometric analysis of the atoms and ions in beams of the halide MX emitted from the surface of hot tungsten filaments (Yonov, 1940; T. L. Bailey, 1958). The lattice energies of the alkali halides (Table VII.7) are seen to range between about 250 kilocalories per mole for lithium fluoride to about 150 for rubidium iodide.

Born's theory of the ionic lattice

The fundamental idea underlying Born's theory of the stability of crystalline salts is that the units of which they are formed are ions. Attractive forces can then be attributed to Coulombic interactions between ions of unlike sign. Repulsive forces arise in part from Coulombic interactions between ions of the same sign, and in part from intrinsic interactions between closed electronic shells of ions of all kinds. We shall here apply the theory to the rock-salt lattice. Figure VII.1 shows that each ion is surrounded by six oppositely charged ions at a distance a away, by twelve similarly charged ions at a distance $a/\sqrt{2}$ away, by eight oppositely charged ions at a distance $a/\sqrt{3}$, and so on. The interaction energy between any single ion and the rest of the crystal is thus

$$-\frac{\varepsilon^2}{a}\left(\frac{6}{\sqrt{1}}-\frac{12}{\sqrt{2}}+\frac{8}{\sqrt{3}}-\cdots\right)$$

The term within the brackets is a number, known as Madelung's constant, and denoted by α. It can be evaluated to any desired degree of precision from the geometry of the crystal. For crystals of the rock-salt type α is 1·747558. The energy of repulsion between two closed shells of electrons whose centres are at a distance a apart may be represented by the term Aa^{-n}, where A is a constant, and n is an integer. The intrinsic repulsion energy of a single ion with all the others in the crystal is seen to be

$$\frac{A}{a^n}\left[\frac{6}{(\sqrt{1})^n}+\frac{12}{(\sqrt{2})^n}+\frac{8}{(\sqrt{3})^n}+\cdots\right]$$
$$=\frac{6A}{a^n}\left[\frac{1}{(\sqrt{1})^n}+\frac{2}{(\sqrt{2})^n}+\frac{(4/3)}{(\sqrt{3})^n}+\cdots\right]$$

The term in the second square bracket may be denoted by the symbol s_n. It has been evaluated (Lennard–Jones and Ingham, 1925) for various values of n. The total energy of interaction of a single ion with the rest of the crystal is the sum of these two contributions. The average potential energy per ion is one-half of this sum. Hence the average potential energy per molecule of salt is simply

$$u = \frac{6As_n}{a^n} - \frac{\alpha\varepsilon^2}{a} \qquad\qquad \text{VII.19}$$

When this energy has its minimum value, du/da is zero, and the equilibrium separation of the ions is given by the equation

$$a_0^{n-1} = \frac{n6As_n}{\alpha\varepsilon^2} \qquad\qquad \text{VII.20}$$

The minimum potential energy per molecule becomes

$$u_0 = -\frac{\alpha\varepsilon^2}{a_0}\left(1 - \frac{1}{n}\right) \qquad\qquad \text{VII.21}$$

On substituting in this expression the experimental lattice energies of Table VII.6 and the internuclear distances of Table VII.1, we obtain the values of n listed in Table VII.8. The nearest integral values of n, shown in brackets, are in satisfactory agreement with those since found from the virial coefficients of the inert gases. Similar numbers are found from data on di-divalent crystals, for which ε^2 of equation must be replaced by $(z\varepsilon)^2$, where z is 2. Thus, for example, the constants for magnesium oxide ($-u_0 = 940$ kilocal; $a_0 = 2\cdot102$ Å) give $n = 6\cdot7$, and those for calcium sulphide ($-u_0 = 722$; $a_0 = 2\cdot84$ Å) give $n = 8\cdot6$. There thus seems little doubt that the forces of intrinsic

Table VII.8 *Values of the constant n in the repulsion term Aa^{-n} for alkali halides*

	F	Cl	Br	I
Li	6·8(7)	9·9(10)	11·0(11)	14·8(15)
Na	8·2(8)	12·0(12)	11·6(12)	14·7(15)
K	9·8(10)	12·5(13)	13·3(13)	15·9(16)
Rb	10·5(11)	13·7(14)	14·0(14)	18·0(18)

repulsion exerted between ions in crystals are the same as those exerted between pairs of inert gas atoms, and that the main features of the stability of salts with different electrovalencies can be interpreted in terms of Born's theory.

It has been improved in various ways. When we include in equation VII.19 a term to allow for dispersion forces, we obtain the more complete equation

$$u = \frac{cs_n A}{a^n} - \frac{\alpha \varepsilon^2}{a} - \frac{cs_6 B}{a^6} \qquad \text{VII.22}$$

where c is the coordination number, s_6 is a second summation constant, resembling s_n, and $-Ba^{-6}$ is the energy of attraction, due to dispersion forces, between a pair of atoms at a distance a apart. The lattice energy is now given by the equation

$$-u_0 = \frac{\alpha \varepsilon^2}{a_0}\left(1 - \frac{1}{n}\right) + \frac{cs_6 B}{a_0^6}\left(1 - \frac{6}{n}\right) \qquad \text{VII.23}$$

from which revised values of n can be estimated. Let us apply this equation to KCl, for which $-u_0 = 169.6$ kilocalories per mole; $a_0 = 3.149$ Å; $\alpha = 1.7476$; $c = 6$; $s_6 = 1.4003$. The value of B afforded by the virial coefficients of argon is 1.034×10^{-58} erg-cm^6. That calculated from the atomic polarisability and the number and frequency of the dispersion electrons, using the Slater–Kirkwood equation, is 1.52 in the same units. They yield the respective values of 9.4 and 8.6 for n. We may therefore assume n to be 9, and the effective value of B becomes 1.404×10^{-58}. The equation for the lattice energy now becomes

$$-u_0 = \frac{\alpha \varepsilon^2}{a_0} \cdot \frac{8}{9} + \frac{cs_6 B}{a_0^6} \cdot \frac{1}{3} \qquad \text{VII.24}$$

$$169.6 = 163.8 + 5.8$$

Thus, although the correction introduced by the dispersion effect is relatively small in the energy, being about 3.4 per cent. of the total, it lowers the estimate of n from 12.5 to 9. Similar corrections when applied to the other salts diminish, but do not remove, the tendency for n to increase with the ionic weight.

If the repulsion between spherical shells of electrons is more reliably represented by an exponential than by an inverse-power term, we may adopt an equation of the form

$$u = cbe^{-(a-a_0)/\rho} - \frac{\alpha\varepsilon^2}{a} - \frac{cBs_6}{a^6} \qquad \text{VII.25}$$

where b and ρ are new constants, and the other terms retain their former meaning. We now have

$$-u_0 = \frac{\alpha\varepsilon^2}{a_0}\left(1 - \frac{\rho}{a_0}\right) + \frac{cBs_6}{a_0^6}\left(1 - \frac{6\rho}{a_0}\right) \qquad \text{VII.26}$$

which is the same as equation VII.23, when a_0/ρ is replaced by n. Applied to KCl, ρ is found to be 0·335 Å or 0·366 Å, according to the value of B adopted. Such a treatment, refined by the resolution of the constant b into three factors and by the inclusion of another energy term to allow for the interaction of quadrupoles, leads to a mean value of $\rho = 0·345$ Å for the alkali halides as a class (Born, 1932; J. E. Mayer, 1933).

The integer n may be independently calculated from the compressibility of the crystal (Born, 1919; Landé, 1921).

Salt molecules

The vapour in equilibrium with a crystalline salt consists of molecules, exerting a pressure which, though small, can be accurately measured by Knudsen's method (equation II.10). Deitz (1936) found that the saturated vapour pressure of crystalline potassium chloride could be represented by the equation $\log_{10}p$ (dynes/cm^2) $= 13·461 - 11\,300/T$ (see Table VII.9). His result has been confirmed and extended by R. S. Bradley (1953). The heat of sublimation at about 900°K is thus $L_T = 51·7$ kilocalories per mole. Because the heat capacities of the crystal and the gaseous molecules differ, it is possible that this figure should be increased to about 54 at the absolute zero of temperature.

Verwey and de Boer (1936) have given an extremely simple account of the stability of salt molecules, based on the assumption that the interionic constants governing the behaviour of ions in crystals may be directly used to determine the behaviour of a pair of ions of opposite sign in the gas phase. Their method can be simplified without loss of validity by using an inverse power term instead of an exponential term to represent the repulsion. Omitting all energies other than those due to intrinsic repulsions and to Coulombic interactions, we

159

then have for a molecule of salt in the crystalline and gaseous phases respectively the expressions:

$$u_{crys.} = \frac{cAs_n}{a^n} - \frac{\alpha\varepsilon^2}{a}; \qquad u_{gas} = \frac{A}{a^n} - \frac{\varepsilon^2}{a} \qquad \text{VII.27}$$

Table VII.9 *The vapour pressure of crystalline potassium chloride*

	Pressure (dynes/cm^2)	
$T°(K)$	Observed	Calculated
847·2	1·35	1·33
855·6	1·89	1·80
879·4	3·95	4·08
892·1	6·22	6·08
903·8	8·86	9·07
910·0	11·10	11·04
918·0	13·8	14·1
929·1	20·3	19·9
936·2	24·9	24·6

The corresponding minimum energies of the molecule are given by the equations:

$$-u_0 = \frac{\alpha\varepsilon^2}{a_0}\left(1 - \frac{1}{n}\right); \qquad -u_e = \frac{\varepsilon^2}{a_e}\left(1 - \frac{1}{n}\right) \qquad \text{VII.28}$$

and the distance apart of the centres of the ions are given by the equations

$$a_0^{n-1} = \frac{ncAs_n}{\alpha\varepsilon^2}; \qquad a_e^{n-1} = \frac{nA}{\varepsilon^2} \qquad \text{VII.29}$$

It follows that

$$\frac{a_0}{a_e} = \left(\frac{cs_n}{\alpha}\right)^{1/(n-1)} \qquad \text{VII.30}$$

and

$$\frac{u_0}{u_e} = \alpha\frac{a_e}{a_0} \qquad \text{VII.31}$$

Both conclusions can be directly tested.

With KCl, we have $a_0 = 3.149$ Å; $\alpha = 1.74756$; $c = 6$; $n = 9$; and $s_9 = 1.1048$. The calculated value of a_e is thus 2.666 Å. That observed is 2.6666 Å. Secondly, since $-u_0 = 169.6$ kilocalories per mole, $-u_e$ becomes 114.7. The latent heat of sublimation of the salt, which is ΔH for the reaction KCl(*crystal*) → KCl(*vapour*), is the difference between these two quantities:

$$\lambda_0 = u_e - u_0 \qquad\qquad \text{VII.32}$$

Hence $\lambda_0 = 54.9$. Values of a_e and λ_0 for the other alkali halides have been computed in a similar way by Verwey and de Boer, with results which, considering the simplicity of their treatment, are in reasonable agreement with experiment.

According to the model upon which these calculations are based a salt molecule consists of a pair of ions of opposite sign, held together by Coulombic attraction, and prevented from coming too close together by an intrinsic repulsion. The dipole moment of such a molecule would be the product of the electronic charge and the inter-ionic separation ($\mu = \varepsilon a_e$), but this is found to be greater than the experimental value. The explanation is that the electric field exerted by each ion induces a moment in the other ion, and that the two induced moments act in a direction opposed to that of the principal moment (see Fig. VII.8). A simple calculation (Born and Heisenberg,

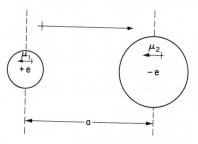

Fig. VII.8 *A diatomic molecule as a polarisable ion-pair*

1916) then shows that the net electric moment is, to a first approximation,

$$\mu = \varepsilon a_e \left[1 - \frac{(\alpha_+ + \alpha_-)}{a_e^3} - \frac{8\alpha_1\alpha_2}{a_e^6} \right] \qquad\qquad \text{VII.33}$$

where α_+ and α_- are the polarisabilities of the cation and anion. In

F*

KCl, $\alpha_+ = 0.840 \times 10^{-24}$ cm^3, and $\alpha_- = 3.685 \times 10^{-24}$ cm^3. The calculated dipole moment is now found to be 8.87×10^{-18} e.s.u., in satisfactory agreement with the experimental value of 8.75×10^{-18} (Rodebush, L. A. Murray and Bixler (1936)).

Induction influences the energy as well as the polarity of the molecule. The chief effect of the interaction between the ions and the dipoles induced by them is to increase the attractive energy by a quantity which varies inversely as the fourth power of the distance apart. It can be shown that, again as a first approximation, the total energy of the pair of mutually polarisable ions, is

$$\phi = \frac{A}{a^n} - \frac{\varepsilon^2}{a} - \frac{C}{a^4} \qquad \text{VII.34}$$

where

$$C = \tfrac{1}{2}\varepsilon^2(\alpha_+ + \alpha_-)$$

That terms involving $-C/a^4$ do not appear in expressions for the crystal energy is due to the fact that the net electric field at the centre of an ion arising from the c equidistant ions of opposite sign surrounding it is zero. There is consequently no induction in the crystal. The energy of the gaseous molecule in its equilibrium state is

$$-\phi_e = \frac{\varepsilon^2}{a_e}\left(1 - \frac{1}{n}\right) + \frac{C}{a_e^4}\left(1 - \frac{4}{n}\right) \qquad \text{VII.35}$$

From the data already cited from KCl, $-\phi$, in kilocalories per mole, is found to be $110.7 + 7.7 = 118.4$, leading to $\lambda_0 = 51.2$, in adequate agreement with experiment. The model can be improved and the treatment refined in various ways to yield results in yet more satisfactory agreement with the facts.

The gain in energy when the ions forming the molecules are displaced from their equilibrium separation is $\phi - \phi_e$. On expanding this expression in a power series of $(a - a_e)$, the linear terms vanish, and, for small displacements, $\phi - \phi_e$ varies as $(a - a_e)^2$. For such displacements, the resulting motion is harmonic, with frequency

$$v_e = \frac{1}{2\pi a_e}\left\{\frac{1}{\mu}\left[(n-1)\frac{\varepsilon^2}{a_e} + 4(n-4)\frac{C}{a_e^4}\right]\right\} \qquad \text{VII.36}$$

Here μ is the reduced mass. The value calculated for the KCl molecule is 1.02×10^{13} sec^{-1}, corresponding to a wave number of 399 cm^{-1}.

The experimental determination of the heat content, entropy and Gibbs free energy of solids

Many thermodynamic properties of solids may be obtained from measurements of the heat capacity at various temperatures. Heat is put into the cooled solid in an adiabatic calorimeter, by passing a steady current, i, for a short time, t, through a metal heating-coil of resistance, R. The electrical energy, $i^2 Rt$, is converted completely into thermal energy of magnitude $i^2 Rt/J$ calories, where $J = 4{\cdot}1840$ joules per defined calories. Since, by definition, $C_P = (dH/dT)_P$, the increase in the heat content of one gram-mole of the solid is

$$dH_P = C_P \, dT$$

The heat content at a temperature, T, is found by integration:

$$H = H_0 + \int_0^T C_P \, dT \qquad\qquad \text{VI.12}$$

where H_0 is the molar heat content at the absolute zero of temperature. Provided there are no phase changes during the heating, C_P increases smoothly as the temperature is raised, and the integration is carried out graphically. The heat capacity of silver at various temperatures is shown in Fig. VII.9, from which $H - H_0$ at $298{\cdot}16°K$ is found to be 1 373 calories/gram-mole. C_P at this temperature is $6{\cdot}092$ cal/mole-degree, and C_V, obtained by means of equation VI.14,

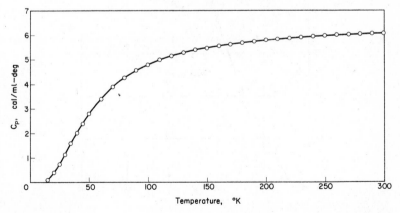

Fig. VII.9 *The heat capacity of silver from 15 to 300°K* (data of Meads, Forsyth and Giauque, 1941)

is 5·851, which is within 2 per cent of the limiting value $3R$ anticipated for a system of three-dimensional, classical oscillators (law of Dulong and Petit).

Anomalous $C_P - T$ curves are found for some of the transitional elements and their salts. With nickel, for example, the curve up to temperatures of about 200°K resembles that found for silver. Beyond this temperature the curve, instead of flattening out to a horizontal line, curves upwards, reaches a sharp maximum value of $C_P = 8\cdot728$ cal/mole-degree when $T = 627$°K, and thereafter falls. The effect has been interpreted in terms of the change in orderliness of the magnets associated with the atoms. At low temperatures, their mutual alignment is one of perfect order; as the temperature is raised, disorder appears, with a consequent increase in the total energy of the system. This energy increases as T is raised, and therefore there appears a magnetic contribution to the heat capacity. At the Curie point, how-

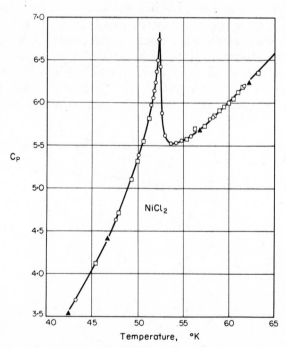

Fig. vii.10 *Anomaly in heat capacity of* NiCl$_2$ (*calories per degree per mole*) (after Busey and Giauque, 1952)

ever, disorder is complete, and remains complete at still higher temperatures. The magnetic component of the energy beyond this point is independent of T, and therefore the magnetic component of the heat capacity vanishes. A similar phenomenon appears with salts of the transition elements, such as anhydrous nickel chloride (Fig. VII.10). Despite the anomalous shape of the $C_P - T$ curve equation VI.12 can still be used to determine $H - H_0$, which, at 298·16°K is found to be 3 448 cal.

The process of heating, even in the region of the anomalous specific heat, is found to be reversible. Hence, by the second law of thermodynamics, the increase in entropy is

$$dS = q_P/T = dH/T = C_P \, dT/T = C_P \, d \ln T$$

On integrating, we obtain, for the molar entropy at $T°K$,

$$S = S_0 + \int_0^T C_P d \ln T \qquad \text{VII.37}$$

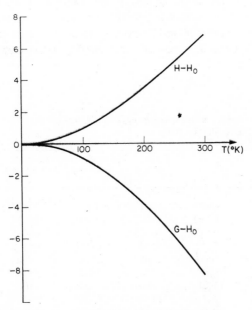

Fig. VII.11 *The molar heat content and free energy, in kilocalories, of crystalline tetramethylammonium iodide at atmospheric pressure*

Since, according to the third law of thermodynamics (equation VI.4), the entropy of all pure solids at the absolute zero of temperature is zero, the entropy of the solid at temperature T is

$$S = \int_0^T C_P d \ln T \qquad \text{VII.38}$$

The integration is again carried out graphically, this time by measuring the area beneath the curve found when C_P is plotted against $\ln T$. The Gibbs free energy is

$$G = H - TS \qquad \text{VI.23}$$

Subtracting H_0 from both sides,

$$G - H_0 = (H - H_0) - TS$$

At the absolute zero of temperature, G and H are naturally equal. An illustrative plot of both is shown in Fig. VII.11. The gradients of the curves are $C_P = (dH/dT)_P$ and $S = -(dG/dT)_P$. A typical set of thermodynamic functions is shown for lithium chloride in Table VII.10. In this way, thanks largely to the work of Clusius, Eucken, Giauque, Nernst, Pitzer and Simon, physical chemists now possess precise data on the heat content, free energy and entropy of a wide variety of solids.

Table VII.10 *The molar heat capacity, entropy, heat content and free energy of crystalline lithium chloride* (D. A. Shirley, 1960)

$T°K$	C_p	S	$(H-H_0)/T$	$-(G-H_0)/T$
15	0·0504	0·0186	0·0131	0·0055
20	0·1356	0·0434	0·0319	0·0115
30	0·5538	0·1652	0·1261	0·0391
50	2·214	0·8027	0·6088	0·1939
100	6·637	3·806	2·600	1·206
150	9·057	7·006	4·392	2·614
200	10·310	9·800	5·729	4·071
250	11·035	12·186	6·724	5·462
298·16	11·470	14·170	7·458	6·712

Table VII.11 *Molar entropy, heat content and Gibbs free energy of certain solids at 298·16°K and 1 atmosphere. All entries in calories/mole-degree*

Solid	S^0	$(H-H_0)/T$	$-(G-H_0)/T$
Li	6·753	3·663	3·090
Na	12·249	5·183	7·067
K	15·262	5·703	9·559
Cu	7·961	4·030	3·931
Ag	10·206	4·605	5·601
Au	11·318	4·810	6·508
Al	6·769	3·668	3·101
Diamond	0·585	0·430	0·153
Graphite	1·361	0·844	0·517
Sn	40·245	4·982	35·263
Pb	15·514	5·515	9·999
Ni	7·137	3·837	3·300
KF	15·91	8·02	7·89
$CdSO_4$	29·408	14·605	14·803
$PbSO_4$	35·509	16·083	19·426
$C_{10}H_8$	80·30	16·47	63·83

VIII Liquids

When a solid is heated, most of its properties vary smoothly with respect to temperature, until at a certain temperature – the melting point, T_m, at atmospheric pressure, or the triple point, T_{tr}, under the system's own pressure – it abruptly becomes fluid. Fusion is attended by an isothermal absorption of heat, an increase in the entropy, the heat capacity and the dielectric constant, a discontinuity in the coefficient of expansion, and, with the exception of bismuth, gallium and ice, an increase in the volume. The range of existence of liquids is from T_m to the boiling point, T_b, at atmospheric pressure, and from T_{tr} to the critical point, T_c, under the system's own pressure. Within these relatively narrow limits, liquids exhibit properties resembling those of solids at low temperatures and those of gases at high temperatures, but contributed in such complicated proportions that no simple theory of the liquid state has yet been formulated. Much, however, can be learned from experimental data, which are extensive and accurate.

The heat capacities of liquids

The heat capacity of monatomic liquids at or near the melting temperature is very nearly $3R$ cal/mole-deg. The exact value for the inert elements is somewhat less, and for the metals somewhat more. C_V for mercury at the melting point, for example, is 6·028 cal/mole-deg., which is 1·1 per cent higher than $3R$. This is more than the experimental error, and is due to a contribution from the free electrons in the metal. The approximate value of $C_V = 3R$ for monatomic liquids at low temperatures indicates that each atom behaves, for most of the time, like a classical three-dimensional oscillator. Nevertheless each atom is mobile, and has access to the whole volume of the liquid. Consequently, the time it spends moving from one position to another must be relatively short. As the temperature is raised, C_V decreases, and liquids become slightly more gas-like in their behaviour.

From the heat capacity measured experimentally at constant

pressure, (usually one atmosphere), the heat capacity at constant volume may be derived provided the molar volume, the coefficients of isobaric expansion and isothermal compressibility are known:

$$C_{V^0} = C_P - \frac{(\alpha^\circ)^2 V^\circ T}{\beta_T^\circ}$$

VI.14

The C_P data cited in Table VIII.1 were measured at one atmosphere, as were also the molar volumes and the two relevant coefficients. The superscript zero is to remind us of this reference state. We note that, very approximately, C_{V° is about one third less than C_P in these

Table VIII.1 *The heat capacities of certain liquids at* 300°K

Liquid	C_P (cal/mole-deg)	V° (cm^3/mole)	$\alpha^\circ \times 10^3$ (deg^{-1})	$\beta^\circ \times 10^6$ (atm^{-1})	$C_P - C_{V^\circ}$ (cal/mole-deg.)	C_{V°
CH_3I	19·76	62·81	1·238	101·9	6·86	12·90
CH_2Br_2	25·17	70·12	1·035	67·6	8·07	17·10
$CHCl_3$	27·11	80·86	1·256	106·0	8·74	18·37
CCl_4	31·29	97·31	1·219	110·1	9·54	21·75

instances. With water, however, the difference between the two heat capacities is slight (Table VIII.2). C_P passes through a minimum value at about 35°C. Similar minima have been found for many liquids at temperatures not far from the melting point, and empirical equations of the form $C_P = K_0 - K_1 T + K_2 T^2$ have been found capable of reproducing the data.

The heat capacity at constant temperature and volume depends on both variables. The volume dependence of the heat capacity at constant volume may be expressed as follows:

$$\left(\frac{dC_V}{dV}\right)_T = \frac{\partial^2 E}{\partial V \partial T} = \frac{\partial^2 E}{\partial T \partial V} = \frac{\partial}{\partial T}\left(\frac{dE}{dV}\right)_T$$

VIII.1

On using equation VI.32, we have

$$\left(\frac{dC_V}{dV}\right)_T = \frac{\partial}{\partial T}\left[-P + T\left(\frac{\partial P}{\partial T}\right)_V\right] = T\left(\frac{d^2 P}{dT^2}\right)_V$$

VIII.2

169

Table VIII.2 *The heat capacities of liquid water* ($M = 18.0156$ g)

$t°C$	$V°$ (cm³/g mol)	$β° \times 10^5$ (atmosphere⁻¹)	$α° \times 10^4$ (degree⁻¹)	Cal/mole-deg.		
				$(α°)^2 V°T/β°$	C_P	$C_{V°}$
0	18.0180	5.11	−0.309	0.002	18.182	18.180
5	18.0157	4.93	+0.340	0.003	18.108	18.105
10	18.0205	4.83	0.939	0.023	18.054	18.031
15	18.0313	4.74	1.489	0.059	18.018	17.959
20	18.0475	4.68	1.996	0.109	17.994	17.885
25	18.0685	4.62	2.493	0.176	17.975	17.799
30	18.0939	4.57	2.937	0.251	17.967	17.716
40	18.1565	4.49	3.771	0.436	17.966	17.530
50	18.2330	4.49	4.517	0.65	17.98	17.33
60	18.3228	4.55	5.192	0.88	18.00	17.12
70	18.4246	4.62	5.828	1.13	18.02	16.89
80	18.5397	4.70	6.424	1.39	18.05	16.66
90	18.6624	4.78	6.989	1.68	18.09	16.41
100	18.7980	4.88	7.533	1.98	18.12	16.14

Given an equation of state for the liquid, it is thus possible to calculate the difference between, say, the heat capacity at the melting volume, V_m, and the heat capacity at the volume, $V°$, obtaining at atmospheric pressure, since

$$C_{V_m} - C_{V°} = T \int_{V°}^{V_m} \left(\frac{\partial^2 P}{\partial T^2} \right)_V dV \qquad \text{VIII.3}$$

The results obtained for liquid mercury (Table VIII.3) show that $(dC_V/dV)_T$ is negative. The same is true for carbon tetrachloride and most liquids. Gibson and Loeffler (1941) have shown that the gradient in the case of water is positive. Michels and his collaborators (1952) find that $(dC_V/dV)_T$ is zero for liquid carbon dioxide at the critical volume.

When the C_V data of Eucken and Hauk (1928) on liquid argon and nitrogen are plotted as a function of the reduced temperature, T/T_c, the curves are found to be wavy but parallel, with a separation of approximately R. It may therefore be concluded that in liquid nitrogen the molecules rotate freely, as they do in the dilute gaseous phase. Such a conclusion cannot be so readily drawn when considering the

Table VIII.3 *The heat capacity of liquid mercury at atmospheric volume and at the melting volume*

$T°K$	$V°$ (cm^3/mole)	C_1 (cal/mole-deg)	C_{V_m}
234·3	14·652	6·028	6·028
273·2	14·756	5·869	5·913
350	14·963	5·601	5·751
450	15·235	5·359	5·637
550	15·516	5·195	5·528
630	15·749	5·081	5·355

heat capacity of more complicated liquids. Following Bernal (1937), Eucken (1948) and Staveley (1953), we may resolve the total heat capacity of a liquid at constant volume into the following contributions:

$$C_V = C_c + C_i + C_r + C_a \qquad \text{VIII.4}$$

where C_c arises from the motion of the centre of gravity of the molecule, and is assumed to be the same as C_V for monatomic liquids; C_i is the contribution from the internal vibrations of the molecule, and is taken to be the same as that in the gaseous molecule; C_r is the rotational heat capacity, lying between $\frac{3}{2}R$ for free rotations and $3R$ for fully torsional rotations; and C_a accounts for the temperature variation of any energy which may be expended in changing the structure of the liquid. An attempt by Harrison and Moelwyn-Hughes (1957) to interpret some of their experimental results along these lines is as follows:

Liquid	CCl$_4$	CHCl$_3$
C_c	5·96	5·96
C_i (from spectroscopic constants of gases)	10·77	5·46
C_r (free rotation about all axes)	2·98	—
C_r (free about one axis; fully torsional about 2 axes)	—	4·98
Sum	19·71	16·40
C_{V_m} (Observed)	21·79	17·97
Difference	2·08	1·57

171

The structural contribution to the total heat capacity thus appears to be approximately R.

Heat and entropy of fusion

The molar increase in entropy attending the fusion of copper, lead, hydrogen and oxygen is very nearly R cal/mole, as shown in Table VIII.4. This is what is to be expected if, as Eyring suggested, fusion consists simply in a change from molecules vibrating in fixed cells to vibrating molecules having free access to all the cells in the system. The higher values of ΔS found in the fusion of the inert elements are more easily explained in terms of the theory of order and disorder (Fröhlich (1937); Lennard–Jones and Devonshire (1937)), according to which the molecules in both the crystal and the liquid at the melting temperature are not in completely ordered states, as they are at the absolute zero of temperature. Some molecules abandon their natural, so-called, α sites, to occupy lattice points hitherto empty — the so-called β sites. Theory then shows that it is possible for two phases to exist at the same temperature, though possessing different degrees of order, s. If, for example, s is taken as 1 for the crystal and $\frac{1}{2}$ for the

Table VIII.4 *Fusion*

	$T_{tr}(°K)$	L_m (cal/mole)	$\Delta S_m = L_m/T_{tr}$
Ne	24·57	80	3·26
A	83·78	280·8	3·25
Kr	115·95	390·7	3·37
Xe	161·36	548·5	3·40
Cu	1 356	2 700	1·99
Pb	600·6	1 220	2·03
H_2	13·96	28	2·01
O_2	54·32	106·75	1·97
F_2	55·20	372	6·74
I_2	386·8	3 720	9·62
H_2O	273·16	1 435·7	5·253
H_2S	187·61	568	3·03
PH_3	139·4	268·2	1·92
CH_4	90·5	225·5	2·49
$CHCl_3$	209·7	2 249	10·73

liquid at the melting point, the gain in entropy on melting would be $\frac{9}{8}R$. Quantitative tests of the theory are, however, difficult, as no precise values are known for s in either system.

We next consider, with reference to the inert elements, the relationship between the molar heat of fusion, L_m, and the lattice energy, L, per mole which, as explained in Chapter VII is the sum of the molar heat of sublimation at the absolute zero of temperature and the residual energy $\frac{3}{2}N_0 h\nu$. These energy terms bear a constant ratio of 7.09 ± 0.11 (Table VIII.5). Let us now assume that the lattice energy may be approximated to by the expression $L/N_0 = -\frac{1}{2}c_{cr}\phi$, where c_{cr} is the coordination number in the crystal, and ϕ is the interaction energy between a neighbouring pair. If a similar expression holds for the liquid, with the same value of ϕ, but with another coordination number, c_{liq}, then

$$L_m/N_0 = -\tfrac{1}{2}\phi(c_{cr} - c_{liq}) \qquad \text{VIII.5}$$

and therefore

$$\frac{L}{L_m} = \frac{c_{cr}}{c_{cr} - c_{liq}} \qquad \text{VIII.6}$$

On using the experimental value for the thermal ratio and 12 for c_{cr}, c_{liq} is found to be 10.31 ± 0.02, in agreement with Gringrich's conclusion (1943) that the average coordination number of liquid argon at the melting point, as revealed by X-ray analysis, is 10.6 ± 0.4.

Table VIII.5 *A comparison of the heat of fusion, L_m, with the lattice energy, L*

Crystal	L_m	(cal/mole) L	L/L_m
Ne	80	558	6·97
A	281	2 030	7·22
Kr	391	2 741	7·01
Xe	549	3 926	7·15

The argument here followed implies, since ϕ is assumed to be the same for near-neighbour pairs in the crystal and the liquid, that the average distance apart of near neighbours in both phases is the same. Taking as round numbers, $c_{cr} = 12$ and $c_{liq} = 10$, this assumption requires the fractional increase in volume on melting to be 0·2, instead of the observed value of 0·15. Nevertheless, the idea is worth pursuing, for it suggests that the N normal sites of the completely ordered lattice have been increased to $\frac{6}{5}N$ in the liquid, of which $\frac{1}{5}N$ are unoccupied. This leads to the following contribution to the molar entropy of fusion:

$$\Delta S = R[\tfrac{6}{5} \ln 6 - \ln 5] = 1\cdot074 \text{ cal/mole-deg}$$

which, when added to the communal entropy gives a total entropy of fusion of 3·06 in the same units.

Heat and entropy of vaporisation

The increase in heat content attending the vaporisation of one mole of liquid may be measured accurately by direct calorimetry or by applying the Clausius–Clapeyron equation to the saturation vapour pressures observed at different temperatures:

$$\frac{dp}{dT} = \frac{L_T}{T\Delta V_T} \qquad\qquad \text{VI.30}$$

The latter method we shall here apply to systems where the saturation vapour pressure is low enough to justify the use of the ideal gas laws to the vapour. Then $\Delta V_T(= V_{vap} - V_{liq})$ is nearly V_{vap}, or RT/p, so that

$$L_T = RT^2 \frac{d \ln p}{dT} \qquad\qquad \text{VIII.7}$$

To obtain a vapour pressure equation which is numerically satisfactory under these conditions, without being computationally awkward, we shall assume that the difference, ΔC_P, between the heat capacities of the liquid and vapour, though both change with respect to temperature, is independent of T. Then

$$L_T = L_s + \int_0^T [C_P(\text{vap}) - C_P(\text{liq})]\, dT$$

$$= L_s + \Delta C_P T \qquad\qquad \text{VIII.8}$$

where L_s is the molar heat of vaporisation which the liquid would have, if it could be sub-cooled to the absolute zero of temperature. On substituting into equation VIII.7 and integrating, we find that

$$\ln p = a' + \frac{\Delta C_P}{R} \ln T - \frac{L_s}{RT} \qquad \text{VIII.9}$$

which can also be written in the form

$$\log_{10}p = a - b \log_{10}T - c/T \qquad \text{VIII.10}$$

where

$$\Delta C_P = -bR \qquad \text{VIII.11}$$

and

$$L_s = 2 \cdot 303 Rc \qquad \text{VIII.12}$$

This well known equation of Kirchhoff (1858), Rankine (1866) and Dupré (1869) has a sound thermodynamic and statistical basis, and has been found adequate, under the conditions indicated, to reproduce experimental vapour pressures with considerable accuracy, and to yield heats of vaporisation and differences in heat capacities in agreement with those measured calorimetrically. Some numerical values are given in Table VIII.6. Fig. VIII.1 shows the linear plot found when $\log_{10}p + b \log_{10}T$ in the case of liquid mercury is plotted against $1/T$.

Table VIII.6 *The vapour pressure constants of certain liquids from the melting point to the boiling point.* $\log_{10}p(mm) = a - b \log_{10}T - c/T$

Liquid	a	b	c	L_s (cal/mole)
Hg	10·5504	0·8403	3 348·6	15 327
N_2	13·0666	2·833	374	1 711
CS_2	15·9206	2·90	1 844	8 444
H_2O	20·9586	4·0843	2 825·4	12 926
CCl_4	24·3085	5·669	2 452·56	11 220
CH_3OH	22·43	4·634	2 661	12 180
$C_{10}H_8$	18·218	3·352	3 099·4	14 180
$o-HOC_6H_4COOCH_3$	36·5929	9·199	4 410·9	20 190
nC_5H_{12}	22·752	5·253	2 099	6 611

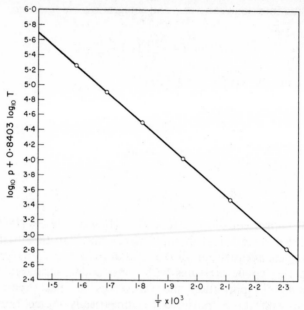

Fig. VIII.1 *Determination of the latent heat of vaporisation of liquid mercury*

On comparing the values of L_s given here with the critical temperatures quoted in Chapter IX, it may be verified that, provided metallic and polar liquids are excluded,

$$\frac{L_s}{RT_c} = 8 \qquad \text{VIII.13}$$

When values of L_s for straight-chained homologous organic compounds are examined, they are found to be linearly dependent on the number, n, of carbon atoms in the chain. Thus, for example, expressing the heat of vaporisation in kilocal/mole, we have, for the normal paraffins and monohydric alcohols:

$$L_s(\text{C}_n\text{H}_{2n+2}) = 1 \cdot 1 + 1 \cdot 7n \qquad \text{VIII.14}$$

and

$$L_s(\text{C}_n\text{H}_{2n+1}\text{OH}) = 2 \cdot 5 + 1 \cdot 88n \qquad \text{VIII.15}$$

The entropy of vaporisation at the boiling point (Table VIII.7) increases as the boiling point increases, and is seen to be 10·69 cal/

Table VIII.7 *The increase in molar heat content (calories) and in molar entropy attending vaporisation at the boiling point*

Substance	$T_b(°K)$	$\Delta H_b = L_b$	$\Delta S_b = \Delta H_b/T_b$
Na	1 172	23 675	20·19
K	1 045	18 975	18·16
Rb	934	16 850	18·05
Hg	630·45	14 275	22·65
Ne	27·17	415	15·27
A	87·44	1 500	17·16
Kr	121·4	2 315	19·06
Xe	164·4	3 210	19·53
Pb	1 887	45 950	24·36
Rn	208·2	4 340	20·84
H_2	20·39	218	10·69
D_2	23·6	302	12·79
CO	81·61	1 444	17·69
N_2	77·32	1 352	17·48
O_2	90·2	1 630	18·07
F_2	85·2	1 581	18·57
Cl_2	239·5	4 865	20·34
Br_2	331·8	7 280	21·95
I_2	457·5	10 120	22·12
$(CN)_2$	251·95	5 576	22·14
HF	377	6 030	16·00
HCl	189	3 538	18·72
HBr	205·5	4 158	20·23
HI	237·4	4 948	20·84
HCN	298·8	6 055	20·27
CS_2	319·3	6 490	20·32
COS	222·87	4 490	20·15
H_2O	373·16	9 705	26·01
H_2S	212·8	4 463	20·97
SO_2	263·08	5 960	22·65
NH_3	239·68	5 581	23·28
PH_3	186·67	3 489	18·69
CH_4	111·73	2 228	19·95
CCl_4	348·41	7 262	20·84
$SnCl_4$	387·2	7 960	20·56
C_2H_6	184·1	3 612	19·61
nC_5H_{12}	309·2	6 383	20·64
nC_6H_{14}	341·9	7 198	21·05
nC_8H_{18}	398·7	8 612	21·62
C_3H_6	225·35	4 402	19·54
CH_3OH	337·8	8 445	25·00
C_2H_5OH	351·4	9 970	28·37
$(CH_3)_3N$	273·06	8 765	32·09
C_6H_6	353·3	7 366	20·84
$C_{10}H_8$	491·05	9 700	19·75

mole-deg for hydrogen and 32·09 for trimethylamine. Many non-polar liquids, like methane, have an entropy of vaporisation of about 20 cal/mole-deg, which was at one time regarded as common to many liquids (Trouton's rule). Hildebrand has shown that more nearly constant entropies of vaporisation are found if they are measured, not at the boiling points, but at temperatures when their vapours have the same molar volumes. To this observation we shall return when dealing with the theory of holes.

Surface tension and surface energy

There exists in the surface of a liquid a tension across any line drawn in it. It is exerted normal to the line, and is the same for all directions of the line. Surface tension, defined by Maxwell (1890) as the (negative) force across an element of the line, divided by the length of that element, and denoted by γ, is one of the most characteristic properties of liquids. Its effects are of great significance in systems with large surface/volume ratios, such as small drops.

When an open capillary tube of radius R stands in a liquid, its level is found to rise to a height L inside it. The force acting upwards on the stationary column of liquid in the tube is $2\pi R\gamma$; that acting downwards is $\pi R^2 L \rho g$, where ρ is the density of the liquid. These forces balance, so that $\gamma = RL\rho g/2$. A more accurate derivation gives us $\gamma = RL(\rho_L - \rho_V)g/2 \cos \alpha$, where ρ_L and ρ_V are the densities of the liquid and vapour phases, and α is the angle between the meniscus and the vertical. This method has been used by Ramsay and Shields (1893) to determine γ for several liquids at equilibrium with their vapours, over the whole temperature ranges up to the critical points, where γ becomes zero. In the forced bubble method of measuring γ, a capillary is again placed in the liquid, and the pressure of a gas filling it is gradually increased until a hemispherical cavity of radius R is formed in the liquid. No further pressure is required to form the second hemisphere. At this point the force forming the bubble, $\pi R^2 p$, equals the contractile force $2\pi R\gamma$ opposing its formation; hence $\gamma = Rp/2$. In practice, a capillary tip with radius of about 10^{-2} is dipped into a specimen of liquid in a vessel of about 5 cm radius, and p is measured from the height h of a manometer liquid of density ρ. Then $\gamma = Rh\rho g/2$. This equation also is subject to a slight correction (Schrödinger, 1915).

The surface tension of mercury at atmospheric pressure, measured by the forced bubble method using hydrogen (Bircumshaw, 1926), varies with respect to temperature according to the equation

$$\gamma(\text{dynes/cm}) = 463\cdot6 + 8\cdot32 \times 10^{-2}T - 3\cdot125 \times 10^{-4}T^2$$

We shall be chiefly interested in the molecular surface energy, defined as the product of γ and the average area, o, occupied by one molecule in the surface. In terms of the distance, a, apart of nearest neighbours in the surface, we have

$$o = \kappa a^2 \qquad\qquad \text{VIII.16}$$

where the structural constant, κ, is unity if, as we shall here assume, the liquid surface corresponds to the 100 face of a face-centred cubic lattice. It is then found that

$$\gamma o \times 10^{13}(\text{ergs/molecule}) = 4\cdot682 + 1\cdot8 \times 10^{-3}T - 3\cdot75 \times 10^{-6}T^2$$

from which the molar heat content of the surface is seen to be

$$H_\sigma = \frac{N_0}{J}\left\{\gamma o - T\left[\frac{d(\gamma o)}{dT}\right]_P\right\} = 6\,761 + 5\cdot431 \times 10^{-3}T^2(\text{cal/mole})$$

where N_0 is Avogadro's number, and J is Joule's constant. The ratio of H_σ at the absolute zero of temperature to L_s for this liquid is seen from Table VIII.8 to be 0·441. Ratios found for further liquids (Wolf and Klapproth, 1940; Haul, 1943; Volkmann, 1947) included in this Table may be interpreted in the same way as the ratio of the heat of fusion to the lattice energy was explained, in terms of near-neighbour interactions, ϕ, and the coordination numbers, c_L for a molecule in the bulk of the liquid, and c_σ for a molecule in the surface. If the numbers of molecules in these two phases are N_L and N_σ, respectively, the total potential energy of the system is

$$U = N_L\left(\frac{1}{2}c_L\phi\right) + N_\sigma(\tfrac{1}{2}c_\sigma\phi) \qquad\qquad \text{VIII.17}$$

It is to be noted that c_σ is the total number of near neighbours surrounding a molecule in the surface phase; it thus includes not only molecules in the surface layer but those in the underlying liquid as well. Since the total number of molecules in the system is $N = N_L + N_\sigma$, we have

$$U = \tfrac{1}{2}Nc_L\phi + \tfrac{1}{2}N_\sigma(c_\sigma - c_L)\phi \qquad\qquad \text{VIII.18}$$

The first term on the right hand side is clearly the potential energy of N molecules in a system without a surface, and the second term is the addition potential energy which appears when N_σ of these exist in the surface:

$$U_\sigma = \tfrac{1}{2}N_\sigma(c_\sigma - c_L)\phi \qquad \text{VIII.19}$$

Since ϕ in all condensed systems is negative, and since c_σ must be less than c_L, it follows that U_σ is positive, and equal, when $N_\sigma = N_0$, to H_σ or E_σ at the absolute zero of temperature. Moreover, $L_s = -\tfrac{1}{2}N_0c_L\phi$. Hence

$$\frac{E_\sigma}{L_s} = 1 - \frac{c_\sigma}{c_L} \qquad \text{VIII.20}$$

From the data of Table VIII.8, c_σ/c_L is seen to lie between 0·545 and 0·724. In a face-centred cubic arrangement, therefore, c_σ has any value from 6·5 to 8·7. After allowing for the approximations necessary in making this assessment, it may be concluded that the number of molecules surrounding any given molecule in the surface layer of a liquid lies between one-half and two-thirds of the number surrounding it in the bulk liquid phase.

Table VIII.8 *Experimental ratios of E_σ (at 0°K) to L_s*

Liquid	E_σ/L_s	Liquid	E_σ/L_s
He	0·455	N_2	0·358
Ne	0·422	N_2O	0·417
A	0·420	CS_2	0·327
Hg	0·411	CCl_4	0·288
H_2	0·418	C_6H_6	0·276

The free surface energy of a system is the component of the total free energy due to the presence of the surface (equation VI.44). In a system at constant volume, the free energy attributable to one mole of surface molecules is

$$A_\sigma = N_0\gamma o \qquad \text{VIII.21}$$

where γ is the surface tension, and o is the average area occupied by one surface molecule. In terms of the molar volume, V_m, and a structural constant, κ, or order of magnitude unity, we can write

$$o = \kappa(V_m/N_0)^{2/3} \qquad \text{VIII.22}$$

Hence

$$A_\sigma = N_0^{1/3}(\gamma V_m^{2/3}) \qquad \text{VIII.23}$$

Eötvös (1886) found that, for non-polar liquids,

$$\gamma V_m^{2/3} = 2(T_c - T - 6)\text{ergs} \qquad \text{VIII.24}$$

By comparing the empirical constant 2 with the corresponding constant obtained with non-polar liquids, it is possible to estimate the degree of polymerisation of molecules in the liquid state. In the case of normal liquids, we have

$$A_\sigma = 2\kappa N_0^{1/3}(T_c - T - 6)\text{ergs/mole} \qquad \text{VIII.25}$$

or

$$A_\sigma = 2 \cdot 029\kappa R(T_c - T - 6)\text{cal/mole} \qquad \text{VIII.26}$$

according to which the molar entropy of the surface phase

$$S_\sigma = 2 \cdot 029\kappa R \qquad \text{VIII.27}$$

and its molar energy

$$E_\sigma = 2 \cdot 029\kappa R(T_c - 6) \qquad \text{VIII.28}$$

should be independent of temperature. Both conclusions are nearly, but not quite, true. Theoretical equations may easily be derived showing that the surface free energy decreases nearly linearly with respect to temperature.

Viscosity

Liquids vary widely in the ease with which they flow, and the coefficient of viscosity, η, as defined in Chapter II, is a quantitative measure of their sluggishness. We have seen that, when the pressure at one end of a capillary (length L, radius R) differs from that at the other end by P, the volume of fluid passing through it in time t is given by Poiseuille's equation $V = \pi P R^4 t / 8\eta L$. If the flow is vertical, and the driving pressure P of equation II.23 is simply that due to the column of liquid, P must be proportional to its density, ρ, and, in a capillary of fixed dimensions, we have $\eta = K\rho t$, where K is an apparatus constant, obtainable by calibrating the capillary with a liquid of known viscosity. Measurement of the time of flow of a given volume of liquid then suffices to determine η (See Fig. VIII.2). In the falling sphere viscometer, a sphere of radius r and density ρ is place on the surface of a liquid of density ρ_0, and the rate at which it falls is measured visually. The rate of fall of a steel sphere in molten glass has also been measured in this way, using X-rays at two points to register its passage. The equation of motion is $m(du/dt) = \frac{4}{3}\pi r^3(\rho - \rho_0)g - 6\pi\eta ru$. The velocity u, initially zero, increases to a terminal value, v, when the gravitational force exactly equals the force of resistance, and there is no further acceleration. Then $\eta = 2r^2(\rho - \rho_0)g/9v$.

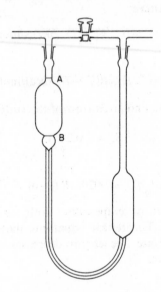

Ostwald's viscometer

Fig. VIII.2

Liquids are frequently from 25 to 75 times as viscous as their corresponding vapours under room conditions. Their viscosities at constant pressure decrease as the temperature is raised, and, at constant temperature, increase as the pressure is increased. The viscosity of a liquid depends largely on the structure of its molecules. Glycerol, for example, is hundreds of times more viscous than propyl alcohol. For non-polar liquids, the product of η and the molar volume, V_m, is an approximate constant at a given temperature (Dunstan, 1905).

The temperature variation of the viscosity of liquids at constant pressure is reproduced roughly, but never with sufficient accuracy, by an equation of the form

$$\eta = Ae^{B/RT} \qquad \text{VIII.29}$$

where A and B are, for a given liquid, approximately constant (Reynolds, 1886). Some typical data are given in Table VIII.9. For generality, a viscous heat is defined as

$$B_P = -RT^2\left(\frac{d\ln\eta}{dT}\right)_P \qquad \text{VIII.30}$$

Table VIII.9 *Viscosity constants of certain liquids at atmospheric pressure*

$$\log_{10}\eta = \log_{10}A + B/RT$$

Liquid	$A \times 10^4$ (gram/cm-second)	B (calories/mole)
Hg	56·63	597
CS_2	5·05	1 204
CCl_4	1·663	2 418
CH_3OH	0·239	2 730
nC_5H_{12}	2·235	1 482
nC_8H_{18}	2·15	1 999

Applied to the precise work of Thorpe and Rodger (1894) on liquid octane, for example, we find that, in calories per mole,

$$B_P = 1\,080 + 3\cdot42T$$

and consequently

$$\ln\eta = \text{constant} - (3\cdot42/R)\ln T + 1\,080/RT$$

The form of this equation (Hovorka, Lankelma and Stanford, 1938) is the same as that found for the vapour pressure under the conditions stipulated earlier.

Typical of the numerous but unavailing attempts to correlate B_P with other thermal properties of liquids is that due to Raman (1923),

183

who suggested that η(vapour)/η(liquid) should equal $\exp(-L_m/RT)$. Certainly, B_P is of the same order of magnitude as the heat of fusion, but there appears to be no common relationship between them. Table VIII.10 shows that L_m/B_P is about 0.94 ± 0.8. If metals and molten salts are omitted, L_s/B_P is often about 5.8 ± 1.6. Higher values of this ratio are naturally found when allowance is made for the temperature variation of B_P. With liquid octane, for example, we find that $L_s/B_{P,0}$ is 7.24. Some rough proportionality thus appears to exist between the energy which a molecule must acquire before it can leave a liquid and the energy it must acquire before being able to flow in it.

Table VIII.10 *A comparison of the viscous heat, B_P, with the latent heats of fusion and of vaporisation, L_m and L_s (in calories/mole)*

Liquid	B_P	L_m	L_m/B_P	L_s	L_s/B
Hg	615	552	0.90	15 327	24.9
Pb	3 150	1 168	0.37	46 210	14.7
Cl_2	875	1 531	1.75	6 473	7.4
Br_2	1 758	2 580	1.47	10 220	5.8
I_2	2 334	3 720	1.59	14 750	6.3
HCl	570	501	0.88	4 228	7.4
AgCl	3 820	2 370	0.62	45 200	11.8
CS_2	1 207	1 047	0.87	8 444	7.0
$CHCl_3$	1 350	2 249	1.67	9 974	7.3
CCl_4	2 375	577	0.24	11.220	4.7
CH_3OH	2 465	760	0.31	12 180	4.9
C_6H_6	2 850	2 372	0.82	11 940	4.2
$C_6H_5COCH_3$	2 980	3 980	1.34	13 419	4.5
$C_6H_5NH_2$	5 330	1 950	0.37	22 392	4.2

In its viscosity as in most of its properties, water is anomalous (Table VIII.11). The viscosity of liquid helium II (lambda point 2.19°K) is also exceptional, and can be reproduced, between 1.4 and 2.2°K, by Reynolds's equation, with a negative value of B_P (Giauque, 1939).

Temperature has a smaller effect on the viscosity at constant volume than it has on the viscosity at constant pressure, but the sign of $d\eta/dT$ is the same. If we define a viscous energy by the equation

$$B_V = -RT^2 \left(\frac{d \ln \eta}{dT}\right)_V \qquad \text{VIII.31}$$

Table VIII.11 *The viscosity of water*

| $t\,°C$ | $\eta \times 10^3$(g/cm sec) | | B_P(cal/mole) | |
	(Slotte, 1883)	(Bingham, 1919)	(Slotte)	(Bingham)
0	18·08	17·89	5 080	5 200
25	8·96	8·94	4 000	4 060
50	5·53	5·50	3 470	3 410
100	2·85	2·82	2 840	2 920

we may derive the following relationship between it and B_P:

$$B_V = B_P - RT^2 \frac{\alpha}{\beta}\left(\frac{d\ln\eta}{dP}\right)_T \qquad \text{VIII.32}$$

where α and β have their usual meaning. As with the heat capacity, B_V does not refer to a strictly constant volume, but to the volume at atmospheric pressure. B_V, as stated, is less than B_P. The work of Bridgman (1930) allows one to evaluate B_V, which, for mercury, carbon disulphide, carbon tetrachloride and n-pentane is found to be about $\frac{1}{2}RT$, so that we may write $(d\ln\eta/dT)_P = -\frac{1}{2}T + \alpha(d\ln C/d\ln V)_T$, where $\eta = C(V)T^{-1/2}$, and

$$\frac{d\ln C}{d\ln V} = \frac{\frac{1}{2} - (B_P/RT)}{\alpha T} \qquad \text{VIII.33}$$

Experiment shows that the term on the right hand side varies from -3 to -7 for various liquids, indicating that the isothermal viscosity varies inversely as the volume raised to some high power. The lowest recorded power is $-\frac{7}{3}$ (Leontieva, 1946). It is clear that much of the effect of temperature on η at constant pressure is due to the effect of temperature on the volume. Batschinski (1913) goes so far as to regard η as a function of the volume only, writing

$$\eta = \frac{K}{V - \Omega} \qquad \text{VIII.34}$$

where K and Ω are constants, the latter resembling the forbidden volume, b, of van der Waal's equation. The fluidity, ϕ, which is the reciprocal of the viscosity, should then vary linearly with respect to

G

the volume:

$$\phi = \frac{1}{\eta} = \frac{V - \Omega}{K} \qquad \text{VIII.35}$$

as is seen to be the case with liquid benzene (Table VIII.12). Generally, however, the equation is inadequate. The viscosity may well be governed by the free volume, but the real free volume of a liquid cannot be represented simply as the total volume less a constant.

Table VIII.12 *The fluidity of liquid benzene, observed and reproduced by the equation* $\phi = (V - 81.76)/0.04535$

$t\,°C$	ϕ, observed	ϕ, calculated
0	111	111
30	178	179
60	256	256
100·5	384	385
131·8	505	510
161·4	647	649
185·7	797	794

Bingham (1922) has argued that viscosity consists of diffusional and collisional components, and can be represented as

$$\eta = K_1 T + \frac{K_2}{V - \Omega} \qquad \text{VIII.36}$$

This equation and a variant due to Macleod (1945) apply to the viscosity of carbon dioxide above and below the critical region. Bridgman (1931) regards viscosity as 'a unique property in regard to the magnitude of the pressure effect and its variation from substance to substance'. A given increase in pressure is seen to produce a greater effect at high pressures than at low pressures (Fig. VIII.3).

As an introduction to the many interesting theories of the viscosity of liquids, we shall first consider the principal features of diffusion in a face-centred cubic system. Let the unit cell be drawn as in Fig. VIII.4. Let a second unit cell, to the right of that drawn, have an empty centre. In terms of the intermolecular distance, a, the concentration

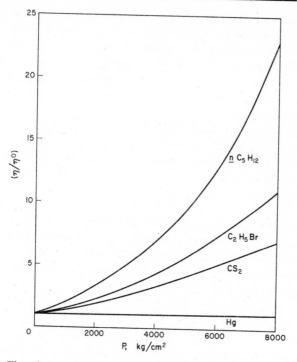

Fig. VIII.3 *The relative viscosity of certain liquids at 303·1°K*

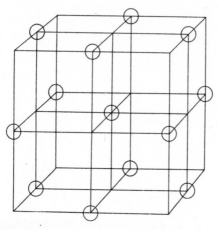

Fig. VIII.4 *The face-centred cubic lattice, as in Fig. VII.3, but displaced by ½ cell length*

187

of molecules in the full cell is $\sqrt{2}/a^3$, and in the incomplete cell is $3\sqrt{2}/4a^3$. The distance apart of the centres of the two cells is $\sqrt{2}a$. Hence that concentration gradient is $-\frac{1}{4}a^4$. The probability per second that the molecule shall hop from the centre of the full cell to the empty site in the other cell may be regarded as the product of its vibration frequency, v, and the probability that it shall possess an energy of at least ε in two quadratic terms. The probability of a successful hop per second is then $ve^{-\varepsilon/kT}$. The area of the wall between the cells is $2a^2$. Hence, the number of molecules crossing per second over unit area under unit concentration gradient, which is the co-efficient of diffusion, is

$$D = 2va^2 e^{-\varepsilon/kT} \qquad \text{VIII.37}$$

This equation, while having the right form, is, of course, greatly over-simplified. It is known that diffusion in solids cannot take place without the cooperation of a number of molecules surrounding the one that moves. We next rely on the Stokes–Einstein equation (II.28) $D = kT/3\pi\eta a$, and find for the viscosity

$$\eta = \frac{nkT}{6\sqrt{2\pi v}} \cdot e^{+\varepsilon/kT} \qquad \text{VIII.38}$$

where n, the molecular concentration is $\sqrt{2}/a^3$. This equation (Frenkel, 1925) resembles Maxwell's equation for the viscosity of a gas, $\eta = (4/\pi)nkT\tau$, where τ is the relaxation time. In liquids this decreases as the temperature is raised due to the potential troughs becoming more shallow. If instead of retaining v as a specific vibration frequency, we substitute for it Herzfeld's expression kT/h, which is discussed in Chapter XV, we see that

$$\eta = \frac{nh}{6\sqrt{2\pi}} \cdot e^{\varepsilon/kT} \qquad \text{VIII.39}$$

In terms of the molar volume, V_m, the molecular concentration is N_0/V_m. Hence

$$\eta V_m = \frac{N_0 h}{6\sqrt{2\pi}} \cdot e^{\varepsilon/kT}$$

$$= 1 \cdot 5 \times 10^{-4} \cdot e^{\varepsilon/kT}$$

The pre-exponential term is smaller by about 100 than the experimental values. Phillips (1921) derives for ηV_m the expression $N_0 h(g/2)$

$[1-(b/V_m)]^{-1}$, where g is an integer, and b a forbidden volume. In Eyring's treatment (1936), the pre-exponential term is written simply as $N_0 h$. Andrade's theory of viscosity (1934) which differs fundamentally from those of Frenkel, Phillips and Eyring in that the viscosity becomes directly proportional to the vibration frequency, yields the expression

$$\eta = \kappa' m v / a \qquad \text{VIII.40}$$

where m is the mass, v the vibration frequency, and a the average distance apart of near neighbours. The structural constant κ', depends on the lattice structure adopted for the liquid, and is of the order of magnitude unity. The equation has been successfully applied by him to determine η from known values of v. A relatively simple expression for the vibration frequency in a condensed system is

$$v = \frac{1}{\pi}\left(\frac{3\kappa a}{2m\beta}\right)^{1/2} \qquad \text{VIII.41}$$

where κ relates the molecular volume, v, to a; $v = \kappa a^3$. The form of this equation was derived, without the numerical constants, by Einstein (1911). When applied to a face-centred arrangement, we thus obtain for the viscosity

$$\eta = \frac{3^{1/2}}{\pi 2^{1/3}}\left(\frac{m}{\beta}\right)^{1/2} v^{-1/6} \qquad \text{VIII.42}$$

For liquid mercury at 20°C, $1/\beta$ is $2{\cdot}488 \times 10^{11}$ dynes/cm^2, and v is $2{\cdot}4426 \times 10^{-23}$cm^3. Hence the calculated viscosity is $2{\cdot}34 \times 10^{-2}$g/cm-sec, which exceeds the observed value of $1{\cdot}57 \times 10^{-2}$ by a factor of $\frac{3}{2}$.

Table VIII.13 *The viscosity and compressibility of liquid mercury*

P(Kg/cm^2)	$\eta \times 10^2$ at 30°C (g/cm.sec)	$\beta \times 10^6$ at 20°C (cm^2/Kg)	$\eta\beta^{1/2} \times 10^5$
1	1·516	3·957	3·02
2 000	1·585	3·715	2·72
4 000	1·663	3·499	3·11
6 000	1·742	3·238	3·13
8 000	1·822	2·958	3·13
10 000	1·912	2·685	3·13
12 000	2·007	2·402	3·11

The value assumed for κ appears to be the only doubtful item in the estimate. An independent approach to the problem (Moelwyn–Hughes, 1932) also stresses that η is proportional to the frequency. If this is true, the product $\eta\beta^{1/2}$ for a given liquid at constant temperature should be constant. Table VIII.13 shows this to be nearly the case with liquid mercury, for which, unfortunately, viscosity and compressibility data (Bridgman) at slightly different temperatures have had to be used. The low pressure gradient $(d \ln \eta / d \ln \beta)_T$ for carbon disulphide is also $-\frac{1}{2}$, but decreases at high pressures.

The heat capacity, heat content, free energy and entropy of liquids

These thermodynamical variables are obtained by the methods used with solids. Provided there are no transitions from one crystalline phase to another, we have

$$H = \int_0^{T_m} C_P(\mathrm{cr})\, dT + L_m + \int_{T_m}^{T} C_P(\mathrm{liq})\, dT \qquad \text{VIII.43}$$

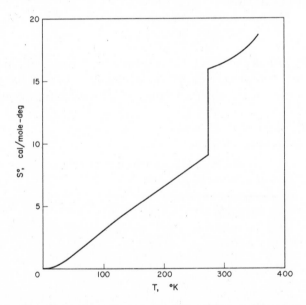

Fig. VIII.5   *The molar entropy of ice and water* (data of Simon and Giauque)

and

$$S = \int_0^{T_m} C_P(\text{cr})\, d\ln T + \frac{L_m}{T_m} + \int_{T_m}^T C_P(\text{liq})\, d\ln T \qquad \text{VIII.44}$$

where T_m is the melting point. Values of the entropy of H_2O obtained by Simon (1926) and Giauque and Stout (1936) are shown in Fig. VIII.5. The entropy of ice at 273·16°K is 10·103, and that of water at the same temperature is 15·940 cal/mole-deg. The increase in heat capacity attending fusion is $18·09 - 9·81 = 8·28$ in the same units. Data for mercury are given in Table VIII.14 and Fig. VIII.6. The value

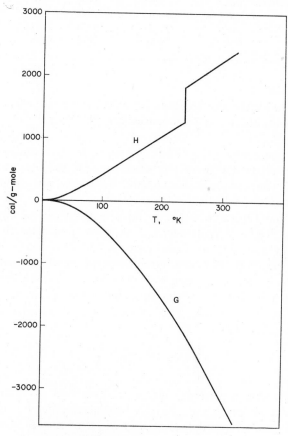

Fig. VIII.6 *The heat content (H) and Gibbs free energy (G) of mercury*

Table VIII.14 *The heat content, entropy and Gibbs energy of solid and liquid mercury*

$T°K$	(Calories/gram-mole-degree)		(Calories/gram-mole)	
	C_P	S	H	$-G$
0	0	0	0	0
40	4·65	3·97	99·5	59·3
80	5·62	7·53	310	292
120	6·02	9·94	545	648
160	6·32	11·64	792	1 070
200	6·51	13·12	1 049	1 574
234·34 (solid)	6·60	14·16	1 274	2 044
234·34 (liquid)	6·85	16·515	1 826	2 044
240	6·81	16·675	1 864	2 138
280	6·68	17·72	2 134	2 828
320	6·59	18·60	2 400	3 551

here accepted for the molar heat of fusion is the mean of those found calorimetrically (555) and piezometrically (548) from the Clapeyron equation.

At each temperature, the Gibbs energy, G, is, by definition, $G = H - TS$. The contrast between the behaviour of H and G as they pass the melting temperature is fundamental; H varies discontinuously, and G smoothly.

We see from Table VIII.14 that the molar entropy of liquid mercury at 320°K is 18·60 cal/g mole-degree. Now the vapour pressure at this temperature, according to Table VIII.6, is 13·5 dynes/cm^2, and the molar heat of vaporisation is 14 760 cals. The gain in entropy attending vaporisation at this temperature is thus $\Delta S = L/T = 14\,760/320 = 46·13$, so that the entropy of the saturated vapour at 320°K is 64·73 cal/g mole-degree. We may also calculate this entropy, using the Sackur-Tetrode formula:

$$S = R\left\{\frac{5}{2} + \ln \frac{(2\pi mkT)^{3/2}}{h^3} \cdot \frac{kT}{P}\right\} \qquad \text{IX.47}$$

obtaining 64·56, in satisfactory agreement. This result is typical of the many results on which the third law of thermodynamics has been founded. It will be noted that a comparison of entropies obtained from thermal data with those computed statistically proceeds directly without introducing the concept of a standard state, though such is a convenient one, especially with complicated molecules.

Theories of the liquid state

Though there are numerous theories of the liquid state, it is clear, even from the brief account given here of their principal properties, that no simple theory can cope with all the facts. Some of the recent theories have been reviewed by de Boer (1952). In most treatments, it is assumed, as in our discussion of heat capacities, that the internal motions of a molecule in a liquid are the same as they are in the gas, so that we are primarily concerned with the motion of the centre of gravity of the liquid molecule, and with the translational partition function

$$f = \frac{1}{h^3} \iiint\iiint_{-\infty}^{\infty} e^{-\varepsilon/kT} dx\, dy\, dz\, dp_x dp_y dp_z \qquad \text{VIII.45}$$

The energy, ε, may be resolved into three components, namely, the kinetic energy, ε_k, which is a function of temperature only, the average potential energy, $u(v)$, which is assumed to depend on the volume only, and the displacement energy, w, which is a function of both:

$$\varepsilon = \varepsilon_k(T) + u(v) + w(T, v)$$

Integrating over all possible values of the momenta from $-\infty$ to $+\infty$, and taking $u(v)$ outside the integral sign because it is assumed to be independent of the absolute values of the coordinates x, y and z, we have

$$f = \frac{(2\pi mkT)^{3/2}}{h^3} \cdot e^{-u(v)/kT} \iint\int_{-\infty}^{\infty} e^{-w(T,v)/kT} dx\, dy\, dz \qquad \text{VIII.46}$$

The remaining problem is to discover the right expression for $w(T, v)$.

If displacement from the position of minimum energy involve an increase, w, in energy expressible as the sum of three quadratic terms, $\frac{1}{2}K(x^2 + y^2 + z^2)$, we would have

$$f = \frac{(2\pi mkT)^{3/2}}{h^3} \left(\frac{2\pi kT}{K}\right)^{3/2} e^{-u(v)/kT} \qquad \text{VIII.47}$$

The molecular motion is now clearly that of a harmonic vibration,

G*

193

since $K = (2\pi v)^2 m$. Hence

$$f = \frac{(2\pi mkT)^{3/2}}{h^3} \left[\frac{1}{v}\left(\frac{kT}{2\pi m}\right)^{1/2}\right]^3 e^{-u(v)/kT} \qquad \text{VIII.48}$$

The term inside the square bracket is the quotient of the average velocity in a given direction (equation II.6) and the vibration frequency, and is therefore one-half of the distance available to the motion of the centre of the molecule. The cube of this distance is proportional to the free space, v_f, per molecule, so that, ignoring a numerical factor, we may write

$$f = \frac{(2\pi mkT)^{3/2}}{h^3} \cdot v_f \cdot e^{-u(v)/kT} \qquad \text{VIII.49}$$

Equation 48 can, of course, be written more briefly as follows:

$$f = \left(\frac{kT}{hv}\right)^3 \cdot e^{-u(v)/kT} \qquad \text{VIII.50}$$

as is consistent with the model of a triply degenerate classical harmonic oscillator. The object of writing it in the other form is to stress the true meaning of free space as the space available to the centre of gravity of the molecule (Boltzmann, 1896; Herzfeld, 1925). The idea that free space may be regarded as the difference between the total volume of the system and the 'incompressible' volume of its molecules, is one that cannot be sustained.

By equating the chemical potentials of molecules in the liquid and vapour phases at equilibrium, we find

$$\frac{v_f(\text{liquid})}{v_f(\text{gas})} = e^{-[u(g)-u(l)]/kT} = e^{-\lambda_i/kT} \qquad \text{VIII.51}$$

where λ_i is the internal heat of vaporisation. When the vapour is dilute, its free volume equals its total volume, and, when the ideal gas laws hold, the following expression emerges for the free molecular volume in a liquid:

$$v_f(\text{liq}) = (kT/p) \cdot e^{-\lambda_i/kT} \qquad \text{VIII.52}$$

The ratio of the free molecular volume to the total molecular volume for liquid water at atmospheric pressure is $1 \cdot 5 \times 10^{-3}$ at the freezing point and $7 \cdot 8 \times 10^{-3}$ at the boiling point. It passes through a point of inflexion at about 35°C.

In a search for other general expressions for the free space in liquids, Dieterici (1898) arrived at the following semi-empirical relationship between the average molecular volume of a liquid and that of its saturated vapour:

$$\frac{v_L}{v_G} = e^{-j\lambda_i/kT}$$ VIII.53

where j is $\frac{3}{5}$ for a variety of non-polar liquids over wide temperature ranges. Since the molar heat of vaporisation is $L = N_0(\lambda_i + kT)$, it follows that the entropy of vaporisation is

$$\Delta S = R\left[\frac{5}{3}\ln\frac{v_G}{v_L} + 1\right]$$ VIII.54

in reasonable agreement with experiment.

The theory of holes has proved to be a stimulating one, whether the holes are regarded as of molecular dimensions (Eyring, 1936) or as having a statistically distributed range of sizes (Altar, 1936). The energy necessary to make a hole of molecular size may be readily obtained in terms of the heat of vaporisation or the surface tension. The decrease in density of liquids in equilibrium with their saturated vapours, as the temperature is raised, is interpreted as an increase in the concentration of holes. Viscosity can be treated as the movement of holes in a direction counter to that of the molecules; and an expression similar to equation 54 may be derived for the entropy of vaporisation.

Lennard–Jones and Devonshire (1937) derived for $w(T, v)$ a rather complicated expression which can explain why liquid molecules at low temperatures simulate harmonic oscillators and at high temperatures more closely resemble gases. The superposition of an order-disorder correction diminishes without eliminating the disparity between theory and experiment.

IX Gases

A discussion of the gaseous state of matter naturally begins with a reconsideration of the ideal gas laws, for these are laws which are approximately obeyed by gases under ordinary conditions of temperature and pressure and to which all gases tend to conform in the limit of high temperatures and low pressures. They may, as we have seen in Chapter I, be stated as follows:

$$PV = NkT = vRT \qquad \text{IX.1}$$

where P is the pressure exerted by N molecules or v gram-moles of gas in a volume V at the absolute temperature T. The coefficient of isobaric expansion of ideal gases is the reciprocal of the absolute temperature,

$$\alpha = \frac{1}{V}\left(\frac{dV}{dT}\right)_P = \frac{vR}{PV} = \frac{1}{T} \qquad \text{IX.2}$$

and the coefficient of isothermal compression is the reciprocal of the pressure,

$$\beta = -\frac{1}{V}\left(\frac{dV}{dP}\right)_T = \frac{vRT}{P^2V} = \frac{1}{P} \qquad \text{IX.3}$$

Since pressure is defined as $-(dA/dV)_T$ (equation VI.20), the increase in the Helmholtz free energy of v gram-moles of gas expanding isothermally by an amount dV is

$$(dA)_T = -(P\,dV)_T = -vRTd\ln V$$

and the free energy itself by integration, is

$$A = -vRT\ln V + \text{constant}$$

For one gram-mole of ideal gas ($v = 1$), we have $A = -RT\ln V + \text{constant}$. If we denote by A° the molar free energy when the gas occupies some particular volume V°, the integration constant becomes $A^\circ + RT\ln V^\circ$. Hence

$$A = A^\circ + RT\ln(V^\circ/V) \qquad \text{IX.4}$$

To obtain an expression for the total energy, we apply the Kelvin–Helmholtz relationship $E = A - T(dA/dT)_V$ to each term. Operation on the first term on the right hand side yields $A° - T(dA°/dT)_V$, which is evidently the total molar energy of the gas when its volume is $V°$. Operation on the second term on the right yields nothing, leaving us with the result

$$E = E^\circ \qquad \text{IX.5}$$

Thus, at any particular temperature, the molar energy of all gases that obey the ideal laws is independent of the volume. It follows that the heat capacity C_V is also independent of V. Thermodynamics can tell us nothing about the magnitude of E or C_V, or predict their dependence on temperature. The kinetic theory, however, tells us that one gram-mole of every ideal gas possesses translational energy $\frac{3}{2}RT$. The total molar energy may then be written as

$$E = E^i + \tfrac{3}{2}RT \qquad \text{IX.6}$$

where E^i denotes the internal energy of one gram-mole. The heat capacity is consequently

$$C_V = C_V^i + \tfrac{3}{2}R \qquad \text{IX.7}$$

Here C_V^i stands for that part of the heat capacity at constant volume which depends on internal molecular motions, principally rotations and vibrations. There can be no internal motion in a monatomic gas, for which, therefore, the heat capacity should be $\frac{3}{2}R = 2\cdot981$ cal/mole-degree if the gas is ideal. The experimental value for helium at ordinary temperatures and pressures is $2\cdot97$.

The entropy expression for an ideal gas may be derived from the free energy equation 4:

$$S = -(dA/dT)_V = -(dA°/dT)_V - R\ln(V°/V) = S° - R\ln(V°/V) \qquad \text{IX.8}$$

If we now choose $V°$ as unity, we can write

$$S = S° + R\ln V \qquad \text{IX.9}$$

which relates the entropy $S°$ of one gram-mole of an ideal gas in a system of unit volume with the entropy of the same amount of gas at the same temperature but at a volume V. Because the pressure of an ideal gas varies inversely as the volume, equation IX.4 may be written as

$$A = A° - RT\ln(P°/P)$$

from which we derive the equation

$$S = S° - R \ln P \qquad \text{IX.10}$$

The term $S°$ now stands for the molar entropy of the gas at unit pressure, and is therefore not the same as the $S°$ of equation 9.

We have next to examine some properties of real gases in systems where their behaviour is far from ideal.

Critical phenomena

In Fig. 1 are shown the isothermals of carbon dioxide at seven temperatures in the neighbourhood of 31°C. Instead of the series of co-axial rectangular hyperbolas which would result if the ideal laws were obeyed, we have a number of curves, each of which shows two discontinuities below the critical point C. Let us study the behaviour of carbon dioxide gas on compressing it at 30·409°C by following its representative point, starting at A. From A to B an increase in pressure is accompanied by a decrease in volume, such that PV diminishes instead of remaining constant. At the point B some liquid appears. No further compression is required to pass from B to G, which corresponds to a change in composition of a liquid-vapour mixture at constant pressure. When a volume corresponding to G is reached, the last trace of vapour disappears. GH shows the compressibility of the pure liquid. The curve upon which the point C lies just misses the formation of the liquid phase. C is the critical point, and is specific for each gas. The pressure, molar volume and temperature at this point are the critical constants, denoted by the symbols P_c, V_c and T_c respectively. The points B and G represent the molar volumes of the saturated vapour and the liquid with which it is in isothermal equilibrium. The locus of points of this type is the bell-shaped curve, with a maximum at C, where B and G coalesce. This inspection of the experimental isothermals provides a second definition of the critical temperature as that temperature at which the molar volumes of the liquid and its saturated vapour are equal. The viscosities, and, with few exceptions, most of the measured physical properties of the two states become identical at the critical point. To obtain our third and final definition of this point, let us again examine Fig. IX.1, looking at the portion of the dotted curve marked $BDFG$. Only a small portion of this curve can be traced experimentally; if a vapour is isothermally compressed, taking care to avoid the presence of any impurity in the

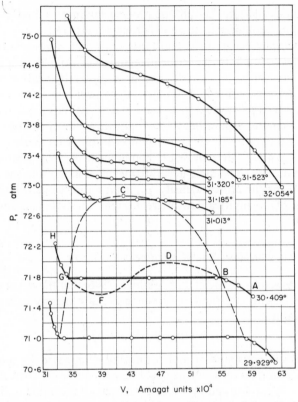

Fig. IX.1 *Isothermals of carbon dioxide in the neighbourhood of the critical point* (after Michels, Blaise and Michels, 1937)

form of dust or surface nuclei, we can go some way along *BD* with a supersaturated vapour. The part marked *DF* is unattainable, and corresponds to the unthinkable process of a simultaneous and isothermal increase of pressure and volume. The point *F* is given analytically by the conditions for a minimum, which are that $(dP/dV)_T$ is zero, and $(d^2P/dV^2)_T$ is positive; the point *D* is defined by the conditions for a maximum, which are $(dP/dV)_T$ is zero and $(d^2P/dV^2)_T$ is negative. The critical point, when the locus of the maxima and minima itself passes through a maximum must therefore satisfy the conditions:

$$\left.\begin{array}{l} (dP/dV)_T = 0 \\ (d^2P/dV^2)_T = 0 \end{array}\right\} \quad T = T_c \qquad \text{IX.11}$$

and

199

All equations of state, i.e. all equations relating P, V and T to one another, must conform to these experimental criteria.

To determine the critical constants, it is not necessary to have detailed isothermals in the critical region. The critical temperature, for example, can be measured with fair accuracy by heating a small, sealed, glass tube containing liquid and its own vapour in the complete absence of air or other gases, and of dust. At the critical temperature, the meniscus separating the two phases abruptly disappears; on cooling, it reappears at the same temperature. If the sealed tube is connected with a high pressure manometer, P_c may similarly be measured directly. The most accurate means of measuring the critical volume, V_c, or the critical density, ρ_c, is an indirect one, which takes advantage of an empirical law of great interest in itself, and now to be discussed.

Cailletet and Mathias's law of rectilinear diameters

It was observed by Cailletet and Mathias (1886) that the mean density of the liquid and its saturated vapour decreases linearly with respect to temperature:

$$\bar{\rho} = \tfrac{1}{2}(\rho_L + \rho_G) = a - bT \qquad\qquad \text{IX.12}$$

The empirical constants, a and b, may be eliminated by assuming that the relation holds from the absolute zero up to the critical point. When $T = 0$, $\rho_G = 0$, and $\rho_L = \rho_s$, the density of the liquid, subcooled to the absolute zero. Hence $a = \tfrac{1}{2}\rho_s$. When $T = T_c$, $\rho_L = \rho_G = \rho_c$, the critical density. Hence $\rho_c = a - bT_c$. Consequently

$$\rho_G + \rho_L = \rho_s - (\rho_s - 2\rho_c)\left(\frac{T}{T_c}\right) \qquad\qquad \text{IX.13}$$

In Fig. IX.2, the extensive data of Amagat (1892) for carbon dioxide have been plotted, along with some supplementary figures due to Lowry (1927) at lower temperatures. The critical density is read off as 0.466 ± 0.002 gram/cc.

On account of the proportionality between density and concentration, n, the Cailletet-Mathias law can be written in the form:

$$\frac{n_G + n_L}{n_c} = \frac{n_s}{n_c} - \left(\frac{n_s}{n_c} - 2\right)\frac{T}{T_c} \qquad\qquad \text{IX.14}$$

As the mean of the molecular concentrations in the liquid and

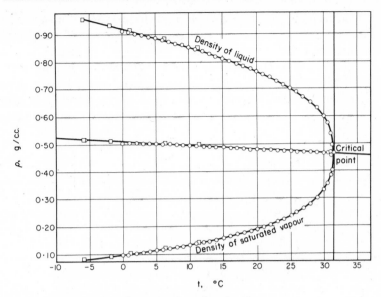

Fig. IX.2   *Cailletet and Mathias curve for carbon dioxide*

saturated vapour phases invariably decreases with a rise in temperature, it follows that $n_s/n_c > 2$ or $V_c/V_s > 2$. Experiment shows that
this condition is only just fulfilled by helium. For most liquids, the
actual ratio of the limiting density, n_s, to the critical density, n_c, is
approximately 4. This ratio can, it will be observed, be obtained from
the intercept and the gradient of the rectilinear diameter. The average
value found by Jüptner (1913) using the first method for 33 liquids
is 3·998, and using the second method 3·984. Approximately, then

$$\frac{n_s}{n_c} = \frac{V_c}{V_s} = 4 \qquad \text{IX.15}$$

Some of the liquid-vapour systems which have been examined with
considerable precision do not accurately obey the linear law. The
results of Young (1918), for example, on carbon tetrachloride can be
expressed in the form

$$\frac{n_G + n_L}{2n_c} = 1.958 - 1.041(T/T_c) + 0.08292(T/T_c)^2$$

The ratio of the limiting density to the critical density is here 3·916. The ratio for the inert gases appears to increase from 3·086 for neon to 3·50 for xenon; non-polar diatomic molecules give $n_s/n_c = 3·67 \pm 0·10$, and hydrocarbons and monosubstituted derivatives of benzene give a ratio of $3·87 \pm 0·06$. The mean value of 3·75 accepted by Lorenz (1916) though correct for many liquids, is not a general one.

The same comment applies to the critical ratio, RT_c/P_cV_c, as may be appreciated by inspection of some representative values in Table IX.1.

Table IX.1 *Critical constants*

Substance	Critical pressure (atmospheres) P_c	Critical volume (cm^3/gram-mole) V_c	Critical temperature (°K) T_c	Critical ratio RT_c/P_cV_c
Kr	45·182	92·08	209·39	3·443
N$_2$	33·49	90·03	125·97	3·422
CO$_2$	72·83	94·23	304·16	3·629
H$_2$O	218·5	55·44	647·3	4·385
NH$_3$	112·2	72·02	405·5	4·118
CCl$_4$	44·98	275·8	556·25	3·681
C$_2$H$_4$	49·98	126·1	282·66	3·680
CH$_3$OH	78·50	117·7	513·1	4·559
CH$_3$COOCH$_3$	46·33	227·7	506·8	3·944
C$_6$H$_6$	47·89	256·4	561·6	3·756
nC$_6$H$_{14}$	29·62	367·4	507·9	3·831

The Joule–Kelvin effect

The energy of a gas obeying the law $PV = vRT$ is, as we have seen, a function of the temperature only, and is independent of the pressure and volume. Hence if a given mass of ideal gas contained at high pressure in one vessel were allowed to expand into a second, evacuated vessel, the total energy, and consequently the temperature, would remain constant. When such an experiment is performed with a real gas, however, there is a temperature change, positive or negative, as observed by Joule and Kelvin. The conditions favourable for a large negative effect are utilised in the attainment of low temperature and in the liquefaction of gases. The sudden expansion of air at room temperature produces a lowering in temperature. This is true also of most gases under the same conditions. With hydrogen however, the reverse effect is found. It can be readily shown that the change in temperature attending a sudden adiabatic change in pressure is given by the equation

$$\Delta T = - \left[\frac{V(1 - \alpha T)}{C_P} \right] \Delta P$$

where α is the coefficient of isothermal expansion. Since α is $1/T$ for the ideal gas, no temperature change attends a change in its pressure. Real gases also can be compressed without change in temperature at a particular temperature given by $T_i = 1/\alpha$. T_i is called the inversion temperature. Because α is a function of the volume (or the pressure), T_i has a whole range of values at different volumes (or pressures). They are all given by the equation:

$$\alpha T_i = 1$$

To apply the inversion condition more easily, we take advantage of the identity (derived on p. 130)

$$\left(\frac{dV}{dT} \right)_P = - \left(\frac{dP}{dT} \right)_V \left(\frac{dV}{dP} \right)_T$$

and express the condition for inversion by the equality:

$$T \left(\frac{dP}{dT} \right)_V = - V \left(\frac{dP}{dV} \right)_T \qquad \text{IX.16}$$

P-V-T relations of real gases

To represent the pressure-volume-temperature relationship of a fixed amount (generally a gram-mole) of any real gas within the accuracy now attainable in the measurement of these variables requires a large number of constants. For example, to relate P with V at a constant temperature sometimes needs five constants; and to relate each of these constants with temperature may require not less than three further constants. Nevertheless, there are numerous equations which contain only three constants and are yet capable of reproducing the experimental results to within 1 or 2 per cent of the observed values. They make up in compactness what they lose in exactness, and we shall restrict our discussion to them.

1. *The equation of van der Waals.* The main deficiency in the original formulation of the kinetic theory of gases is the omission of inter-molecular forces. Without these, gases would not condense, as they all do at low temperatures, when the kinetic energy ceases to play the dominant role. By an argument which can no longer be sustained, van der Waals concluded that the effect of intermolecular forces was to establish an internal pressure, P_i, which is negative in sign (i.e. a cohesive pressure) and varies as the square of the concentration of the molecules; $P_i = -a'(N/V)^2$. Another innovation was to express the kinetic pressure as $P_k = NkT/[V-\frac{2}{3}\pi N\sigma^3]$, where σ is the molecular diameter. The argument underlying this amendment to the ideal expression, $P_k = NkT/V$, is somewhat as follows. The volume accessible to the centre of gravity of a molecule is less than the total volume of the system because the molecules, assumed spherical, themselves occupy a volume $N(\pi/6)\sigma^3$. To obtain the free volume, we do not simply subtract this term from the total volume, because, when two spheres of diameter σ are in contact, the forbidden volume for the pair is $\frac{4}{3}\pi\sigma^3$, as is evident from Fig. II.3. The average forbidden volume per molecule is thus $\frac{2}{3}\pi\sigma^3$, and the total forbidden volume in the system is $N\frac{2}{3}\pi\sigma^3$. The equation of van der Waals is thus

$$P = P_k + P_i \qquad \text{IX.17}$$

$$= \frac{NkT}{V-\frac{2}{3}\pi N\sigma^3} - \frac{a'N^2}{V^2} \qquad \text{IX.18}$$

The constants σ and a' are regarded as independent of temperature and volume. When applied to a gaseous system containing one gramme-mole, the equation becomes

$$P = \frac{RT}{V-b} - \frac{a}{V^2} \qquad \text{IX.19}$$

where

$$b = \frac{2}{3}\pi N_0\sigma^3; \qquad a = N_0^2 a' \qquad \text{IX.20}$$

The isotherms obtained from equation IX.19 resemble the curve $ABDFGH$ of Fig. IX.2. The equation is a cubic in V, giving three roots of V for one value of P. These are all real below the critical temperature, but two of the roots are imaginary above it. Equations IX.11 suffice to relate a to b to the critical constants. They may also be readily obtained without the aid of the calculus. Let equation

204

IX.19 be written in the order of descending powers of V:

$$V^3 - V^2 \left(b + \frac{RT}{P} \right) + \frac{aV}{P} - \frac{ab}{P} = 0$$

If the roots of this equation are x, y and z, then $(V-x)(V-y)(V-z) = 0$. At the critical point, all the roots are equal, and $V = V_c$; hence $(V - V_c)^3 = 0$. Expanding

$$V^3 - 3V^2 V_c + 3V V_c^2 - V_c^3 = 0$$

comparing coefficients of like powers of V, and rearranging, we have

$$V_c = 3b = 2\pi N_0 \sigma^3 \qquad \text{IX.22}$$

$$P_c = a/27b^2 \qquad \text{IX.22}$$

$$T_c = \frac{8a}{27bR} \qquad \text{IX.23}$$

and

$$\frac{RT_c}{P_c V_c} = \frac{8}{3} = 2\cdot67 \qquad \text{IX.24}$$

A comparison of the last equation with the data of Table IX.1 shows that agreement with experiment is moderate only. A more serious drawback to an equation which is an admitted improvement on the ideal gas law is that the experimental values of a and b are found to be functions of the temperature and molar volume.

Let us rewrite equation IX.18 in a slightly different way, namely

$$\frac{PV}{NkT} = \left(1 - \frac{2\pi N\sigma^3}{3V} \right)^{-1} - \frac{Na'}{VkT}$$

At relatively low concentrations, the first term on the right hand side may be expanded by means of the binomial theorem. Retaining only two terms in the expansion, we then find

$$\frac{PV}{NkT} = 1 + \left(\frac{2}{3}\pi\sigma^3 - \frac{a'}{kT} \right) \frac{N}{V} \qquad \text{IX.25}$$

When gas laws are expressed in this way, as a power series in the concentration, the coefficients of the various powers of N/V appearing on the right hand side are called virial coefficients. The second virial coefficient of a van der Waals gas is thus $\frac{2}{3}\pi\sigma^3 - (a'/kT)$.

2. *The equation of Dieterici.* From the many semi-empirical equations advanced by Dieterici, the version we shall consider may be written, for one gram-mole of gas, as follows

$$P = \frac{RT}{V-b} e^{-A/RT^{3/2}V} \qquad \text{IX.26}$$

It gives isothermals of the same shape as van der Waals' equation, and it can therefore be similarly treated. By differentiation, the first condition for the critical point is

$$\left(\frac{dP}{dV}\right)_T = \frac{RT}{V-b} e^{-A/RT^{3/2}V}\left[\frac{A}{RT^{3/2}V^2} - \frac{1}{V-b}\right] = 0$$

The exponential obviously cannot be zero at the critical point, hence the term inside the square brackets must be zero, or

$$V^2 - \frac{A}{RT^{3/2}}V + \frac{Ab}{RT^{3/2}} = 0$$

This is a quadratic equation in V, giving the locus of maxima and minima. At the critical point the two roots of the equation coincide, so that, by comparison with the equation

$$V^2 - 2VV_c + V_c^2 = 0$$

we obtain

$$V_c = 2b, \qquad \text{IX.27}$$

and

$$T_c = \left(\frac{A}{4bR}\right)^{3/2} \qquad \text{IX.28}$$

Substituting in equation IX.26, we have

$$P_c = \frac{R}{b}\left(\frac{A}{4bR}\right)^{3/2} e^{-2} \qquad \text{IX.29}$$

whence

$$\frac{RT_c}{P_cV_c} = \tfrac{1}{2}e^2 = 3\cdot695 \qquad \text{IX.30}$$

The data of Table IX.1 show that the last equation is in better agreement with the facts than is equation IX.24.

On using equation IX.16, we also find (see Fig. IX.3) that the equation of Dieterici excels in reproducing the inversion conditions of nitrogen and carbon dioxide. The pressure unit adopted in this figure is the critical pressure, and the temperature unit is the critical temperature, for each gas. When the pressure, volume and temperature of a gas are written as fractions of their values at the critical

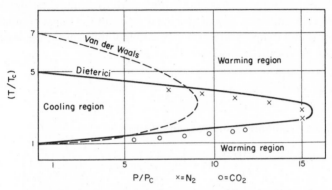

Fig. IX.3 *The relationship between inversion pressure and inversion temperature* (after W. C. McC. Lewis, 1925)

point, say $P/P_c = \pi$, $V/V_c = \phi$, and $T/T_c = \theta$, the variables are called reduced variables, and the equation of state a reduced equation of state. In these terms, Dieterici's equation becomes

$$\pi(2\phi - 1) = \theta \exp\left\{2\left[1 - \frac{1}{\phi\theta^{3/2}}\right]\right\} \qquad \text{IX.31}$$

If two substances were found to obey equations of state of exactly the same form, their isotherms and other representative curves showing their behaviour could be superimposed, however different the absolute magnitude of P, V and T. Moreover, if any two of the variables π, ϕ and θ were the same for two different substances, the other variable must also have a common value. States of two substances with two identical values of these variables are said to be corresponding states. Seldom, however, even with monatomic crystals, do two different systems obey the equations of state of exactly the same form.

3. *The equation of D. Berthelot*. The empirical equation of Berthelot, which, for one gram-mole of gas may be written in the form

$$PV = RT\left\{1+\frac{9}{128}\left(\frac{P}{P_c}\right)\left(\frac{T_c}{T}\right)\left[1-6\left(\frac{T_c}{T}\right)^2\right]\right\} \qquad \text{IX.32}$$

clearly does not apply to the critical region, for, according to it, RT_c/P_cV_c would be as low as 128/83. It is, however, convenient and sufficiently reliable to express the behaviour of real gases at moderate temperatures and pressures, and is often used to estimate the difference between the entropies of real and ideal gases. In the range of moderate pressures and temperatures, the increase in Gibbs energy on compressing the gas isothermally from P_1 to P_2 is

$$\Delta G = \int_{P_1}^{P_2} V\,dP = RT\ln\left(\frac{P_2}{P_1}\right)+\frac{9}{128}\frac{RT_c}{P_c}\left[1-6\left(\frac{T_c}{T}\right)^2\right](P_2-P_1) \qquad \text{IX.33}$$

and the corresponding increase in entropy is

$$\Delta S = -\left[\frac{d(\Delta G)}{dT}\right]_P = R\left[\ln\left(\frac{P_1}{P_2}\right)-\frac{27}{32}\left(\frac{T_c}{T}\right)^3\left(\frac{P_2-P_1}{P_c}\right)\right] \qquad \text{IX.34}$$

The first term is the entropy of compression of an ideal gas, and the second term the entropy change arising from the imperfection of the gas.

4. *The Leiden equation.* Much of the very accurate work done by the Dutch physical chemists has been summarised in isothermals using power series of the density, ρ, expressed in Amagat units (1 Amagat unit = 0·044617 gram-mole/litre):

$$PV = A+B\rho+C\rho^2+D\rho^3+Y\rho^4+Z\rho^5 \qquad \text{IX.35}$$

where A is NkT, and the constants, B, C, ... are independent of the density. The experimental accuracy of 1 in 10,000 can be reproduced by this equation, though at fairly low densities, only the terms involving A, B and C are required. The experimental values for argon, obtained by Michels (1949) using the method of least squares, are reproduced in Table 2. They refer to the equation

$$PV = NkT+B\rho+C\rho^2 \qquad \text{IX.36}$$

If we express the concentration as n, the number of molecules per cc,

208

the results may clearly be expressed in the form:

$$\frac{PV}{NkT} = 1 + B^*n + C^*n^2 \qquad \text{IX.37}$$

where

$$B^* = \frac{B}{A \times 2 \cdot 7037 \times 10^{19}}.$$

Values of B^* are given in the last column of Table IX.2. Beattie and Bridgman (1930) have based an equation of state on equation IX.35, taken as far as the fourth term, and have expressed the coefficients A, B and C in terms of T and empirical constants.

Table IX.2 $PV = A + B\rho + C\rho^2$ for argon, with ρ in Amagat units

$T°$K	A	$B \times 10^3$	$C \times 10^6$	$B^* \times 10^{23}$ (cc/molecule)
273·16	1·00097	−0·958737	2·53657	−3·54262
298·16	1·09258	−0·768605	2·52178	−2·60193
323·16	1·18419	−0·594282	2·66717	−1·85617
348·16	1·27581	−0·412911	2·64590	−1·19706
373·16	1·36742	−0·244114	2·73653	−0·66029
398·16	1·45902	−0·076899	2·81476	−0·19494
423·16	1·55065	+0·095810	2·73347	+0·22852

5. *A theoretical equation.* A general equation of state for gases has been derived by Rayleigh on the basis of Boltzmann's law and the virial theorem of Clausius. In terms of the interaction energy, ϕ, of an isolated pair of molecules at a distance r apart, it takes the from:

$$\frac{PV}{NkT} = 1 + \frac{2\pi N}{V} \int_0^\infty (1 - e^{-\phi/kT}) r^2 \, dr \qquad \text{IX.38}$$

Before the integration can be performed, it is, of course, necessary to know how ϕ depends on the intermolecular distance, r. We here adopt Mie's expression for ϕ, which is valid when the forces exerted between the molecules are spherically symmetrical (equation VII.9):

$$\phi = Ar^{-n} - Br^{-m} \qquad \text{IX.39}$$

Here A and B are constants, and n and m integers, of which n is the larger. Rayleigh's equation, after substituting Mie's potential, has been integrated by Lennard–Jones (1924). Its form is complicated, and, on comparison with the experimental virial coefficients does not allow of an absolute evaluation of the four constants concerned. We shall here greatly simplify the procedure, by first resolving the integral into two parts, where r has values below and above the molecular 'diameter', σ:

$$\frac{PV}{NkT} = 1 + \frac{2\pi N}{V}\left[\int_0^\sigma (1 - e^{-\phi/kT})\, r^2\, dr + \int_\sigma^\infty (1 - e^{-\phi/kT})\, r^2\, dr\right]$$

The form of Mie's equation is such that, when r is small, ϕ is positive and increases rapidly as r diminishes. As a first approximation, therefore, we can ignore $\exp(-\phi/kT)$ in comparison with unity when r is less than σ, obtaining $\sigma^3/3$ as the first integrand. When r is greater than σ, we shall use only the first two terms in the expansion of the exponential. Then

$$\frac{PV}{NkT} = 1 + \frac{2\pi N}{V}\left[\frac{\sigma^3}{3} - \frac{B}{(m-3)kT\sigma^{m-3}}\right] \qquad \text{IX.40}$$

A comparison of this equation with the second virial coefficient for a van der Waals gas (equation IX.25) shows that

$$a' = \frac{2\pi B}{(m-3)\sigma^{m-3}}$$

and

$$a = \frac{2\pi N_0^2 B}{(m-3)\sigma^{m-3}} \qquad \text{IX.41}$$

which provides a theoretical interpretation of the van der Waals constant, a.

According to London's theory (Chapter IV) $m = 6$, and the energy of attraction of a pair of identical, non-polar molecules at a distance, r, apart is

$$\phi = -\frac{B}{r^6} = -\frac{3}{4}\frac{h\nu_i\alpha_0^2}{r^6} \qquad \text{IV.53}$$

where ν_i is the frequency of the electronic oscillator, and α_0 the static polarisability. London identifies hv_i with the ionisation potential. The constant a may thus be evaluated in terms of B and b, since

$$a = \frac{2\pi N_0^2 B}{3\sigma^3} = \frac{4\pi^2 N_0^3 B}{9b} \qquad \text{IX.42}$$

The satisfactory agreement with experiment which London found for the elements of group 0 is apparent in Table IX.3.

Table IX.3. *A comparison of the observed and calculated constant, a, of van der Waals' equation (after London)*

Molecule	$hv_i \times 10^{11}$ (ergs)	$\alpha_0 \times 10^{24}$ (cc/mole)	$(B = \frac{3}{4}hv_i\alpha_0^2) \times 10^{60}$(erg-cm^6)	b (cc/gram-mole)	$a \times 10^{-4}$ (atm-cc^2) observed	calculated
He	3·898	0·2036	1·212	24	3·5	4·87
Ne	3·415	0·3926	3·950	17	21	22·4
A	2·496	1·6264	49·52	32·3	135	151·4
Kr	2·217	2·4559	100·3	39·8	240	243·2
Xe	1·921	3·9989	230·4	51·5	410	431·8

The second virial coefficient may be analysed in such a way as to yield independent values of both σ and B, and thus to dispense with the need of van der Waals' experimental value b or of London's theoretical expression for B. From equation IX.40, the second virial coefficient, with $m = 6$, is

$$\frac{2}{3}\pi\sigma^3\left(1 - \frac{B}{\sigma^6 kT}\right)$$

On plotting it as a function of $1/T$, we can obtain the value of σ from the intercept, and that of B from the gradient. Using Michels' data for argon (Table IX.2), we thus find $\sigma = 3\cdot218\,\text{Å}$, and $B = 62\cdot41 \times 10^{60}$ erg-cm^6.

The translational partition function for ideal gases

The dynamical property which all ideal gases have in common is free translational motion, and this is a property the consequences of which may be studied without regard to the structural complexity or the internal motions of the molecules. The most direct way of arriving at satisfactory expressions for the translational component of the entropy, free energy, and other macroscopic properties of an ideal gas is *via* the translational component of the partition function, which we shall now derive, in easy stages.

Free linear motion. The energy of a point particle of mass m, moving linearly and freely along a length l, is $\varepsilon = \frac{1}{2}mv^2 = (1/2m)(mv)^2 = (1/2m)(h/\lambda)^2$, where λ is the de Broglie wavelength, one-half of which must be an integral fraction of l, i.e. $\lambda = 2l/n$. The discrete energy levels allowed by quantum laws are then

$$\varepsilon = \frac{h^2 n^2}{8ml^2} ; (n = 1, 2, 3, \ldots)$$

IV.13

According to its general definition, the partition function in this instance is

$$f = \sum_{n=1}^{n=\infty} e^{-h^2 n^2/8ml^2 kT}$$

When the coefficient of n^2 in the exponent is small, we may replace the summation by the integration

$$f = \int_0^\infty e^{-an^2} dn$$

where a is $h^2/8ml^2 kT$. The physical conditions implied are those of a dilute system of massive particles at high temperatures. The approximate treatment is not valid for condensed systems of light particles at low temperatures. The integral is $\frac{1}{2}(\pi/a)^{1/2}$. Hence, with sufficient accuracy for most purposes the summation yields the result

$$f = \frac{(2\pi mkT)^{1/2} l}{h}$$

IX.43

When an atom, or a coherent group of atoms, is being torn from the remainder of a complex molecule, its relative motion when it is about to break away resembles linear translation in a force-free field. Equation IX.43 is therefore of interest in chemical kinetics.

Free superficial motion. The same considerations, applied to the motion of a point particle free to move simultaneously along a length l_1 in one direction and a length l_2 in another direction at right angles to it, lead to the partition function

$$f = \frac{(2\pi mkT)^{1/2}l_1}{h} \frac{(2\pi mkT)^{1/2}l_2}{h}$$

But l_1l_2, which may be denoted by o, represents the area accessible to the molecule, so that

$$f = \frac{2\pi mkTo}{h^2} \qquad \text{IX.44}$$

This equation is the general jumping-off ground afforded by statistical theory for the treatment of surface phenomena, such as interfacial tension and superficial adsorption.

Free motion in a confined space. Suppose the particle were capable of performing free superficial translation on a plane area, o, and simultaneously of executing free linear motion of extension l_3, in a direction at right angles to the plane. We should then find for the partition function the product

$$f = \frac{2\pi mkTo}{h^2} \frac{(2\pi mkT)^{1/2}l_3}{h}$$

Now ol_3 is the volume, v, accessible to the molecule; hence

$$f = \frac{(2\pi mkT)^{3/2}v}{h^3} \qquad \text{IX.45}$$

which is the partition function for a point particle of mass m free to move in, but confined to, a cell of volume v at temperature T.

Free motion in a shared space. We shall denote the partition function just derived for a point particle of mass m moving freely in a cell of volume v by f_c, where the subscript is to remind us that the molecule is captive:

$$f_c = \frac{(2\pi mkT)^{3/2}v}{h^3}$$

If we apply this partition function to an ideal gas molecule, taking v as V/N, we derive the correct isotherm, specific heat and most of its properties, with the exception of the entropy, which turns out to be less by k than the experimental value. The reason for the apparent discrepancy is that the ideal gas is not a system of N molecules each confined to a volume v, but a system of N molecules each of which has access to the total volume, V, of the system. If, therefore, we require the partition function for an ideal gas molecule, we must modify our expression, f_c, so as to allow for molecular mobility from one cell to another. This may be done in the following way.

Let us consider two neighbouring cells, each of volume v, and each containing one molecule. If each molecule is kept in its own cell, the partition function for the system is $f_1 f_2 = (qv)^2$, where q is $(2\pi mkT)^{3/2}/h^3$. Now let us remove the wall which we have imagined to separate the two cells. There are two consequences: (1) each molecule now has access to the volume $2v$, and (2) the new system is more disordered than the original one, for it can be constructed in two indistinguishable ways. If the wall were re-erected, it would be impossible to say which molecule is in which cell. The partition function is always proportional to the number of distinguishable ways in which the system can be formed. The true partition function for the new system is thus

$$f_1 f_2 = f_m^2 = \frac{(q \cdot 2v)^2}{2!}$$

where f_m is the molecular partition function for either molecule in the new system. Proceeding to a system of three molecules each having access to the total volume $3v$, we have

$$f_1 f_2 f_3 = f_m^3 = \frac{(q \cdot 3v)^3}{3!}$$

In the general case where N molecules are free to move among N cells, we have

$$f_m^N = (q \cdot Nv)^N/N!$$

For large values of N, we may use Stirling's approximation,

$$\frac{N^N}{N!} = e^N$$

and thus obtain the result

$$f_m^N = (qve)^N,$$

or

$$f_m = \frac{(2\pi mkT)^{3/2}ve}{h^3}$$

The partition function for the mobile molecule is thus greater by a factor e than that for the captive molecule. As explained in Chapter VI, we must include the degeneracy, g. Hence, after replacing v by V/N, we have the desired expression:

$$f = \frac{g(2\pi mkT)^{3/2}Ve}{h^3 N}$$

IX.46

from which the translational component of all the thermodynamic properties of ideal gas systems may be derived.

The statistical evaluation of some properties of gaseous monatomic systems

1. *Entropy.* On applying the general relation

$$S = Nk\left[\ln f + T\left(\frac{d\ln f}{dT}\right)_V\right]$$

VI.54

to the present partition function, we find, after substituting kT/P for V/N,

$$S = Nk\left\{\ln\left[\frac{g(2\pi mkT)^{3/2}}{h^3}\cdot\frac{kT}{P}\right]+\frac{5}{2}\right\}$$

IX.47

a result independently derived by Sackur and Tetrode. There is no objection to using this equation as it stands. Frequently, however, it is more convenient to work with the molar weight, M, instead of the molecular weight, m ($= M/N_0$), and to express the pressure, P, in atmospheres rather than in dynes per cm^2. Finally, if we want the molar entropy, we must restrict N to N_0, when Nk becomes R, the gas constant per mole. After inserting the values of the fundamental constants, we then find for the translational component of the molar entropy of an ideal gas:

$$S_{\text{trans}} = R\ln g+\tfrac{3}{2}R\ln M+\tfrac{5}{2}R\ln T-R\ln P(\text{atm})-2\cdot315,$$

or

$$S_{\text{trans}}/R = \ln g+\tfrac{3}{2}\ln M+\tfrac{5}{2}\ln T-\ln P(\text{atm})-1\cdot165$$

IX.48

The correction for gas imperfection can be made by adopting a reliable equation of state, and is usually small at a pressure of one atmosphere, which is frequently taken as a reference or standard

215

pressure. Some standard molar entropies of monatomic gases and vapours computed in this way are compared in Table IX.4 with those found experimentally by the method described on p. 192. For each gas, the agreement lies within the limits of experimental error. For monatomic gases there is clearly no need to distinguish between the translational component of the entropy and the total entropy, for they are identical.

Table IX.4 *Molar entropies of monatomic gases and vapours at atmospheric pressure and at a temperature of 298·16°K*

Element	g	$S^0_{298 \cdot 16}$ (cal/g-mol-deg)	
		obs	calc
He	1	30·4	30·11
Ne	1	35·0$_5$	34·93
A	1	36·8$_5$	36·98
Na	2	37·2	36·70
K	2	38·3	38·28
Cu	2	37·8	39·74
Ag	2	42·8	41·32
Mg	1	35·2$_5$	35·50
Zn	1	38·5	38·44
Cd	1	40·4	40·10
Hg	1	42·2	41·78
Pb	3	43·6	44·06

2. *Free energies and chemical potential.* The general relation between the free energy and the molecular partition function of a pure substance is $A = -NkT \ln f$. Let us define the variable q as follows:

$$q = \frac{Nf}{Ve} = n \cdot \frac{f}{e} \qquad \text{IX.49}$$

Then

$$A = -NkT \ln q - NkT \ln V - NkT + NkT \ln N$$

On differentiating this expression with respect to N at constant temperature and volume, we obtain the chemical potential:

$$\mu = -kT \ln (q/n)$$

With the particular partition function now discussed, we have

$$\mu = -kT \ln \left[\frac{g(2\pi mkT)^{3/2}}{h^3} \right] + kT \ln n \qquad \text{IX.50}$$

The first term on the right-hand side is clearly the chemical potential of one molecule in a system the concentration of which is unity, i.e. one molecule per cc. Denoting this chemical potential by μ^0, there results the familiar and much-used relation:

$$\mu = \mu^0 + kT \ln n \qquad \text{IX.51}$$

Alternatively, we may be interested in using a practical unit of concentration, such as one gram-mole per litre. Then $n = c(N_0/1,000)$, and

$$\mu = -kT \ln \left[\frac{g(2\pi mkT)^{3/2}}{h^3} \frac{1\,000}{N_0} \right] + kT \ln c$$

$$= \mu^0 + kT \ln c \qquad \text{IX.52}$$

where c is the concentration in moles per litre, and μ^0 is now the chemical potential of one molecule in a system at molar concentration.

The general relation between the Gibbs free energy and the molecular partition function readily follows from equations VI.20 and VI.23:

$$G = A + PV = -NkT \left[\ln f - \left(\frac{d \ln f}{d \ln V} \right)_T \right]$$

On using equations IX.1 and IX.46, we obtain the expressions:

$$G = -NkT \ln \left[\frac{g(2\pi mkT)^{3/2} V}{h^3 N} \right] = -NkT \ln \left[\frac{g(2\pi mkT)^{3/2} kT}{h^3 P} \right]$$

$$\text{IX.53}$$

Differentiation of G with respect to N at constant T and P gives, of course, the same chemical potential as that obtained by the other method. The molar Gibbs energy ($N = N_0$), expressed in calories, is found, by substituting numerical values for the universal constants, to be

$$-\frac{G}{T} = R \ln g + \tfrac{3}{2} R \ln M + \tfrac{5}{2} R \ln T - R \ln P(\text{atm}) - 7 \cdot 267$$

H

or

$$G/RT = \ln g + \tfrac{3}{2} \ln M + \tfrac{5}{2} \ln T - \ln P(\text{atm}) - 3 \cdot 665 \qquad \text{IX.54}$$

Thus, for example, G for one gram atom of sodium vapour at atmospheric pressure and at a temperature of $1\,000°\text{K}$ becomes $-37\,871$ calories.

The partition function for diatomic molecules

Before similar calculations can be made for diatomic molecules, we must formulate its molecular partition function, assuming that the translation of the molecule in a shared space, its rotation about its centre of gravity and the vibration of the atoms in the molecule have no effect on one another. Then

$$f = f_{\text{trans}} f_{\text{rot}} f_{\text{vibr}} \qquad \text{IX.55}$$

f_{trans} is given by equation IX.46, and f_{vibr} by equation VII.1. To obtain an expression for f_{rot}, we note that the energy levels allowed by the quantum theory for the free rotation of a rigid particle of moment of inertia I is

$$\varepsilon = \frac{J(J+1)h^2}{8\pi^2 I}; \qquad (J = 1, 2, 3, \ldots) \qquad \text{IV.44}$$

and that a given rotational energy can be realised in $2J+1$ ways, each corresponding to a separate solution of the Schrödinger equation. The partition function is accordingly

$$f = \sum_{1}^{\infty} (2J+1)e^{-J(J+1)h^2/8\pi^2 IkT} \qquad \text{IX.56}$$

The summation is readily evaluated when $\{(2J+1)h^2\}/8\pi^2 I \ll kT$, which holds for massive molecules generally, but for light molecules only at high temperatures. Let $x = J(J+1)$, so that $dx = (2J+1)\,dJ$. On replacing the summation by the integration

$$f = \int_0^{\infty} e^{-bx}\,dx$$

where $b = h^2/8\pi^2 IkT$, we see that

$$f = \left[-\frac{e^{-bx}}{b}\right]_0^{\infty} = \frac{1}{b} = \frac{8\pi^2 IkT}{h^2}$$

If the rotator is symmetrical, this partition function must be reduced by an integer σ, which is equal to the number of indistinguishable permutations obtained by the rotation of the molecule. Then,

$$f = \frac{8\pi^2 I k T}{\sigma h^2} \qquad \text{IX.57}$$

and the total effective molecular partition function for a diatomic molecule becomes

$$f = g\frac{(2\pi m k T)^{3/2} v e}{h^3} \frac{8\pi^2 I k T}{\sigma h^2}(1 - e^{-hv/kT})^{-1} \qquad \text{IX.58}$$

provided the translational, rotational and vibrational motions are mutually independent. For homonuclear diatomic molecules, g is 2.

The statistical evaluation of some properties of gaseous diatomic systems

The total energy, entropy and the free energy of systems of gaseous diatomic molecules can now be calculated by inserting this partition function in equations VI, 51, 54 and 55.

1. *Energy and heat capacity.* The average energy per molecule is

$$\varepsilon = kT^2\left(\frac{d\ln f}{dT}\right)_V = \tfrac{3}{2}kT + kT + \frac{hv}{e^{+hv/kT} - 1}$$

and per gram-mole is

$$E = N_0\varepsilon = RT\left[\frac{5}{2} + \left(\frac{hv/kT}{e^{+hv/kT} - 1}\right)\right] \qquad \text{IX.59}$$

On differentiating with respect to temperature, the heat capacity at constant volume is found to be

$$C_V = R\left[\frac{5}{2} + \left(\frac{hv}{2kT}\operatorname{cosech}\frac{hv}{2kT}\right)^2\right] \qquad \text{IX.60}$$

On adding R, and making use of the characteristic temperature,

$$\theta = \frac{hv}{k} = 4.799 \times 10^{-11} \times v \qquad \text{IX.61}$$

219

we see that

$$C_P = R\left[\frac{7}{2} + \left(\frac{\theta}{2T}\,\text{cosech}\,\frac{\theta}{2T}\right)^2\right] \qquad \text{IX.62}$$

By subtracting $\frac{7}{2}R$ from the total heat capacity, we obtain the vibrational contribution, which is seen to be, with the appropriate value of θ, one third of the heat capacity of a monatomic solid (equation III.19). Eucken (1932) found the observed values of C_{vibr} of chlorine between 243°K and 452°K to be in satisfactory agreement with the second term in equation IX.60, with $\theta = 810$°K. This value corresponds to $v = 1\cdot693 \times 10^{13}$ sec^{-1} (cf. Table X.2).

2. *Entropy.* Because of the assumed independence of the three components of the partition function, we find independent contributions to the total entropy, i.e.

$$S = S_{\text{trans}} + S_{\text{rot}} + S_{\text{vibr}} \qquad \text{IX.63}$$

On using the general relationship between S and f, we obtain the result

$$\frac{S}{R} = \ln\left\{\frac{g[2\pi(m_A + m_C)kT]^{3/2}}{h^3}\frac{kT}{P}\right\} + \frac{5}{2}$$

$$+ \ln\left(\frac{8\pi^2 IkT}{\sigma h^2}\right) + 1$$

$$- \ln\left(1 - e^{-hv/kT}\right) + \frac{hv}{kT}(e^{+hv/kT} - 1)^{-1} \qquad \text{IX.64}$$

When hv/kT is small, the vibrational entropy becomes

$$S_{\text{vibr}} = R\left[1 + \ln\left(\frac{kT}{hv}\right)\right] \qquad \text{IX.65}$$

The specific constants for the nitrogen molecule are $g = 1$, $(m_A + m_C) = 4\cdot624 \times 10^{-23}$ g, $I = 13\cdot81 \times 10^{-40}$ g-cm^2, $\sigma = 2$ and $v/c = 2\,359\cdot61$ cm^{-1}. Then, at a pressure of one atmosphere and a temperature of 298·16°K, we find

$$S = 35\cdot95 + 9\cdot84 + 0\cdot000309 = 45\cdot79 \text{ cal/mole-deg.}$$

The vibrational contribution to the entropy is seen to be, in this instance, negligible in comparison with the other contributions.

220

3. *Free energy*. The calculation of the Gibbs free energy of diatomic molecules in the gaseous state presents no features which are not dealt with in the calculation of the entropy. G, for a system of N diatomic molecules of mass m, at temperature T, behaving like rigid rotators with moment of inertia I and like harmonic oscillators with frequency v is, according to equations (VI.96 and (VIII.51)

$$G = -NkT \ln\left\{\frac{g(2\pi mkT)^{3/2}}{h^3}\frac{kT}{P}\frac{8\pi^2 IkT}{\sigma h^2}(1-e^{-hv/kT})^{-1}\right\} \qquad \text{IX.66}$$

If we apply this equation to bromine vapour at the standard pressure and temperature, using the constants of Table x.2, we find that $-(G^0/RT) = 25\cdot5994$, so that $G^0_{298\cdot16}$ is $-15\,162\cdot4$ calories per mole. Here is an example of an energy which can be calculated with greater precision than it has been measured.

The present method of calculation makes use of the effective molecular partition function, f, and the general relationship for ideal gases to give the Gibbs free energy

$$G = -NkT \ln(f/e) \qquad \text{IX.67}$$

without including the residual energy. The complete molecular partition function is greater by the factor $e^{-(1/2)hv/kT}$, and the complete free energy by the amount $N\frac{1}{2}(hv/kT)$, or E_0. In conformity with the convention introduced by Giauque, we therefore re-label the effective free energy as

$$G-E_0 = -NkT \ln(f/e) \qquad \text{IX.68}$$

After inserting numerical constants into equation IX.66, it may be written in the form

$$-\frac{G-E_0}{T} = R\ln g + \tfrac{3}{2}R\ln M + \tfrac{7}{2}R\ln T - R\ln P + R\ln(10^{40}I/\sigma)$$

$$- R\ln(1-e^{-hv/kT}) - 14\cdot628 \qquad \text{IX.69}$$

where G is given in calories per mole, M is the molar weight (oxygen $= 32$), T is the absolute temperature, P is the pressure in atmospheres, and $R = 1\cdot9872$ cal/mole-deg. Although this equation, like others in this section, is an over-simplification, it yields values of the free energy only slightly different from those which take account of the fact, revealed spectroscopically, that the rotational and vibrational

221

motions influence each other. Thus, for example, for carbon monoxide at $1\,000°K$, the accurate value of $-(G^0 - E_0)/T$ is $48\cdot882$ cal/mole-deg, (Gordon and Barnes, 1933), while that given by equation IX.66 is $48\cdot893$.

The statistical evaluation of some properties of gaseous triatomic systems

We shall again assume that the rotational motions are classical, the vibrational motions harmonic, and that they do not influence each other. Since the linear molecule has only one moment of inertia and two degrees of freedom of rotation, and since the bending motion is doubly degenerate, we have

$$f = \frac{g[2\pi(m_1 + m_2 + m_3)kT]^{3/2} \, Ve}{h^3 N} \frac{8\pi^2 I kT}{\sigma h^2}$$

$$\times (1 - e^{-hv_1/kT})^{-1}(1 - e^{-hv_2/kT})^{-2}(1 - e^{-hv_3/kT})^{-1} \quad \text{IX.70}$$

The non-linear molecule has three moments of inertia, and three degrees of freedom of rotation; hence

$$f = \frac{g[2\pi(m_1 + m_2 + m_3)kT]^{3/2} \, Ve}{h^3 N} \frac{\pi^{1/2}(8\pi^2 kT)^{3/2}(I_A I_B I_C)^{1/2}}{\sigma h^3}$$

$$\times (1 - e^{-hv_1/kT})^{-1}(1 - e^{-hv_2/kT})^{-1}(1 - e^{-hv_3/kT})^{-1} \quad \text{IX.71}$$

The symmetry factor, σ, is unity for asymmetric molecules, whether linear or angular, and 2 for symmetrical molecules, linear or angular. We shall now use these expressions, in conjunction with the data of Table X.3, to calculate the entropy and the free energy of gaseous systems under standard conditions of pressure and temperature, taking g to be unity.

Standard entropies

1. *Linear symmetrical molecules. Example, $S = C = S$.* From the general relation between entropy and partition function, we have, since the various motions are assumed to be mutually independent,

$$S = S_{\text{trans}} + S_{\text{rot}} + S_{\text{vibr}}$$

Because the symmetry factor is now 2, and the system obeys the ideal gas laws, we have

$$S = Nk\left\{\ln\frac{[2\pi(m_1+m_2+m_3)kT]^{3/2}}{h^3}\frac{kT}{P}+\frac{5}{2}\right\}$$

$$+Nk\left\{\ln\frac{4\pi^2IkT}{h^2}+1\right\}$$

$$+Nk\sum_{i=1}^{4}\left\{\frac{kv_i}{kT}\left(\frac{e^{-hv_i/kT}}{1-e^{-hv_i/kT}}\right)-\ln(1-e^{-hv_i/kT})\right\} \qquad \text{IX.72}$$

With $v_1 = 655 \cdot 5$ cm^{-1}, $v_2 = 396 \cdot 8$ (double weight) and $v_3 = 1{,}532$, all of which are only slightly different from the figures listed in Table x.3, $(S^0_{298 \cdot 16})_{vibr}$ consists of the respective contributions $0 \cdot 441$, $2 \cdot 167$ and $0 \cdot 016$. Hence $(S^0_{298 \cdot 16})_{vibr} = 2 \cdot 624$, most of which is due to the degeneracy and weakness of the bending frequency. S^0_{rot} and S^0_{trans} at the same temperature are calculated as $15 \cdot 725$ and $39 \cdot 255$; hence the total molar entropy in the standard gaseous state is estimated as $57 \cdot 60$.

2. *Angular symmetrical molecules. Example, H—O—H.* We must now use equation IX.70, with $\sigma = 2$. From the data of Table x.3, we then find the standard entropy of water vapour to be

$$S^0_{298 \cdot 16} = 34 \cdot 61 + 10 \cdot 48 + 0 = 45 \cdot 09 \text{ cal/mole-deg.}$$

The vibrational contribution to the entropy is negligible.

3. *Linear asymmetrical molecules, Example $N \equiv N = O$.* The infrared spectrum of this gas shows it to have only one moment of inertia. It is, therefore, a linear molecule, and we employ equation IX.70 with $\sigma = 1$. Using the moment of inertia $I = 66 \cdot 0 \times 10^{40}$ g-cm^2 given by Barker (1932), the contributions to the standard molar entropy of the gas at the boiling point of the liquid are found to be

$$S^0_{184 \cdot 59^\circ} = S_{trans} + S_{rot} + S_{vibr}$$

$$= 34 \cdot 91 + 13 \cdot 38 + 0 \cdot 232$$

$$= 48 \cdot 522 \text{ cal/mole-deg.}$$

Standard free energies

As with diatomic molecules, the thermodynamic potential which counts is the effective value obtained from the partition function involving the total internal energy minus the residual energy. This quantity is obtained directly for ideal gases from the relation

$$G_{\text{effective}} = (G_{\text{total}} - E_0) = -NkT \ln \frac{f}{e} \qquad \text{IX.68}$$

where f is the effective partition function which we have consistently used. The general equation for the Gibbs free energy of a system of triatomic molecules which behave like rigid three-dimensional rotators of moments I_A, I_B and I_C, and which vibrate in such a way that the oscillatory motion may be analysed into three simple harmonic vibrations, is thus

$$-\left(\frac{G - E_0}{T}\right)$$
$$= Nk \ln \left\{ \frac{(2\pi mkT)^{3/2}}{h^3} \frac{kT}{P} \frac{\pi^{1/2}(I_A I_B I_C)^{1/2}(8\pi^2 kT)^{3/2}}{\sigma h^3} \sum_{i=1}^{3} (1 - e^{-hv_i/kT})^{-1} \right\}$$

$$\text{IX.73}$$

The effective free energy of 1 g-mole ($N = N_0$, hence $Nk = R$) in the standard state ($P = P^0$) is thus

$$-\left(\frac{G^0 - E_0^0}{T}\right) = R \ln \left\{ \frac{4\pi(m\bar{I})^{3/2}(2\pi kT)^4}{h^6 P^0 \sigma \Sigma (1 - e^{-hv/kT})} \right\} \qquad \text{IX.74}$$

where $\bar{I} = (I_A I_B I_C)^{1/3}$; and for a linear molecule,

$$-\left(\frac{G^0 - E_0^0}{T}\right) = R \ln \left\{ \frac{2\pi^{1/2} m^{3/2} I (2\pi kT)^{7/2}}{h^5 P^0 \sigma \Sigma (1 - e^{-hv/kT})} \right\} \qquad \text{IX.75}$$

where the bending frequency is doubly degenerate.

The statistical evaluation of some properties of polyatomic molecules in the gaseous phase

Let us consider a few gaseous systems composed of molecules containing more than three atoms each, but of such simple geometric construction that the foregoing treatment can, with but slight modification, be applied in the determination of their principal properties.

The partition function for linear symmetrical tetratomic molecules, such as acetylene H—C $\equiv$ C—H is

$$f = \frac{g(2\pi m k T)^{3/2} V e}{h^3 N} \frac{8\pi^2 I k T}{\sigma h^2} \prod_{i=1}^{7} (1 - e^{-h v_i/kT})^{-1} \qquad \text{IX.76}$$

where m is the molecular weight, $\sigma = 2$, and the vibrational component contains seven terms; two of the five vibratory motions are degenerate. It is to these weak bending motions that acetylene owes many of its properties, e.g. a molar heat capacity at constant volume which is 8·4 calories per degree at 273°K, instead of the 4·968 expected of a rigid molecule.

The molar entropy of gaseous acetylene at atmospheric pressure is found directly by means of the usual equations:

$$S^0_{\text{trans}} = R[\tfrac{3}{2} \ln M + \tfrac{5}{2} \ln T] - 2·315 \qquad \text{IX.48}$$

$$S^0_{\text{rot}} = R \left[\ln \left(\frac{8\pi^2 I k T}{\sigma h^2} \right) + 1 \right] = R \ln (IT/\sigma) + 177·672$$

and

$$S^0_{\text{vibr}}/R = - \sum_{i=1}^{7} \ln (1 - e^{-h v_i/kT}) + \sum_{i=1}^{7} \left(\frac{h v_i}{kT} \right) (e^{+h v_i/kT} - 1)^{-1}$$

Two of the five fundamental vibration frequencies are doubly degenerate. From the spectroscopic constants given by Herzberg (1945), we find

$$S^0_{298·16} = S^0_{\text{trans}} + S_{\text{rot}} - S_{\text{vibr}}$$
$$= 35·714 + 10·905 + 1·423 = 48·042$$

The partition function for pentatomic molecules of the symmetrical top type, such as methyl bromide, CH_3Br, bromoform, $CHBr_3$, and the thiosulphate ion $[SO_3S]^{--}$ is

$$f = \frac{(2\pi m k T)^{3/2} V e}{h^3 N} \frac{1}{\pi \sigma} \left[\frac{8\pi^3 (I_x I_y I_z)^{1/3} k T}{h^2} \right]^{3/2} \prod_{i=1}^{9} (1 - e^{-h v_i/kT})^{-1} \qquad \text{IX.77}$$

where I_x, I_y and I_z are the moments of inertia for rotations about the corresponding axes. The symmetry number is obviously 3. Of the nine vibrational contributions, three come from non-degenerate vibrations, and six from three pairs of double degenerate vibrations.

For methyl bromide at 298·16°K, and at atmospheric pressure, we find

$$S_{\text{trans}} = \tfrac{3}{2}R \ln M + \tfrac{5}{2}R \ln T - R \ln P(\text{atm.}) - 2\cdot315 \qquad = 39\cdot564$$

$$S_{\text{rot}} = \tfrac{1}{2}R \ln (I_x I_y I_z) + \tfrac{3}{2}R \ln T - R \ln 3 + 267\cdot645 \qquad = 18\cdot442$$

$$S_{\text{vibr}} = R \sum_{i=1}^{9} [(h\nu_i/kT)(e^{+h\nu_i/kT} - 1)^{-1} - \ln(1 - e^{-h\nu_i/kT})] = \;\; 0\cdot720$$

$$58\cdot726$$

Estimates for other pentatomic systems of this type have been calculated by Gelles and Pitzer (1953).

The molecular partition function of the benzene molecule in the ideal gaseous state is

$$f = \frac{(2\pi mkT)^{3/2}kTe}{h^3 P} \; \frac{\pi^{1/2}(8\pi^2 kT)^{3/2}(I_x I_y I_z)^{1/2}}{\sigma h^3} \prod_{i=1}^{30} (1 - e^{-h\nu_i/kT})^{-1} \qquad \text{IX.78}$$

where I_x is the moment of inertia about the x axis (Fig. IX.4). This is

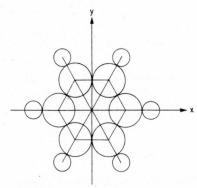

Fig. IX.4 *The benzene molecule*

equal to I_y and is $\tfrac{1}{2}I_z = 147\cdot63 \times 10^{-40}$ g-cm². The symmetry number, σ, is 12, because the molecule can be rotated into six positions in the plane of the paper without losing its identity, and because it can, when turned upside-down, similarly occupy six indistinguishable configurations. Of the thirty vibrational components of the partition function, ten relate to non-degenerate frequencies, and twenty to ten pairs of doubly degenerate motions. Herzberg's frequencies, and

226

the entropy contributions calculated from them are given in Table IX.5.

The three contributions to the entropy at 298·16°K are given by the equations:

$$S_{trans} = R[\tfrac{3}{2} \ln M + \tfrac{5}{2} \ln T - \ln P(\text{atm})] - 2.315 = 38·99$$

where M is the molar weight;

$$S_{rot} = R[\tfrac{3}{2} \ln T + \tfrac{1}{2} \ln (I_x I_y I_z) - \ln \sigma] + 267·645 = 20·77$$

where σ is 12; and,

$$S_{vibr} = R \sum_{i=1}^{30} [x_i(e^{x_i} - 1)^{-1} - \ln (1 - e^{-x_i})] = 4·77$$

Here x_i stands for $h\nu_i/kT$. The calculated molar entropy of benzene in the standard gaseous state is thus 64·53 cal/mole-deg (Lord and Andrews, 1937).

Table IX.5 *Vibrational contributions to the entropy of benzene at 298·16°K*

	Non-degenerate vibrations			Doubly degenerate vibrations	
Label	ω (cm^{-1})	S (cals/mole-degree)	Label	ω (cm^{-1})	S (cals/mole-degree)
1	3 062	0·00001	11	849	0·34738
2	992	0·09949	12	3 045	0·00002
3	1 190	0·04412	13	1 485	0·02584
4	671	0·34634	14	1 037	0·16488
5	3 063	0·00001	15	3 047	0·00002
6	1 008	0·09232	16	1 596	0·01611
7	1 520	0·01094	17	1 178	0·09246
8	538	0·57435	18	606	0·88848
9	1 854	0·00321	19	1 160	0·09974
10	1 145	0·05314	20	404	1·90900
	$\Sigma S = 1·22393$			$\Sigma S = 3·54393$	

A molecule containing N atoms is capable of $3N$ modes of motion, which may be resolved into the three modes of motion of the molecule

227

in space, its three modes of rotation about the centre of gravity, and the remaining $3N-6$ modes of internal motions. If the latter correspond to harmonic vibrations, the molecular partition function becomes

$$f = g\frac{(2\pi mkT)^{3/2}Ve}{h^3N}\frac{\pi^{1/2}(8\pi^2kT)^{3/2}(I_AI_BI_C)^{1/2}}{\sigma h^3}\sum_{i=1}^{3N-6}(1-e^{-h\nu_i/kT})\quad\text{IX.79}$$

and it becomes possible, in principle, to calculate the properties of gaseous systems composed of complicated polyatomic molecules. Seldom, however, can the internal motions be so simply resolved, for some of them are hindered motions, resembling harmonic oscillators at low temperatures and free rotators at high temperatures, and computations become difficult.

The calorimetric determination of the heat content, entropy and free energy of gaseous systems

The thermal method of obtaining the properties of gaseous systems, depends entirely on experimental results, codified according to the laws of thermodynamics, and can be applied to systems of any degree of complexity. We have seen in Chapter VII how these properties can be measured for solids. A knowledge of the saturation pressure of the vapour in equilibrium with the solid at various temperatures is all that is required to provide information on the molar properties of the gases in the reference state of unit pressure. From the first law of thermodynamics, we have for the molar heat content

$$H(\text{sat vap}) = H(\text{crystal})+L_{\text{sub}}$$

where L_{sub} is the molar heat of sublimation. From the thermodynamic condition for equilibrium between two phases of a pure substance, we have

$$G(\text{sat vap}) = G(\text{crystal})$$

Provided the vapour obeys the ideal gas laws, we can write

$$G^\circ = G(\text{sat vap})+RT\ln(p^\circ/p_{\text{sat}})$$

where G° is the molar free energy of the vapour at a pressure p°. The reference state is taken to be that of the vapour at unit pressure; hence

$$G^\circ = G(\text{sat vap})-RT\ln p_{\text{sat}}$$

$$= G(\text{crystal})-RT\ln p_{\text{sat}}$$

On differentiating each term in this equation with respect to T, and recalling that $S = -(dG/dT)$, we see that

$$S° = S(\text{crystal}) + R \ln p_{\text{sat}} + RT(d \ln p_{\text{sat}}/dT)$$

According to the Clausius–Clapeyron equation, the last term is L_{sub}/T. Hence

$$S° = S(\text{crystal}) + L_{\text{sub}}/T + R \ln p_{\text{sat}}$$

The same result is obtained from the expressions derived for H and G, since $TS = H - G$. As an example of the application of this equation, we shall consider magnesium at 298·16°K, when $S(\text{crystal}) = 7·76$ cal/mole-deg, $L_{\text{sub}} = 35\,655$ cal/mole and p_{sat}, extrapolated from data

Table IX.6 *The calorimetric determination of the standard molar entropy*

(i) Nitrogen, N_2 Stage	ΔS (cal/g-mol-deg)
0–10° ($\theta = 68°$)	0·458
10–35·61 (graph of C_P for solid phase I)	6·034
Transition from solid phase I to solid phase II; absorption of latent heat 54·71 cal at 35·61 : 54·71/35·61	1·536
35·61–63·14 (graph of C_P for solid phase II)	5·589
Fusion: 172·3/63·14	2·729
63·14–77·32 (graph of C_P for liquid)	2·728
Vaporisation: 1332·9/77·32	17·239
Correction for gas imperfection	0·22
Total observed entropy of ideal gas at its boiling-point	36·53
77·32–298·1 (graph of C_P for gas)	9·37
Observed value of molar entropy in standard state	45·90
(ii) Water, H_2O	
0–10°K ($\theta = 192°$)	0·022
10–273·1; C_P curve for ice	9·081
Fusion at 273·1; 1435·7/273·1	5·257
273·1–298·1; C_P curve for liquid	1·580
Vaporisation at 298·1; 10 499/298·1	35·220
Compression to 760 mm; $R \ln 2·3756/760$	−6·886
Correction for gas imperfection	0·002
Observed value of molar entropy in standard state	44·28 ± 0·05

obtained at high temperatures, is $7 \cdot 18 \times 10^{-21}$ atm. The standard molar entropy of magnesium vapour is consequently

$$S = 7 \cdot 76 + 119 \cdot 65 - 92 \cdot 13 = 35 \cdot 29 \text{ cal/mole-deg}$$

Two further instances, due to Giauque and his collaborators (1933, 1936), are given in Table IX.6.

Table IX.7 *The standard molar entropies of certain gases, other than monatomic, in calories/mole-degree*

Element or Compound	g	σ	$S^0_{298 \cdot 16}$	
			Thermal	Spectroscopic
H_2	1	2	31·33	31·23
N_2	1	2	45·90	45·79
O_2	3	2	49·1	49·03
Cl_2	1	2	52·8	53·31
Br_2	1	2	59·5	58·68
I_2	1	2	63·1	62·29
HCl	1	1	44·5	44·64
HBr	1	1	47·6	47·53
HI	1	1	49·7	49·36
NO	2	1	49·64	50·43
CO	1	1	46·22	47·33
CO_2	1	2	51·11	51·07
CS_2	1	2	57·5±0·5	57·60
COS	1	1	55·27	55·37
N_2O	1	1	51·44	52·581
H_2O	1	2	44·28	45·101
D_2O	1	2	46·69	47·46
H_2S	1	2	51·74	51·905
HCN	1	1	47·92	48·23
SO_2	1	2	59·24	59·18
CH_4	1	12	44·49±0·10	44·536
C_6H_6	1	12	64·46±0·12	64·531

A comparison of standard entropies of gases obtained in two ways

The satisfactory agreement, shown in Table IX.7, between standard gaseous entropies obtained, on the one hand, by the statistical treatment of spectroscopic constants and, on the other hand, by the thermodynamic treatment of thermal data establishes the validity of the third law of thermodynamics. There are, however, a few apparent discrepancies. The thermal value of $S°$ for carbon monoxide, for example, exceeds the spectroscopic estimate by $1·11$ cal/mole-deg. This lies so near to $R \ln 2 (= 1·376)$ that Clayton and Giauque (1932— suggested that the true symmetry number of this molecule is 2, and not 1, as if the crystal lattice were unable to distinguish the carbon end of the molecule from the oxygen end. Expressed in another way, we infer that, for the purpose of building the crystal, a molecule of carbon monoxide lying in one direction is as effective as one lying in the opposite direction. This interpretation explains the apparent anomaly, and makes $S°$ for CO experimentally indistinguishable from $S°$ for nitrogen, which has the same molar weight and electronic configuration. The same interpretation is now accepted for the apparent disparity found with nitrous oxide, which is isoelectronic with carbon dioxide. Somewhat similar considerations have been suggested by Pauling to explain the difference of $0·82$ cal/mole-deg between the two values of $S°$ derived for the water molecule. If ice, at the lowest temperature attainable, is not completely ordered, but allows the hydrogen bridges a completely random orientation, its entropy at the absolute zero of temperature would not be zero, but $R \ln \frac{3}{2} = 0·806$, which is numerically satisfactory.

X Molecular structure

There are many methods for determining molecular structure, by which is meant the spatial arrangement of atoms in a molecule, the average values of the distances apart of neighbouring atoms, the angles of inclination of the bonds joining one atom to two others, and the distribution of electricity. Internuclear distances, angles of inclination between bonds and the density of electricity fluctuate about their mean values, and it is essential to know the frequency with which these oscillations take place. We shall begin this brief survey by considering the simplest example.

The determination of internuclear distances in diatomic molecules

The basic structural constant of a diatomic molecule is the equilibrium distance apart, r_e, of the nuclei of the two atoms, which, as we have seen, is related as follows to the moment of inertia, I, of the molecule and the atomic masses, m_A and m_M:

$$I = \left(\frac{m_A m_B}{m_A + m_B}\right) r_e^2 \qquad \text{II.40}$$

When the nuclei remain at a fixed distance apart, the only internal energy of the molecule is the kinetic energy due to its rotation, which, according to wave-mechanical theory is given in terms of an integer, J, and Planck's constant, h:

$$\varepsilon_J = \frac{J(J+1)h^2}{8\pi^2 I}; \qquad J = 0, 1, 2, \ldots \qquad \text{IV.44}$$

The quantum of radiation absorbed when the molecule is raised from the energy state characterised by J to that characterised by $J+1$ is given by Bohr's frequency relationship:

$$hv = \varepsilon_{J+1} - \varepsilon_J \qquad \text{III.35}$$

The wave number, ω, of the radiation absorbed is v/c; hence

$$\omega = (J+1)\frac{h}{4\pi^2 Ic} \qquad \text{x.1}$$

Transitions between systems performing simple harmonic motions, of which free rotation is an example, occur only with unit change in the quantum number. The absorption spectrum should therefore consist of a number of lines with wave numbers which are integral multiples of the fundamental wave number $B = h/4\pi^2 Ic$, as first deduced by Bjerrum (1911). The value of B obtained from the infra-red spectrum of gaseous hydrogen chloride, for example, is 20.793 cm^{-1}, from which I is found to be 2.6629×10^{-40} g cm^2. It follows that r lies between 1.2840×10^{-8} and 1.2831×10^{-8} cm, depending on the proportion of the isotopes Cl^{35} and Cl^{37} present in the ordinary gas. Moments of inertia and internuclear distances determined in this way for some diatomic molecules are given in Table x.1. In homo-nuclear diatomic molecules formed from elements of the first period, r decreases as the valence increases. In heteronuclear molecules, r may be equal to, greater than or less than $\frac{1}{2}(r_1 + r_2)$, as instanced by the respective data cited for NO, HF and HI.

A more satisfactory expression than equation IV.44 for the rotational energy of a diatomic molecule is

$$\varepsilon_J = J(J+1)\frac{h^2}{8\pi^2 I} - \alpha hc[J(J+1)]^2 \qquad \text{x.2}$$

where α is a semi-empirical constant. The wave numbers of the absorption lines now become

$$\omega = \frac{h}{4\pi^2 Ic}(J+1) - 8\alpha(J+1)^3 \qquad \text{x.3}$$

agreeing with the empirical equations of Czerny, who with HCl, for example found the series of absorption lines to be reproduced by the equation

$$\omega = 20.793M - 0.00163M^3; \qquad M = 1, 2, 3, \ldots \qquad \text{x.4}$$

The term involving M^3 or $(J+1)^3$ is relatively small. Even omitting it, we see that the energy spacing between neighbouring quantum levels increases with the quantum number (Fig. x.1). This, as we shall now see, contrasts with the spacing and quantum number relationship in the vibrational absorption spectrum of diatomic molecules.

233

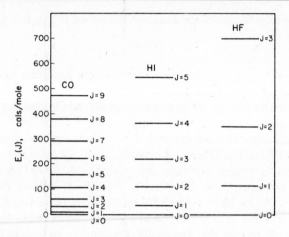

Fig. x.1 *Some of the lower rotation energy levels of the molecules carbon monoxide, hydrogen iodide and hydrogen fluoride*

Table x.1 *Moments of inertia and internuclear distances of certain diatomic molecules*

Molecule	$I \times 10^{40}$ (g cm^2)	$r_e \times 10^8$ (cm)
H_2	0·4598	0·7415
D_2	0·9185	0·7414
N_2	14·005	1·0976
O_2	19·360	1·2074
F_2	32·80	1·442
I_2	749·06	2·6666
HF	1·338	0·9175
HI	4·289	1·608
CO	14·490	1·1282
NO	16·420	1·1508

The spectroscopic determination of the vibration frequency and dissociation energy of diatomic molecules

If the vibration of the nuclei in a diatomic molecule were strictly harmonic, the allowed energy levels would be given in terms of the quantum number, v, by the equation $\varepsilon_v = (v + \frac{1}{2})h\nu_e$, according to which the only line in the absorption spectrum would be at a frequency of radiation equal to the vibration frequency, ν_e, of the nuclei. Moreover, since, in harmonic motion the restoring force is directly proportional to the displacement of the particles from their position of minimum energy, there would be no dissociation into atoms. Both these consequences are contrary to the facts. There are numerous bands of lines in the absorption spectrum of each diatomic molecule, with head positions determined by transitions between various vibrational energy levels, and the many absorption lines in each band determined by transitions between rotational energy levels. Moreover, there is also a limit to the amount of energy which a molecule can absorb, because it will eventually break up. To account for these facts, a more reasonable expression for the allowed vibrational energy levels is the following:

$$\varepsilon_v = h\nu_e(v+\tfrac{1}{2}) - xh\nu_e(v+\tfrac{1}{2})^2 \qquad \text{x.5}$$

where x, the anharmonicity constant is relatively small. Bohr's frequency relationship now gives the following frequencies of the absorption lines due to transitions between the levels denoted by quantum numbers v'' and v':

$$\nu_{v'' \to v'} = \nu_e(v'-v'')[1-x(v'+v''+1)] \qquad \text{x.6}$$

Thus, for example, transitions from the ground state to the first and second vibrational levels account for the following absorption lines:

$$\nu_{0 \to 1} = \nu_e(1-2x)$$

and

$$\nu_{0 \to 2} = 2\nu_e(1-3x) \qquad \text{x.7}$$

Because, according to Boltzmann's distribution law, low energy levels are the most populated, the first of these expressions corresponds to the head of the intensest band in the spectrum, and the second to the next most intense. The experimental data for hydrogen chloride are

$$\nu/c = 2885 \cdot 88 + 20 \cdot 562M - 0 \cdot 3030M^2 - 0 \cdot 0020M^3,$$
$$\nu/c = 5667 \cdot 96 + 20 \cdot 291M - 0 \cdot 6028M^2 - 0 \cdot 0025M^3, \qquad \text{x.8}$$

where M is $1, 2, 3, \ldots$ for the R branch lines and $-1, -2, -3, \ldots$ for the P branch lines. By equating the leading terms in these empirical equations with the theoretical expression, we find that x is $1 \cdot 735 \times 10^{-2}$

235

and that v_e is $8\cdot996 \times 10^{13}$ sec^{-1}. Some results similarly obtained for other molecules are given in Table x.2 (Hertzfeld, 1950).

We shall deal with only one of the many spectroscopic methods of measuring the energy of dissociation of heteronuclear diatomic molecules. The energy absorbed when the vibrational quantum number is raised from v to $v+1$ is given by equation x.6 as

$$\Delta\varepsilon_{v \to v+1} = hv_e[1 - 2x(v+1)] \qquad \text{x.9}$$

The energy absorbed in the transition from $v-1$ to v is

$$\Delta\varepsilon_{v-1 \to v} = hv_e[1 - 2xv] \qquad \text{x.10}$$

We may therefore regard the increment

$$\Delta\varepsilon_v = hv_e[1 - 2x(v+\tfrac{1}{2})] \qquad \text{x.11}$$

as the average difference in the energies of two neighbouring vibrational levels. Absorption lines due to such transitions thus have the frequencies

$$v = v_e[1 - 2x(v+\tfrac{1}{2})] \qquad \text{x.12}$$

which are seen to diminish as the quantum number increases, and to vanish when v reaches a limiting value given by the equation

$$v_{\text{lim}} + \tfrac{1}{2} = \frac{1}{2x} \qquad \text{x.13}$$

The limiting vibrational energy which the molecule can have, that is, its dissociation energy, is found by substituting this value of v in equation x.5. It is

$$\varepsilon_{\text{lim}} = hv_e/4x = D_e \qquad \text{x.14}$$

Equation x.5 may consequently be written in the form

$$\varepsilon_v = hv_e(v+\tfrac{1}{2}) - \frac{(hv_e)^2}{4D}(v+\tfrac{1}{2})^2 \qquad \text{x.15}$$

as obtained by solving Schrödinger's equation (Chapter IV). Its application to hydrogen bromide is shown in Fig. x.2.

Analysis of the absorption spectra of homonuclear diatomic molecules shows that the energy which they absorb before dissociating into atoms exceeds the dissociation energy as measured by van't

236

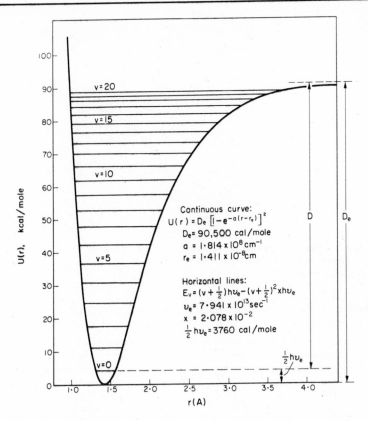

Fig. x.2 *The potential energy function and anharmonic vibrational energy levels of the hydrogen bromide molecule*

Hoff's isochore by an amount which coincides with the energy required by one of the atoms to rise from the ground to the first electronically excited state (Fig. x.3). Thus there is a sharp distinction between the thermal and photochemical decomposition of such molecules, which may be represented schematically as follows:

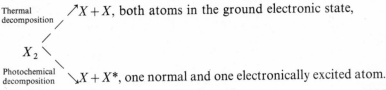

Thermal decomposition $\nearrow X + X$, both atoms in the ground electronic state,

X_2

Photochemical decomposition $\searrow X + X^*$, one normal and one electronically excited atom.

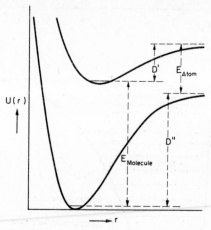

Fig. x.3 *Potential energy diagram representing the dissociation of a diatomic molecule from the ground state and from an excited state* (after Jevons, 1932)

Table x.2 *Interatomic vibration frequencies and energies of dissociation of certain diatomic molecules*

Molecule	ω_e (cm^{-1})	$r_e \times 10^8$ (cm)	D (kilocalories)
H_2	4 395·2$_4$	0·7415	103·19
HD	3 817·09	0·7413$_6$	103·99
D_2	3 118·4$_6$	0·7416$_1$	104·97
Li_2	351·43$_5$	2·672$_5$	23·7
Na_2	159·23	3·078$_6$	16·8
K_2	92·96	3·923	11·85
Hg_2	29·6	3·38	1·58
F_2	892·1	1·442	36·7
Cl_2	564·9	1·988	57·06
Br_2	323·2	2·283$_6$	45·43
I_2	214·57	2·666$_6$	35·539
HF	4 143·01	0·9175	134
HCl	2 989·74	1·2744	102·13
HBr	2 649·67	1·408	86·5$_4$
HI	2 309·5$_3$	1·608	70·5$_6$
KCl	280	2·6666	114·6
OH	3 735·21	0·9706	100·2
O_2	1 580·361	1·20739$_8$	117·10
CO	2 170·21	1·1281$_9$	254·0
N_2	2 359·61	1·0976	225

The limiting value of the molecular energy is given directly as $h\nu_{conv}$ where ν_{conv} is the frequency at which absorption becomes continuous. D'', the energy required to dissociate the molecule from its ground electronic state into two normal atoms is known from thermochemical sources: and the excitation energy of the atom is known from its atomic spectrum. In this way, potential energy curves may be computed for electronically excited molecules. The D values of Table x.2 refer to dissociation into atoms in the ground electronic state.

Rotational, vibrational and electronic energies have all to be considered, even in an elementary account of the simplest type of molecule. The relationship between them is illustrated in Fig. x.4, where the

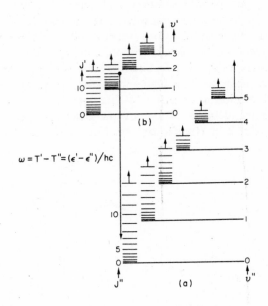

Fig. x.4 *Schematic representation of electronic, vibrational and rotatory energy levels* (after Jevons)

lowest horizontal line refers to the ground state of the molecule, which possesses only its residual energy, and the topmost horizontal line depicts an electronically excited molecule in its third vibrational and fourth rotational quantum state.

239

The spectroscopic determination of the moments of inertia and valence angles in triatomic molecules

Because each atom is capable of moving in three mutually perpendicular directions, a molecule containing n atoms is capable of $3n$ modes of motion. These are conveniently resolved into three modes of bulk translation of the molecule as a whole and $3n-3$ modes of internal motions, which are unaffected by the position of the molecule in space, and depend only on the relative motion of the atoms within the molecule. These again may be resolved into $3n-6$ internal vibrations and three rotational motions about the Cartesian axes passing through the centre of gravity of the molecule. When, however, the molecule is linear, it is capable of only two modes of rotation; consequently the number of modes of internal vibration is now $3n-5$. Applied to triatomic molecules, these principles tell us that each angular molecule has three vibrational and three rotational degrees of freedom. With linear triatomic molecules, however, there are only two modes of rotation, and four modes of internal vibration. This does not mean that four fundamental frequencies are to be found from its absorption spectrum. In fact, only three are detected, because two are identical. These are the wagging motions, denoted by the subscript 2 in Hund's diagram (Fig. x.5), and referred to as

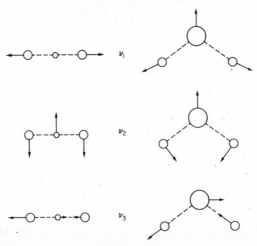

Fig. x.5 *Vibrations of the three-particle systems. The dotted line represents the valency bond, and the full line one of the directions of motion of the oscillating atom*

doubly degenerate. To formulate the dynamical problem, the molecule may be thought of as lying in the plane $z = 0$, with the internuclear distances and the valency angle as labelled in Fig. x.6.

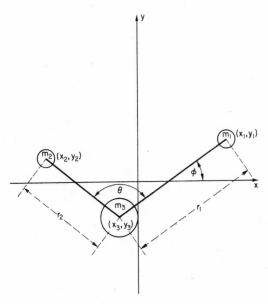

Fig. x.6 *Axes of reference for the triatomic molecule*

The moments of inertia are obtained, as usual, by taking moments about each axis in turn. The simplest example is that of a linear symmetric molecule, for which $m_1 = m_2 = m$, $\theta = \pi$, and $r_1 = r_2 = \frac{1}{2}R$, where R is the distance apart of the wing atoms. Then $I = \frac{1}{2}mR^2$, as with the homonuclear diatomic molecule. The simplest example of an angular molecule is again the symmetrical one, when $m_1 = m_2 = m$. The moments of inertia about the x and y axes are now

$$I_x = \left(\frac{2m_1 m_3}{2m_1 + m_3}\right) r^2 \cos^2\left(\frac{\theta}{2}\right) \qquad \text{x.16}$$

and

$$I_y = 2m_1 r^2 \sin^2\left(\frac{\theta}{2}\right) \qquad \text{x.17}$$

From the ratio of these two moments, the valency angle may be determined, since

$$\cot^2\left(\frac{\theta}{2}\right) = \left(1 + \frac{2m_1}{m_3}\right)\frac{I_x}{I_y} \qquad \text{x.18}$$

By eliminating the angle, the distance r may be found, since

$$r^2 = I_x\left(\frac{2m_1 + m_3}{2m_1 m_3}\right) + \frac{I_y}{2m_1} \qquad \text{x.19}$$

Both moments of inertia, and their sum ($I_z = I_x + I_y$) may be found from the magnitudes of the Bjerrum separations, B, of lines in the pure rotational spectrum or in the rotational fine structure of the vibrational spectrum. Thus, for example, with water vapour, the two lower values of I found (Eucken, 1920) are 0.996×10^{-40} and 1.908×10^{-40} g-cm^2, but it was not then certain which was I_x and which I_y. If we take them to be in this order, the valency angle θ becomes 105° 2′. If we take them the other way round, θ becomes 68° 30′. The latter is rejected because it would endow the water molecule with a much higher dipole moment than it possesses.

Table x.3 *Certain spectroscopically determined constants of triatomic molecules*

Molecule	Internuclear distance (Å)		Valency angle	Fundamental frequencies (cm^{-1})		
2, 3, 1	$r_{2,3}$	$r_{1,3}$		ν_1	ν_2	ν_3
O=C=O	1·163	1·163	180	1 286	667	2 349
S=C=S	1·554	1·554	180	660	397	1 523
H—O—H	0·96	0·96	105	3 652	1 595	3 756
D—O—D	0·96	0·96	105	2 666	1 179	2 784
H—S—H	1·345	1·345	97	2 611	1 290	2 684
F—O—F	1·36	1·36	104	830	490	1 110
Cl—O—Cl	1·71	1·71	105	680	330	973
O=S=O	1·46	1·46	122	1 152	524	1 361
O=N=O	1·20	1·20	114	1 320	648	1 621
O$_3$	1·29	1·29	127	1 037	710	1 740
O=C=S	1·161	1·560	180	859	527	2 079
N≡N≡O	1·126	1·191	180	1 285	589	2 224
H—C≡N	1·059	1·157	180	2 089	712	3 312

In order to solve the equations of the internal motions, it is assumed that small changes in r_1, r_2 and θ from their average values of r_1^0, r_2^0 and θ^0 are opposed by restoring forces varying linearly with respect to the displacements, so that the potential energy, V, of the displaced system is related as follows to that of the undisplaced system:

$$V = V^0 + \tfrac{1}{2}[k_1(r_1 - r_1^0)^2 + k_2(r_2 - r_2^0)^2 + \tfrac{1}{2}k_3(r_{1,0}^2 + r_{2,0}^2)(\theta - \theta^0)^2]$$

There result three equations giving the squares of the three frequencies in terms of the atomic masses, the restoring force constants, k, and the valency angle, θ. Comparison with the frequencies of lines in the absorption spectrum, which often appear in combinations such as $v_1 + v_2$ and $v_1 + 3v_3$, yield numerical results for the force constants and the valency angles (Table x.3).

The shapes of tetratomic molecules

The principal configurations of molecules containing four atoms are shown in Fig. x.7. The determination of these forms, and the magnitudes of the internuclear distances and valency angles, have not been established solely on measurements of moments of inertia, obtained from absorption spectra, but has made use of molecular polarity, as in the case of the water molecule. The effect of isotopic substitution and experimental heat capacities have also been used. One example of each of these supplementary evidences will now be described.

Types of tetratomic molecules

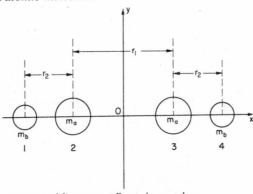

Fig. x.7a *The symmetrical linear type. Example, acetylene*

$$H—C\equiv C—H$$

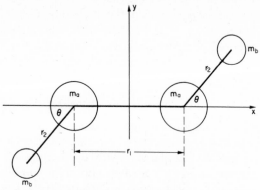

Fig. x.7b *The arm chair type. Example, possibly sulphur monochloride,*
Cl—S—S—Cl

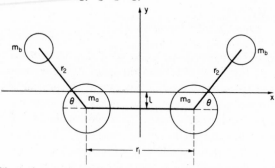

Fig. x.7c *The bath type. Example, when skewed, hydrogen peroxide,*
H—O—O—H

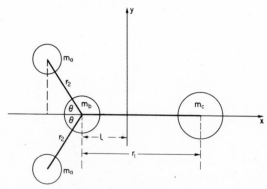

Fig. x.7d *The Y type. Example, formaldehyde*

$$\begin{matrix} H \\ H \end{matrix}\!\!\diagdown\!\!C = 0$$

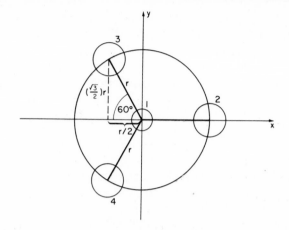

Fig. x.7e *The cart wheel type. Example, boron trifluoride,* BF_3

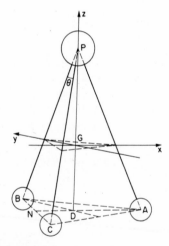

Fig. x.7f *The symmetrical pyramidal type. Example, ammonia,*
NH_3

There are only two modes of rotation of the acetylene molecule, because it is linear. Rotations about the two relevant axes involve the common moment of inertia

$$I_y = I_z = I = 2m_C(\tfrac{1}{2}r_1)^2 + 2m_H(\tfrac{1}{2}r_1 + r_2)^2$$
$$= \tfrac{1}{2}m_C r_1^2 + \tfrac{1}{2}m_H(r_1 + 2r_2)^2 \qquad \text{x.20}$$

where C and H denote carbon and hydrogen, and the r terms are as in Fig. x.7a. Measurement of a single Bjerrum separation is clearly insufficient to give the two internuclear distances. If, however, we replace hydrogen by deuterium, and assume the r values to be unaffected, they can both be evaluated, since

$$r_1^2 = \frac{2}{m_C}(2I_{C_2H_2} - I_{C_2D_2}) \quad \text{and} \quad r_2 = \left(\frac{I_{C_2D_2} - I_{C_2H_2}}{2m_H}\right)^{1/2} - \tfrac{1}{2}r_1. \quad \text{x.21}$$

In this way, r_1 is found to be $1{\cdot}203 \times 10^{-8}$ cm, and r_2 is $1{\cdot}060 \times 10^{-8}$ cm.

As an example of the supplementary guidance to be obtained from thermal data, we shall consider the phosphine molecule, PH_3, which has the structure of a regular pyramid, like the ammonia molecule. Denoting by r the distance between the phosphorus atom and any one of the hydrogen atoms, and by m and M the respective atomic weights of the hydrogen and phosphorus atoms, it can be shown that

$$r^2 = \left(\frac{1}{3m} + \frac{1}{M}\right)I_x + \frac{1}{2}\left(\frac{1}{3m} - \frac{1}{M}\right)I_z, \qquad \text{x.22}$$

from which r could be evaluated if both moments of inertia were known. Rotation about the z axis, however, does not affect the dipole moment of the molecule, and the separation B corresponding to I_z cannot therefore be found from the infra-red spectrum. Now the partition function for the symmetrical, pyramidal, tetratomic molecule is:

$$f = \frac{g[2\pi(3m+M)kT]^{3/2}Ve}{h^3N} \frac{\pi^{1/2}(8\pi^2kT)^{3/2}(I_xI_yI_z)^{1/2}}{\sigma h^3} \prod_{i=1}^{6}(1-e^{-h\nu_i/kT})^{-1}$$

$$\text{x.23}$$

The ground electronic state is a singlet state ($g = 1$), and the symmetry number, σ, is 3. We shall apply this equation to determine the molar entropy of gaseous phosphine at atmospheric pressure and at its boiling temperature ($185{\cdot}70°K$). Under these conditions, and for this particular molecule, each of the $h\nu/kT$ terms is so large that the vibrational motion makes no appreciable contribution to the entropy. On substituting numerical values for the constants, S, in calories per gram-mole degree becomes:

$$S = R[\tfrac{3}{2}\ln \overline{M} + 4\ln T + \tfrac{1}{2}\ln(I_xI_yI_z) - \ln \sigma] + 265{\cdot}305, \qquad \text{x.24}$$

where $\overline{M}$ is the molar weight ($O_2 = 32$).

Despite the existence of three crystalline phases of phosphine, Clusius and A. Frank (1936) were able to measure its specific heats and the latent heats of transition, fusion and vaporisation with such accuracy that the calorimetric entropy could be given as $46\cdot39\pm0\cdot10$. Combined with the spectroscopic value of $I_x = I_y = 6\cdot296\times10^{-40}$ g cm^2, this leads to a value of $8\cdot26\times10^{-40}$ for I_z, from which, by means of equation x.22, r can be found. The moment of inertia about the z axis is seen, from the diagram to be

$$I_z = 4mr^2 \sin^2(\theta/2), \qquad \text{x.25}$$

where θ is the valency angle. It is 118° in the phosphine molecule, but less (111°) in ammonia, and greater (118–123°) in the trihalides of phosphorus, arsenic and bismuth.

Molecular polarity

Molar polarisation is defined by an equation due to Clausius and Mosotti in terms of the dielectric constant, D, and the molar volume, V_m, and is related as follows to the molecular polarisability, α:

$$P = \frac{D-1}{D+2}V_m = \tfrac{4}{3}\pi N_0\alpha \qquad \text{x.26}$$

Molar refraction is defined in terms of the refractive index, n, and the optical polarisability, α_0;

$$R = \frac{n^2-1}{n^2+2}V_m = \tfrac{4}{3}\pi N_0\alpha_0 \qquad \text{x.27}$$

According to Maxwell's electromagnetic theory of light, $D = n^2$, and P should therefore equal R. Such is the case with systems of symmetrical molecules, like carbon dioxide, methane and benzene. For a given compound, moreover, P (or R) is independent of its physical state. In systems formed of molecules which are asymmetric, such as carbonyl sulphide, methyl chloride and chlorobenzene, P exceeds R, and the difference between them is attributed to what is known as orientational polarisation, which is now to be considered.

A charge e, separated by a distance l from a charge $-e$, is said to constitute a permanent electrical dipole, of moment μ, defined as $\mu = el$. Just as the potential energy of a magnet of magnetic moment, M, in a magnetic field of strength H and inclined at an angle θ to its direction is $-MH\cos\theta$, the potential energy of a dipole of moment

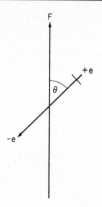

Fig. x.8 *Permanent dipole in a uniform electrical field*

μ in an electrical field of strength F is

$$V = -\mu F \cos \theta \qquad \text{x.28}$$

In the absence of any other influence, the dipole would occupy the position of minimum energy, which corresponds to $\theta = 0$. Thermal motion, however, affects its average position, and, on applying the Boltzmann law to a system of dipoles rotating in a uniform electrical field (equations II.39, II.44), the average potential energy is given directly by the equation

$$\overline{V} = \frac{\int e^{-V/kT} V . d \cos \theta}{\int e^{-V/kT} d \cos \theta} = \frac{\int e^{(\mu F/kT)\cos\theta}(-\mu F \cos \theta) \, d \cos \theta}{\int e^{(\mu F/kT)\cos\theta} d \cos \theta} \qquad \text{x.29}$$

Integrations are over all values of $\cos \theta$ from -1 to $+1$. If we denote $\cos \theta$ by x, and $\mu F/kT$ by a, we have

$$\overline{V} = \frac{-\mu F \displaystyle\int_{-1}^{+1} e^{ax} x \, dx}{\displaystyle\int_{-1}^{+1} e^{ax} \, dx}$$

The denominator, as shown in Appendix 1, is

$$\left[\frac{1}{a} e^{ax}\right]_{-1}^{+1} = \frac{1}{a}(e^a - e^{-a}) = \left(\frac{2}{a}\right) \sinh a$$

and the numerator is

$$-\mu F\left[\frac{e^{ax}}{a^2}(ax-1)\right]_{-1}^{+1} = \frac{-\mu F}{a^2}[a(e^a+e^{-a})-(e^a-e^{-a})]$$

$$= \frac{-\mu F}{a^2}.\,2[a\cosh a-\sinh a]$$

Hence

$$\bar{V} = -\mu F\left[\coth a-\left(\frac{1}{a}\right)\right] \qquad \text{x.30}$$

In strong fields, when a is large and $\coth a$ approximates to unity, $\bar{V} = -\mu F$, reminding us that thermal agitation has been unable to deflect the molecules from their position of minimum energy. When, however, μF is much smaller than kT, $\coth(\mu F/kT)-(kT/\mu F)$ may be expanded to give $\frac{1}{3}(\mu F/kT)-\frac{1}{45}(\mu F/kT)^3+\ldots$. Taking the first term only, we have

$$\bar{V} = -\frac{1}{3}\frac{(\mu F)^2}{kT} \qquad \text{x.31}$$

From equation x.28, we can also write

$$\bar{V} = -\mu F\,\overline{\cos\theta}$$

so that

$$\overline{\cos\theta} = \frac{1}{3}\frac{\mu F}{kT} \qquad \text{x.32}$$

But

$$\bar{\mu} = \overline{\mu\cos\theta} = \frac{1}{3}\frac{\mu^2 F}{kT}$$

and since polarisability is the moment induced in unit field,

$$\tilde{\alpha} = \frac{1}{3}\frac{\mu^2}{kT}$$

To this orientational polarisability must be added the optical polarisability, which, being a property of the electrons, is possessed by all types of atoms and molecules, whether symmetrical or asymmetrical. Then

$$\alpha = \alpha_0+\frac{1}{3}\frac{\mu^2}{kT} \qquad \text{x.33}$$

I

and

$$P = \frac{4}{3}\pi N_0 \left(\alpha_0 + \frac{1}{3}\frac{\mu^2}{kT}\right) \qquad \text{x.34}$$

The dipole moment, μ, may thus be found from the difference between the molar polarisation and the molar refraction, or, more accurately, by plotting the molar polarisation against $1/T$. (Langevin, 1905; Debye, 1929). The order of magnitude of the dipole moments (10^{-18} e.s.u.) is anticipated from the orders of magnitude of the electronic charge and the internuclear distance (Table x.1). Reasonable estimates of internuclear distances in the salt molecules are, in fact, obtained by dividing μ by the electronic charge, and exact values are found when allowance is made for the intrinsic repulsion of the electronic shells of the two ions and the moments induced by each in the other. These gaseous salt molecules clearly approximate to ion pairs, held by Coulombic forces or electrovalent bonds. It is seen from Table x.4 that homonuclear diatomic molecules, symmetrical linear triatomic molecules, symmetrical tetrahedral molecules

Table x.4 *Dipole moments*

Molecule	$\mu \times 10^{18}$ e.s.u.	Molecule	$\mu \times 10^{18}$ e.s.u.
N_2	0	CH_4	0
O_2	0	CH_3F	1·81
NO	0·07	CH_3Cl	1·87
CO	0·12	CH_3Br	1·80
HF	1·91	CH_3I	1·64
HCl	1·045	$CHCl_3$	1·07
HBr	0·802	C_6H_6	0
HI	0·386	C_6H_5F	1·45
KCl	8·01	C_6H_5Cl	1·55
KBr	9·12	C_6H_5Br	1·53
KI	9·33	C_6H_5I	1·31
OCO	0	$oC_6H_4(NO_2)_2$	6·0
SCS	0	$mC_6H_4(NO_2)_2$	3·8
OCS	0·65	$pC_6H_4(NO_2)_2$	0
HOH	1·83	$pC_6H_4(NH_2)_2$	1·50
OSO	1·67	$pC_6H_4(NO_2)(NH_2)$	6·5
NH_3	1·48	$pC_6H_4(NO_2)Cl$	2·5

and benzene have zero dipole moments. This does not mean that bonds such as $C{=}O$, $C{=}S$ and $C{-}H$ have zero moments. On account of molecular symmetry, bond moments cancel out one another's effects. There are, for example, four $C{-}H$ bonds in methane of 0·2 to $0·3 \times 10^{-18}$ e.s.u. each. If we denote this bond moment by μ_1, that of the molecule must be $\mu_1 + 3\mu_1 \cos \theta$, since the moment of one bond is opposed by the resolved components of the three other bonds in the direction of its axis. The fact that μ for the molecule is zero requires that $\cos \theta = -\frac{1}{3}$, or that $\theta = 109° 28'$, as previously established by organic chemistry. The six $C{-}H$ bonds in benzene have no components perpendicular to the plane of the ring, and in it cancel one another's influence.

Experiments give us the magnitude, but not the sign, of the dipole moments. Since, however, the hydrogen halides, HX, ionise to H^+ and X^-, it is fair to infer that the sign of their moments is $H \leftrightarrow X$, the crossed tail indicating the positive end. Thus, for example, if we accept $\mu = -0·25 \times 10^{-18}$ for the $C \leftarrow H$ bond, the dipole moment of the $C \leftrightarrow NO_2$ bond becomes $+3·73 \times 10^{-18}$. With these values of the bond moments (Smyth, 1937), we may consider the observed moments of the three di-nitrobenzenes (Fig. x.9). The dipole moment of *para*–dinitrobenzene is zero, indicating that the oxygen atoms in the NO_2 groups lie in the plane of the benzene ring. Vectorial addition of the bond moments in *meta*–dinitrobenzene lead us to expect the component along the x axis to be $3·73 + 0·25 - 3·73 \cos 60° = 2·11$, and along the y axis to be $3·73 \cos 30° = 3·23$, giving a total moment of $3·86$, which compares well with the observed value of $3·80$. In general, however, the simple vectorial addition of bond moments is not satisfactory. Using the same bond moments, μ for *ortho*–dinitrobenzene is calculated as $6·7$, which is 10 per cent too high (Table x.4), and μ for *para*–nitraniline ($6·5$) is not the sum of the μ's for nitrobenzene ($3·98$) and aniline ($1·54$). If simple vectorial addition were adequate, $\mu(CH_3X) - \mu(C_6H_5X)$ should be zero, instead of $0·32$ (Sutton, 1932), and μ for CH_3Cl should equal that for $CHCl_3$. As previously stated, several other factors, including intrinsic repulsion and mutual induction, must be included in a proper assessment.

It is to be observed that the moment of *para*–phenylene–diamine is not zero; the hydrogen atoms of the amino groups cannot, then, be in the plane of the benzene ring. Their positions, as calculated from the total moment recorded here are, however, average positions, which vary with the temperature.

251

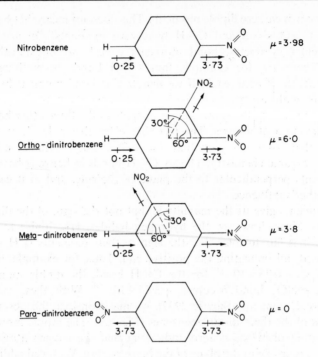

Fig. x.9 *Dipole moments, multiplied by 10^{18} e.s.u. of nitrobenzene and the dinitrobenzenes*

The structure of the water molecules

Attempts to construct on classical foundations an acceptable model of the water molecule have proved unavailing. Some of the properties requiring mutual reconciliation are the valency angle (105°), the distance apart of the oxygen and hydrogen nuclei (0·958 Å), the dipole moment ($1·834 \times 10^{18}$ e.s.u.), the polarisability ($1·444 \times 10^{24}$ cc) and the energy of complete separation into atoms (218·8 kilocalories per mole). The classical treatments implied that the molecule was planar, overlooking the possibility that, although the nuclei necessarily lie in one plane, the electrons may lie outside it.

Wave mechanics offers a more satisfactory account of the water molecule. It is known that when an oxygen atom ($1s^2\ 2s^2\ 2p^4$) unites with two hydrogen atoms ($1s^1$), two of the $2p$ electrons contribute with the $1s$ electrons of the hydrogen atoms to form two univalent bonds.

This leaves two non-participating $2p$ electrons. Verwey (1941) pointed out that the wave functions associated with these unpaired electrons "give rise to a concentration of negative electricity in two regions at right angles to the plane of the HOH nuclei. As a consequence of this effect, the water molecule itself would show a charge distribution somewhat resembling a tetrahedron, with two corners of positive and

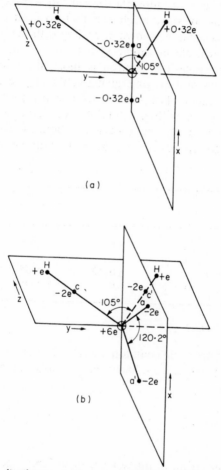

Fig. x.10 *Charge distributions in the water molecule, according to Rowlinson (A) and Pople (B)* (reproduced from Hirschfelder, Curtiss and Bird, *The Molecular Theory of Gases and Liquids*, Wiley, New York, 1954)

253

two of negative charge." A model of the water molecule based on this conclusion, and using fractional charges derived from its dipole moment (Fig. x.10a) has been given by Rowlinson (1951). Pople (1950), using the method of molecular orbitals, also concludes that the clouds of electricity due to the lone pair of electrons are concentrated on the side of the oxygen nucleus remote from the hydrogen atoms. Moreover, the orbitals of the $2s$ and $2p$ electrons hybridise, as in Pauling's treatment of methane, to endow the oxygen with tetrahedral symmetry. It is in the nature of wave mechanics that no fixed position can be ascribed to an electron. As shown in dealing with the hydrogen atom, however, it is possible in simple systems to calculate the position which, on an average, the electron is most likely to be found in. Different methods of averaging, giving conflicting results, have been used by Pople and Duncan (1953), who finally propose the point-charge model shown in Fig. x.10b. The coordinates of the charge, in Ångstrom units, are given in Table x.5. Both models have been so constructed as to reproduce the experimental dipole moment.

Table x.5

Charge	x	y	z	$\mu_2 \times 10^{18}$
$+e$ (protons)	0	± 0.764	0.586	$+5.63$
$+be$ (oxygen ion)	0	0	0	—
$-2e$ (bond electrons)	0	± 0.463	0.355	-6.83
$-2e$ (lone pairs)	± 0.275	0	-0.158	$+3.03$

Pentatomic molecules

Although there are some pentatomic molecules, such as vinyl cyanide, alumina and urea which are linear, bent or forked respectively,

those of greater chemical interest are of the top type. We shall consider only the symmetrical top (Fig. x.11), the base of which consists of three identical and equidistant atoms, a, and the apex of which is occupied by atom b. Within the pyramid thus formed lies atom c,

254

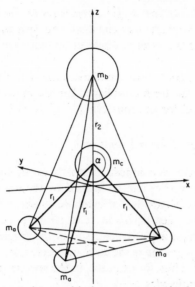

Fig. x.11 *The symmetrical top model of a pentatomic molecule*

at the apex of the smaller tetrahedron. From the Bjerrum separations, and the theoretical equations for the moments of inertia, such as $I_z = 3m_a r_1^2 \sin^2 \alpha$, the internuclear distances and the valency angle may be determined, as with smaller molecules. With m_a as the hydrogen atom, m_b as a halogen atom and m_c as the carbon atom, we have the structures of the methyl halides, and the spectroscopic constants summarised in Table x.6. The slight increase in I_z with increase in

Table x.6 *Moments of inertia, internuclear distances and valency angles in molecules of the CH_3X type*

Molecule	$I_z \times 10^{-40}$ (g-cm²)	$I_x \times 10^{-40}$ (g-cm²)	$r_{c-x} \times 10^{8}$ (cm)	α (degrees)
CH_3H	5·337	5·337	1·0936	109° 28′
CH_3D	5·337	7·218	1·0936	109° 28′
CH_3F	5·489	32·95	1·398	111° 48′
CH_3Cl	5·492	63·6	1·767	111° 52′
CH_3Br	5·508	87·83	1·936	112° 6′
CH_3I	5·514	111·84	2·144	112° 12′
CH_3NH_2	8·00	—	1·48	—

molecular weight shows that $r_1 \sin \alpha$ increases in the same direction; if r_1, the *C-H* distance, remains constant, the drift must be due to a gradual widening of the valency angle, as shown by the figures in the last column.

The regular tetrahedral structure of methane is thus fully confirmed. The same structure has been established for the molecules SiH_4, CF_4, CCl_4, and CBr_4, and for the ions NH_4^+, ClO_4^-, SO_4^{--} and PO_4^{---}.

Hexatomic molecules; hindered rotation

Complicated molecules decompose thermally or photochemically into fragments; conversely, they can be formed by the union of such fragments, as di-nitrogen tetroxide, for example, is made by the union of two molecules of nitrogen peroxide. It is, perhaps, natural to expect absorption lines which are characteristic of the fragments not to be modified beyond recognition in the large molecule; and the expectation is generally realised. Thus, for example, in the spectra of the ostensibly planar hexatomic molecules

$$
\begin{array}{ccc}
O\diagdown \quad \diagup O & H\diagdown \quad \diagup H & H\diagdown \quad \diagup H \\
N{-}N & N{-}N & C{=}C \\
O\diagup \quad \diagdown O & H\diagup \quad \diagdown H & H\diagup \quad \diagdown H
\end{array}
$$

there appear absorption lines made familiar in the study of the triatomic molecules or radicals from which they can be formed. Hexatomic molecules built on the tetrahedral plan illustrate the same truth. The spectrum of methyl cyanide, CH_3CN, resembles that of methane, CH_4, and differs from it in revealing lines at 918 and $2\,249\ \text{cm}^{-1}$, which are characteristic of the C—C bond, as in ethane, and the C≡N bond, as in hydrogen cyanide. Similarly, the spectrum of methyl alcohol, CH_3OH, resembles that of methane, with two new lines, one typical of the C—O bond, and the other (of wave number $3\,682$) easily recognisable as belonging to the O—H bond, as in water. This rule of the approximate constancy of bond frequencies, simplifies the theoretical treatment of complex molecules, and forms the basis of quantitative analysis by means of infra-red absorption spectra.

Having compared the structures of methyl cyanide and methyl alcohol, let us next contrast them. It is known from the study of simpler molecules that the two bonds represented by C—C≡N are linear, and that the two bonds represented by C—O—H are bent, so that the configurations of the atoms in methyl cyanide and methyl alcohol must be as shown in Fig. x.12. Let us consider the methyl group to act as a fixed pedestal, supporting the substituted atoms. We know from the specific heat of gaseous cyanogen that the cyanide group does not spin round the principal axis of the molecule. The hydrogen atom attached to the oxygen atom, however, is capable of such a motion, the nature of which is that of a hindered rotation.

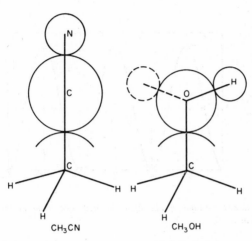

Fig. x.12   *Methyl cyanide.*   *Methyl alcohol*

Small displacements of the hydrogen atom perpendicular to the plane of the paper result in a harmonic oscillation; given sufficient energy, however, the atom may make the complete cycle round the principal molecular axis. In doing so, it passes through three planes each of which contains another hydrogen atom. The motion is like that of the hobby-horse in a fair-ground, which rises and falls three times during a complete revolution round the pole. The simplest assumption concerning the potential energy which can explain these effects is that

$$V = \tfrac{1}{2}V_0(1 - \cos n\phi) = V_0 \sin^2(n\phi/2), \qquad \text{x.35}$$

where V_0 is the maximum potential energy, or the height of the barrier, ϕ is the angle subtended between the plane in which the hydrogen atom is found and the reference plane, and n is the number of maxima

I*

257

or minima passed during a complete revolution. This potential energy equation, with $n = 3$, is shown in Fig. x.13. Hindered rotation, like all other molecular motions, contributes to the entropy and heat capacity, and the height of the barrier may be estimated from such thermodynamical quantities (Kassel, 1936; Pitzer, 1951). For the motion, described above, of the hydroxyl hydrogen atom in methanol V_0 is 1·3 kilcal/mole, and for the hindered rotational motion of the hydrogen atoms in acetone the barrier is about twice as high.

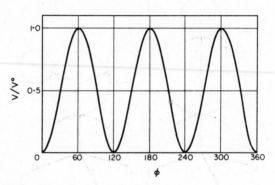

Fig. x.13 *Hindered rotation of the hydroxyl hydrogen atom in the methyl alcohol molecule*

Raman spectra

When monochromatic radiation is allowed to pass through matter, there is detected, in a direction perpendicular to that of the incident beam, light of the original frequency and also light of other frequencies, in numbers and intensities which depend on the scattering medium. The difference between the frequencies of the incident and scattered radiation is termed the Raman frequency

$$\nu_R = \nu_1 - \nu_2$$

Its magnitude is independent of the frequency of the incident radiation and, to a first approximation, of the physical state of the scatterer. By applying the law of the conservation of energy to the head-on collision of a photon with a molecule which has internal energy E_1 and kinetic energy $\frac{1}{2}mv_1^2$, we see that

$$h\nu_1 + E_1 + \tfrac{1}{2}mv_1^2 = h\nu_2 + E_2 + \tfrac{1}{2}mv_2^2 \qquad \text{x.37}$$

By applying the law of the conservation of momentum, we have

$$hv_1/c + mv_1 = hv_2/c + mv_2 \qquad \text{x.38}$$

from which, as Smekal (1923) showed, the fraction of the energy absorbed by the molecule in the kinetic form is quite negligible. Hence

$$v_R = v_1 - v_2 = \frac{1}{h}(E_2 - E_1) \qquad \text{x.39}$$

which explains why the Raman frequency, being an intrinsic property of the molecule, is unaffected by the frequency of the incident light. The mechanism of the absorption is best understood by considering the moment, μ_i, induced by the electric component of light, in a molecule vibrating with frequency v_R. In terms of the polarisability, α, and the electrical field strength, F, we have $\mu_i = \alpha F$. Now $F = F_0 \cos 2\pi v_L t$, where v_L is the frequency of the incident radiation and α is assumed to vary linearly with respect to the internuclear displacement, x, so that α may be written as $\alpha_0 + Kx$. Then, using equation II.46,

$$\mu_i = (\alpha_0 + Ka \cos 2\pi v_R t)(F \cos 2\pi v_L t) \qquad \text{x.40}$$

where a is the amplitude of the nuclear vibration. Using the trigonometrical equation $\cos A \cos B = \frac{1}{2}[\cos(A + B) + \cos(A - B)]$, we see that

$$\mu_i = \alpha_0 F_0 \cos 2\pi v_L t + \tfrac{1}{2} Ka F_0 \cos[2\pi(v_L + v_R)t]$$
$$+ \tfrac{1}{2} Ka F_0 \cos[2\pi(v_L - v_R)t] \qquad \text{x.41}$$

The induced moment thus consists of three parts; the first is that which would be induced in the molecule in the absence of internuclear vibrations; the other two vary harmonically with respect to time, with frequencies lying above and below v_L. We can then write:

$$u_i = \mu_i^0 + \mu_i^+ + \mu_i^- \qquad \text{x.42}$$

The polarisation energy and the intensity of the electromagnetic vibration in each case vary as the square of μ_i. Since the intensity of the scattered radiation is weak, it follows that Ka, which is simply $a(\partial\alpha/\partial x)$, is small compared with α_0. When $\partial\alpha/\partial x$ is zero, there is no Raman effect. Similarly, in the infra-red spectrum, when $\partial\mu/\partial x$ is zero, there is no absorption. These are the classical equivalents of the selection rules of the quantum theory.

259

Raman spectra supplement electronic, vibrational and rotational spectra by revealing absorption lines which are absent in them. For example, the P and R branches of the vibration-rotation spectra of gaseous heteronuclear diatomic molecules correspond, respectively, to changes of -1 and $+1$ in the rotational quantum number, J, and the null line, which corresponds to transition between two vibrational states with the same rotational quantum number, is absent, though its position at the head of the band can be accurately interpolated. The wave numbers inferred for these lines which are absent from the infra-red spectra of the hydrogen halides are reproduced in the last column of Table x.7, along with the single lines

Table x.7 *Raman and infra-red wave numbers of the hydrogen halides and hydrogen sulphide*

Molecule	Raman wave number (cm^{-1})			Wave number of missing null line in infra-red spectrum of gas
	Solid	Liquid	Gas	
HCl	2 760	2 778	2 880	2 887
HBr	2 465	2 487	2 558	2 559
HI	2 160	2 165	2 233	2 230
H_2S	2 523	2 578	2 615	2 615

observed in the Raman spectra of the molecules in the three states of matter. The agreement of the figures in the last two columns is satisfactory. Significant changes in the Raman wave numbers appear for the condensed states, showing that the internuclear vibration frequency of a polar molecule which is hemmed in by close neighbours is less than the value for the isolated molecule in the gaseous state. There is no detectable change in ν_R for carbon dioxide and carbon disulphide. A slight effect is found in solution, where solvent molecules bring about a diminution in the Raman frequency similar to that exercised by the neighbouring molecules in the pure liquid or solid.

A given bond in a complicated molecule often gives rise to a Raman frequency which is but slightly affected by variations in the remaining portion of the molecule. All aliphatic compounds which are not fully substituted, for example, exhibit a Raman shift in the neighbourhood of $2\,924\,\text{cm}^{-1}$. A line near $1\,700\,\text{cm}^{-1}$ is invariably found in the Raman spectra of carboxylic acids, aldehydes, ketones, acid chlorides and esters, and is naturally attributed to the presence of the carbonyl group $>\!C\!\!=\!\!O$. Some characteristic Raman shifts which may be allotted to atom pairs in polyatomic molecules are shown in Table x.8.

Table x.8 *Characteristic Raman wave numbers (cm^{-1}) of certain univalent bonds*

Bond	v_R/c	Bond	v_R/c
H—H	4 158	C—C	993
C—H (aromatic)	3 050	C—N	1 033
C—H (aliphatic)	2 924	C—O	1 030
N—H	3 370	C—S	650
O—H	3 650	C—Cl	710
S—H	2 572	C—Br	597
		C—I	526

The mechanisms of tautomerism and polymerisation, established by other means, have been confirmed by the Raman spectra. Thus, for example, the typical lines ($1\,632$ and $1\,725\,\text{cm}^{-1}$) of the ethylenic link are present in the spectrum of ethyl acetoacetate, but are absent from that of ethyl dimethylacetoacetate, which shows, however, the doublet ($1\,707$ and $1\,738$) which characterises the carbonyl group. The Raman line due to the double bond in methyl methacrylate gradually disappears during polymerisation, and is almost absent in the spectrum of the final polymer, which indicates that linking is due to opening of the double bond.

Corroboration is also afforded to some established facts in connexion with solutions. Thus, during the dimerisation of carboxylic acids, the characteristic Raman lines due to the unattached carbonyl and hydroxyl groups are both modified. The great similarity of the Raman spectrum of the tetramethylammonium ion, $[(CH_3)_4N]^+$, to that of tertiary pentane, $(CH_3)_4C$, confirms the regular tetrahedral structure assigned by stereochemistry to the ion. Aqueous solutions of nitric and sulphuric acid of moderate concentrations, on being examined by their Raman spectra, give definite proof of the existence of unionised molecules.

Ionisation potentials

The ionisation potential of triatomic and even more complicated molecules may be measured as described in Chapter III from constants required to reproduce the wave numbers of lines emitted in the ultraviolet region of the spectrum;

$$\omega = v/c = (v_\infty/c) - \frac{R}{(n+a)^2}, \qquad \text{X.43}$$

where R is Rydberg's constant and n is an integer. Some of the results obtained by W. C. Price (1935) are given in Table x.9. The values of v_∞ for triatomic molecules are generally lower than those derived from optical constants. Ionisation potentials may also be measured by the method of electron impact. From these three sources accurate information is slowly accruing on the energy states of electrons in simple molecules.

Table x.9 *Ionisation potentials derived from Rydberg series in the ultra-violet spectra* ($R = 109\ 678\ cm^{-1}$)

Molecule	a	n	$(v_\infty/c)\ cm^{-1}$	V (volts)
CO_2	0·21	2, 3, ...	111 250	13·73
CS_2	0·55	3, 4, ...	81 734	10·083
	0·55	3, 4, ...	81 298	10·027
N_2O	0·92	3, 4, ...	102 567	12·66
H_2O	1·05	4, 5, ...	101 780	12·56
H_2S	1·57	4, 5, ...	84 520	10·425
	2·04	5, 6, ...	84 420	10·415
CH_3Cl	0·50	2, 3, ...	90 500	11·17
	0·50	2, 3, ...	91 180	11.25
CH_3Br	0·90	3, 4, ...	85 020	10·488
	0·90	3, 4, ...	87 560	10·803
CH_3I	0·75	6, 7, ...	76 930	9·490
	0·80	6, 7, ...	81 990	10·115
HCOOH	0·40	2, 3, ...	91 370	11·29
$CH_2{=}CH{-}CH{=}CH_2$	0·90	2, 3, ...	73 115	9·02
	0·50	3, 4, ...	73 066	9·02

Magnetic resonance spectra

In a magnetic field of strength H, the potential energy of a magnet, of moment M, is $u = -MH \cos \theta$ (equations x.28 and III.47). Its maximum value is MH, and its minimum value, $-MH$. Classically, the potential energy can have any value within these limits. Quantally, only $2I + 1$ energy levels are allowed, where I is the spin quantum number. The total energy span of $2MH$ is thus divided into $2J$ intervals, so that the difference between any two neighbouring levels is MH/I. If a system of such magnets were irradiated with photons of energy hv, there should be sharp absorption when $hv = MH/I$. For the electron and the proton, I is $\frac{1}{2}$, and the resonance frequency is accordingly $v = 2MH/h$. Their magnetic moments are 9.29×10^{-21} and 1.41×10^{-23} erg/gauss, respectively, and v becomes 2.80×10^{10} and 4.26×10^7 $\sec^{-1}$, corresponding to micro-wave and radio frequencies. In practice, the field H is kept constant, and absorption is measured at varying frequencies about the resonance value. As with the absorption of visible radiation, it is not a sharp line but a band that is found. On the other hand, the mechanism of absorption and emission of energy in the present instance is more complicated, because the total influence on a nuclear magnet is due to several causes: (1) the direct action of the applied field, H, (2) the action of the magnetic component of the radiation, and (3) the magnetic field set up by neighbouring nuclear magnets. It is to the third of these effects that the broadening in the nuclear magnetic resonance spectra of proton-containing compounds is due. Since the field exerted by a magnet at a distance r from its centre is $(M/r^3)(1 - 3\cos^2\theta)$ in the direction of its axis, and $-(3M/r^3)\sin\theta\cos\theta$ in the direction perpendicular to that of the axis, it becomes possible, from a careful analysis of the shape of the absorption band, to estimate internuclear distances, and to describe the magnetic environment of the proton.

From the nuclear magnetic resonance spectrum of crystalline ammonium chloride, the N–H bond length in the ammonium ion has been found to be 1.025 ± 0.005 Å, in agreement with the results of neutron diffraction. Estimates have also been made of the height of the energy barrier hindering free rotation of the ammonium ion in crystalline ammonium halides, the water molecules in various hydrates, and the methyl group in compounds such as CH_3CCl_3 and CH_3NO_2. The nuclear magnetic resonance technique has confirmed the structure assigned by other methods to the hydroxonium ion in crystals such as $[H_3O]^+[NO_3]^-$ and $[H_3O]^+[ClO_4]^-$, formerly written HNO_3, H_2O and $HClO_4$, H_2O.

Electron magnetic resonance is more restricted in its application than nuclear magnetic resonance, because in most molecules the magnets arising from the movements of orbital electrons cancel out one another's effect. Most of the electrons are paired, and therefore show no magnetic resonance. Electron magnetic resonance is exhibited by all molecules containing unpaired or incompletely paired electrons. Free radicals and molecules in the triplet state have accordingly been widely investigated by the method of electron magnetic resonance. The presence of free radicals trapped in crystals which have suffered radiation damage by X-rays or gamma rays has been detected in this way, and their concentrations estimated from the integrated area of the absorption band. Liquid sulphur contains molecules of S_8, which are puckered rings of sulphur atoms, in which the electrons are paired, and chain molecules S_n with an unpaired electron at each end. The chain length, n, has been found by this method to be about $1 \cdot 5 \times 10^6$.

The determination of internuclear distances from measurements on the scattering of X-rays and electrons

To measure the distances between the atomic nuclei, there are two further methods, which though distinct from each other have much in common. They depend on the fact that the effectiveness with which matter can scatter X-rays or electrons is proportional to the electron density in the scattering material, and thus varies, as the rays pass through matter, with a certain regularity from which can be derived the mutual separation and arrangement of the atoms.

To gain an elementary notion of the principle underlying the scattering of electrons, let us first estimate the electronic radius. We consider two electrons, of mass m and of charge $-e$ each, to approach each other with velocities u_1 and u_2 at a distance a apart. The total energy of the system is $\frac{1}{2}mu_1^2 + \frac{1}{2}mu_2^2 + e^2/a = $ constant. Let the initial velocities be c and $-c$, where c is the (unattainable) velocity of light, and the initial separation be infinite. Then $\varepsilon = mc^2$. Let the final velocities be zero, and the distance be a_0, when $\varepsilon = e^2/a_0$. On equating the two expressions, we see that the nearest distance of approach is $a_0 = e^2/mc^2$, which we shall take to be the radius, rather than the diameter of the electron. More accurate estimates give higher values (Born, 1935). Now let us imagine a beam of photons or electrons, of intensity I_0, to alight on unit area of a hypothetical piece of matter containing only one electron, and suppose that the resulting collision leads to complete scattering. Then the intensity, I_s, of the scattered radiation bears the same ratio to that of incident radiation as the area of the electron does to unit area, i.e. $I_s/I_0 = 4\pi a_0^2 = 4\pi(e^2/mc^2)^2$. This is the fraction of the incident radiation scattered by a single electron at a distance a_0 from its centre. At a distance R from the scattering electron, the intensity of the scattered radiation is $I_s/4\pi R^2$, so that, as J. J. Thomson showed,

$$\frac{I_s}{I_0} = \left(\frac{a_0}{R}\right)^2 = \left(\frac{e^2}{Rmc^2}\right)^2 \qquad \text{x.44}$$

If all the Z extra-nuclear electrons in an atom were distributed at random, and each acted independently, we would expect this ratio for the atom to be Z^2 times as great. Then, using de Broglie's law ($mc = h/\lambda$), we would have

$$\frac{I_s}{I_0} = \left(\frac{me^2\lambda^2}{Rh^2}\right)^2 Z^2 \qquad \text{x.45}$$

We now introduce a reciprocal distance, s, defined as follows in terms of λ and the glancing angle, ϕ

$$s = \frac{4\pi}{\lambda} \sin\frac{\phi}{2} \qquad \text{x.46}$$

and, giving $\sin^2(\phi/2)$ its average value of $\frac{1}{2}$, obtain the ratio

$$\frac{I_s}{I_0} = \left(\frac{8\pi^2 me^2}{Rh^2 s^2}\right)^2 Z^2 \qquad \text{x.47}$$

It is known, however, that the distribution of electrons in an atom is by no means random (Chapter IV). If $P(r)$ denotes the probability that an electron shall be in a shell of thickness dr at a distance r from the nucleus, then

$$4\pi n_e \int P(r)r^2 \, dr = \int U(r) \, dr = Z \qquad \text{x.48}$$

where n_e is the concentration of the electrons, and Z the nuclear charge. $U(r)$ is known as Hartree's function (1928), and can be evaluated by wave-mechanical methods. The average value of the atomic scattering number is then found to be

$$f = \int_0^\infty U(r)\frac{\sin sr}{sr} \, dr \qquad \text{x.49}$$

265

Consequently

$$\frac{I_s}{I_0} = \left[\frac{e^2}{Rmc^2} \int_0^\infty U(r)\frac{\sin sr}{sr} dr \right]^2 \qquad \text{x.50}$$

By comparing the observed ratio of the intensities of the scattered and incident radiation with the ratio given by this equation, it is possible to calculate the density of (negative) electricity as a function of the distance, r, from the nucleus. Such comparisons form the basis of X-ray diffraction analysis.

The simplest and most direct application of these phenomena is that which leads to Bragg's law of the reflexion of X-rays from a crystal surface. Each atom or ion in the crystal acts like a centre from which radiation is scattered in all directions consonant with the optical laws; radiation scattered in the direction of an atom-atom link, however, is strongly reinforced by radiation scattered in the same direction by other atoms. Cumulative diffraction in a selected direction amounts to a Bragg's reflexion. A second application (Debye, Mencke and Prins), is directed to determining the distribution of atoms in a liquid. Finally, much labour has been saved by means of the mixed powder device, (Hull and Debye and Scherrer), in which X-rays are scattered in all directions by a small specimen of a mixture of crystals, one of which (usually rock salt) has a known structure. The determination of internuclear distances is then a comparative process, which reduces to measuring the diameters of diffraction rings due to the known and unknown scatterers.

In a system containing two kinds of nuclei, the scattering ratio for electrons is based on equation x.47, and takes the form

$$\frac{I_s}{I_0} = \frac{8\pi^2 me^2}{Rh^2 s^2} \sum_i \sum_j (Z_i - f_i)(Z_j - f_j)\frac{\sin sr_{ij}}{r_{ij}}, \qquad \text{x.51}$$

where the summation is to be carried over all near-neighbour atomic pairs. When applied to gaseous molecules, the atomic scattering factors, f, can be omitted. The experimental plot of I_s/I_0 against s is compared with plots computed from this equation, with different values of r_{ij}, until the curves become superimposable. Internuclear distances and valency angles of many molecules have been determined in this way, confirming and extending the information afforded by other means.

XI Solutions of non-electrolytes

As most known chemical changes take place in solution, it is clearly important to discover what happens to molecules when they dissolve in a solvent, and what are the general laws that govern miscibility and solubility. In a rule-of-thumb way, chemists have long worked on the principle that like dissolves like. Sugars, for example, which are carbohydrates, dissolve readily in water; many metals form amalgams of all composition with mercury; and neighbouring members of most homologous series are mutually soluble. Apart from ionisation – dealt with in Chapter XII – many changes accompany the process of dissolution. Heat may be absorbed or evolved; the volume may increase or decrease, and the state of aggregation of the solute may alter. Carboxylic acids, for example, occur partly as double molecules, or dimers, in most solvents. Sulphur dissolved in non-polar solvents has a molecular weight corresponding to S_8, as in the gaseous state. Combination of solute with solvent is frequently met with, as Faraday showed when he isolated a crystalline hydrate from an aqueous solution of chlorine.

A solution, for the purpose of this chapter, is defined as a homogeneous, fluid, condensed system of not less than two components. We thus exclude from the discussion solid solutions and mixed gases. The fundamental laws of such solutions emerged as empirical observations, many of which have now been adequately interpreted theoretically.

Raoult's law: ideal solutions

Raoult (1888) found that the vapour pressure, p, of di-ethyl ether over a solution of methyl salicylate in the liquid ether was proportional to the molar fraction, x, of ether in the liquid phase. If the proportionality held over the whole composition of the liquid solution, it is clear that the proportionality factor is p^0, the vapour pressure of the pure ether; that is:

$$p = p^0 x \qquad \text{XI.1}$$

267

or, in terms of the numbers of molecules in the liquid:

$$p_1 = p_1^0 \frac{N_1}{N_1 + N_2}$$
XI.1a

The total pressure of a binary liquid mixture obeying Raoult's law should, therefore, vary linearly with respect to the molar fraction:

$$P = p_1 + p_2 = p_1^0 x_1 + p_2^0 x_2 = p_1^0 x_1 + p_2^0 (1 - x_1) = p_2^0 + (p_1^0 - p_2^0) x_1$$
XI.2

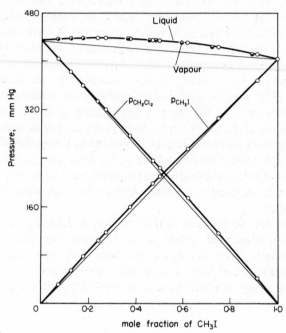

Fig. XI.1

Fig. XI.1 shows that this relationship is very nearly obeyed by liquid mixtures of methylene dichloride and methyl iodide. Deviations from Raoult's law are said to be positive or negative, respectively, when the total pressure exceeds or is less than that calculated by equation XI.2. The carbon disulphide-methylal and chloroform-acetone systems are, respectively, typical examples of systems exhibiting positive and negative deviations.

Solutions which obey Raoult's law at all temperatures are said to be ideal. If the components of the vapour in equilibrium with such solutions obey the ideal gas laws, we can clearly write for the chemical potential of the first component in the vapour phase:

$$\mu_1(\text{vap}) = \mu_1^0(\text{sat vap}) + kT \ln (p_1/p_1^0) \qquad \text{XI.3}$$

But $\mu_1(\text{vap})$ must equal μ_1 for the component in solution, and $\mu_1^0(\text{sat vap})$ must equal μ_1^0 for the pure liquid. Hence Raoult's law leads to the following expressions for the chemical potential of a component in solution:

$$\mu_1 = \mu_1^0 + kT \ln \frac{N_1}{N_1 + N_2} \qquad \text{XI.4}$$

Here μ_1^0 refers to the pure liquid component at the pressure of the system.

Lowering in the freezing point of the solvent

Let us suppose that, when the solubility, x_1, of the first component has reached a certain value, s, its crystals appear. From the general condition of equilibrium, we then have

$$\mu_{\text{cr}} = \mu_1^0 + kT \ln s$$

where s is the solubility expressed in molar fractions. Rearranging, we write

$$kT \ln s = \mu_{\text{cr}} - \mu_1^0 = -(\mu_1^0 - \mu_{\text{cr}}) = -\Delta\mu(\text{fusion})$$

or, in molar notation,

$$RT \ln s = -\Delta G^0(\text{fusion}) = -\Delta H_T + T\Delta S_T \qquad \text{XI.5}$$

If the excess of the heat capacity of the liquid over that of the crystal remains constant in the temperature interval considered, we may substitute as follows:

$$\Delta H_T = L_T = L_m + \int_{T_m}^{T} \Delta C_p dT = L_m + \Delta C_p(T - T_m) \qquad \text{XI.6}$$

and

$$\Delta S_T = \Delta S_m + \int_{T_m}^{T} \Delta C_p d \ln T = \frac{L_m}{T_m} + \Delta C_p \ln \frac{T}{T_m} \qquad \text{XI.7}$$

269

where L is the heat of fusion, and the subscript m refers to the melting temperature. Then

$$RT \ln s = -L_T + L_m \frac{T}{T_m} + T\Delta C_P \ln \frac{T}{T_m} \qquad \text{XI.8}$$

When the difference between T and T_m is small, we may approximate as follows. $T/T_m = 1 - (T_m - T)/T_m$; $\ln(T/T_m) = -(T_m - T)/T_m$; hence

$$RT \ln s = -L_T + \frac{T}{T_m}[L_m - \Delta C_P(T_m - T)]$$

From equation XI.6, we see that the term inside the square bracket is L_T, so that

$$RT \ln s = -L_T\left(1 - \frac{T}{T_m}\right)$$

and

$$T_m - T = -\frac{RTT_m}{L_T} \ln s = \frac{RTT_m}{L_T} \ln\left(\frac{N_1 + N_2}{N_1}\right)_{\text{sat}} \qquad \text{XI.9}$$

which is an approximate expression for the depression in the freezing point of a solvent. Measurements of freezing point depressions are usually made on dilute solutions, so that, without great loss of precision, we have

$$T_m - T = \frac{RTT_m}{L_T} x_2 = \frac{RTT_m}{L_T} \frac{N_2}{N_1 + N_2} \qquad \text{XI.10}$$

Fig. XI.2 shows the linear relationship of the depression of the freezing point of cyclohexane containing low molar fractions of n-hexane. From the gradient, which is 222°, a value of L_T is found which compares favourably with the calorimetric value. In solutions as dilute as those examined, N_2 can be ignored in comparison with N_1, and equation XI.10 reduces to

$$T_m - T = \frac{RTT_m}{L_T} \frac{N_2}{N_1}$$

When w grams of solute, of molar weight M_2, are dissolved in 100 grams of solvent, of molar weight M_1, the molar ratio is $(w/M_2)/(100/M_1)$. Hence

$$T_m - T = \left(\frac{RTT_m}{100 l_T}\right) \frac{w}{M_2} \qquad \text{XI.11}$$

270

where $l_T = L_T/M_1$ is the heat of fusion per gram of solvent. This equation is frequently used to determine the molar weight of compounds. The term inside the brackets, which can be calculated from thermal data relating to the solvent, is termed the freezing point constant. It is the computed depression in the freezing point which would result if one formula weight of the solute were dissolved in 100 g of solvent.

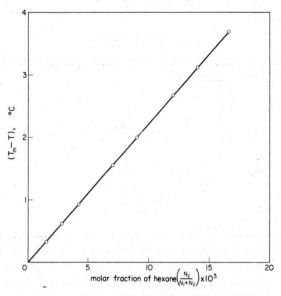

Fig. xi.2 *Depression in the freezing point of cyclohexane by hexane as solute*

The osmotic pressure of ideal solutions

There are membranes, both natural and artificial, which allow molecules of solvent to pass through them, but prohibit the passage of solute molecules. This phenomenon, called osmosis, is quantitatively studied by measuring the difference between the pressure, P, exerted on a solution, placed on one side of such a membrane, and the pressure, P^0, exerted on the pure solvent placed on the other side of the membrane. When the system is at equilibrium, the chemical potential of the solvent must be the same on both sides. Then

271

μ_1 (solvent in solution at pressure P) $= \mu_1^0 + kT \ln x_1$;

μ (pure solvent at pressure P^0) $= \mu_1^0 + \int_P^{P^0} \left(\frac{\partial \mu_1}{\partial P} \right) dP = \mu_1^0 + \int_P^{P^0} v_1 \, dP$

where v_1, as explained in later sections of this chapter, is the partial molecular volume of the solvent. If the solvent is incompressible,

$$\mu = \mu_1^0 + v_1(P^0 - P)$$

and therefore

$$v_1(P^0 - P) = kT \ln x_1$$

and the osmotic pressure, which is the excess pressure on the solution over that on the solvent, is

$$\prod = P - P^0$$

$$= -\frac{kT}{v_1} \ln x_1 = \frac{kT}{v_1} \ln \frac{N_1 + N_2}{N_1} \qquad \text{XI.12}$$

or, since $\qquad x_1 = p_1/p_1^0,$

$$\prod = \frac{kT}{v_1} \ln \frac{p_1^0}{p_1} \qquad \text{XI.13}$$

This expression (Arrhenius, 1889) relates the osmotic pressure of an ideal solution to the partial vapour pressure of the solvent. Allowance for the compression of the solvent is readily made, especially when its compressibility, β, (equation VI.16) is regarded as constant over the pressure range considered, for then,

$$v_1 = v_1^0 \cdot e^{-\beta(P - P^0)}$$

We now have

$$\int_P^{P^0} v_1 \, dP = \frac{v_1^0}{\beta} [e^{-\beta(P - P^0)} - 1]$$

Expansion of the exponential term to the second place gives us

$$\int_P^{P^0} v_1 \, dP = v_1^0 (P^0 - P)[1 - (\beta/2)(P^0 - P)]$$

and

$$\prod = \left[\frac{kT}{v_1^0} \ln \frac{N_1 + N_2}{N_1} \right] \times \left[1 - (\beta/2)(P^0 - P) \right]^{-1} \qquad \text{XI.14}$$

At the highest osmotic pressure (137 atmospheres) measured with aqueous solutions of sucrose, the correction amounts to 0·3 per cent.

Equation XI.12, applied to dilute solutions, reduces to

$$\Pi = \frac{kT}{v_1} \frac{N_2}{N_1}$$

or, since under these conditions $N_1 v_1$ is effectively the total volume, V, of the solution,

$$\Pi = kTn_2 \qquad \text{XI.15}$$

where n_2 is the concentration of solute, in molecules per cm^3. This is the celebrated equation of van't Hoff (1887), whose conclusion was that the osmotic pressure exerted by solutes in dilute solution is the same as the ordinary pressure they would exert if they existed as a gas at the same temperature and concentration. It is obeyed in aqueous and non-polar solvents at solute concentrations not exceeding about 20 millimoles per litre. At higher concentrations, the observed osmotic pressure exceeds that calculated by means of equation XI.15.

Thermodynamic properties of ideal solutions; regular solutions

The free energy of a system consisting of N_1 molecules of one type and N_2 molecules of another type is, according to the definition of the chemical potential, μ,

$$G_{12} = N_1\mu_1 + N_2\mu_2 \qquad \text{XI.16}$$

The free energy of an ideal solution, according to equation XI.4, is thus

$$G_{12} = N_1(\mu_1^0 + kT \ln x_1) + N_2(\mu_2^0 + kT \ln x_2) \qquad \text{XI.17}$$

To obtain the free energy of one mole of solution, we let $N_1 + N_2 = N_0$, the Avogadro number. On dividing N_1 and N_2 by this number, and multiplying each term within the brackets by the same number, we find

$$G_{12} = x_1(G_1^0 + RT \ln x_1) + x_2(G_2^0 + RT \ln x_2) \qquad \text{XI.17a}$$

where G^0, the molar chemical potential is $N_0\mu^0$. The gain in free energy on making one mole of solution is evidently

$$\Delta G = G_{12} - x_1 G_1^0 - x_2 G_2^0$$
$$= x_1 RT \ln x_1 + x_2 RT \ln x_2 \qquad \text{XI.18}$$

273

and the gain in entropy is

$$\Delta S = -\left(\frac{d\Delta G}{dT}\right)_P = -x_1 R \ln x_1 - x_2 R \ln x_2 \qquad \text{XI.19}$$

as in the formation of an ideal gas mixture. Since x is less than 1, the entropy of mixing is always positive. It follows from equations XI.18 and XI.19 that $\Delta H = 0$, i.e., there is no change in heat content when an ideal solution is formed from its components. With the exception of isotopic mixtures, few real solutions are ideal. There are numerous examples, however, of solutions formed with absorption or evolution of heat, while still having an entropy of mixing in reasonable agreement with equation XI.19. Such solutions have been termed regular by Hildebrand (1929). They are 'like ideal solutions in that thermal agitation is able to overcome any tendency towards molecular orientation, combination or association, and to give the same completely random distribution as exists in ideal solutions'.

A simple statistical derivation of the laws of regular solutions may be derived as follows, by considering, in the first place, the partition function, F, of an ideal gaseous system containing N_1 molecules of the first type and N_2 molecules of the second type in a total volume, V, at a temperature, T. Using equation IX.46 for the molecular partition functions, and applying the multiplicative rule, we have

$$F = \left[\frac{(2\pi m_1 kT)^{3/2} Ve}{h^3 N_1}\right]^{N_1} \left[\frac{(2\pi m_2 kT)^{3/2} Ve}{h^3 N_2}\right]^{N_2}. \qquad \text{XI.20}$$

The pressure of the system is

$$P = kT\left(\frac{d \ln F}{dV}\right)_{T, N_1, N_2} = (N_1 kT/V) + (N_2 kT/V)$$

which is Dalton's law. We may re-write the result as follows:

$$V = (N_1 + N_2)kT/P = (N_1 + N_2)v \qquad \text{XI.21}$$

where v, which is a constant at constant temperature and pressure, is the average volume which one molecule of either component would occupy if it existed in the pure state at the total pressure of the system. By making use of this result and Stirling's approximation, we may re-cast the system partition function into the form

$$F = \frac{(N_1 + N_2)!}{N_1! N_2!} f_1^{N_1} f_2^{N_2} \qquad \text{XI.22}$$

where
$$f_1 = (2\pi m_1 kT)^{3/2} ev/h^3, \quad \text{and} \quad f_2 = (2\pi m_2 kT)^{3/2} ev/h^3$$

For the chemical potential of either component, we derive the expression
$$\mu_i = -kT \ln(f_i/x_i)$$

where f_i is the partition function of the pure component i at the temperature and pressure of the mixture, and x_i is its molar fraction. This equation may clearly be written in the form

$$\mu_i = \mu_i^0 + kT \ln x_i \qquad \text{XI.4}$$

so that equation XI.22 is applicable, not only to ideal gas mixtures, but to ideal liquid mixtures. Moreover, if for f_1 and f_2 we substitute the vibrational partition functions of two similar solids, we arrive directly at equation XI.22 in the case of ideal solid solutions, provided, as Tolman (1938) points out, the 'molecules of the two types of substances become so nearly alike as to the volume they occupy and the forces they exert on their neighbours, that they can be used indiscriminately for constructing crystals of any desired composition without changing the structure or dimensions of the lattice or affecting the lattice properties of the solid.' When applying equation XI.22 to one and the same binary system in the gaseous, liquid and solid states, F must be multiplied by $\exp(-U/kT)$, where U is the total potential energy of the system:

$$F = \frac{(N_1+N_2)!}{N_1!N_2!} f_1^{N_1} f_2^{N_2} e^{-U/kT} \qquad \text{XI.23}$$

For gases, U is zero, for solids a constant, and for regular solutions can be derived as follows.

Let each molecule of either kind be surrounded by a number c of neighbours. Of the c molecules surrounding a molecule of type 1, there are, in a random distribution, $c\left(\dfrac{N_1}{N_1+N_2}\right)$ molecules of its own kind, and $c\left(\dfrac{N_2}{N_1+N_2}\right)$ molecules of the second kind. Hence, the energy of its interaction with its c neighbours, which is also its effective energy of interaction with the whole system, is

$$c\left(\frac{N_1}{N_1+N_2}\right)\phi_{1,1} + c\left(\frac{N_2}{N_1+N_2}\right)\phi_{1,2}$$

275

where $\phi_{1,1}$ is the energy of interaction of a pair of molecules of type 1, and $\phi_{1,2}$ is the interaction energy of a dissimilar pair. As there are N_1 molecules of the first kind, their total interaction energy with the system is

$$\frac{N_1^2}{N_1+N_2}c\phi_{1,1}+\frac{N_1N_2}{N_1+N_2}c\phi_{1,2}$$

Arguing from the other side, by starting with a consideration of one molecule of type 2, we obtain a similar expression for the interaction energy of all molecules of this kind with the system:

$$\frac{N_2^2}{N_1+N_2}c\phi_{2,2}+\frac{N_1N_2}{N_1+N_2}c\phi_{1,2}$$

where $\phi_{2,2}$ is the energy of interaction of a pair of molecules of the second kind. The total potential energy of the system is one-half of the sum of these two expressions, for we must not count the contacts twice. Then

$$U = \frac{N_1^2}{N_1+N_2}(\tfrac{1}{2}c\phi_{1,1})+\frac{N_2^2}{N_1+N_2}(\tfrac{1}{2}c\phi_{2,2})+\frac{N_1N_2}{N_1+N_2}(c\phi_{1,2}) \quad \text{XI.24}$$

Now on making two isolated pairs of molecules of the mixed type 1,2 from two isolated molecular pairs, each of the type 1,1 and 2,2, the gain in potential energy is $2\phi_{1,2}-\phi_{1,1}-\phi_{2,2}$. Therefore, the gain in potential energy on making one dissimilar pair under the same condition is

$$\Delta\phi = \phi_{1,2}-\tfrac{1}{2}\phi_{1,1}-\tfrac{1}{2}\phi_{2,2} \quad \text{XI.25}$$

The corresponding gain in potential energy when c dissimilar pairs are formed in solution from $c/2$ similar pairs of either kind is

$$\Delta u^0 = c(\phi_{1,2}-\tfrac{1}{2}\phi_{1,1}-\tfrac{1}{2}\phi_{2,2}). \quad \text{XI.26}$$

The physical meaning of the term Δu^0 is illustrated in Fig. XI.3; it is one-half of the difference between the energy of the two configurations shown in the upper half and the energy of the two configurations shown in the lower half of the diagram. Δu^0 may be referred to as the interchange energy, because it stands for the average increase in energy which one molecule of either kind acquires when it exchanges all its own neighbours for neighbours of another kind.

276

Equation XI.24 can now be put into a more convenient form, for, if we add $\left(\dfrac{N_1 N_2}{N_1 + N_2}\right)(\tfrac{1}{2}c\phi_{11})$ to the first term, $\left(\dfrac{N_1 N_2}{N_1 + N_2}\right)(\tfrac{1}{2}c\phi_{22})$ to the to the second, term, and subtract their sum from the third term, we find that

$$U = N_1(\tfrac{1}{2}c\phi_{1,1}) + N_2(\tfrac{1}{2}c\phi_{2,2}) + \frac{N_1 N_2}{N_1 + N_2}\Delta u^0$$

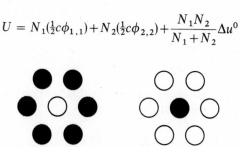

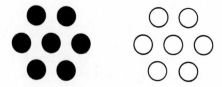

Fig. XI.3 *The molecular rearrangement contemplated in deriving the interchange energy, Δu^0*

One has only to examine the form taken by this equation when N_1 and N_2, respectively, are zero, to realise that $\tfrac{1}{2}c\phi_{2,2}$ is the average potential energy of one molecule of the second type when it exists in the pure liquid (or solid), and that $\tfrac{1}{2}c\phi_{1,1}$ is the average potential energy of one molecule of the first type when it exists in the pure condensed state. Denoting these quantities by the symbols u_2^0 and u_1^0, respectively, we arrive at the final form of our expression for the total potential energy of the system:

$$U = N_1 u_1^0 + N_2 u_2^0 + \frac{N_1 N_2}{N_1 + N_2}\Delta u^0 \qquad \text{XI.27}$$

From the system partition function (equation XI.23), the Helmholtz free energy is

$$A = -kT \ln F$$

$$= N_1 \left[-kT \ln f_1 + kT \ln \frac{N_1}{N_1 + N_2} + u_1^0 \right]$$

$$+ N_2 \left[-kT \ln f_2 + kT \ln \frac{N_2}{N_1 + N_2} + u_2^0 \right]$$

$$+ \left(\frac{N_1 N_2}{N_1 + N_2} \right) \Delta u^0 \qquad \text{IX.28}$$

If Δu^0 is independent of temperature, it follows that the total energy and entropy are given by the equations

$$E = N_1(\varepsilon_1 + u_1^0) + N_2(\varepsilon_2 + u_2^0) + \left(\frac{N_1 N_2}{N_1 + N_2} \right) \Delta u^0 \qquad \text{XI.29}$$

and

$$ST = E - A = N_1 \left[\varepsilon_1 + kT \ln f_1 - kT \ln \frac{N_1}{N_1 + N_2} \right]$$

$$+ N_2 \left[\varepsilon_2 + kT \ln f_2 - kT \ln \frac{N_2}{N_1 + N_2} \right] \qquad \text{XI.30}$$

The increase in free energy, when the system is formed from its components at constant temperature and volume is

$$\Delta A = A - (A_1 + A_2)$$

where A_1 is the free energy of N_1 molecules of the first kind, and A_2 the free energy of N_2 molecules of the second kind. Hence

$$\Delta A = N_1 kT \ln \frac{N_1}{N_1 + N_2} + N_2 kT \ln \frac{N_2}{N_1 + N_2} + \left(\frac{N_1 N_2}{N_1 + N_2} \right) \Delta u^0 \qquad \text{XI.31}$$

Similarly, the increase in total energy on forming the solution is

$$\Delta E = \left(\frac{N_1 N_2}{N_1 + N_2} \right) \Delta u^0 \qquad \text{XI.32}$$

The gain in the free energy and the gain in the total energy attending the formation of one gram-mole of solution (obtained as we derived equation XI.17a) are

$$\Delta A = x_1 RT \ln x_1 + x_2 RT \ln x_2 + x_1 x_2 \Delta U^0 \qquad \text{XI.31}$$

and

$$\Delta E = x_1 x_2 \Delta U^0 \qquad \text{XI.32}$$

where

$$\Delta U^0 = N_0 \Delta u^0 \qquad \text{XI.33}$$

It follows from equation XI.31 that, provided ΔU^0 is independent of temperature, the entropy of mixing is the ideal value given by equation XI.19.

Partial differentiation of equation XI.28 leads to the chemical potential

$$\mu_1 = -kT \ln f_1 + kT \ln\left(\frac{N_1}{N_1 + N_2}\right)$$

$$+ u_1^0 + \left(\frac{N_2}{N_1 + N_2}\right)^2 \Delta u^0 \qquad \text{XI.34}$$

Clearly, when N_2 is zero, the chemical potential of the pure component is

$$\mu_1^0 = -kT \ln f_1 + u_1^0$$

Hence

$$\mu_1 = \mu_1^0 + kT \ln\left(\frac{N_1}{N_1 + N_2}\right) + \left(\frac{N_2}{N_1 + N_2}\right)^2 \Delta u^0 \qquad \text{XI.35}$$

These equations are simplified forms of more general ones derived by van Laar (1894), but the statistical method of derivation adopted here was suggested by Heitler (1926). They relate in the first instance to spherical molecules of the same size, forming solutions without a volume change; such solutions have been termed isomegethic. They have been found, however, to give close approximations to the behaviour of solutions formed from asymmetric molecules of very different shapes and sizes. We shall therefore consider some of the properties of solutions, without restriction to size or symmetry of their components, in the light of these equations.

1. *Partial pressure.* By equating the chemical potential of the gaseous component (equation XI.3) with that for the same component in solution (equation XI.35), we find for either component

$$\frac{p}{p^0} = x e^{(1-x)^2 \alpha} \qquad \text{XI.36}$$

where

$$\alpha = \Delta u^0 / kT \qquad \text{XI.37}$$

279

This relationship, with integral values of α, is illustrated in Fig. XI.4, which makes an impressive comparison with the experimental partial pressures of the lower aliphatic alcohols in water at 25°C (Fig. XI.5).

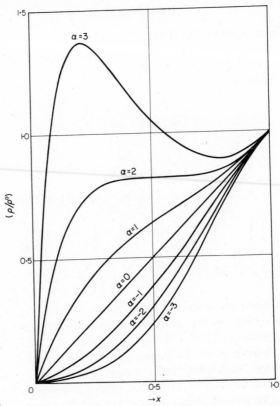

Fig. XI.4

When α exceeds 2, there are, according to equation XI.36, two values of x which give the same ratio, p/p^0. This is, of course, inadmissible in one phase. The consolute temperature, T_c, above which there is only partial miscibility, is consequently related as follows to Δu^0:

$$kT_c = \Delta u^0/2 \qquad \text{XI.38}$$

As no solute has yet been found to exert a greater partial pressure in solution than it does as a pure liquid at the same temperature, the maximum value of p/p^0 with physical significance is unity. The two values of x which may be read off the experimental curve for n-butanol in water when p/p^0 is 0·63 correspond to two phases, i.e.

an aqueous solution saturated with butanol, and a butanol solution saturated with water. Raoult's law (equation XI.1) is seen to be the special case of van Laar's law when α is zero.

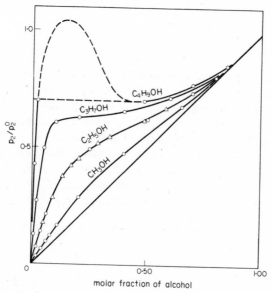

Fig. XI.5 *The relative partial pressures of aliphatic alcohols in water at 298·16°K* (after J. A. V. Butler, D. W. Thomson and W. H. Maclennan, 1933)

2. *Total pressure.* By adding the partial pressures of the two components, we obtain, for the total pressure of the solution:

$$P = p_1 + p_2 = p_1^0 \left(\frac{N_1}{N_1 + N_2}\right) e^{\left(\frac{N_2}{N_1 + N_2}\right)^2 \frac{\Delta u^0}{kT}} + p_2^0 \left(\frac{N_2}{N_1 + N_2}\right) e^{\left(\frac{N_1}{N_1 + N_2}\right)^2 \frac{\Delta u^0}{kT}}$$

If we let x stand for the molar fraction $(N_1/(N_1 + N_2))$ of the first component, we obtain for the pressure of the system:

$$P = p_1^0 x e^{(1-x)^2 \Delta u^0/kT} + p_2^0 (1-x) e^{x^2 \Delta u^0/kT} \qquad \text{XI.39}$$

Let $P_{1/2}$ denote the total pressure of the equimolar solution: then

$$\frac{\Delta u^0}{kT} = 4 \ln\left(\frac{2P_{1/2}}{p_1^0 + p_2^0}\right) \qquad \text{XI.40}$$

K

which is one of many expressions enabling us to evaluate the interchange energy.

A solution exerting a maximum or a minimum pressure is termed an azeotrope. Its composition, found by equating $(dP/dx_1)_T$ to zero, is

$$x_1^{az} = \frac{1}{2}\left[1 + \frac{kT}{\Delta u^0}\ln\left(\frac{p_1^0}{p_2^0}\right)\right] \qquad \text{XI.41}$$

Fig. XI.1 shows the total experimental pressure of the methyl iodide-methylene dichloride system at 25°C, and the experimental partial pressures of the components. The faint straight lines are the predictions of Raoult's law. In this instance, there is a slight positive deviation, with $\Delta U^0 = 90$ cal/mole. Figure XI.6 is the corresponding plot for the methyl iodide-chloroform system, where there is a smaller deviation, in the negative sense, with $\Delta U^0 = -32$ cal/mole. A greater negative deviation (-570 cal) has been recorded for the acetone-chloroform system, which consists of such highly polar molecules

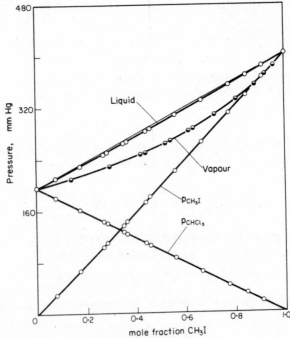

Fig. XI.6 *Vapour pressure of* CH_3I-$CHCl_3$ *at 25°C*

that many of them doubtless form binary complexes

$$H_3C \diagdown \qquad \leftrightarrow \qquad \leftrightarrow \diagup Cl$$
$$C = O \quad H - C - Cl$$
$$H_3C \diagup \qquad \diagdown Cl$$

For these solutions, van Laar's theory, in so far as it is based on random mixing, is less relevant than an alternative theory, to be discussed later.

3. *Osmotic pressure.* By following the treatment which led to equation XI.12, we obtain the following expression for the osmotic pressure of a regular solution:

$$\Pi = \frac{kT}{v_1}\left[\ln\left(\frac{N_1+N_2}{N_1}\right) - \left(\frac{N_2}{N_1+N_2}\right)^2 \frac{\Delta u^0}{kT}\right] \qquad \text{XI.42}$$

Table XI.1 gives a comparison of the observed osmotic pressure of aqueous solutions of sucrose with those calculated from equation XI.42, taking $\Delta u^0/kT$ as -7.06, which is the value afforded by equation XI.36. The partial molecular volumes of the solvent (column 1) are experimental values obtained as described later. More rigorous and general treatments of osmosis have been developed by Adair (1929) and Scatchard (1946).

4. *Excess thermodynamic functions of binary solutions.* It is expedient to subtract from the total change in free energy of mixing that part which is anticipated if liquids mix like ideal gases, and to refer to the

Table XI.1 *Observed osmotic pressure of solutions of sucrose in water at 0°C compared with those calculated on van Laar's theory*

$v_1 \times 10^{22}$ (cc per mole)	Weight fraction of sucrose	Molar fraction of water	II (atmospheres)	
			calculated from van Laar's equation	observed by Berkeley and collaborators
2·9588	0·3610	0·9712	43·87	43·84
2·9499	0·4481	0·9592	66·95	67·67
2·9419	0·5283	0·9445	99·08	100·43
2·9384	0·5851	0·9311	132·02	134·71

remainder as the excess free energy of mixing. This quantity we shall denote by the symbol ΔA^{ex}, which for isomegethic solutions formed at constant volume is, according to equations XI.31 and XI.32,

$$\Delta A^{ex} = \Delta E^{ex} = x_1 x_2 \Delta U^0 \qquad \text{XI.43}$$

Consequently

$$\Delta S^{ex} = 0 \qquad \text{XI.44}$$

Because experimental data refer to solutions formed at constant pressure, corrections are necessary before they can be compared with theoretical equations. Since $G = A + PV$, it follows that, for any change at constant pressure, $dG_P = dA_P + PdV_P$. At ordinary pressures, the last term is negligible, and ΔG^{ex} can be taken as equal to ΔA^{ex}. The excess increase in free energy on forming one mole of a binary solution may be measured from the composition and partial pressures of the vapour in equilibrium with the solution:

$$\Delta G^{ex} = x_1 \mu_1^{ex} + x_2 \mu_2^{ex} \qquad \text{XI.45}$$

The excess chemical potential of the first component is given by

$$\mu_1^{ex} = RT \ln(p_1/p_1^0)/x_1 \qquad \text{XI.46}$$

The increase in heat content attending the mixing of two liquids may be measured calorimetrically. The initial system consists of known amounts of the two pure liquids at thermal equilibrium in compartments separated by a thin tin foil. The lower compartment contains a steel bullet with a head sharp enough to pierce the diaphragm when the cell is inverted. By means of a thermistor, temperature changes can be measured to an accuracy of $0.001°$. From the temperature change and the amount and composition of the solution, ΔH_P can be measured correctly to within 1 calorie per mole, the standard deviation being usually about 0.6. The excess entropy of mixing is then given by the equation

$$T\Delta S^{ex} = \Delta H_P - \Delta G^{ex} \qquad \text{XI.47}$$

Results obtained in this way for solutions of methyl iodide in methylene dichloride, chloroform and carbon tetrachloride (Fig XI.7) show that the symmetrical equation

$$\Delta G^{ex} = x_1 x_2 \Delta U^0 \qquad \text{XI.48}$$

is obeyed with the respective ΔU^0 values of 90 ± 2, -32 ± 3, and

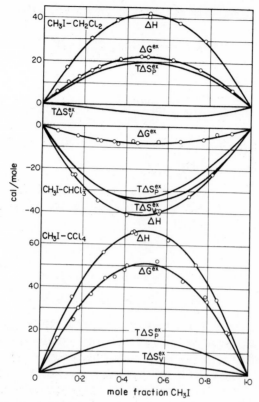

Fig. XI.7 *Excess thermodynamic functions:* CH_3I + *chloromethanes at* 25°C

204 ± 8 calories per mole of solution. These mean values reproduce the isotherms with a standard deviation of 0·4 mm Hg.

A correction due to Scatchard (1937) may be derived by considering the isothermal mixing of two liquids, first at a constant pressure, when the gain in energy of the system is dE_P, and secondly at a constant volume, when the gain in energy is dE_V. The two gains are clearly related as follows:

$$dE_P - dE_V = \left(\frac{dE}{dV}\right)_T dV$$

where dV is the increase in volume attending the mixing at constant

285

pressure. From equation VI.8 we have $dH_P = dE_P + PdV_P$. Hence

$$dH_P - dE_V = \left[P + \left(\frac{dE}{dV} \right)_T \right] dV_P$$

On using equations VI.32, we see that

$$dH_P - dE_V = T \left(\frac{dP}{dT} \right)_V dV = (\alpha T/\beta) \, dV_P$$

If, during the isothermal change, the ratio (α/β) is constant, we have

$$\Delta H_P - \Delta E_V = (\alpha T/\beta) \Delta V_P \qquad\qquad \text{XI.49}$$

which is Scatchard's equation. Now $T\Delta S_P = \Delta H_P - \Delta G$, and $T\Delta S_V = \Delta E_V - \Delta A$, and, as we are ignoring the difference between ΔG and ΔA, it follows that

$$\Delta S_P - \Delta S_V = (\alpha/\beta) \Delta V_P \qquad\qquad \text{XI.50}$$

Both entropy changes, less the ideal entropy change

$$\Delta S_i = -R(x_1 \ln x_1 + x_2 \ln x_2),$$

are shown in Fig. XI.7. The terms $T\Delta S_P^{ex}$ and $T\Delta S_V^{ex}$ for the first system considered are found to be 19·75 and $-4·0$ calories at the equimolar point. These are to be compared with $T\Delta S_i$, which is 411 calories. The theory under consideration thus accounts for the total entropy change to within 1 per cent. For an equimolar solution of methyl iodide and chloroform, the entropy of mixing is, even after correction, as much as 8 per cent below the ideal value. With these solutions, however, it is found that $d(\Delta U^0)/dT$ is about 0·5 cal/mole-deg. The excess entropy arising from this fact is seen from equation XI.43 to be

$$\Delta S^{ex} = -x_1 x_2 \frac{d(\Delta U^0)}{dT} \qquad\qquad \text{XI.51}$$

In sign and magnitude, therefore, all the experimental curves can be interpreted.

By contrast, solutions of methanol in the same three solvents are highly irregular. One instance is shown in Fig. XI.8. This difference in behaviour cannot be due to polarity, for methyl iodide and methanol have nearly the same dipole moment. It probably arises, as Zachariasen (1935) has suggested, from the transient hydrogen bridges in liquid methanol, which hold the molecules together in chain-like polymers. There is no evidence that liquid methyl iodide has such a structure. The positive excess entropy of mixing found in solutions weak in alcohol may thus be in part attributed to increased rotational entropy

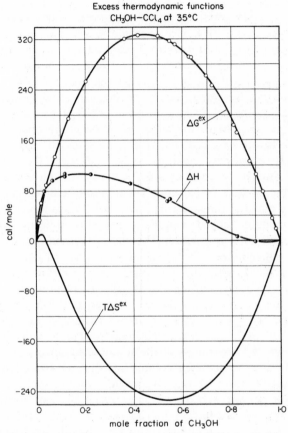

Fig. XI.8 *Excess thermodynamic functions:* CH_3OH-CCl_4 *at 35* (after Moelwyn-Hughes and Missen)

as the hydrogen-bridged network breaks up endothermally. Scatchard (1938) has suggested that the large negative excess entropies of mixing found over the greater part of the composition are due to clustering between like or unlike molecules.

Discussion of van Laar's treatment of isomegethic solutions

The treatment of solutions as if they consisted of molecules of approximately equal size, mixed randomly and exerting specific interactions on one another has, as we have seen, led to a relatively simple expression for the free energy of the solution, and to a consistent set of equations for other physicochemical properties which can be derived from the free energy. We may conclude that about one-half of the observed properties are satisfactorily explained in terms of the present form of van Laar's theory. Data on partial pressures, solubility and freezing-points, however, all indicate the falsity of the assumption that the interchange energy Δu^0 is independent of temperature. This conclusion is borne out by the data on solutions of chloroform, iodine and benzene in carbon disulphide. Many ways are open for us to amend the theory in the direction demanded by the facts. We can, for example, reconsider equation XI.24, and make the probability that a site shall be occupied by a particular type of molecule proportional to the product of its molar fraction and a Boltzmann factor, rather than equal to the molar fraction itself. This is a method which has been much employed; it leads to rather complicated equations which we shall not here consider. The physical reason why Δu^0 should vary with temperature is best realised by examining equation XI.26, from which we see that the interchange energy depends on the co-ordination number, c, and on the specific interaction energies, $\phi_{i,j}$. If, on heating a solution at constant volume, both the coordination number and the average distance apart of the molecules remained constant, Δu^0 would also remain constant. It is much more probable, however, that the orderliness of the solution diminishes as the temperature is raised at constant volume and that the two coordination numbers and the three interaction energies which characterise binary solutions all change. Finally, we must recall that the theory as it stands is one of near-neighbour interactions only, and takes no account of the attraction of a molecule for molecules beyond the first coordination shell. Such an additional attraction is known, from the study of pure liquids, to amount to as much as 20 per cent in certain cases. Moreover, it is dependent on temperature.

Important extensions to the present theory have been made by Scatchard (1931) and Hildebrand (1936), who have shown that volume fraction is more relevant than molar fraction in determining the properties of solutions. To their developments we shall return in a later section, after dealing with the general treatment of partial volumes in solution. In the meantime, we shall consider briefly some alternative approaches to the general theory of solutions.

Other theories of solutions

1. *The solvate theory of Poynting and Callendar.* It is a consequence of Raoult's law that the relative lowering in the vapour pressure of one component in a binary solution shall be equal to the molar fraction of the other component:

$$\frac{p_1^0 - p_1}{p_1^0} = \frac{N_2}{N_1 + N_2} \qquad \text{XI.1a}$$

Poynting (1896) posed the question of how a second component, if involatile, can lower the vapour pressure of the first component, and suggested that it did so by combining with it and rendering it incapable of vaporising. Deviations from Raoult's law exhibited by aqueous solutions could then be attributed to the formation of relatively involatile hydrates. The fact that even non-polar solutes such as bromine, carbon dioxide and the hydrocarbons form stable crystalline hydrates suggests that a similar, if weaker, fixation of solvent molecules persists in solution. Callendar (1908) applied the idea to explain deviations of the observed osmotic pressures from those given by van't Hoff's law (equation XI.15). If each of the N_2 molecules of solute is permanently attached to c molecules of solvent, the number of solvent molecules to be reckoned with is reduced from N_1 to $N_1 - cN_2$, and the conventional molar fraction of the solvent is reduced from $N_1/(N_1 + N_2)$ to $(N_1 - cN_2)/N_1 - cN_2 + N_2$. Equation XI.12 consequently becomes

$$\pi = \frac{kT}{v_1} \ln \left[1 + \left(\frac{N_2}{N_1 - cN_2} \right) \right]. \qquad \text{XI.52}$$

The value of $c = 5$ proposed by Callendar is less satisfactory than that of $c = 6$, proposed by Findlay (1913). Adopting the latter value, which is supported by cryoscopic evidence (Washburn, 1910), we calculate the osmotic pressures of aqueous solutions of sucrose listed in the last column of Table XI.2. The molar ratios (column 2) have been calculated from the densities. Except for the most concentrated solution, equation XI.52, despite its simplicity, suffices to reproduce the facts. The Poynting–Callendar theory has been extended by allowing

K*

for the fact that the degree of hydration of the solute is a function of temperature and composition (Moelwyn-Hughes, 1951).

Table XI.2 *The osmotic pressures of aqueous solutions of sucrose at 0°C*

Concentration of solute, in grams per litre of solution	Molar ratio $\left(\dfrac{N_2}{N_1}\right) \times 10^4$	Osmotic pressure in atmospheres		
		observed (Berkeley and Hartley, 1906)	equation (15) (van't Hoff)	equation (52) (Callendar)
2·02	1·064	0·134	0·132	0·133
10·0	5·294	0·66	0·655	0·661
20·0	10·64	1·32	1·310	1·332
45·0	24·22	2·97	2·947	3·056
93·75	51·99	6·18	6·141	6·662
150·8	87·42	11·8	9·877	11·43
300	193·6	26·8	19·65	26·99
558·5	445·3	71·8	39·59	73·41
750	737·2	134·7	49·14	154·5

2. *Dolezalek's theory.* The basic assumptions underlying Dolezalek's theory of binary liquid mixtures are that Raoult's law is applicable to each species in solution, and that, due to association between like molecules or complex formation between unlike molecules, the so-called binary system consists in fact of more than two species. Ideal solutions are those in which the molecules of types A and B neither associate nor combine to form a complex, AB. Positive deviations from Raoult's law are due to dimerisation (A_2, B_2) or polymerisation (A_n, B_n) of either or of both components. Negative deviations are due to the formation of a complex or complexes between unassociated components. From his analysis of the data of Raoult and von Zawidski, Dolezalek (1908) argued that the system ethylene dibromide—propylene dibromide consisted solely of unpolymerised molecules, that the system methyl salicylate—diethyl ether contained double molecules of the ester, and that the system acetone—chloroform contained complex molecules of the type AB.

One example shall suffice to illustrate the method of analysis. Let us consider a system which contains, in all, N_1 molecules of the first type and, in all, N_2 molecules of the second type. We shall suppose that the equilibrium system contains also a number, N_c, of complex molecules of the type AB, so that

$$N_1 = N_1' + N_c$$

and

$$N_2 = N_2' + N_c$$

where the dashed numbers refer to free molecules. The equilibrium constant for the reaction,

$$A + B \rightleftarrows AB$$

in terms of molar fractions is consequently

$$K = \frac{N_c/\Sigma N}{(N_1'/\Sigma N)(N_2'/\Sigma N)} = \frac{N_c\Sigma N}{(N_1 - N_c)(N_2 - N_c)} \qquad \text{XI.53}$$

where

$$\Sigma N = N_1' + N_2' + N_c = N_1 + N_2 - N_c$$

Hence

$$K = \frac{N_c(N_1 + N_2 - N_c)}{(N_1 - N_c)(N_2 - N_c)}$$

Now

$$\frac{p_1}{p_1^0} = \frac{N_1'}{\Sigma N} = \frac{(N_1 - N_c)}{\Sigma N}$$

and

$$\frac{p_2}{p_2^0} = \frac{N_2'}{\Sigma N} = \frac{(N_2 - N_c)}{\Sigma N}$$

so that

$$N_c = \frac{N_1(p_2/p_2^0) - N_2(p_1/p_1^0)}{(p_2/p_2^0) - (p_1/p_1^0)}$$

The number of complex molecules in the system can thus be found in terms of its composition and the partial pressures of the components; and the equilibrium constant is then determined by means of equation XI.53. For example, K for the formation of the acetone–chloroform

291

complex at $35 \cdot 17°C$ is found to be $1 \cdot 25$, and for the dimerisation of methyl salicylate in ether solution at $14 \cdot 1°$ is $2 \cdot 9$. By applying the van't Hoff isochore to values of K obtained in this way, Schulze (1919) derives increases in heat content, ΔH, which are in reasonable agreement with the calorimetric data. The Dolezalek–Schulze theory has been extensively applied to the determination of many other properties of solution.

That dimers and intermolecular complexes frequently exist in solution is no longer in doubt. Indeed, our quantitative information concerning them is now both extensive and precise. The carboxylic acids, the phenyl halides and the monohydric alcohols form double molecules and sometimes higher polymers in many solvents. The thermodynamic constants governing their formation have been measured, and in certain cases have been given quantitative interpretations in terms of intermolecular forces. Complexes have been equally well characterised. Beryllium benzolcamphor in chloroform solution forms a complex with two molecules of the solvent, which has been isolated as a crystal (Lowry and Traill, 1931). Trinitrobenzene forms complexes with dibenzyl, tolan and stilbene (Briegleb and Kambeitz, 1934). The equilibrium constant for the formation of a 1–1 complex between p-toluidine and p-chlorophenol in benzene solution has been shown to be, in terms of activities, constant while the molar ratio of the reactants is varied by a factor of 100 (Madgin, 1937). Thus the basic assumption of the Dolezalek–Schulze theory is well founded in fact. The two subsidiary assumptions, that equilibrium is determined by molar fractions, and that Raoult's law is obeyed by each species, are not only suspect but now known to be false. Nevertheless, the appearance of the theory served a salutory service in directing attention to the more chemical aspects of the problem of solutions.

Van Laar and Dolezalek, regarding their theories as mutually exclusive, had bitter comments to make about each other's efforts, and failed to see that their theories differed only in emphasis. Van Laar's treatment, being a thermodynamic one, would have been also a general one had he not restricted it to fluids which were assumed, without sufficient evidence, to obey the equation of van der Waals. When the intermolecular forces, which he envisaged as diffuse and of a physical nature, become directional and specific, we arrive automatically at the definite chemical complexes and polymers in terms of which Dolezalek preferred to treat the problem.

3. *Free space theories.* On expanding equation XI.52 to the first term only, we obtain for the osmotic pressure of dilute solutions the relation

$$\Pi = \frac{kT}{v_1}\left(\frac{N_2}{N_1 - cN_2}\right)$$

If the total volume, V, of solution is the sum of the volume, $(N_1 - cN_2)v_1$, of the free solvent molecules and the volume, $N_2 v_c$, of the solvated solute molecules, it follows that

$$\Pi = \frac{n_2 kT}{1 - n_2 v_c,}$$
XI.54

where n_2 is the concentration (N_2/V) of the solute, in molecules per cc of solution. Theories of hydration thus lead to osmotic laws of the free-space type. This equation is most conveniently applied in the form

$$\frac{\Pi}{n_2} = kT + v_c\Pi$$
XI.55

or, if we denote concentrations by c moles per litre of solution, and the forbidden volume by B ccs per mole,

$$\frac{\Pi}{c} = RT + B\Pi$$
XI.56

Many of the older data can be well reproduced by this equation. In water of 0°C, for example, B is found to be 50 cm³ for methyl alcohol, 72 for ethyl alcohol, 150 for glucose and 300 for sucrose. (Sackur, (1912).) At the same temperature, the osmotic pressure of haemo-globin in water is given by the equation

$$\Pi = \frac{n_2 kT}{1 - 3\cdot24 n_2 v_2},$$
XI.57

where v_2 is the partial molecular volume of the solute. (Adair, (1947).)

Partial molar quantities: the Gibbs–Duhem–Margules equation

A deep-seated belief in an additivity law has brought into thermo-dynamics a set of conventional equations designed to express the magnitude of any extensive property, X, of a homogeneous system

293

containing many components in the form

$$X = N_1X_1 + N_2X_2 + N_3X_3 + \cdots \qquad \text{XI.58}$$

where the N's are the numbers of molecules of the various components in the system at a constant temperature and pressure, and X_i is the partial molecular value of the extensive property, X, of component i. Assuming that X can be expressed as a function of temperature, pressure and composition,

$$X = f(T, P, N_i, N_j \ldots)$$

any change in X may be formulated as follows:

$$dX = \left(\frac{\partial X}{\partial T}\right)_{P,N_1,N_2,N_3\ldots} dT + \left(\frac{\partial X}{\partial P}\right)_{T,N_1,N_2,N_3\ldots} dP$$

$$+ \left(\frac{\partial X}{\partial N_1}\right)_{T,P,N_2\ldots} dN_1 + \left(\frac{\partial X}{\partial N_2}\right)_{T,P,N_1,\ldots} dN_2 + \cdots$$

In particular, any change in $\overset{\cdot}{X}$ at constant temperature and pressure is

$$dX_{T,P} = \left(\frac{\partial X}{\partial N_1}\right)_{T,P,N_2,N_3,N_4\ldots} dN_1 + \left(\frac{\partial X}{\partial N_2}\right)_{T,P,N_1,N_3,N_4\ldots} dN_2$$

$$+ \left(\frac{\partial X}{\partial N_3}\right)_{\overset{\cdot}{T},P,N_1,N_2,N_4\ldots} dN_3 + \cdots$$

Omitting but not forgetting the subscripts, we have

$$dX = X_1dN_1 + X_2dN_2 + X_3dN_3 + \cdots = \sum X_i dN_i \qquad \text{XI.59}$$

Now let us build up a system, at constant T and P, which finally is to contain N_1 molecules of type 1, N_2 molecules of type 2, and so on, by the simultaneous addition of small numbers dN_1, dN_2, and so on, in the constant proportions finally required. Because of the stipulation of constancy of composition, the partial molecular values X_1, $X_2, \ldots$ remain constant during the construction of the system. This equation may thus be integrated directly to give

$$X = X_1N_1 + X_2N_2 + X_3N_3 + \cdots = \sum X_i N_i$$

If the numbers N_i refer to moles rather than molecules, X_i is termed the partial molar value of X for species i. Let us now differentiate equation XI.58, at constant T and P, without imposing the artificiality required in its derivation. Then

$$dX = X_1 dN_1 + N_1 dX_1 + X_2 dN_2 + N_2 dX_2 + \cdots = \sum X_i dN_i + \sum N_i dX_i.$$

On subtracting equation XI.59, we find

$$N_1 dX_1 + N_2 dX_2 + \cdots = \sum N_i dX_i = 0$$

In the particular case when X is G,

$$\sum N_i \, d\mu_i = 0 \qquad \qquad \text{XI.60}$$

which is the equation of Gibbs, Duhem, and Margules.

The partial molar volumes of a binary solution

Let us apply this convention to determine the partial molar volumes of the two components in a homogeneous binary system. Its volume may be written as follows:

$$V = v_1 V_1 + v_2 V_2 \qquad \qquad \text{XI.61}$$

where V_1 and V_2 are the partial molar volumes of components 1 and 2 respectively. On dividing each term by the total number $v_1 + v_2$ of gram-moles in the system we have

$$\bar{V} = \frac{V}{v_1 + v_2} = x_1 V_1 + x_2 V_2 \qquad \qquad \text{XI.62}$$

where x denotes the molar fraction, and $\bar{V}$ is the molar volume of the solution, i.e. the volume of a solution which contains in all one gram-mole of substance. In terms of the weight fractions, w, the molar weights, M, and the density, ρ, of the solution, we have

$$\bar{V} = \frac{1}{\rho \left(\dfrac{w_1}{M_1} + \dfrac{w_2}{M_2} \right)}, \qquad \qquad \text{XI.62}$$

or, since $w_1 + w_2 = 1$,

$$\bar{V} = \frac{1}{\rho} \left[\frac{M_1 M_2}{M_2 + (M_1 - M_2) w_2} \right]. \qquad \qquad \text{XI.63}$$

From experimental values of the specific volume, $1/\rho$, and the weight fraction of one component, the molar volume $\bar{V}$ of the solution may thus be found. Because $x_1 + x_2 = 1$, equation XI.62 takes the form

$$\bar{V} = V_1 + (V_2 - V_1) x_2, \qquad \qquad \text{XI.64}$$

from which, by the method of intercepts, the partial molar volumes, V_1 and V_2 may be determined. The tangent of the $\bar{V}-x_2$ curve at any composition intercepts the two ordinates ($x_2 = 0$ and $x_2 = 1$) to give the values of V_1 and V_2 at that composition (Fig. XI.9). Table XI.3 gives values of the partial molar volumes of water and methanol in water-methanol mixtures at 15°C. If V_1^0 and V_2^0 denote, respectively, the molar volumes of pure water and methanol at the same temperature, the increase in volume on making one mole of solution is clearly

$$\Delta V = x_1 V_1 + x_2 V_2 - (x_1 V_1^0 + x_2 V_2^0)$$

$$= (V_1 - V_1^0) + [(V_2 - V_2^0) - (V_1 - V_1^0)]x_2 \qquad \text{XI.65}$$

Numerical values for the system under consideration are given in Table XI.3 and are shown in Fig. XI.10, from which we see that ΔV has a value of -1 cm^3 when x_2 is 0·475. At low concentrations of

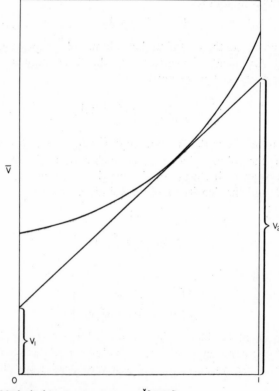

Fig. XI.9 *Method of intercepts* $x_2 \longrightarrow$

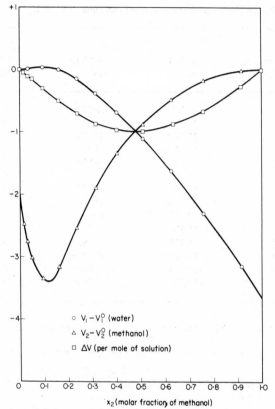

Fig. XI.10   *The partial molar volumes of water and methanol at 288·16°K*

methanol, the partial molar volume of water exceeds that of pure water. Over most of the range, however, the reverse is true. $V_2 - V_2^0$ passes through a minimum when x_2 is 0·125.

Heats of mixing and heats of dissolution

Heat content is another extensive property of solutions which may be examined in the same way. Analysis of thermal data on the methanol-water system serves as an example.

The heat evolved when a gram of solution is made is given in column 3 of Table XI.4 (E. and M. Bose, 1912). To evaluate the heat

297

Table XI.3 *Partial molar volumes of water and methanol at 288·2°K*

x_2 (molar fraction of methanol)	V_1 (water) cm³	V_2 (methanol) cm³	ΔV (cm³ per mole of solution)
0	18·0318	(38·27)	0
0·01437	18·0317	37·7951	−0·0336
0·02940	18·0319	37·5269	−0·1147
0·04377	18·0468	37·2879	−0·1161
0·09102	18·0683	36·9303	−0·2795
0·15871	18·0435	37·1185	−0·4943
0·23341	17·8964	37·7294	−0·6961
0·36127	17·6584	38·3644	−0·8569
0·40871	17·3510	38·9079	−0·9579
0·51249	16·9361	39·4022	−0·9771
0·62983	16·4249	39·7922	−0·8369
0·76360	15·7291	40·1016	−0·6698
0·91750	14·8960	40·2660	−0·2587
1·00000	(14.37)	40·2661	0

Table XI.4 *Heats of mixing and heats of dissolution in the methanol-water system at 292·85°K*

w_2 (Weight fraction of methanol)	x_2 (molar fraction of methanol)	Heat evolved (in calories)			
		per gram of solution formed	per mole of solution formed	per mole of methanol dissolved	per mole of water dissolved
0	0	—	0	(1 740)	0
0·05	0·0288	2·63	48·5	1 686	50
0·10	0·0588	5·02	94·6	1 608	101
0·15	0·0903	6·88	132·6	1 470	146
0·20	0·1233	8.31	160·7	1 304	183
0·30	0·1942	9·96	205·5	1 065	256
0·40	0·2747	10·07	219·9	807	302
0·50	0·3599	9·38	216·3	601	338
0·60	0·4576	8·31	203·0	443	374
0·70	0·5675	6·93	179.9	317	416
0·80	0·6923	5·26	145·9	211	474
0·90	0·8347	3·13	93·1	111	564
1·00	1·0000	—	0	0	(770)

when one gram-mole of solution is formed from its components, we must find the weight W of solution which contains one gram-mole of substance. In the present instance it is clearly $W = x_1 M_1 + x_2 M_2 = M_1 + (M_2 - M_1)x_2 = 18 \cdot 016 + 14 \cdot 027\ x_2$, where the molar fraction x_2 of methanol can be derived from its weight fraction w_2 by means of the equation

$$x_2 = \left[1 + \frac{M_2}{M_1} \left(\frac{1 - w_2}{w_2} \right) \right]^{-1}$$

The resulting values x_2 and of $-\Delta H$ are given in columns 2 and 4 of Table XI.4, and are plotted in Fig. XI.11, as a function of x_2. In the

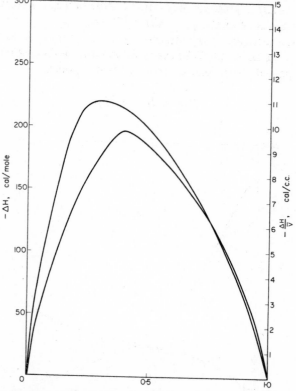

Fig. XI.11   *Molar heat of mixing methanol and water at 292·85°C. Upper curve: left ordinate, heat evolved on forming one mole of solution; abscissa, molar fraction. Lower curve: right ordinate, heat evolved on forming one cc of solution, abscissa volume fraction*

same diagram will be found the heat evolved per unit volume of solution formed, plotted as a function of the volume fraction θ_2 of methanol. This curve is seen to be a more symmetrical one, as anticipated in Scatchard's theory, which is discussed later. The integral heat of dissolution, defined as the heat evolved when one gram-mole dissolves, is usually a function of the composition of the solution formed. To evaluate it, regarding methanol as the solute, we multiply the heat evolved on making one gram of solution (column 3) by the weight of solution which contains one gram-mole of solute: this is clearly M_2/w_2. The results for methanol and water are given in columns 5 and 6. Slight extrapolations of the curves in Fig. XI.12 indicate that, when 1 mole of methanol dissolves in an infinite amount of water, $-\Delta H$ is 1 740 cal, and when 1 mole of water dissolves in an infinite amount of methanol, $-\Delta H$ is 770 cal.

The heat content of one gram-mole of a binary system can, like its volume (equation XI.61) be expressed in terms of the molar fractions and the partial molar heat contents of its components:

$$\bar{H} = x_1H_1 + x_2H_2 \qquad \text{XI.66}$$

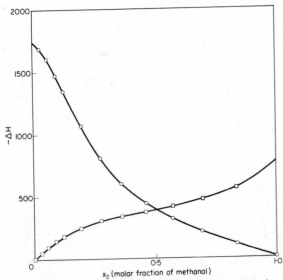

Fig. XI.12   *Integral heats of dissolution (cals. per mole of solute) of methanol in water (circles) and of water in methanol (squares) at 292·85°K*

Denoting by H_1^0 and H_2^0 the molar heat contents of the pure components, the increase in heat content attending the formation of one gram-mole of solution is

$$\Delta H = x_1(H_1 - H_1^0) + x_2(H_2 - H_2^0)$$
$$= (H_1 - H_1^0) + x_2[(H_2 - H_2^0) - (H_1 - H_1^0)]$$
$$= \Delta H_1 + x_2(\Delta H_2 - \Delta H_1), \qquad \text{XI.67}$$

where ΔH_1 is the partial molar increase in heat content attributable to the first component, and $-\Delta H_1$ is the partial molar heat of its dissolution. This quantity, and the analogous term ΔH_2, can be found by the method of intercepts. Some values so derived for the present system are given in Table XI.5.

Table XI.5 *Partial molar heats of dissolution of water in methanol* $(-\Delta H_1)$ *and of methanol in water* $(-\Delta H_2)$ *at* 298·85°K (cal/mole)

x_2	$-\Delta H_1$	$-\Delta H_2$
0	0	1 740
0·25	194	310
0·50	309	79
0·75	356	40
1·00	770	0

A comparison of Figs. XI.10 and XI.11 shows that ΔV and ΔH are both negative over the whole composition. A rough parallelism between these two quantities is fairly general, not only for a given system at various compositions, but for different systems. Contraction is usually associated with the evolution of heat, and expansion with its absorption.

The heats of escape of one gram-mole of solute from an infinitely dilute solution to the vapour phase can be obtained by combining these results with the heats of vaporisation of pure liquids. We have

$$\Delta H(\text{cal/mole})$$

H_2O (inf. dilute soln. in methanol)	$\rightarrow H_2O$(liq.)	770
H_2O (liq.)	$\rightarrow H_2O$(vap.)	10 556
H_2O (inf. dilute soln. in methanol)	$\rightarrow H_2O$(vap.)	11 326

Similarly,

CH_3OH (inf. dilute aq. solution)	$\rightarrow CH_3OH$(liq.)	1 740
CH_3OH (liq.)	$\rightarrow CH_3OH$(vap.)	9 120
CH_3OH (inf. dilute aq. solution)	$\rightarrow CH_3OH$(vap.) .	10 860

If the molecules were symmetrical and of equal volume, we would expect the two heats of escape to be equal, as both processes would then entail the breaking of bonds of the same number and type.

The Hildebrand–Scatchard theory of binary solutions

The more general theory of solutions due to Hildebrand and Scatchard may be outlined here, using the same notation as in our treatment of van Laar's theory.

We again consider a solution containing N_1 molecules of the first kind, with a molecular volume v_1, each capable of making c_1 contacts with other molecules. Let N_2, v_2 and c_2 be the corresponding values for the molecules of the second type. Each contact of the 1–1 type contributes an interaction energy of magnitude ϕ_{11}; single contacts of the 2–2 and 1–2 types contribute interaction energies of magnitude ϕ_{22} and ϕ_{12}, respectively. We assume, as in the previous discussion, that first-neighbour interactions alone need be taken into account. Further, we assume that the chance that a single contact shall be of a given type is proportional to the volume fraction, rather than the molar fraction, of that type of molecule. Then the energy of interaction of one molecule of the first type with those molecules which immediately surround it is

$$c_1\phi_{11}\frac{N_1v_1}{V}+c_1\phi_{12}\frac{N_2v_2}{V},$$

Following the procedure which led to equation XI.27, we now find the total potential energy to be

$$U = N_1(\tfrac{1}{2}c_1\phi_{11})+N_2(\tfrac{1}{2}c_2\phi_{22})+\tfrac{1}{2}\frac{N_1N_2}{N_1v_1+N_2v_2}[\phi_{12}(c_1v_2+c_2v_1)$$
$$-\phi_{11}c_1v_2-\phi_{22}c_2v_1] \qquad \text{XI.68}$$

which is as far as the problem can be formulated, without introducing further assumptions. Denoting $\tfrac{1}{2}c_1\phi_{11}$ by u_1^0, and differentiating with respect to N_1, we find the partial molecular potential energy of a

302

molecule of the first type to be

$$u_1 = \left(\frac{dU}{dN_1}\right)_{N_2} = u_1^0 + \beta\left(\frac{N_2 v_2}{N_1 v_1 + N_2 v_2}\right)^2$$

where

$$\beta = \tfrac{1}{2}\left[\phi_{12}\left(c_1 + c_2\frac{v_1}{v_2}\right) - \phi_{11}c_1 - \phi_{22}c_2\frac{v_1}{v_2}\right] \qquad \text{XI.69}$$

To eliminate ϕ_{12}, Scatchard assumes that

$$\tfrac{1}{2}\phi_{12}\left(\frac{c_1}{v_1} + \frac{c_2}{v_2}\right) = \sqrt{\frac{c_1\phi_{11}}{v_1}\frac{c_2\phi_{22}}{v_2}} \qquad \text{XI.70}$$

After some slight algebraic rearrangement, the expression for the total potential energy of the system may then be written as follows:

$$U = N_1 u_1^0 + N_2 u_2^0 - \frac{N_1 N_2 v_1 v_2}{N_1 v_1 + N_2 v_2}\left(\sqrt{\frac{u_1^0}{v_1}} - \sqrt{\frac{u_2^0}{v_2}}\right)^2 \qquad \text{XI.71}$$

or, replacing each u^0 term by $-\lambda$, where λ is positive,

$$U = -N_1\lambda_1 - N_2\lambda_2 + \frac{N_1 N_2 v_1 v_2}{N_1 v_1 + N_2 v_2}\left(\sqrt{\frac{\lambda_1}{v_1}} - \sqrt{\frac{\lambda_2}{v_2}}\right)^2 \qquad \text{XI.72}$$

The partial molecular potential energy of the molecules now takes on the simple forms

$$u_1 = \left(\frac{dU}{dN_1}\right)_{N_2} = u_1^0 + \left(\frac{N_2 v_2}{N_1 v_1 + N_2 v_2}\right)^2 v_1\left(\sqrt{\frac{\lambda_1}{v_1}} - \sqrt{\frac{\lambda_2}{v_2}}\right)^2$$

and

$$u_2 = \left(\frac{dU}{dN_2}\right)_{N_1} = u_2^0 + \left(\frac{N_1 v_1}{N_1 v_1 + N_2 v_2}\right)^2 v_2\left(\sqrt{\frac{\lambda_1}{v_1}} - \sqrt{\frac{\lambda_2}{v_2}}\right)^2 \qquad \text{XI.73}$$

If the potential energy is independent of temperature, the gain in heat content on forming a solution becomes

$$\Delta H = \Delta E = U - (U_1 + U_2)$$

$$= \frac{N_1 N_2 v_1 v_2}{N_1 v_1 + N_2 v_2}A_{12} \qquad \text{XI.74}$$

where the constant, A_{12}, known as the solubility parameter, is

$$A_{12} = \left(\sqrt{\frac{\lambda_1}{v_1}} - \sqrt{\frac{\lambda_2}{v_2}}\right)^2 \qquad \text{XI.75}$$

303

This result we can more conveniently express as follows:

$$\Delta H = \frac{N_1 N_2 v_1 v_2}{N_1 v_1 + N_2 v_2} A_{12} = \frac{N_1 v_1}{V} \frac{N_2 v_2}{V} V A_{12}$$
$$= \theta_1 \theta_2 V A_{12}$$
$$= \theta_1 (1 - \theta_1) V A_{12} \qquad \text{XI.76}$$

where the θ terms are volume fractions, and V is the total volume of the solution. Hence,

$$\frac{\Delta H}{V} = \theta_1 (1 - \theta_1) A_{12} \qquad \text{XI.77}$$

On plotting the term on the left against the volume fraction, we should thus obtain a symmetrical curve, with a maximum or a minimum when θ_1 is $\frac{1}{2}$. The constant A_{12} is then four times the magnitude of $\Delta H/V$ at the maximum or minimum. The upper curve of Fig. XI.13 illustrates

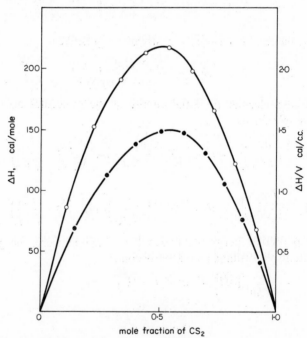

Fig. XI.13 *Increases in heat content attending the formation of one gram-mole of carbon disulphide–chloroform mixtures at 290°K. Lower curve: ΔH plotted against molar fraction of CS_2. Upper curve: $\Delta H/V$ plotted against volume fraction of CS_2 (after Scatchard, Wood and Mochel, 1939).*

304

this relationship for the carbon disulphide-chloroform system. In this case there is no doubt that the present treatment gives the more symmetrical curve. The computed value of A_{12}, however, is lower by a factor of about 14 than that obtained from the analysis of the calorimetric data. Thus although quantitative confirmation of the theory is not always available, it gives qualitative expression to a useful solubility rule, i.e. substances are mutually soluble according to the similarity in their energy densities, or, as Hildebrand first assumed, their statical pressure, $-dE/dV$.

A statistical treatment of binary solutions formed from molecules of different sizes

As there seems at present no prospect of formulating an exact theory of the type of binary solution here contemplated, we shall be content with one which has the correct form, adopting as the system partition function:

$$F = \left(\frac{q_1 Ve}{N_1}\right)^{N_1} \left(\frac{q_2 Ve}{N_2}\right)^{N_2} e^{-U/kT} \qquad \text{XI.78}$$

where the q terms, which include the molecular partition functions for internal motions, are functions of the temperature only, and

$$U = N_1 u_1^0 + N_2 u_2^0 + \left(\frac{N_1 N_2 \sqrt{v_1 v_2}}{N_1 v_1 + N_2 v_2}\right) \Delta u^0$$

$$= N_1 u_1^0 + N_2 u_2^0 + (N_1 N_2 \theta_1 \theta_2)^{1/2} \Delta u^0 \qquad \text{XI.79}$$

and

$$\Delta u^0 = \tfrac{1}{2}\left[\phi_{12}\left(c_1 \sqrt{\frac{v_2}{v_1}} + c_2 \sqrt{\frac{v_1}{v_2}}\right) - \phi_{11} c_1 \sqrt{\frac{v_2}{v_1}} - \phi_{22} c_2 \sqrt{\frac{v_1}{v_2}}\right] \quad \text{XI.80}$$

as derived in the last section (equation XI.68). We shall not, however, limit ourselves to the special form of Δu^0 assumed by Scatchard, but note that Δu^0, like u_1^0 and u_2^0, is a function of the partial molecular volumes, v_1 and v_2. Progress can now be made only when these partial molecular volumes, occurring in the equation

$$v = N_1 v_1 + N_2 v_2 \qquad \text{XI.81}$$

are independent of the composition. The treatment is thus limited to solutions which, on being formed from their liquid components, do not

305

change in volume. The methods of deriving the thermodynamic properties of the solution are those previously used, and the resulting equations resemble those derived earlier, with volume fractions replacing molar fractions. There are, however, other, less easily predictable, differences. The chemical potentials, for example, expressed in terms of molecular concentrations ($n_1 = N_1/V; n_2 = N_2/V$), are

$$\mu_1 = \mu_1^0 + kT \ln n_1 v_1 + kTn_2(v_2 - v_1) + (P - P^0)v_1 + n_2^2 v_2 \sqrt{v_1 v_2} \Delta u^0$$

$$\mu_2 = \mu_2^0 + kT \ln n_2 v_2 + kTn_1(v_1 - v_2) + (P - P^0)v_2 + n_1^2 v_1 \sqrt{v_1 v_2} \Delta u^0$$

$$\text{XI.82}$$

where μ^0 is the chemical potential of the pure component, at the temperature of the solution, and at some reference pressure, P^0.

Osmotic equilibrium obtains when μ_1 for the solvent in solution at T and P equals μ_1^0 for the pure solvent at T and P^0, i.e. $\mu_1(T, P) = \mu_1^0 (T, P^0)$. The osmotic pressure is thus

$$\prod = P - P^0 = \frac{kT}{v_1}\left[-\ln n_1 v_1 - n_2(v_2 - v_1) - n_2^2 v_2 \sqrt{v_1 v_2}\frac{\Delta u^0}{kT} \right]$$

or, since $n_1 v_1 = 1 - n_2 v_2$,

$$\prod = \frac{kT}{v_1}\left[-\ln (1 - n_2 v_2) - n_2(v_2 - v_1) - n_2^2 v_2 \sqrt{v_1 v_2}\frac{\Delta u^0}{kT} \right] \quad \text{XI.83}$$

On expanding the logarithmic term, and ignoring powers of $n_2 v_2$ beyond the second, we see that deviations from van't Hoff's laws at low concentrations vary linearly as the volume fraction of the solute:

$$\prod = kTn_2\left[1 + n_2 v_2\left(\frac{1}{2}\frac{v_2}{v_1} - \sqrt{\frac{v_2}{v_1}} \cdot \frac{\Delta u^0}{kT} \right) \right] \quad \text{XI.83a}$$

The condition of equilibrium between either component of the solution and that component in the vapour phase is obtained by equating the chemical potentials in the two phases. Let the reference pressure, P^0, be now taken as the saturation pressure, p_1^0, for the first component, so that in solution, we have

$$\mu_1 = \mu_1^0 + kT \ln n_1 v_1 + kTn_2(v_2 - v_1)$$
$$+ (P - p_1^0)v_1 + n_2^2 v_2 \sqrt{v_1 v_2}\, \Delta u^0 \quad \text{XI.84}$$

in which P is the pressure of the system, and μ_1^0 the chemical potential of the first component in the pure state at a pressure p_1^0. If the vapour obeys the ideal gas laws, we have

$$\mu_1(\text{vapour}, p_1) = \mu_1^0(\text{sat vap}, p_1^0) + kT \ln (p_1/p_1^0), \qquad \text{XI.3}$$

and

$$\mu_1(\text{vapour}, P) = \mu_1^0(\text{liq or sat vap}, p_1^0) + kT \ln (p_1/p_1^0) + (P - p_1^0)v_1.$$

On equating μ_1 for both phases at the common total pressure P, we have

$$\ln \frac{p_1}{p_1^0} = \ln n_1 v_1 + n_2(v_2 - v_1) + n_2^2 v_2 \sqrt{v_1 v_2}(\Delta u^0/kT). \qquad \text{XI.85}$$

In terms of the volume fractions, the relative partial pressures of the components are:

$$\frac{p_1}{p_1^0} = \theta_1 e^{\theta_2 \left(1 - \frac{v_1}{v_2}\right)} . e^{\theta_2^2 \left(\frac{v_1}{v_2}\right)^{1/2} \frac{\Delta u^0}{kT}}$$

$$\text{XI.86}$$

Applied to aqueous solutions of sucrose (Table XI.6), equation XI.86 gives a consistent value of Δu^0, which, unlike that obtained from equation XI.42, is positive, and, therefore, more consistent with thermal data.

Table XI.6 *Partial pressures and composition of aqueous solutions of sucrose at* 273·16°K
($v_1 = 29·72 \times 10^{-24}$ cm³ $v_2 = 336·3 \times 10^{-24}$ cm³ $v_2/v_1 = 11·32$)

$\dfrac{N_1}{N_1+N_2}$	$\dfrac{N_1 v_1}{N_1 v_1 + N_2 v_2}$	$\dfrac{p_1}{p_1^0}$ (obs)	$\dfrac{p_1}{p_1^0}$ (calc)	Δ	$\left(\dfrac{v_1}{v_2}\right)^{1/2} \dfrac{\Delta u^0}{kT}$	$\dfrac{\Delta u^0}{kT}$
0·9712	0·7460	0·9655	0·9648	+0·0007	0·412	1·387
0·9592	0·6725	0·9486	0·9477	+0·0009	0·429	1·443
0·9445	0·6039	0·9233	0·9264	−0·0031	0·407	1·370
0·9311	0·5444	0·8988	0·8993	−0·0005	0·418	1·406
0·9120	0·4794	0·8632	0·8632	0	0·421	1·417
0·8973	0·4346	0·8321	0·8312	+0·0009	0·422	1·420
0·8865	0·4085	0·8133	0·8108	+0·0025	0·429	1·443
				Average	0·420	1·412

The interchange energy

If we assume that the number of contacts, c, is proportional to the molecular volume, v, equation XI.80 becomes

$$\Delta u^0 = \tfrac{1}{2}\sqrt{(c_1 c_2)}(2\phi_{12} - \phi_{11} - \phi_{22}), \qquad \text{XI.87}$$

which reduces, when $c_1 = c_2$, to equation XI.26. With the same supposition, equation XI.70 becomes

$$\phi_{12} = \sqrt{(\phi_{11}\phi_{22})}, \qquad \text{XI.88}$$

which is Scatchard's assumption in its original form. That the inter-action energy of a dissimilar pair should be the geometric mean of the interaction energies of like pairs at the same separation is a conse-quence of Coulomb's law for ions with charges e_i and e_j, because, at a common distance, r, apart, $\phi_{ii} = e_i^2/r$; $\phi_{jj} = e_{jj}^2/r$, and $\phi_{ij} = e_i e_j/r$ The improbable assumption of a common r leads to equation XI.88 (Berthelot, 1898). To derive a relationship between ϕ_{12} and $\phi_{11} + \phi_{22}$ when, as is usually the case, the interaction energies vary inversely as some high power of the intermolecular separation, is a recondite theoretical problem, and one to which the most precise experimental data cannot give an authoritative answer. The simplest expression for the interchange energy,

$$\Delta u^0 = c(\phi_{12} - \tfrac{1}{2}\phi_{11} - \tfrac{1}{2}\phi_{22}) \qquad \text{XI.26}$$

on being multiplied by N_0 gives us the molar interchange energy ΔU^0. If we ignore the energy contribution due to thermal motion, we may identify $-\tfrac{1}{2}c\phi_{11}$ with λ_1, the heat of vaporisation per molecule so that

$$-N_0 c\phi_{12} = L_1 + L_2 - \Delta U^0 \qquad \text{XI.8}$$

which enables us to evaluate ϕ_{12}. In the acetone-chloroform system for example, ϕ_{12} is found to exceed $2kT$, even allowing for the highe conceivable value of c. From equation XI.69, however, it follows tha in dilute solution,

$$u_2 - u_2^0 = \tfrac{1}{2}\left[\left(c_1 + c_2\frac{v_1}{v_2}\right)\phi_{12} - c_1\phi_{11} - c_2\left(\frac{v_1}{v_2} - 1\right)\phi_{22}\right] \qquad \text{XI.9}$$

which acknowledges that interactions of the 1–2 type consist of two components. J. A. V. Butler and Ramchandani (1935) have resolve

308

ϕ_{12} into as many components as are required by the structure of the solute:

$$u_2(\text{aq}) - u_2^0(\text{vap}) = \tfrac{1}{2}(\sum c_i\phi_i - c_1\phi_{11}) \qquad \text{XI.91}$$

From distribution data, they have ascribed values of ϕ_i for the interaction of water with the methylene, hydroxyl and amino groups, and with the ketonic and etheric oxygen atoms. There is no doubt that the theory of solutions of biological interest, such as those of carbohydrates and proteins in water, can be profitably developed along these lines.

Activity, and activity coefficient

In a solution which obeys van't Hoff's law (equation XI.15), the chemical potential of the solute is given by the equation

$$G_i = G_i^0 + RT\ln c_i, \qquad \text{XI.92}$$

where c_i is the concentration, in gram-moles per litre of solution, and G_i^0 is the chemical potential of one mole of the solute in a solution of unit concentration. In an ideal solution, we have used the analogous expression in terms of molar fractions, viz.

$$G_i = G_i^0 + RT\ln x_i, \qquad \text{XI.4}$$

where G_i^0 is now the chemical potential of the pure liquid component i at the temperature and pressure of the solution. van Laar's theory of isomegethic solutions provides an improved equation, which, for binary systems, is

$$G_i = G_i^0 + RT\ln x_i + (1-x_i)^2\Delta U^0, \qquad \text{XI.35}$$

and the Hildebrand–Scatchard theory goes a stage further by providing an expression for the chemical potential of a component in a solution containing molecules of different sizes, viz.

$$G_i = G_i^0 + RT\ln x_i + (1-\theta_i)^2\Delta U^0, \qquad \text{XI.93}$$

where θ_i is the volume fraction, and the exchange energy, ΔU^0, has a different meaning from that in equation XI.35. We shall see, in the next chapter, that the chemical potential of a gram-mole of ion in an aqueous solution when the concentration is in the neighbourhood of one millimole per litre of solution, has the form

$$G_i = G_i^0 + RT\ln c_i - Bc_i^{1/2}, \qquad \text{XII.65}$$

309

where B is a positive constant, dependent in magnitude on the ionic charge, and the temperature and dielectric constant of the solution, but independent of the composition. These are a few examples of incomplete but helpful attempts to relate the chemical potential of a solute with its concentration. Deviations from them vary, in the case of ions, in proportion to the square root of their concentration, and, in the case of molecules of the same size, in proportion to the square of the molar fraction of the other component. When there is no theoretical guide as to the form of the deviation, it may be represented empirically by a term of the same form as the basic term, i.e. by $RT \ln \gamma$, where γ is an empirical factor termed by G. N. Lewis the activity coefficient. We then have a set of empirical equations of the form

$$G_i = G_i^0 + RT \ln z_i + RT \ln \gamma_i = G_i^0 + RT \ln a_i \qquad \text{XI.94}$$

where z stands for concentration, c, in moles per litre of solution, or molality, m, expressed as moles of solute per kilogram of solvent, or mole fraction, x, of solute, or its volume fraction, θ, and the activity a is, by definition, $z\gamma$ in each case. By comparing equations XI.35 and XI.94, we see that the activity coefficient of component, A, in a binary solution which obeys van Laar's theory is given in terms of the inter change energy by the relation

$$\ln \gamma_A = (1 - x_A)^2 (\Delta U^0 / RT). \qquad \text{XI.9}$$

By comparing equation XI.94 and XII.65, the activity coefficient of ions in aqueous solutions at concentrations in the neighbourhood of one millimole per litre is seen to be given by the equation

$$\ln \gamma_i = -(B/RT)c_i^{1/2} \qquad \text{XI.9}$$

Finally, in order to appreciate the significance of changing from one reference state to another, let us apply equation XI.82 to a solution containing molecules of type A and S. Then

$$G_A = G_A^L + RT \ln \theta_A + (1 - \theta_A)^2 \sqrt{\frac{V_A}{V_S}} \Delta U^0$$

$$+ RT(1 - \theta_A)\left(1 - \frac{V_A}{V_S}\right) \qquad \text{XI.8}$$

Here G_A^L manifestly stands for the free energy of one mole of pure component, A, in the liquid state at the temperature and pressure of the system. If we desire to examine the solution over the complete range of composition, this is a suitable reference state. On the other hand, we may be limited by the nature of things to solutions wherein the amount of S is always greatly in excess of the amount of A, i.e. to relatively dilute solutions of A in S. The pure liquid is then a cumbrous reference state to adopt, and may be replaced by one which, as far as numbers are concerned, is that of one gram-mole of A in a litre of solution, but, as far as behaviour is concerned, is that corresponding to a zero value of the interchange energy, ΔU^0. Let us replace θ_A by the product of the concentration, c_A, in moles per litre of solution, and the partial molar volume, V_A, adjusted by the necessary numerical factor:

$$\theta_A = c_A V_A / 1\ 000.$$

The chemical potential of the solute now becomes

$$G_A = G_A^0 + RT \ln c_A - K_1 c_A + K_2 c_A^2, \qquad \text{XI.97}$$

where

$$G_A^0 = G_A^L + RT \ln (V_A/1\ 000) + \sqrt{\frac{V_A}{V_S}} \Delta U^0 + RT \left(1 - \frac{V_A}{V_S}\right),$$

$$K_1 = 2(V_A/1\ 000) \sqrt{\frac{V_A}{V_S}} \Delta U^0 + RT(V_A/1\ 000) \left(1 - \frac{V_A}{V_S}\right),$$

and

$$K_2 = (V_A/1\ 000)^2 \sqrt{\frac{V_A}{V_S}} \Delta U^0.$$

The equation in this more convenient form can be compared with the empirical extension of van't Hoff's equation,

$$G_A = G_A^0 + RT \ln c_A + RT \ln \gamma_A, \qquad \text{XI.98}$$

giving us the result

$$RT \ln \gamma_A = -K_1 c_A + K_2 c_A^2. \qquad \text{XI.99}$$

On this basis, the activity coefficient is unity at infinite dilution, i.e. when c_A is zero, and also at an often unattainable concentration given by the equation

$$c_A(\gamma = 1) = \frac{1\ 000}{V_A} \left[2 - \left(\sqrt{\frac{V_S}{V_A}} - \sqrt{\frac{V_A}{V_S}}\right) \frac{RT}{\Delta U^0}\right]. \qquad \text{XI.100}$$

311

Having defined the activity and the activity coefficient, and shown how these may be related to certain fundamental properties of the components of solutions in cases where the nature of the molecular interaction is known, we turn now to discuss one of the many methods which have been used to determine these variables in solutions concerning which nothing is known about the nature of the intermolecular forces.

The determination of the activity of a solvent from the depression of its freezing-point

Let us, assuming that the nearest law to which the solution conforms is Raoult's law, denote departures therefrom by the conventional term $RT \ln \gamma$. Denoting the solvent by the subscript 1, its chemical potential, per gram-mole, is then

$$G_1 = G_1^0 + RT \ln x_1 + RT \ln \gamma_1$$
$$= G_1^0 + RT \ln a_1 \qquad \text{XI.101}$$

where a_1 is its activity. Clearly, when x_1 is unity, the solution is simply the pure solvent, for which γ_1 by definition is also unity. Then G_1^0 is G_L, the free energy of one mole of the pure liquid solvent, and

$$G_1 = G_L + RT \ln a_1$$

We next suppose that, on cooling the solution, component 1 separates out in the crystalline form, while component 2, the solute, remains in solution, and is insoluble in the crystalline solvent. When, at temperature T, the solution is in equilibrium with the crystalline solvent, T is the freezing-point, and the chemical potentials of this component must be the same in the two phases, so that

$$G_{\text{cr.}} = G_L + RT \ln a_1$$

The treatment from now on is the same as that used in dealing with the solubility of solids in liquids, and leads to equations XI.6 and XI.8, except that the term s of the latter equation is replaced by the activity, a_1, of the solvent. After eliminating L_T from these equations, we find that

$$\ln a_1 = -\left(\frac{L_m - \Delta C T_m}{RT_m}\right)\left(\frac{T_m}{T} - 1\right) - \frac{\Delta C}{R} \ln\left(\frac{T_m}{T}\right) \qquad \text{XI.102}$$

where L_m is the molar heat of fusion of the solvent at its melting point, T_m, and T is the freezing point of the solution.

Let us apply this equation to water as a solvent, for which we have $L_m = 1\,435 \cdot 7$ calories per mole, $T_m = 273 \cdot 16°K$, $R = 1 \cdot 9872$ calories per mole-degree, and ΔC, though increasing rapidly as the temperature is lowered, is $9 \cdot 122$ calories per mole-degree at T_m. We find

$$\ln a_1 = +1 \cdot 9462 \left(\frac{T_m}{T} - 1\right) - 4 \cdot 5920 \ln\left(\frac{T_m}{T}\right) \qquad \text{XI.103}$$

from which the activity of water is readily found. On dividing a_1 by the mole fraction, x_1, we obtain the activity coefficient, γ_1. Thus, for example, when $7 \cdot 804$ gram-moles of acetone are dissolved in 1 kilogram of water, the lowering, $T_m - T$, in the freezing point is $12 \cdot 35°$; x_1 is $0 \cdot 8768$, and γ_1 is consequently $1 \cdot 0158$. The chemical potential of water in this solution is greater than that anticipated by Raoult's law by $RT \ln \gamma$, which, at the freezing point of the pure solvent, is $8 \cdot 486$ calories. Somewhat greater influences are exerted on the solvent when the solute is ionised. The depression in the freezing point of an aqueous solution of hydrogen chloride containing $1 \cdot 003$ gram-mole in $1\,000$ grams of water is $3 \cdot 965°$, which is about twice as great as that caused by an equivalent amount of acetone, and leads to a value of $0 \cdot 9765$ for the activity coefficient of the solvent.

L

XII Solutions of electrolytes

Acids, bases and salts dissolved in polar solvents such as water, sulphur dioxide and acetonitrile conduct electricity well. The solutions exhibit other properties distinguishing them so markedly from non conducting solutions that they are treated as a separate class, known as electrolytes.

Specific conductivity and equivalent conductivity

The specific conductivity, κ, of any substance is the quotient of the current, i, carried across unit area, and the electrical field strength, E

$$\kappa = i/E \qquad \text{XII.}$$

Of greater physicochemical interest than κ is the equivalent conducti vity, Λ, which is the product of κ and the volume, in cubic centi metres, of a solution containing 1 gram-equivalent of the electrolyte. If the concentration is expressed as c gram-equivalents per litre clearly

$$\Lambda = 1\ 000\ \kappa/c \qquad \text{XII.}$$

The mental picture conjured up by this equation is that of two parallel plane electrodes, separated by a distance of 1 cm, and having sufficient area to enclose that volume of solution which contains one gram equivalent of solute. When the electrolyte is uni-univalent, like sodium chloride, we can also write

$$\Lambda = N_0 \kappa/n \qquad \text{XII.}$$

where N_0 is Avogadro's number, and n is the number of molecule per cm^3 of solution ($n = cN_0/1\ 000$).

The specific conductivity of electrolytic solutions is measured by determining its resistance R in a Wheatstone bridge circuit, using a cell such as that shown in Fig. XII.1. If the current were to flow in precisely parallel streams between the two electrodes, each of area O cm^2 at a distance L cm apart, we would have, by Ohm's law $R = (L/O)/\kappa$. Actual conductance is not quite so simple, and in practice the term (L/O) is replaced by a cell constant, C, so that $R = C/\kappa$. The cell constant is determined by using a standard electrolyte solution, such as $M/10$ potassium chloride in water, for which highly accurate values of κ are already known.

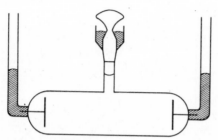

Fig. XII.1   *A convenient form of a conductivity cell*

F. Kohlrausch (1900) found that the equivalent conductivity, Λ_V, of aqueous electrolytic solutions at concentrations below about 1 millimole per litre decreased linearly with respect to the square-root of the concentration, so that

$$\Lambda_V = \Lambda_\infty - A\sqrt{c} \qquad \text{XII.4}$$

where A is an empirical constant. Figure XII.2, drawn from the data of Walden and Birr (1929), illustrates the law. It provides a convenient method of estimating the equivalent conductivity at infinite dilution, and is the first of many laws relating the properties of extremely dilute electrolytic solutions with the square-root of the concentration.

It was Kohlrausch also who established the fact that values of Λ_∞ for various solutes in a common solvent at the same temperature consist of contributions independently made by the cations and anions:

$$\Lambda_\infty = U + V \qquad \text{XII.5}$$

Some of his data are compared in Table XII.1 with values of Λ_∞ found by adopting $U = 33 \cdot 47$ for Li^+, $43 \cdot 52$ for Na^+ and $64 \cdot 58$ for K^+ in water at 18°C, with $V = 65 \cdot 37$ for Cl^- and $61 \cdot 77$ for NO_3^-. This illustrates Kohlrausch's law of the independent mobilities of ions in infinitely dilute solutions.

315

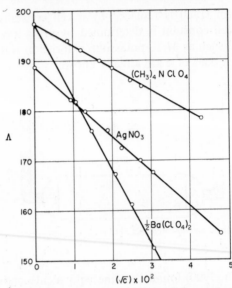

Fig. XII.2 *The equivalent conductance of tetramethylammonium perchlorate, silver nitrate and barium perchlorate in methyl cyanide solution at 298·1°K*

Arrhenius's theory of electrolytic dissociation

Arrhenius (1887) attributed the decrease in equivalent conductivity with increasing concentration to the decrease in the degree of ionisation (α) of the electrolyte, which he regarded as consisting partly of un-ionised molecules and partly of cations and anions. If this supposition

Table XII.1 *Equivalent conductivities, extrapolated to infinite dilution, of certain salts in water at 18°C*

Salt	Λ_∞		Salt	Λ_∞	
	observed	calculated		observed	calculated
LiCl	98·89	98·84	$LiNO_3$	95·18	95·24
NaCl	108·87	108·89	$NaNO_3$	105·30	105·20
KCl	129·91	129·95	KNO_3	126·40	126·35

is true, a solution of a uni-univalent electrolyte containing in all n molecules per cm^3 of solution contains a concentration $n\alpha$ of either ion. The current carried across unit area is then given in terms of the charge $(+\varepsilon)$ on the cation, the charge $(-\varepsilon)$ on the anion, and their velocities of migration, u and v:

$$i = n_+\varepsilon u + n_-(-\varepsilon)(-v)$$

$$= n\varepsilon(u+v)\alpha$$

The velocity of migration of the anion is written as $-v$ because it moves in a direction opposite to that of the cation. Mobility is defined as velocity in a field of unit strength: $u^0 = u/E$; $v^0 = v/E$. Hence, from equation XII.1 the specific conductivity is

$$\kappa = n\varepsilon(u^0 + v^0)\alpha \qquad\qquad \text{XII.6}$$

and the equivalent conductivity is

$$\Lambda_V = N_0\varepsilon(u^0 + v^0)\alpha \qquad\qquad \text{XII.7}$$

But $N_0\varepsilon$ is Faraday's constant, $\mathfrak{F}$, so that

$$\Lambda_V = \mathfrak{F}(u^0 + v^0)\alpha \qquad\qquad \text{XII.8}$$

At infinite solution, ionisation is assumed to be complete, i.e. $\alpha = 1$, so that

$$\Lambda_\infty = \mathfrak{F}(u^0 + v^0) \qquad\qquad \text{XII.9}$$

and the degree of ionisation is consequently

$$\alpha = \Lambda_V/\Lambda_\infty \qquad\qquad \text{XII.10}$$

The law of the independent mobilities of ions at infinite dilution is evidently interpreted, since $U = \mathfrak{F}u^0$ and $V = \mathfrak{F}v^0$.

Arrhenius's theory, in the elementary form given here, proved to be directly applicable to certain aqueous solutes, like ammonia and acetic acid, which are only slightly ionised, but appeared to be in-applicable to highly ionised solutes like lithium hydroxide and nitric acid. Relatively recent work has shown, however, that its apparent inapplicability to the so-called strong electrolytes is due less to inadequacy of the theory, which on the whole has been confirmed, than to inaccuracy of certain of the data used to test it.

If this theory is sound, the ratio of the actual concentration of solute particles to the concentration imagined if there were no ionisation

317

is $[n(1-\alpha)+vn\alpha]/n = 1+(v-1)\alpha$, where v is the number of ions into which a single molecule dissociates. This ratio, sometimes referred to as van't Hoff's factor, tends in the limit of infinite dilution to the integer v. The ratio of the actual osmotic pressure (or lowering in the vapour pressure of the solvent) to the value anticipated were there no ionisation is, in fact, found to yield integral values when extrapolated to infinite dilution. The limiting values found for $NaNO_3$, $Ba(NO_3)_2$ and $La(NO_3)_3$, for example, are 2, 3 and 4 respectively.

Ostwald's dilution law

Let us, following Ostwald (1888), apply the law of mass action to a uni-univalent electrolyte ionising according to the scheme $AB \rightleftarrows A^+ + B^-$. The condition of equilibrium is that the chemical potential μ_{AB} of the undissociated molecule shall equal the sum of the chemical potentials μ_{A^+} and μ_{B^-} of the ions. In solutions sufficiently dilute to justify the use of van't Hoff's law, we may express μ for each species of solute as $\mu^0 + kT \ln c$, where c is its equilibrium concentration, and μ^0 its chemical potential in a solution of unit concentration. It follows that

$$\frac{c_{A^+} \cdot c_{B^-}}{c_{AB}} = e^{-\Delta\mu^0/kT} = K \qquad \text{XII.11}$$

where the constant K, though a function of temperature and pressure, is independent of the concentration, and $\Delta\mu^0 = \mu_{A^+}^0 + \mu_{B^-}^0 - \mu_{AB}^0$. In terms of the total concentration c, $c_{AB} = c(1-\alpha)$, and $c_{A^+} = c_{B^-} = c\alpha$, so that

$$K = \frac{c\alpha^2}{1-\alpha} \qquad \text{XII.12}$$

On substituting Arrhenius's expression for α, we have

$$K = \frac{c\Lambda_V^2}{\Lambda_\infty(\Lambda_\infty - \Lambda_V)} \qquad \text{XII.13}$$

which is Ostwald's dilution law.

To apply this equation we rearrange it as suggested by Kraus (1922) into the form

$$c\Lambda_V = -K\Lambda_\infty + \frac{K\Lambda_\infty^2}{\Lambda_V} \qquad \text{XII.14}$$

so that, by plotting $c\Lambda_V$ as a function of $1/\Lambda_V$, we obtain a straight line, with an intercept of $-K\Lambda_\infty$ and a gradient of $K\Lambda_\infty^2$. As an example, the data of McInnes and Shedlovsky (1932) on acetic acid in water at 298·16°K have been analysed in this way (Fig. XII.3). We find $K\Lambda_\infty = 7·00 \times 10^{-3}$ and $K\Lambda_\infty^2 = 2·74$. It follows that $\Lambda_\infty = 391·6$ and that $K = 1·787 \times 10^{-5}$ gram-equivalents per litre. Both values have been confirmed by independent experiments.

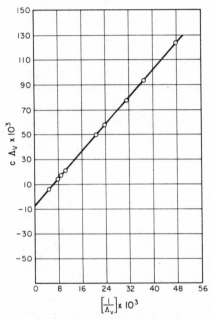

Fig. XII.3 · *Determination of the ionisation constant of acetic acid in aqueous solution at 298·1°K from conductivity measurements*

In the early days of the electrolytic theory of solutions, the distinction between strong electrolytes, like hydrochloric acid, and weak electrolytes, like formic acid, was regarded as a fundamental one, though a few cautious experimenters, such as Bogdan (1907), held it to be one of degree only. In the absence of more precise data than those available to him, Kohlrausch wisely refrained from expressing an opinion. The more accurate information which we now possess on the conductivity of hydrochloric acid (H. C. Parker, 1923) shows that Ostwald's dilution law in the form of equation XII.13 is obeyed at concentrations below 0·2 millimoles per litre, with $K = 0·105$ gram-ion per litre at 25°C. Other evidences have since accured to confirm the view that even strong electrolytes are not completely ionised. The Raman spectrum of nitric acid, for example, contains not only those lines which are attributable to the nitrate ion, but three lines known to be characteristic of the nitric acid molecule (Woodward, 1934). Representative data are listed in Table XII.2.

Table XII.2 *Ionisation constants in water at 25°C and 1 atmosphere pressure*

Electrolyte	K (g moles/litre)	ΔH (cals/g mole)	$-\Delta C_E$ (cals/g mole-deg)
H_2O	$1·81 \times 10^{-16}$	$+13465$	$42·7$
d-Glucose	$5·10 \times 10^{-13}$	$+8100$	40
C_6H_5OH	$1·09 \times 10^{-10}$	$+6015$	$43·5$
m-$NO_2C_6H_4OH$	$5·30 \times 10^{-9}$	$+4980$	48
HCOOH	$1·77 \times 10^{-4}$	-13	41
CH_3COOH	$1·75 \times 10^{-5}$	-112	34
NH_4OH	$1·81 \times 10^{-5}$	$+790$	$52·5$
$HOCH_2COOH$	$1·48 \times 10^{-4}$	$+210$	39
$ClCH_2COOH$	$1·38 \times 10^{-3}$	-1170	35
C_6H_5COOH	$6·52 \times 10^{-5}$	$+180$	42
m-IC_6H_5COOH	$1·60 \times 10^{-4}$	$+2670$	36
o-IC_6H_5COOH	$1·40 \times 10^{-3}$	-2670	23
H_3PO_4	$7·52 \times 10^{-3}$	-1765	43
			Average 40

When van't Hoff's law is not obeyed, the chemical potential of a solute may be expressed as follows, in terms of a corrected concentration, a, which is known as the activity, and is so chosen that the equation is true:

$$\mu = \mu^0 + kT \ln a \qquad \text{XII.15}$$

The activity coefficient, γ, is the quotient of a and the molality, m, so that

$$\mu = \mu^0 + kT \ln m + kT \ln \gamma \qquad \text{XII.16}$$

The molality is defined as the number of gram-moles of electrolyte in 1 000 grams of solvent. Adopting equations of this form for the ions and the unionised molecules, we have

$$\mu_+ = \mu_+^0 + kT \ln m\alpha + kT \ln \gamma_+$$

$$\mu_- = \mu_-^0 + kT \ln m\alpha + kT \ln \gamma_-$$

and

$$\mu = \mu^0 + kT \ln m(1-\alpha) + kT \ln \gamma_{+-}$$

The μ^0 terms are the chemical potentials of the solutes in hypothetical states where both m and γ are unity, i.e. they refer to solutions which, as far as concentrations are concerned, are molar, but as far as behaviour is concerned are ideal. On equating $\mu_+ + \mu_-$ with μ, and denoting $(\gamma_+ \gamma_-)^{1/2}$ by γ_i, we see that

$$K = e^{-\Delta\mu^0/kT} = \frac{m\alpha^2}{(1-\alpha)} \cdot \frac{\gamma_i^2}{\gamma_{+-}} \qquad \text{XII.17}$$

where

$$\Delta\mu^0 = \mu_+^0 + \mu_-^0 - \mu^0 \qquad \text{XII.18}$$

The activity coefficient, γ_{+-}, of the unionised solute can often be taken as unity over a considerable concentration range. γ_+ and γ_- are, by definition, unity at infinite dilution. Hence, if K^0 denotes the ionisation constant extrapolated to infinite dilution, we can write

$$K = K^0 \gamma_i^2 \qquad \text{XII.19}$$

The mean ionic activity coefficient can be measured in many ways, one of which is described in later sections of this chapter. Combined with a knowledge of K, we can thus obtain K^0, which is sometimes referred to as the thermodynamic ionisation constant.

The variation of K^0 with respect to temperature is given for most electrolytes by the equation

$$\log_{10} K^0 = A' - B' \log_{10} T - C'/T \qquad \text{XII.20}$$

where A', B', and C' are empirical constants. With benzoic acid, for example, we find

$$\log_{10} K^0 = 57 \cdot 411 - 21 \cdot 13 \log_{10} T - 2\,774/T \qquad \text{XII.21}^\cdot$$

The empirical equation may also be written in the following way:

$$\ln_e K^0 = A - \frac{B}{R} \ln_e T - \frac{C}{RT} \qquad \text{XII.22}$$

L*

321

The increase in heat content attending the ionisation of one gram-mole of electrolyte at constant temperature is

$$\Delta H = RT^2\left(\frac{d \ln_e K^0}{dT}\right)_P = C - BT \qquad \text{XII.23}$$

from which it is clear that

$$C = \Delta H_0 \qquad \text{XII.24}$$

and

$$B = -\Delta C_P \qquad \text{XII.25}$$

Numerical values of these constants for various electrolytes in water are given in Table XII.2. A rough average value of ΔC_P for them all is 40 calories/gram-mole-degree. The loss in heat capacity when one gram-mole of water freezes is 8·1 in these units. The results can therefore be explained in terms of the freezing in of 5 moles of water per mole of electrolyte. This is the so-called iceberg hypothesis of Ulich. Since ΔC_P is not highly specific, we conclude that it is the hydrogen ion that is mainly responsible for its value.

In terms of the constants of equation XII.22, the standard increase in entropy attending ionisation is

$$\Delta S^0 = (\Delta H/T) + R \ln_e K^0 = R \ln_e A - B(1 + \ln_e T) \qquad \text{XII.26}$$

The numerical value for benzoic acid in water at 25°C is $-18\cdot7$ cal/mole-degree.

Transport numbers

The fraction of the total current carried by any species of ion is known as the transport number of that ion. In an electrolyte consisting of cations and anions of the same valency, the transport number of the cation is clearly $t_+ = u/(u+v)$; that of the anion is $t_- = v/(u+v)$. The sum of the ionic velocities may, as we have seen, be obtained from the equivalent conductivity, but separate experiments are needed to obtain individual values of u and v. The most direct method is a visual one, due to Lodge (1896). Its principle is illustrated in Fig. XII.4. The electrolyte is an aqueous solution of a strong acid, kept in two vessels at a distance of about 50 cm apart. The horizontal tube contains aqueous set gelatin impregnated with a little sodium chloride to render it conducting and coloured red with slightly alkaline phenol-phthalein. When an electric current flows through the system, hydro-gen ions migrate to the cathode, removing the red colour as they go. The rate of movement of the boundary between the coloured and colourless parts of the solution is the rate, u, of migration of the hydrogen ions in the field applied. By measuring the refractive index of the solution, the moving boundary method can be extended to colour-less ions.

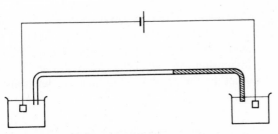

Fig. XII.4   *Lodge's moving boundary apparatus*

A method due to Hittorf (1901) consists of analysing the solution of an electrolyte in the vicinity of the cathode and the anode after a known quantity of electricity has passed through it. In the anolyte of a cell containing aqueous silver nitrate between plane parallel silver electrodes of unit area (Fig. XII.5), the rate of increase of concentration of silver ions is $k - nu$, where k is the rate at which silver dissolves from the anode, and n is the uniform, initial concentration of silver

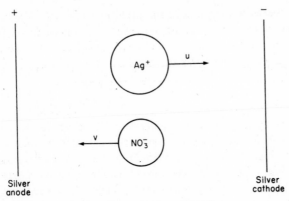

Fig. XII.5   *The principle of Hittorf's transport experiment*

323

ions or of nitrate ions. The rate of increase of concentration of silver ions in the catholyte is clearly $nu - k$. The total current may be expressed in two ways; $i = k\varepsilon = n\varepsilon(u + v)$, so that $k = n(u + v)$. It follows that the rate of increase in concentration in the anolyte is nv, and that this also is the rate of decrease in the concentration of silver ions in the catholyte. After a time t, the total change in concentration is nvt, positive in the anolyte and negative in the catholyte. Gravimetric analysis of the silver in either compartment thus provides the value of v.

Values of the transport numbers afforded by the two methods are in agreement. Transport numbers vary slightly and in an unpredictable way with respect to concentration. They also depend on temperature, increasing or decreasing with a rise in temperature according to whether the transport number is less than or greater than 0·5.

Elementary theory of ionic migration; Stokes radii

If the only forces acting on an ion in solution are the driving force due to the external electrical field, E, and the force of resistance, assumed to vary as the velocity, u, the equation of motion is $m(du/dt) = Ez\varepsilon - Cu$, where m is the mass, z the valency, ε the charge on a proton, and C is the resistance constant. When steady motion has been reached, du/dt is zero, and the steady velocity is thus $Ez\varepsilon/C$. Since the mobility is u/E, we have

$$u^0 = z\varepsilon/C \qquad\qquad \text{XII.27}$$

Some experimental values of the mobility of ions in aqueous solution are given in Table XII.3, along with the ionic conductances from which have been derived. For spherical ions of radius r, $C = 6\pi\eta r$, where η is the viscosity of the medium. Hence

$$u^0 = z\varepsilon/6\pi\eta r \qquad\qquad \text{XII.28}$$

Ionic radii given by this equation, and termed Stokes radii, are seen to be, on the whole, abnormally small, and mutually inconsistent. Thus, for example, r_- for the iodide ion in water is much less than its value in crystalline alkali iodides, and the radius of the silver ion is greater than that of the perchlorate ion. The most mobile ions are H^+ and OH^-, i.e. precisely those ions which the solvent can generate. Grotthus suggested that the conduction of electricity in pure water

324

Table XII.3 *Ionic conductances, mobilities and Stokes radii of certain ions in water at 25°C*

Cation	U (ohm^{-1}cm^2 per g eq.)	$u^0 \times 10$ (cm sec^{-1} per e.s.u.)	r_+ (Å)	Anion	V (ohm^{-1}cm^2 per g eq.)	$v^0 \times 10$ (cm sec^{-1} per e.s.u.)	r_- (Å)
H$^+$	316·6	9·61	0·253	OH$^-$	176·6	5·49	0·443
Cs$^+$	67·7	2·10	1·155	F$^-$	46·7	1·45	1·675
Cu^{++}	45·9	1·43	1·70	I$^-$	67·4	2·09	1·16
Ag$^+$	53·8	1·67	1·455	ClO$_4^-$	56	1·74	1·40
Ra^{++}	58	1·80	1·35	HCOO$^-$	47·0	1·46	1·67
NH$_4^+$	64	1·99	1·23	CH$_3$COO$^-$	35·9	1·09	2·25

may entail frequent ionisation of water molecules, and recombinations of the ions. On combining equations XII.9 and XII.28, we see that

$$\eta\Lambda_\infty = \frac{\mathfrak{F}z\varepsilon}{6\pi}\left(\frac{1}{r_+}+\frac{1}{r_-}\right) \qquad \text{XII.29}$$

The product of the viscosity and the equivalent conductance at infinite dilution should therefore be a constant, independent of temperature and of the solvent. This conclusion has been proved correct by Walden, but only for electrolytes like tetraisoamylammonium picrate which yield large ions.

Determination of the valency of ions

Of the many methods available for finding the valency of an ion, one is based on equation XII.27. On combining it with the equation $D = kT/C$ derived in Chapter II, we see that

$$z = \frac{kT}{\varepsilon} \cdot \frac{u^0}{D} \qquad \text{XII.30}$$

From measurements of their mobilities and coefficients of diffusion Hevesy in this way (1935) established or confirmed the valencies of thirteen radioactive cations.

The heat of dissolution of electrolytes

The heat change occurring when an electrolyte dissolves may be measured with great accuracy by the calorimetric method. It is generally found to vary slightly with the concentration of the resulting solution. Thus, for example, when 1 gram-mole of gaseous hydrogen chloride dissolves in $55{\cdot}51/m$ gram-moles of water at 29°K, according to the equation

$$HCl(gas) + (55{\cdot}51/m)H_2O(liquid) \rightarrow HCl(aqueous, m)$$

the increase in heat content, expressed in calories, is found to be

$$\Delta H = -17\,777 + 451{\cdot}4m^{1/2}$$

This relationship (Roth and Richter, 1934) holds for molalities (m) between 0·005 and 0·095, and indicates that, when 1 gram-mole of HCl dissolves in an infinite volume of water at the temperature stated, 17 777 calories of heat are evolved.

There are also indirect methods, particularly applicable to sparingly soluble salts, of measuring the heat of dissolution. The one which we shall describe is that which depends on the variation of the solubility with respect to temperature. The condition that a crystalline salt MX shall be in equilibrium with its saturated solution in any solvent is that $\mu(MX, cr) = \mu(M^+, sat) + \mu(X^-, sat)$. In very dilute solutions, μ for each ion takes the form $\mu^0 + kT \ln c(sat)$. Moreover, if the unionised part of the solute can be ignored, we may replace $c(sat)$ by s, the solubility of the salt. Then

$$\mu(MX, cr) = \mu_{M^+}^0 + \mu_{X^-}^0 + 2kT \ln s \qquad \text{XII.31}$$

On multiplying throughout by N_0, and denoting the standard increase in free energy by $\Delta G^0 = N_0(\mu_{M^+}^0 + \mu_{X^-}^0 - \mu_{MX,cr})$, we have the result

$$-\Delta G^0 = 2RT \ln s \qquad \text{XII.32}$$

from which, by means of the Kelvin–Helmholtz equation, the standard increase in heat content becomes

$$\Delta H^0 = 2RT^2(d \ln s/dT)_P \qquad \text{XII.33}$$

Kohlrausch used the electrical conductivity method (equation XII.2) to determine the solubility of numerous sparingly soluble salts. His data for silver chloride show that the increase in molar heat content attending its dissolution in water decreases linearly with respect to temperature:

$$\Delta H^0 = 47\,110 - 105 \cdot 0T \qquad \text{XII.34}$$

At 298·16°, the heat absorbed is thus 15 803 calories. This should be the same as the heat evolved in the familiar analytical reaction $Ag^+(aq) + Cl^-(aq) \to AgCl(cr)$, and is, in fact reasonably near to the calorimetric value of 15 740.

The heat of solvation of ions

When the standard increase in heat content, ΔH_2, accompanying the dissolution of an electrolyte is subtracted from its lattice energy, ΔH_1, we obtain the sum of the increases in heat content attending the escape of the ions from solution into the gaseous phase;

$$MX_{cr} \to M^+(gas) + X^-(gas) \qquad \Delta H_1$$

$$MX_{cr} \to M^+(solv) + X^-(solv) \qquad \Delta H_2$$

$$M^+(solv) + X^-(solv) \to M^+(gas) + X^-(gas) \qquad \Delta H_1 - \Delta H_2$$

How this sum is to be resolved into contributions attributable to the separate processes

$$M^+(solv) \to M^+(gas)$$

$$X^-(solv) \to X^-(gas) \qquad \text{XII.36}$$

has not yet been unambiguously decided. Unlike the resolution of the equivalent conductance, the additional experimental factor corresponding to the transport number is here lacking. Fajans (1928) has argued that the potassium and fluoride ions can be regarded as contributing in equal measure; Latimer (1939) considers the lithium and fluoride ions as thermally equivalent. Some numerical estimates of the heats of escape of ions from water at 298·16°K are given in Table XII.4. The data for H_3O^+ are based on J. Sherman's estimate (1932) of $\Delta H = 182$ kilocalories for the gaseous reaction $H_3O^+ \to H_2O + H^+$.

The relative entropies of aqueous ions

The solubility of silver iodide at 25°C is $(2 \cdot 4 \pm 0 \cdot 1) \times 10^{-7}$ g per 100 g of solution. The increase in free energy associated with the conversion of one gram-mole of the crystalline salt into aqueous ions in a

Table XII.4 *Estimated molar increases in heat content attending the escape of ions from water to the gas phase at* 298·1°K *(kilocalories/gram-ion)*

$$\Delta H_{escape} = H_{gas} - H_{solution}$$

Ion	$Li^+ \equiv F^-$	$Na^+ \equiv F^-$	$K^+ \equiv F^-$	$r_i \times 10^8$ cm
H^+	259	268	278	0·597
Li^+	122	135	145	1·15
Na^+	96	109	119	1·40
K^+	76	89	99	1·68
Rb^+	70	83	93	1·78
H_3O^+	73	86	96	1·73
F^-	122	109	99	1·68
Cl^-	89	76	66	2·52
Br^-	81	68	58	2·86
I^-	72	59	49	3·39

hypothetical solution containing one gram-equivalent of each kind of ion per litre is thus $\Delta G^0 = 21\,810 \pm 50$ calories. The corresponding increase in heat content is $\Delta H^0 = 26\,710$. Hence, $\Delta S^0 = (\Delta H^0 - \Delta G^0)/T = 16·44$ cal/mole-degree. This is the excess entropy of the ions (more accurately, the solution) in this reference state over the entropy of the crystalline salt, which is 27·6 cal/mole-degree. It follows that the sum of the molar entropies of the silver and iodide ions under these conditions is 44·04. If the molality, m, of a saturated solution is so low that the activity coefficient, γ, differs significantly from unity, we may write for the dissolution process $-\Delta G^0 = vRT \ln m_{sat}$, where v is the number of ions into which one molecule of salt dissociates. Since ΔS^0 is $\Sigma S^0_{ions} - S_{crystal}$, it follows that the sum of the entropies of the ions in the reference solution (unit molality, as far as composition is concerned; unit activity coefficient as far as behaviour is concerned) is

$$\sum S^0_{ions} = S^0_{crystal} + \frac{\Delta H^0_{diss}}{T} + vR \ln m_{sat} \qquad \text{XII.37}$$

There are many other ways of determining the sum of the standard entropies of ions. The ionic product of water, for example, is $K_w = c_{H^+} \cdot c_{OH^-} = 10^{-14}$ (mole/litre)² at 298·16°K, and the increase in heat content attending the ionisation $H_2O \rightarrow H^+ + OH^-$ is

13 480 calories. Hence $\Delta S^0 = -18\cdot84$ cal/mole degree. But the entropy of 1 gram-mole of liquid water under these conditions is $15\cdot94$. Hence $S^0_{H^+} + S^0_{OH^-} = -2\cdot9$ cal/mole degree.

If we conventionally take the standard entropy of the hydrogen ion in water at $298\cdot16°K$ to be zero, that of the hydroxyl ion in the same solvent at the same temperature is $-2\cdot9$, and relative values can be ascribed to the standard entropies of other ions in water. Some of these are given in calories per gram-ion-degree in Table XII.5. Gurney (1953) has given reasons for accepting $-5\cdot5$ for $S^0(H^+)$.

Table XII.5 *Relative molar entropies of certain ions in water at $298\cdot16°K$, at a concentration of one gram-ion per litre, and at unit activity coefficient*

Cation	S^0	Anion	S^0
H^+	0	OH^-	$-2\cdot9$
Cs^+	$31\cdot8$	F^-	$-2\cdot3$
Cu^{++}	$-28\cdot5$	I^-	$36\cdot6$
Ag^+	$17\cdot5$	ClO_4^-	$43\cdot6$
Ba^{++}	$2\cdot3$	HCO_3^-	$22\cdot2$
NH_4^+	$26\cdot5$	CO_3^{--}	$-13\cdot0$

Theories of ionic solvation

There have been numerous attempts, none wholly adequate, to explain the magnitudes and trends in the heats and entropies of solvation of ions.

The first theory, due to Born (1920), treats an ion as a sphere of radius r_i and a solvent as a uniform medium with dielectric constant, D. The electrostatic energy of such an ion is $e_i^2/2Dr_i$; and the contribution to the free energy of a solution independently made by N_i identical ions is

$$G_e = N_i e_i^2/2Dr_i \qquad \text{XII.38}$$

It is to be observed that G_e is always positive. It follows that the electrostatic contributions to the entropy and heat content of the solution are

$$S_e = -N_i e_i^2 L/2Dr_i \qquad \text{XII.39}$$

329

and

$$H_e = \frac{N_i e_i^2}{2Dr_i}(1 - LT) \qquad \text{XII.40}$$

where the positive constant L stands for $-(d \ln D/dT)_P$. It is specific to the solvent. According to this theory, the electrostatic component of the entropy of an aqueous ion is always negative, owes its origin to the fact that the dielectric constant of the solvent varies with respect to temperature, and has a magnitude which varies inversely as the ionic radius. Latimer and others have plotted the total relative entropies of aqueous ions against the reciprocal of their 'radii' in crystals, finding an approximate linearity, which is much improved when the anions and cations are treated separately, and when to the radii of each kind of ion is added a specific but arbitrary length.

The gain in heat content when N_i ions escape from a solvent to a vacuum $(D = 1; L = 0)$ is

$$\Delta H_e = H_e^{vac} - H_e^{sol} = \frac{N_i e_i^2}{2r_i} \left[1 - \frac{(1 - LT)}{D} \right] \qquad \text{XII.41}$$

For water at 25°C, the term in the square bracket is 1·005, so that, if we express the molar heat of escape in kilocalories, and the radius in Ångstrom units

$$\Delta H_e = 166/r_i \qquad \text{XII.42}$$

Qualitatively, the equation is satisfactory; small ions have high heats of hydration. The radii given in Table XII.4, which are based on Fajans's assignment of ΔH_e, are, for the fluoride and the alkali metal ions, greater by 0·38 Å than the corresponding 'radii' in crystals. In many ways, however, Born's theory is unsatisfactory. Bernal and Fowler (1933), while retaining Born's expression as the principal component of the electrostatic free energy of aqueous solutions, added other significant terms.

An alternative approach to the problem can be made, without appealing to the concepts of ionic radii or dielectric constant, by considering the forces exerted between an ion and the c solvent molecules which are assumed to surround it symmetrically. If the additional repulsions between solvent molecules thus radially situated, and the energies of induction are ignored, the principal electrostatic energy of the solvated ion is $c(Aa^{-n} - |z|\varepsilon\mu a^{-2})$ where a is the distance between the centres of the ion and the solvent molecule. The first

330

term is the energy of intrinsic repulsion between the ion and the c solvent molecules; the second term is the energy of attraction between the ion, of valency $|z|$, and the solvent molecules, each with a dipole moment μ. The electrostatic contribution to the free energy of a solution containing N_i ions, each at its equilibrium distance a_0 is

$$G_e = -N_i c |z| \varepsilon u \left(1 - \frac{2}{n}\right) a_0^{-2} \qquad \text{XII.43}$$

It is to be observed that G_e is always negative. According to this treatment (Moelwyn-Hughes, 1948), the electrostatic contribution to the ionic entropy,

$$S_e = N_i c |z| \varepsilon \mu \left(1 - \frac{2}{n}\right) a_0^{-2} \left[\frac{1}{c}\left(\frac{dc}{dT}\right)_P - \frac{2}{a_0}\left(\frac{da_0}{dT}\right)_P\right] \qquad \text{XII.44}$$

may, in principle, be positive or negative, and owes its origin to the variation, with respect to temperature, of the coordination number c and the ion-solvent separation, a_0. Of these two possible effects, the latter is certainly the more important, as may be judged from such evidence as we have on the temperature variation of the partial molar volumes of ions at infinite dilution. If the term in the square bracket in equation XII.44 does not vary much from ion to ion, we may expect the electrostatic contribution to the ionic entropy to vary in proportion to the ionic charge, and in inverse proportion to the square of the ion-solvent distance. The more recent reviews of the data (Powell, 1954) do, in fact, show that this is approximately true, and that S_e can be expressed as a constant minus $|z|/(r_i + 1\cdot3)^2$, where r_i is the crystal 'radius' in Ångstrom units. This experimental fact is to be contrasted with equation XII.39, according to which S_e should vary as the square of the ionic charge, and inversely as the ionic 'radius'. If, instead of eliminating the constants A, we adopt the values afforded by the second virial coefficients of gases or by Born's theory of ionic crystals, it is possible to compute absolute values of a_0 and ΔH_e. These and their trends are found to be reasonable. The theory, moreover, explains the difference in the heats of hydration of ions of opposite valency but of the same size.

According to either theory, the hydrogen ion appears as an anomalous entity. It is, perhaps, best regarded as the highly stable monohydrate, H_3O^+, which responds to its four immediate neighbours in the same way as the unhydrated ions Li^+ and F^-.

331

The interionic attraction theory of electrolytic solutions

After this discussion of the absolute magnitude of some of the properties of ions in infinitely dilute solution, we shall discuss the different and much more extensively investigated problem of how their behaviour at very low concentrations differs from that of non-electrolytic solutions. This difference is naturally attributable to the Coulombic forces exerted between the ions. Milner (1913), using the virial theorem, succeeded in formulating the effect of these forces on the osmotic pressure. The main outcome of his theory is to show that the total effect of the Coulombic forces is to decrease the average free energy of each ion by an amount which, in very dilute regions, varies as the square-root of the concentration. An elementary proof of this conclusion, correct to within a factor of $\sqrt{2}$, may be given as follows.

On combining Boltzmann's law with Coulomb's expression for the interaction energy of a pair of ions at a distance r apart, in a medium of dielectric constant D, we obtain the following expressions for the concentrations of cations and anions at a distance r from some selected cation:

$$n_+ = ne^{-\varepsilon^2/DrkT}; \qquad n_- = ne^{+\varepsilon^2/DrkT} \qquad \text{XII.45}$$

where n is the bulk concentration of either kind of ion in a solution of a 1–1 electrolyte. When the electrostatic interaction of a pair of ions is small compared with kT, the following approximations suffice:

$$n_+ = n\left(1 - \frac{\varepsilon^2}{DrkT}\right); \qquad n_- = n\left(1 + \frac{\varepsilon^2}{DrkT}\right) \qquad \text{XII.46}$$

The total number of cations surrounding the selected central cation is

$$N_+ = 4\pi n\int\left(1 - \frac{\varepsilon^2}{DrkT}\right)r^2\,dr = 4\pi n\left[\frac{r^3}{3} - \frac{\varepsilon^2 r^2}{2DkT}\right]_{r=a}^{r=b} \qquad \text{XII.47}$$

The lower limit of integration is the closest distance, a, to which the centres of two real ions can come. The upper limit, b, is determined by the concentration of the solution. When a can be ignored in comparison with b, we have

$$N_+ = \frac{4}{3}\pi nb^3\left(1 - \frac{3\varepsilon^2}{2DbkT}\right) \quad \text{and} \quad N_- = \frac{4}{3}\pi nb^3\left(1 + \frac{3\varepsilon^2}{2DbkT}\right)$$

The condition of electrical neutrality ($N_- - N_+ = 1$) leads to the result

$$b = \left(\frac{DkT}{4\pi n \varepsilon^2}\right)^{1/2} \qquad \text{XII.48}$$

The energy of interaction of the selected cation with the system is

$$\int^b \left(\frac{\varepsilon^2}{Dr} n_+ - \frac{\varepsilon^2}{Dr} n_-\right) 4\pi r^2 \, dr$$

and the average potential energy of a single cation is one half of this quantity, i.e.

$$u' = -\frac{\varepsilon^2}{D}\left(\frac{4\pi n \varepsilon^2}{DkT}\right)^{1/2} \qquad \text{XII.49}$$

Fuller treatments show that the true average potential energy per ion is greater by a factor of $2^{1/2}$, and is consequently

$$u = -\frac{\varepsilon^2}{D}\left(\frac{8\pi n \varepsilon^2}{DkT}\right)^{1/2} = -\frac{\varepsilon^2 \kappa}{D} \qquad \text{XII.50}$$

where

$$\kappa = \left(\frac{8\pi n \varepsilon^2}{DkT}\right)^{1/2} \qquad \text{XII.51}$$

More generally, the reciprocal distance κ is defined in terms of the concentrations and valencies of all the ions by the equation

$$\kappa^2 = \frac{4\pi \Sigma n_i e_i^2}{DkT} = \frac{4\pi \varepsilon^2 \Sigma n_i z_i^2}{DkT} \qquad \text{XII.52}$$

Henceforth in this chapter, we shall confine attention to 1–1 electrolytes ($z_i = +1 ; z_j = -1$). The algebraic steps necessary to extend the present treatment to the general case are straightforward, though sometimes cumbrous.

The interionic attraction theory in a more recent and accurate form (Debye and Hückel, 1923) is based on a relationship derived by Poisson between the electric potential, ψ, and the electric density, Π, in a field of spherical symmetry:

$$\frac{\partial^2(\psi r)}{\partial r^2} = -\frac{4\pi r \Pi}{D} \qquad \text{XII.53}$$

As before, Boltzmann's law governs the radial distribution of cations

333

and anions around a selected cation. Their respective concentrations at a distance r from the centre are:

$$n_+ = ne^{-\psi\varepsilon/kT}; \qquad n_- = ne^{+\psi\varepsilon/kT} \qquad \text{XII.54}$$

The electric density

$$\Pi = n_+\varepsilon + n_-\varepsilon = -2n\varepsilon \sinh(\psi\varepsilon/kT) \qquad \text{XII.55}$$

reduces, when $\psi\varepsilon$ is small compared with kT, to

$$\Pi = -2n\varepsilon^2\psi/kT \qquad \text{XII.56}$$

and Poisson's equation thus takes the approximate form

$$\frac{\partial^2(\psi r)}{\partial r^2} = \left(\frac{8\pi n\varepsilon^2}{DkT}\right)\psi r = \kappa^2\psi r \qquad \text{XII.57}$$

Of the constants A and B in the general solution ($\psi r = Ae^{-\kappa r} + Be^{+\kappa r}$), the latter must be zero, in order to ensure that ψ itself is zero when r is infinite. The relevant solution is thus $\psi r = Ae^{-\kappa r}$. In a solution of zero concentration ($\kappa = 0$), ψ must clearly be ε/Dr. Hence $A = \varepsilon/D$, and the required expression for the potential is

$$\psi = \frac{\varepsilon}{Dr}e^{-\kappa r} \qquad \text{XII.58}$$

It is easily verified that the integral of $\Pi 4\pi r^2\, dr$ from zero to infinite r is $-\varepsilon$, as required. The work done in reversibly bringing a charge ε on to a sphere of radius r_i is clearly

$$\int_{e=0}^{e=\varepsilon} \frac{e}{Dr_i}e^{-\kappa r_i}\, de$$

In integrating we must allow for the fact that κ at any instant is proportional to the element of charge e, and increases in a solution of constant concentration as the charges on all the ions increase. The integral represents the average free energy per ion;

$$\frac{A_i}{N_i} = \frac{1}{Dr_i}\left(\frac{\varepsilon}{\kappa r_i}\right)^2 [1 - (1 + \kappa r_i)\, e^{-\kappa r_i}]$$

On expanding the exponential to four terms, we find

$$A_i = N_i\left(\frac{\varepsilon^2}{2Dr_i} - \frac{\varepsilon^2\kappa}{3D} + \frac{\varepsilon^2 r_i\kappa^2}{8D}\cdots\right) \qquad \text{XII.59}$$

The first term is clearly the gain in electrostatic free energy of N_i ions each charged separately, as in Born's treatment. The leading term that follows is the key term in the interionic theory of extremely dilute solutions of electrolytes. It denotes the extent to which the average electrostatic free energy of an ion in a solution of concentration corresponding to κ differs from its average free energy at infinite dilution. The additional electrostatic energy of an extremely dilute electrolyte solution containing different kinds of ions is

$$A_e = -\sum \frac{N_i e_i^2 \kappa}{3D} \qquad \text{XII.60}$$

where $e_i = z_i \varepsilon$, and z_i is the valency. Because κ is proportional to the square-root of the molar concentration, c_i, or, more generally to the square-root of the ionic strength, j, defined as

$$j = \tfrac{1}{2}\sum c_i z_i^2 = \left(\frac{1\,000\,DkT}{8\pi N_0 \varepsilon^2} \right) \kappa^2 \qquad \text{XII.61}$$

the additional electrostatic energy of dilute electrolytes also varies as the square-root of the ionic strength; and it is natural to expect the magnitude of most properties of electrolytes at great dilution to differ from the corresponding magnitudes at infinite dilution by an amount which varies as the square-root of the concentration. For 1–1 electrolytes j is identical with c. This is indeed found to be the case, not only for the equivalent conductivity and the heat of dissolution already discussed, but for partial ionic volumes, coefficients of diffusion, partial ionic heat capacities, and many other properties.

1. *Heats of dilution.* Ignoring the difference between A_e and G_e, we obtain, from equation XII.60, the following expression for the heat content of an ionic solution:

$$H = H^0 - \sum (N_i e_i^2 \kappa / 2D)(1 - LT) \qquad \text{XII.62}$$

Applied to an aqueous solution containing one gram-mole of a 1–1 electrolyte at 25°C, the heat content, in calories, becomes

$$H = H^0 + 537 c^{1/2} \qquad \text{XII.63}$$

where c is the concentration in gram-moles per litre. It is to be noted that $(1 - LT)$ for this solvent at this temperature is negative. The limiting experimental value of $dH/d\sqrt{c}$ for 1–1 electrolytes is 480 ± 88

335

(Seligmann, 1938). The heat of dilution of most salts at moderate concentrations is, however, in a direction opposite to that indicated by this equation.

2. *Activity coefficients.* The contribution to the chemical potential of an ion due to its additional electrostatic energy is $(dA_e/dN_i)_{N_j,T,V}$. From equation XII.60 this is seen to be $\mu_e = -e_i^2\kappa/2D$. The factor $\frac{1}{2}$ appears, instead of $\frac{1}{3}$, because κ is proportional to $N_i^{1/2}$. Instead of writing for the chemical potential of an ion the empirical equation

$$\mu_i = \mu_i^0 + kT\ln c_i + kT\ln \gamma_i \qquad \text{XII.64}$$

we can now write

$$\mu_i = \mu_i^0 + kT\ln c_i - (e_i^2\kappa/2D) \qquad \text{XII.65}$$

The proportionality between the logarithm of the activity coefficient and the square-root of the concentration (Mellanby's rule) thus finds its interpretation, since

$$\ln \gamma_i = -e_i^2\kappa/2DkT \qquad \text{XII.66}$$

For 1–1 electrolytes $(e_i = \varepsilon)$ in water at 25°C $(D = 78\cdot53$ and $\varepsilon^2/2DkT = 3\cdot55\,\text{Å})$, we have

$$\log_{10}\gamma = -0\cdot506c^{1/2} \qquad \text{XII.67}$$

At a concentration of 1 millimole per litre $(c = 0\cdot001)$ the observed value of γ is found to be within 2 per cent of the computed value. At higher concentrations the gradient $d\log\gamma/dc^{1/2}$ deviates widely from this limiting value, and changes its sign. Activity coefficients at these higher concentrations are discussed in a later section.

3. *Equivalent conductivity.* The force acting on an isolated ion of charge ε in a field of strength E is $E\varepsilon$. The net charge on the swarm of ions around a single cation is $-\varepsilon$. Thus the effect of the external field is to push the selected ion in one direction and to pull the cloud around it in the opposite direction. This electrophoretic effect can be accounted for by regarding the effective charge on the selected ion as $\varepsilon(1 - \kappa r_i)$ where r_i is the ionic radius. A second retarding force arises from the fact that the movement of an ion in a given direction destroys the symmetry of its attendant cloud. Brownian motion tends to restore it, and the effect is known as the relaxation effect. The total force acting on a single cation can be shown (Debye and Hückel, 1923;

336

Onsager, 1926), to be

$$X = E\varepsilon\left[1 - \kappa r_i - \left(\frac{2}{2+\sqrt{2}}\right)\frac{\varepsilon^2\kappa}{6DkT}\right]$$

Both retarding forces are seen to be proportional to κ. The velocity, u, of migration is X/C_+, where C_+ is a resistance factor, given by Stokes as $6\pi r_+\eta$ for a spherical ion. The mobility, u^0, is u/E. Hence

$$u^0 = \frac{\varepsilon}{C_+}\left[1 - \kappa r_i - \left(\frac{2}{2+\sqrt{2}}\right)\frac{\varepsilon^2\kappa}{6DkT}\right] \qquad \text{XII.68}$$

On making use of the expressions already derived for the mobilities ($u^0 = \varepsilon/C_+$; $v^0 = \varepsilon/C_-$) and for the equivalent conductance $\Lambda = N_0\varepsilon(u^0+v^0)$ we find

$$\Lambda = \Lambda_\infty\left[1 - \left(\frac{2}{2+\sqrt{2}}\right)\frac{e^2\kappa}{6DkT}\right] - \frac{N_0\varepsilon^2\kappa}{3\pi\eta} \qquad \text{XII.69}$$

The gradient $d\Lambda/dc^{1/2}$ can be thus evaluated in terms of parameters and natural constants used in the theory (η, D, T, ε, k and N_0). They are found to compare favourably with the empirical constant A of equation XII.4.

Electrolytic solutions of moderate concentrations

The square-root law has been often qualitatively, and not infrequently quantitatively, established in aqueous solutions containing not more than 1 millimole per litre of electrolyte. The narrowness of the concentration range where it holds has elicited the comment that it is less a law of electrolytes than of slightly polluted water. This observation, though cynical, is not without justification. To construct a theory of electrolytic solutions on such narrow foundations would be as perilous as if we attempted to derive the intermolecular energy constants of the inert atoms from our knowledge of their behaviour at pressures below 15 mm. The tail must not wag the dog. In a saturated aqueous solution of ammonium chloride at 298·16°K, the interionic energy between the ions is less than one tenth of the interaction energy between the ions and the solvent molecules. Nevertheless, there have been advanced many extensions of the square-root law. A more careful solution of Poisson's equation shows that the electrostatic contribution to the chemical potential ($-e_i^2\kappa/2D$) should be

337

multiplied by the factor $(1+\kappa a_i)^{-1}$, where a_i is the mean value of the nearest distances of approach of the various ions. Instead of equation XII.66, we then have

$$\ln \gamma = \frac{z_i z_j \varepsilon^2 \kappa}{2DkT}\left(\frac{1}{1+\kappa a}\right) \qquad \text{XII.70}$$

For 1–1 electrolytes in water at 25°, it follows that

$$\log_{10}\gamma = -\frac{0\cdot5092\sqrt{c}}{1+0\cdot3286\mathring{a}\sqrt{c}} \qquad \text{XII.71}$$

where $\mathring{a}$ is the value of a expressed in Ångstrom units. There is no justification for ignoring the higher terms in the expansion of equation XII.59; the next term to be included is positive, and varies in proportion to c. The revised expression for $\ln \gamma$, and the corresponding one for the equivalent conductivity, give better representations of the facts. The value of $\mathring{a}$ required to fit the data is, however, sometimes unreasonably small.

Ion association

The idea that the ionic atmosphere surrounding an ion in solution can be treated as a continuous cloud of electricity is mathematically convenient but physically far from acceptable. If a positive ion were to approach a negative ion of equal valency and the pair were to rotate freely in solution, they would present to the remainder of the system a neutral region. The equilibrium distance apart of the ions, a_0, is obtained, as in the treatment of the hydrogen atom, from the condition $I\omega^2 = \varepsilon^2/Da_0$, where I is the moment of inertia and ω the angular velocity. We have seen that the average value of the kinetic energy of a free rotator is $\frac{1}{2}I\omega^2 = kT$. Hence $a_0 = \varepsilon^2/2DkT$. In water at 25°C, a_0 is 3·55 Å. Bjerrum (1926) has greatly improved the theory of electrolytes by allowing for the presence of ion pairs. Pairs of oppositely charged ions closer together than a_0 are regarded as associated; those further apart as free, and subject to the Milner–Debye distribution. The application of his theory is one of successive approximations, but can be carried out with precision. C. W. Davies (1949) finds, for example, that the equilibrium constants governing the dissociation of the ion pairs $Ag^+NO_3^-$ and $Ba^{++}S_2O_3^{--}$ into free ions in water at 25°C are $1\cdot17 \times 10^0$ and $6\cdot1 \times 10^{-3}$ respectively, and that the corresponding values of a_0 are 2·7 and 4·9 Å. These and similarly derived equilibrium distances are much more reasonable than the closest distances of approach obtained in the earlier treatments. Ion triplets have also been studied (Fuoss and Kraus, 1933). Further reference is made in Chapter XIII to the influence of the solvent on the extent of ion association.

Concentrated electrolyte solutions

The solvent molecules forming the first coordination shell around elementary ions in aqueous solution are so different from ordinary water molecules that it is misleading not to emphasise the difference. They are so firmly clamped that they cannot, for example, exert an appreciable vapour pressure. The idea that each molecule of electrolyte, while ionising into v ions combines with n molecules of water, has been applied by R. A. Robinson and R. H. Stokes (1948) to explain properties of electrolyte solutions at concentrations of many moles per litre. We shall consider activity coefficients only in aqueous solutions.

The conventional mean ionic activity coefficient, γ_2, of an electrolyte is defined in terms of the chemical potential, μ_2 the molality, m, and the number of ions, v, into which each molecule dissociates:

$$\mu_2 = \mu_2^0 + vkT \ln m + vkT \ln \gamma_2 \qquad \text{XII.72}$$

For the solvent it is customary to write

$$\mu_1 = \mu_1^0 + kT \ln a_1 \qquad \text{XII.73}$$

where a_1 the activity coefficient, is p_1/p_1^0, as in the treatment of non-electrolytes. The Gibbs–Duhem equation $N_1 \, d\mu_1 + N_2 \, d\mu_2 = 0$ in the notation of molality (number of moles per 1 000 grams of water, or, nearly, per 55·5 moles of water) is $55·5 \, d\mu_1 + m \, d\mu_2 = 0$. Hence

$$d \ln \gamma_2 = -d \ln m - (55·5/mv) \, d \ln a_1 \qquad \text{XII.74}$$

In terms of a corrected molality m', defined as the number of moles of hydrated solute per 1 000 grams of free water, we introduce a corrected activity coefficient by the similar equation

$$d \ln \gamma_2' = -d \ln m' - (55·5/m'v) \, d \ln a_1 \qquad \text{XII.75}$$

Hence

$$d \ln \gamma_2' - d \ln \gamma_2 = -(d \ln m' - d \ln m) - \frac{55·5}{mv}\left(\frac{m}{m'} - 1\right) d \ln a_1 \qquad \text{XII.76}$$

339

But clearly

$$\frac{m'}{m} = \frac{55\cdot5}{55\cdot5 - mn} = (1 - 0\cdot018mn)^{-1} \qquad \text{XII.77}$$

On eliminating $d \ln m' - d \ln m$ and m/m', we obtain an equation which can be integrated to give

$$\ln \gamma'_2 - \ln \gamma_2 = \ln(1 - 0\cdot018mn) + (n/v) \ln a_1 \qquad \text{XII.78}$$

Finally, the rational activity coefficient γ of the hydrated ions is obtained by means of Scatchard's relation $\gamma/\gamma'_2 = 1 + 0\cdot018vm'$, so that

$$\ln \gamma_2 = \ln \gamma - \ln[1 - 0\cdot018(n-v)m] - (n/v) \ln a_1 \qquad \text{XII.79}$$

Stokes and Robinson contend that the expression of Debye and Hückel may be adopted for the rational activity coefficient, γ, of the hydrated ions, so that, for a 1–1 electrolyte in water at 25°C, the

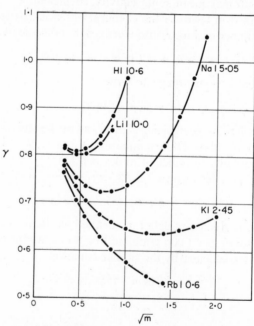

Fig. XII.6 *Mean activity coefficients of certain iodides in water at 298·16°K. Points are experimental. Curves are calculated from equation*

logarithm of the conventional activity coefficient takes the form:

$$\log_{10}\gamma_2 = -\frac{0.509\sqrt{c}}{1+0.329\mathring{a}\sqrt{c}} - \log_{10}[1-0.018(n-v)m] - (n/v)\log_{10}a_1$$

$$\text{XII.80}$$

Comparison with experiment allows the evaluation of the constants $\mathring{a}$ and n. (See Fig. XII.6.) The mean value found for n for the halides of hydrogen and lithium is 8.

XIII Equilibria in homogeneous systems

Equilibria in homogeneous systems

There are three distinct approaches to the subject of chemical equilibria. In terms of molecular statistics, the equilibrium state is that having the maximum inherent probability; any displacement from that state results in the formation of a less probable one. From the standpoint of thermodynamics, the equilibrium state is the state of minimum free energy; a virtual displacement of the system from its equilibrium position, consonant with constancy of volume, temperature and molecular population, cannot be effected without the expenditure of energy. According to chemical kinetics, the equilibrium state is that in which the rate of formation of each type of molecule is equal to its rate of destruction. We shall see in Chapter XV that the elimination of time from kinetic expressions leads to the law of mass action, and that the equilibrium state is one of balanced activity rather than of rest. We shall here treat equilibria in homogeneous systems by the methods of statistical mechanics and of chemical thermodynamics, using the former in simple and the latter in complex cases.

The general expression for the molecular partition function,

$$f = \sum_0^\infty p_i e^{-\varepsilon_i/kT} \qquad \text{VI.48}$$

when applied to N ideal gas molecules in a system of volume V at a temperature T becomes

$$f = \frac{g(2\pi mkT)^{3/2} Ve}{h^3 N} f_{\text{rot}} f_{\text{vib}} f_{\text{elec}} \, e^{-u/kT} \qquad \text{XIII.1}$$

where the first term is the translational component of the total partition function, as previously derived (equation IX.46), and the remaining components are the rotational, vibrational and electronic partition functions. u is the average potential energy of the molecule at the absolute zero of temperature if it were completely static. Since, when $T = 0$, the molecule is assumed to be static, u is also the total energy per molecule at this temperature. It is convenient to work

342

with the variable, q, defined as follows:

$$q = \frac{Nf}{Ve} = n\frac{f}{e} \qquad \text{IX.48}$$

where n is the concentration, in molecules per cc. It is to be noted that q has the dimensions of a concentration, that its magnitude depends on many specific properties of the molecule, and that it is a function of the temperature, but is independent of the pressure or volume of the system. The system partition function for a mixture of ideal gases, not necessarily convertible one into another by chemical change, but at equilibrium in a system of constant volume V at temperature T is

$$F = f_i^{N_i} \cdot f_j^{N_j} \cdots = \left(\frac{q_i Ve}{N_i}\right)^{N_i} \left(\frac{q_j Ve}{N_j}\right)^{N_j} \qquad \text{XIII.2}$$

where N_i, N_j, ... are the numbers of the various kinds of molecules present. The Helmholtz free energy of the system is

$$A = -kT \ln F = -kT \sum (N_i \ln q_i V + N_i - N_i \ln N_i) \qquad \text{XIII.3}$$

and the chemical potential of a molecule of the ith type is, according to equation VI.36,

$$\mu_i = \left(\frac{dA}{dN_i}\right)_{T,V,N_j...} = -kT \ln\left(\frac{q_i}{n_i}\right) \qquad \text{XIII.4}$$

If we wish to work on a molar basis, we may replace N_i, N_j, ... in equation XIII.3 by $v_i N_0$, $v_j N_0$, ..., where v is the number of gram-moles, and N_0 is Avogadro's number. Then, since $N_0 k = R$, the gas constant, we have

$$A_i = \left(\frac{dA}{dv_i}\right)_{T,V,v_j...} = -RT \ln\left(\frac{q_i}{n_i}\right) \qquad \text{XIII.5}$$

Now it has been shown that when a homogeneous system is at equilibrium,

$$\sum v_i \mu_i (\text{reactants}) = \sum v_j \mu_j (\text{resultants}) \qquad \text{VI.39}$$

The v terms in this equation are stoichiometric numbers, $1, 2, 3, \ldots$. On applying this condition to the homogeneous gas reaction represented by the equation

$$bB + cC \rightleftarrows lL \qquad \text{XIII.6}$$

343

we see that

$$\frac{n_L^l}{n_B^b n_C^c} = \frac{q_L^l}{q_B^b q_C^c} = K_n \qquad \text{XIII.7}$$

Because q for each participant depends on temperature only, it follows that K_n, the equilibrium constant, is also dependent on T only. This is the law of mass action, (Guldberg and Waage, 1864) which we may now apply to a few well investigated systems.

Equilibria of the type $2AB \rightleftarrows A + B$

In this type of equilibrium, $l = b + c$, and K is consequently dimensionless, and independent of the units in which the concentrations are expressed. The subscript to K may thus be dropped. The decompositions of the hydrogen halides into hydrogen and halogen molecules come under this heading. They have been investigated by Bodenstein (1893–99) with a thoroughness hardly yet surpassed. The hydrogen iodide system $2HI \rightleftarrows H_2 + I_2$ gives us:

$$K = \frac{n_{H_2} n_{I_2}}{n_{HI}^2} = \frac{[H_2][I_2]}{[HI]^2} \qquad \text{XIII.8}$$

The square brackets are a conventional and typographically convenient means of expressing concentrations. Bodenstein worked with small glass tubes which were filled with hydrogen iodide at a known pressure, sealed off, and analysed for the remaining acid and for the iodine produced, after having been kept in the vapour of boiling mercury ($T = 630 \cdot 4°K$) or boiling sulphur ($T = 717 \cdot 7°K$) for a sufficient time to allow equilibrium to be established. Let the initial amount of hydrogen iodide be $2c$ g-mol; then, if the initial amounts of hydrogen and iodine are zero, and the fraction decomposed at equilibrium is x,

$$[HI] = 2c(1 - x)/V$$

$$[H_2] = [I_2] = cx/V$$

and

$$K = \frac{[H_2][I_2]}{[HI]} = \left[\frac{x}{2(1 - x)}\right]^2$$

The real check on the attainment of equilibrium is now to start with tubes containing pure hydrogen and iodine, and, after heating them

344

for a sufficient time, to determine whether the amount of hydrogen iodide formed may be satisfactorily estimated from this value of K and from the known initial concentrations, a and b respectively, of hydrogen and iodine. Let the equilibrium concentration of hydrogen iodide for these experiments be $2y$ g-mol per litre. Then

$$K = \frac{(a-y)(b-y)}{4y^2}$$

and

$$y = \frac{a+b}{2(1-4K)} - \left\{\frac{(a+b)^2}{4(1-4K)^2} - \frac{ab}{1-4K}\right\}^{1/2}$$

the other root of the quadratic equation being an impossible one. Bodenstein found close agreement between the observed and calculated values of y.

The temperature variation of the equilibrium constant for many reactions of this type can be reproduced by the empirical equation written over Table XIII.1, which contains data for other reactions in this category.

Table XIII.1 *Experimental equilibrium constants for gaseous reactions of the type* $2AB \rightleftarrows A_2 + B_2$. $K = [A_2][B_2]/[AB]^2$. $\quad \log K = a + b \log T - c/T$.

Reaction	a	b	c	ΔE_0 (cals/mole)
$2HD \rightleftarrows H_2 + D_2$	-0.627	0	-34.3	-157
$2HCl \rightleftarrows H_2 + Cl_2$	-2.16	0.44	9 586	43 860
$2HBr \rightleftarrows H_2 + Br_2$	-2.835	0.50	5 187	23 730
$2HI \rightleftarrows H_2 + I_2$	-2.450	0.45	508.3	2 325
$2HCN \rightleftarrows H_2 + (CN)_2$	-2.24	0	2 348	10 740
$2BrI \rightleftarrows Br_2 + I_2$	0.1075	0	805	3 683
$2NO \rightleftarrows N_2 + O_2$	-1.63	0	$-9 452$	$-43 240$

Thermodynamic formulation of equilibria by the method of standard states

Let us denote $-kT \ln q_i$ by μ_i^0 and $-RT \ln q_i$ by A_i^0, so that equations XIII.4 and XIII.5 for the molecular and molar chemical potentials, respectively, become

$$\mu_i = \mu_i^0 + kT \ln n_i \qquad \text{XIII.9}$$

M

345

and

$$A_i = A_i^0 + RT \ln n_i \qquad \text{XIII.10}$$

where μ_i^0 and A_i^0 are the chemical potentials of species i when at unit concentration. The general condition of equilibrium in homogeneous systems,

$$\sum v_i \mu_i = \sum v_j \mu_j \qquad \text{VI.39}$$

now becomes

$$\sum [v_i(\mu_i^0 + kT \ln n_i)] = \sum [v_j(\mu_j^0 + kT \ln n_j)]$$

provided the concentrations are those prevailing at equilibrium. On rearranging, we have

$$\sum v_i \mu_i^0 - \sum v_j \mu_j^0 = kT \ln \frac{\Pi n_j^{v_j}}{\Pi n_i^{v_i}}$$

or

$$\Delta \mu^0 = -kT \ln K \qquad \text{XIII.11}$$

where K is the equilibrium constant (products in the numerator), and $\Delta \mu^0$ is the algebraic sum of the standard chemical potentials of reactants and resultants (the resultants reckoned positive). Similarly

$$\Delta A^0 = -RT \ln K \qquad \text{XIII.12}$$

We may apply the Kelvin–Helmholtz operation to both sides of this equation, and obtain the result

$$\Delta E^0 = \Delta A^0 - T \frac{d(\Delta A^0)}{dT} = RT^2 \frac{d \ln K_n}{dT} = -R \frac{d \ln K_n}{d(1/T)} \qquad \text{XIII.13}$$

We may also use equation (VI.21), and obtain

$$\Delta A^0 = \Delta E^0 - T \Delta S^0 \qquad \text{XIII.14}$$

where the Δ refers to increases attending the reaction at constant temperature and volume. It should be pointed out that the reaction need not be measured at constant volume; K_n is independent of the total volume, and equilibria may well be studied at constant pressure over a range of temperatures. On eliminating ΔA^0 from equations XIII.12 and XIII.14, we find that

$$\ln K_n = \frac{\Delta S^0}{R} - \frac{\Delta E^0}{RT},$$

or

$$K_n = e^{\Delta S^0/R} e^{-\Delta E^0/RT}. \qquad \text{XIII.15}$$

It must not be thought, from the form of this equation, that K_n is dimensionless. The entropy term for each participant consists of the product of one term, which has the same dimensions as R, and another term which is the logarithm of a concentration. Hence, unless the same number of molecules appear on both sides of the chemical equation, K_n has the dimensions of a concentration raised to an integral power.

As explained in earlier chapters, the entropy of a pure substance may be measured from thermal data. Moreover, ΔE^0 is the molar heat, q_V, absorbed when the reaction proceeds from left to right. K_n can thus be found completely from thermal data, which is a valuable chemical consequence of the laws of thermodynamics.

We shall illustrate the usefulness of equation XIII.15 with reference to the gaseous decomposition of three of the hydrogen halides, for which Bodenstein and his collaborators have measured equilibrium constants at room temperatures by an electromotive force method which is described in Chapter XIV. Drawing our data from Chapter IX, we obtain the increases in standard entropies shown in Table XIII.2.

Table XIII.2

x	$S^0_{298 \cdot 1}(H_2) + S^0_{298 \cdot 1}(X_2) - 2S^0_{298 \cdot 1}(HX) = \Delta S^0_{298 \cdot 1}$		
Cl	$31 \cdot 23$ + $53 \cdot 31$	− $2 \times (44 \cdot 64) =$	$-4 \cdot 74$
Br	$31 \cdot 23$ + $58 \cdot 68$	− $2 \times (47 \cdot 48) =$	$-5 \cdot 07$
I	$31 \cdot 23$ + $62 \cdot 29$	− $2 \times (49 \cdot 36) =$	$-5 \cdot 20$

The concentration in the reference state is $(1/22 \cdot 41)$ mole/litre, i.e. the molar concentration at a pressure of one atmosphere. With the thermochemical values provided by Thomsen and by Berthelot in the first two reactions, the equilibrium constant, K_n, may now be evaluated from purely thermal data. Since small errors in ΔE^0 produce a magnified effect on K_n, it is fairer to compare the experimental values of ΔE^0 with those obtained from equation XIII.15, i.e.

$$\Delta E^0_{\text{calc.}} = T(\Delta S^0 - R \ln K_n) \qquad \text{XIII.15}$$

The results are set forth in Table XIII.3. The calculated value of ΔE^0 in each case agrees with, and is probably more reliable than, the experimental figure found calorimetrically or from equation XIII.13.

Table XIII.3

Reaction	$K^0_{298.1}$	$\Delta S^0_{298.1}$	$\Delta E^0_{298.1}$ (calc)	ΔE^0 (obs)
$2HCl \rightleftarrows H_2 + Cl_2$	5.50×10^{-34}	-4.74	43 960	44 000 (room temp.)
$2HBr \rightleftarrows H_2 + Br_2$	1.05×10^{-19}	-5.07	24 380	24 200 $\pm$ 400 (room temp.)
$2HI \rightleftarrows H_2 + I_2$	5.01×10^{-4}	-5.20	2 950	2 940 (300–800°K)

Many gaseous equilibria have been examined at a constant total pressure, P. Analogous to equations XIII.12 and XIII.15, we now have

$$\Delta G^0 = -RT \ln K \qquad \text{XIII.16}$$

and

$$\ln K_p = \frac{\Delta S^0}{R} - \frac{\Delta H^0}{RT}$$

$$K_p = e^{\Delta S^0/R} \, e^{-\Delta H^0/RT} \qquad \text{XIII.17}$$

The same warning must be given concerning the use and interpretation of this equation as with equation XIII.15: each S^0 term is proportional to the logarithm of a pressure, and, therefore, unless $b + c = l$, K_P has the dimensions of a pressure, raised to some integral power.

Statistical computation of equilibria based on spectroscopic data

The statistical expression (equation XIII.7) is a general one, but it is of practical value only when the q terms can be explicitly formulated in terms of known molecular constants, such as vibration frequencies, and moments of inertia. Such is the case with the reactions now under consideration, all of which involve diatomic molecules only. Using the partition function IX.57 to obtain the q values, we have the following theoretical expression for the equilibrium constant in the hydrogen iodide system:

$$K = \frac{[H_2][I_2]}{[HI]^2} = \left(\frac{g_{H_2} g_{I_2}}{g_{HI}^2}\right)\left\{\frac{m_{H_2} m_{I_2}}{m_{HI}^2}\right\}^{3/2}\left\{\frac{\sigma_{HI}^2}{\sigma_{H_2} \sigma_{I_2}}\right\}\left\{\frac{I_{H_2} I_{I_2}}{I_{HI}^2}\right\}$$

$$\times \frac{(1-e^{-hv(HI)/kT})^2}{(1-e^{-hv(H_2)/kT})(1-e^{-hv(I_2)/kT})} e^{-\Delta E_0/RT} \qquad \text{XIII.18}$$

g is unity for the three types of molecules. σ, however, is 1 for HI and 2 for H_2 and I_2. From the spectroscopic data given in Table x.2, the term preceding the Boltzmann factor can be evaluated. ΔE_0 can also be evaluated from the same set of constants, by considering the following simple cycle of operations:

$$
\begin{array}{lll}
2HI \rightarrow 2H + 2I; & \Delta E = 2D_{HI} \\
2H \rightarrow H_2 & ; & \Delta E = -D_{H_2} \\
2I \rightarrow I_2 & ; & \Delta E = -D_{I_2} \\
\hline
2HI \rightarrow H_2 + I_2; & \Delta E = 2D_{HI} - (D_{H_2} + D_{I_2})
\end{array}
$$

ΔE_0 is thus the algebraic sum of the energies of dissociation of reactants and products:

$$\Delta E_0 = \sum D_i - \sum D_j \qquad \text{XIII.19}$$

If, instead of the energies of dissociation used here, we regard D for each type of molecule as the energy required to atomise it, the equation is true for reactions of any degree of complexity. Values of ΔE_0 for the dissociation of hydrogen chloride and hydrogen bromide found from the spectroscopically determined energies of dissociation of the various molecules are in close agreement with those found earlier by means of equation XIII.13. The spectroscopic evaluation of D_{HI}, however, has proved to be difficult, and the most reliable value for it is that obtained by combining the spectroscopic values of D_{H_2} and D_{I_2} with the ΔE_0 value found from the temperature variation of the equilibrium constant (equation XIII.13).

The common energy level

The various potential energies, u, which are included in the partition functions of the different molecules (equation XIII.1) must obviously refer to a level which is common to them all. In systems of the kind examined here, the logical reference level is that of zero potential

349

energy for all atoms when infinitely far apart, and at rest. Two hydrogen atoms and two iodine atoms under such conditions may descend into regions of lower potential energy in two different ways, forming either two molecules of hydrogen iodide or one molecule each of hydrogen and iodine. The difference between the losses is the gain in potential energy attending the conversion of two static molecules of HI into its static products. More generally, we may write

$$\Delta\varepsilon_s = \sum u_j - \sum u_i \qquad\qquad \text{XIII.20}$$

It is known, however, that even at the absolute zero of temperature, the atoms in a molecule are not at rest. As may be seen from Fig. XIII.1, the maximum observable increase in energy attending a reaction

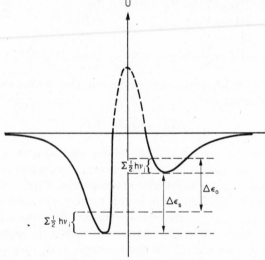

Fig. XIII.1 *Schematic representation of energy changes attending a chemical reaction*

at the absolute zero of temperature is related as follows to the static increase in potential energy:

$$\Delta\varepsilon_0 + \sum \tfrac{1}{2}h\nu_i = \Delta\varepsilon_s + \sum \tfrac{1}{2}h\nu_j$$

Hence

$$\Delta\varepsilon_0 = \sum(u_j + \tfrac{1}{2}h\nu_j) - \sum(u_i + \tfrac{1}{2}h\nu_i)$$

$$= \sum \varepsilon_{0,j} - \sum \varepsilon_{0,i} \qquad\qquad \text{XIII.21}$$

where ε_0 is the total energy of a molecule at the absolute zero of temperature, and includes its residual energy.

Reverting to our expression for the partition function of a diatomic molecule, we see that

$$f = f_{trans} f_{rot} f_{vibr} f_{elec} e^{-u/kT}$$
$$= f_{trans} f_{rot} f_{elec} e^{-(1/2)hv/kT} (1 - e^{-hv/kT})^{-1} e^{-u/kT}$$
$$= f_{trans} f_{rot} f_{elec} (1 - e^{-hv/kT})^{-1} e^{-\varepsilon_0/kT} \qquad \text{IX.57}$$

Thus, by using the effective vibrational partition functions, $(1 - e^{-hv/kT})^{-1}$ instead of the complete vibrational partition function, $2 \sinh (hv/2kT)$, we conveniently obtain equilibrium constants in terms of $\Delta\varepsilon_0$, which is what is required.

Equilibria of the type $BC \rightleftarrows B + C$

Let us consider a gaseous system containing v formula-weights of phosphorus pentachloride, of which a fraction α is dissociated into phosphorus trichloride and chlorine:

$$PCl_5 \rightleftarrows PCl_3 + Cl_2$$
$$v(1 - \alpha) \quad v\alpha \quad v\alpha$$

The total number of gram-moles in the system is thus $v(1 + \alpha)$. If each component obeys the ideal gas laws, we have

$$PV = v(1 + \alpha)RT \qquad \text{XIII.22}$$

where P is the pressure of the system, V its volume, and T the absolute temperature. Let us denote by V^0 the computed volume which the system would have, at the same pressure and temperature, if there were no dissociation. Then

$$PV^0 = vRT$$

and consequently,

$$V/V^0 = 1 + \alpha$$

But, at constant temperature and pressure, the volume of a system of constant mass varies inversely with respect to its density, ρ, so that $\rho^0/\rho = 1 + \alpha$, or

$$\alpha = (\rho^0/\rho) - 1 \qquad \text{XIII.23}$$

351

The degree of dissociation can thus be found from measurements of the actual density, ρ, of the system, and a knowledge of the computed density, ρ^0, which the system would have, at the same pressure and temperature, if there were no dissociation. This is a method which has been frequently used. Alternatively, let P^0 denote the pressure which the system would have if there were no dissociation. Then

$$P^0 V = \nu R T.$$

On comparing with equation XIII.22, we have

$$P/P^0 = 1 + \alpha,$$

or

$$\alpha = (P/P^0) - 1 \qquad\qquad \text{XIII.23a}$$

The fraction dissociated can thus be found by measuring the actual pressure, P, of the system, and comparing it with the computed pressure, P^0, which the system would have, at the same volume and temperature in the complete absence of dissociation. This is the method used by Holland (1913), who, after filling a reaction vessel of known volume with decomposing phosphorus pentachloride at a high temperature, sealed it off, and measured the equilibrium pressure at various lower temperatures, before analysing its contents for the total amount of substance used.

In terms of the partial pressures, the equilibrium constant is expressed as follows:

$$K_p = \frac{p_{PCl_3} \times p_{Cl_2}}{p_{PCl_5}}$$

By Dalton's law the partial pressure of a component in an ideal gas system bears the same relation to the total pressure as the number of moles of that component bears to the total number of moles. Hence, provided our system is nominally pure phosphorus pentachloride, with no addition of the other gases,

$$p_{Cl_2} = p_{PCl_3} = P\left(\frac{\alpha}{1+\alpha}\right); \quad p_{PCl_5} = P\left(\frac{1-\alpha}{1+\alpha}\right)$$

and

$$K_p = P\frac{\alpha^2}{1-\alpha^2} \qquad\qquad \text{XIII.24}$$

This quadratic equation has only one real root, which is

$$\alpha = \left(\frac{K_p}{K_p + P}\right)^{1/2} \qquad\qquad \text{XIII.25}$$

We note that α is unity, i.e. dissociation is complete, at zero pressure, and that α can be extremely small at high pressures. The analogy with Ostwald's dilution law (Chapter XII) is complete. Equation XIII.25 also provides a quantitative expression of le Chatelier's general principle of mobile equilibria; when an external agency, such as pressure or heat, is brought to bear on a system at equilibrium, the equilibrium is displaced in a direction which tends to undo the effect of the external agent.

By plotting against $1/T$ the values of log K_p obtained from Holland's data over a temperature range of 200°, the constants of equation XIII.17 are found to be $\Delta H = 21\,850$ cal/mole and $\Delta S^0 = 42\cdot46$ cal/mole-degree, where the reference state is that of 1 atmosphere. The latter value allows S^0 for PCl_5 to be determined, since S^0 for PCl_3 and Cl_2 are known from spectroscopic sources.

Other gaseous equilibria belonging to the same category are the dissociation of the halogen molecules into atoms. Here the spectrometric evaluations have fully confirmed the earlier thermal results

Table XIII.4 *A comparison of the energies of dissociation of the halogen molecules obtained by two independent methods (calories/mole)*

Reaction	ΔE_0^0 from equilibrium constants	ΔE_0^0 from spectroscopic sources
$Cl_2 \rightleftarrows 2Cl$	57 650	57 030
$Br_2 \rightleftarrows 2Br$	45 180	45 196
$I_2 \rightleftarrows 2I$	35 785	35 550

(Table XIII.4). The most reliable values of the energies of dissociation of numerous diatomic molecules are summarised in Table XIII.5.

General thermodynamic formulation of chemical equilibria in homogeneous systems

Equation VI.12, on being applied to a chemical reaction, gives us Kirchhoff's law:

$$\Delta H^0 = \Delta H_0^0 + \int_0^T \Delta C_P \, dT \qquad \text{XIII.26}$$

M*

Table XIII.5 *Energies of dissociation of gaseous diatomic molecules at the absolute zero of temperature, in kilocalories per mole*

Molecule	ΔE_0	Molecule	ΔE_0
H_2	103·05	BrI	42·27
D_2	104·91	HF	134·1
Li_2	26·3	HCl	102·13
Na_2	17·5	HBr	85·99
K_2	11·8	HI	71·3
Hg_2	1·59	HLi	56·9
F_2	36·8	HCu	69·2
Cl_2	57·34	HAg	53·0
Br_2	45·19	HAu	92·0
I_2	35·67	HZn	21·0
N_2	224·86	HCd	15·5
P_2	115·98	HHg	8·5
As_2	34·3	HAl	70·5
O_2	117·20	AgCl	71·7
S_2	102·6	AgBr	59·9
NO	149·41	AgI	48·4
CO	255·77	TlCl	87·4
ClBr	52·64	TlBr	73·8
ClI	49·84	TlI	59·0

The constant pressure analogue of equation XIII.13 is

$$\frac{d \ln K_P}{dT} = \frac{\Delta H^0}{RT^2} \qquad \text{XIII.27}$$

Hence

$$\frac{d \ln K_p}{dT} = \frac{\Delta H_0^0}{RT^2} + \frac{1}{RT^2} \int_0^T \Delta C_P \, dT$$

and, therefore,

$$\ln K_p = -\frac{\Delta H_0^0}{RT} + \int_0^T \frac{dT}{RT^2} \int_0^T \Delta C_P \, dT + J$$

where J is constant. Integration by parts leads to the expression

$$\ln K_P = -\frac{\Delta H_0^0}{RT} - \frac{1}{RT} \int_0^T \Delta C_P \, dT + \frac{1}{R} \int_0^T \Delta C_P \, d \ln T + J \qquad \text{XIII.28}$$

which, according to equation XIII.26, can also be written as follows:

$$\ln Kp = -\frac{\Delta H^0}{RT} + \frac{1}{R} \int_0^T \Delta C_P \, d \ln T + J$$

Now in any homogeneous phase, we have

$$\Delta S^0 = \Delta S_0^0 + \int_0^T \Delta C_P \, d \ln T$$

so that

$$\ln K_P = -\frac{\Delta H^0}{RT} + \frac{1}{R}(\Delta S^0 - \Delta S_0^0) + J$$

But, by definition,

$$\ln K_P = -\frac{\Delta H^0}{RT} + \frac{\Delta S^0}{R} \qquad \text{XIII.17}$$

Hence

$$\Delta S_0^0 = RJ \qquad \text{XIII.29}$$

which is the third law interpretation of the empirical constant, J. In the solid phase, ΔS_0^0 is zero. To derive an expression of the right form to represent $\ln K_P$ for homogeneous gas reactions, we proceed as follows. The heat capacity of a pure substance can be reproduced as a power series in T; $C_P = a + bT + cT^2 + \dots$. Similarly, we have

$$\Delta C_P = \alpha + \beta T + \gamma T^2 + \dots$$

where α, β and γ are the algebraic sums of the terms a, b and c, the resultants taken as positive. Restricting the expansions to three constants only, we have

$$\int_0^T \Delta C_P \, dT = \alpha T + \tfrac{1}{2}\beta T^2 + \tfrac{1}{3}\gamma T^3$$

and

$$\int_0^T \Delta C_P \, d \ln T = \alpha \ln T + \beta T + \tfrac{1}{2}\gamma T^2$$

After inserting these expressions in equation XIII.28 and taking advantage of equation XIII.29, we find that

$$R \ln K_P = (\Delta S_0^0 - \alpha) + \alpha \ln T + \tfrac{1}{2}\beta R + \tfrac{1}{6}\gamma T^2 - \frac{\Delta H_0^0}{T} \qquad \text{XIII.30}$$

which is in a form that has been much used.

Haber (1913), for example, studied the water-gas reaction

$$H_2 + CO_2 \rightleftarrows H_2O + CO; \qquad K = [H_2O][CO]/[H_2][CO_2]$$

at temperatures in the neighbourhood of $1\,200°K$, employing a streaming method, with platinised asbestos as catalyst. He summarised the temperature effect on the equilibrium constant by the equation:

$$\log_{10} K = 0.02858 + 0.979 \log_{10} T - 1.082 \times 10^{-3} T + 1.734 \times 10^{-7} T^2$$
$$- 2\,170/T \qquad \text{XIII.31}$$

His work on the synthesis of ammonia,

$$2NH_3 \rightleftarrows N_2 + 3H_2; \qquad K_P = p_{N_2} p_{H_2}^3 / p_{NH_3}^2$$

can be expressed by an equation of the same form, namely

$$\log_{10} K_P (\text{atm})^2 = 5.6988 + 5.6122 \log_{10} T - 1.924 \times 10^{-4} T$$
$$- 2.90 \times 10^{-7} T^2 - 4\,196/T \qquad \text{XIII.32}$$

ΔH_0^0 for these reactions are consequently $9\,926$ and $19\,200$ calories respectively, but corrections for gas imperfection reduce the latter result by about $1\,000$ calories (Gillespie and Beattie, 1930).

On multiplying both sides of equation XIII.30 by $-T$, we obtain another expression which is frequently used to represent the temperature variation of the equilibrium constant:

$$\Delta G^0 = \Delta H_0^0 - \alpha T \ln T - \tfrac{1}{2}\beta T^2 - \tfrac{1}{6}\gamma T^3 - \ldots - RJT. \qquad \text{XIII.33}$$

The following two instances are taken from *International Critical Tables* and give the energy, as usual, in calories:

$$2H_2O \rightleftarrows 2H_2 + O_2; \qquad K_p = p_{H_2}^2 p_{O_2} / p_{H_2O}^2;$$

$$\Delta G^0 = -RT \ln K_P(\text{atm}) = 114\,820 - 1.88 T \ln T - 3.30 \times 10^{-3} T^2$$
$$+ 7.4 \times 10^{-7} T^3 - 7.84 T \qquad \text{XIII.34}$$

$$2Cl_2 + 2H_2O \rightleftarrows 4HCl + O_2; \qquad K_P = p_{HCl}^4 p_{O_2} / p_{Cl_2}^2 p_{H_2O}^2;$$

$$\Delta G^0 = -RT \ln K_P(\text{atm}) = 27\,340 - 0.08 T \ln T - 3.4 \times 10^{-3} T^2$$
$$+ 7.4 \times 10^{-7} T^3 - 29.08 T \qquad \text{XIII.35}$$

The energy of atomisation of certain inorganic molecules in the gas phase

By combining the data of Table XIII.5 with equations XIII.30, 31, 34 and 35 of this chapter, we readily find the energy of decomposition of polyatomic molecules into atoms. The energies required to atomise molecules of water and ammonia, for example, are found as follows:

		ΔE_0
(1) H_2O	$2H_2O \rightleftarrows 2H_2 + O_2$	114·82
	$2H_2 \rightleftarrows 4H$	206·10
	$O_2 \rightleftarrows 2O$	117·20
	$2H_2O \rightleftarrows 4H + 2O$	438·12
	$\therefore H_2O \rightleftarrows 2H + O$	219·06
(2) NH_3	$2NH_3 \rightleftarrows N_2 + 3H_2$	18·32
	$N_2 \rightleftarrows 2N$	224·86
	$3H_2 \rightleftarrows 6H$	309·15
	$2NH_3 \rightleftarrows 2N + 6H$	552·33
	$\therefore NH_3 \rightleftarrows N + 3H$	276·17

Some further data are given in Table XIII.6.

The energy to atomisation of organic compounds in the vapour phase

Most of our knowledge of the energies required completely to disrupt organic molecules into atoms derives from their heats of combustion. Thomsen (1908) found the heat of combustion of amorphous carbon at 18°C to be 96·96 kilocals per gram-atom. Berthelot found 97·65.

$$C(amorph) + O_2(g) \rightarrow CO_2(g); \qquad \Delta H_{291 \cdot 1} = -97 \cdot 31 \pm 0 \cdot 34$$

On allowing for the heat of transition,

$$C(diamond) \rightarrow C(amorph); \qquad \Delta H_{291 \cdot 1} = +2 \cdot 25 \pm 0 \cdot 75$$

we have

$$C(diamond) + O_2(g) \rightarrow CO_2(g); \qquad \Delta H_{291 \cdot 1} = -95 \cdot 06 \pm 1 \cdot 09$$

The more recent work of Roth, as analysed by Rossini (1936) gives the heat of combustion of diamond at the same temperature as $94 \cdot 45 \pm 0 \cdot 10$ kilo-cal. This increases the accuracy tenfold. Adjustment of this value to that which holds at the absolute zero of temperature, yields the generally accepted result:

$$C(diamond) + O_2(g) \rightarrow CO_2(g); \qquad \Delta H_0 = -94 \cdot 50 \pm 0 \cdot 10$$

Table XIII.6 *Energies of atomisation, at the absolute zero of temperature, of certain gaseous inorganic molecules, in kilocalories per mole*

Molecule	ΔE_0
H_2O	219·1
H_2S	174·0
F_2O	89·9
Cl_2O	97·7
N_2O	264·0
CO_2	382·1
CS_2	274·1
COS	329·6
HCN	304·3
$ONBr$	178·3
SO_2	254·4
NO_2	222·2
NH_3	276·2
AsH_3	142·4
$AsCl_3$	181·0
$AsBr_3$	155·4
AsI_3	99·3
As_4	90·8
H_2O_2	252·1
$(CN)_2$	495·0
N_2O_4	458·1

Let us now consider the combustion of gaseous methyl chloride, for which Thomsen gives the following value at $291 \cdot 1°K$:

$$4CH_3Cl(g) + 7O_2(g) \rightarrow 4CO_2(g) + 6H_2O(liq) + 2Cl_2(g);$$

$$\Delta H_T = -707 \cdot 80$$

On adding the heat of vaporisation of 6 moles of water at this temperature,

$$6H_2O(liq) \rightarrow 6H_2O(g); \qquad \Delta H_T = +63 \cdot 84$$

and calculating from spectroscopic constants that

$$\Delta H_0 = \Delta H_T - \sum (H_T - H_0) = \Delta H_T - 2 \cdot 79$$

we obtain the heat of combustion into gaseous products at the absolute zero of temperature. The remaining steps are:

$$\Delta H_0$$

		ΔH_0
$4CH_3Cl + 7O_2$	$\rightarrow 4CO_2 + 6H_2O + 2Cl_2$	$-646 \cdot 75$
$4CO_2$	$\rightarrow 4C + 8O$	$+1\,528 \cdot 36$
$6H_2O$	$\rightarrow 12H + 6O$	$+1\,312 \cdot 62$
$14O$	$\rightarrow 7O_2$	$-820 \cdot 40$
$2Cl_2$	$\rightarrow 4Cl$	$+114 \cdot 68$
$4CH_3Cl$	$\rightarrow 4C + 12H + 4Cl$	$+1\,488 \cdot 51$
CH_3Cl	$\rightarrow C + 3H + Cl$	$+372 \cdot 13.$

The results of applying similar steps to the heats of combustion of some organic molecules measured by Thomsen are summarised in Table XIII.7

Table XIII.7 *The energies of atomisation of certain organic compounds in the vapour phase at the absolute zero of temperature, in kilocalories per mole*

Molecule	Energy of atomisation	
	observed	calculated
CH_4	394·3	394·8
C_2H_6	671·6	671·5
$C(CH_3)_4$	1 501·8	1 501·6
$CH_2{=}CH_2$	538·1	538·1
$CH_3{-}CH{=}CH_2$	814·1	814·1
$CH{\equiv}CH$	389·9	389·9
$CH{\equiv}C{-}CH_3$	668·7	669·0
C_6H_6(benzene)	1 302·4	1 302·6
$1:3:5C_6H_3(CH_3)_3$	2 126·6	2 126·7
CH_3Cl	372·1	372·1
$CHCl_3$	323·4	323·7
CCl_4	303·2	303·2
CH_3Br	359·4	359·4
CH_3I	343·3	343·3
$COCl_2$	339·8	339·8
$CH_3{-}CHO$	647·3	647·3
$(CH_3)_2CO$	928·5	928·5
$(CH_3)_2O$	751·5	751·4
CH_3OH	479·7	480·4
C_2H_5OH	757·7	757·1
CH_3NH_2	546·0	546·0
CH_3NO_2	569·8	569·8

The experimental determination of bond energies

The properties of chemical bonds in which physical chemistry is chiefly interested are the internuclear distance, the nature and magnitude of the interatomic force, and the density and distribution of electrical charges—in brief, their length, strength and polarity. Like all other properties of a bond, these depend primarily on the nature of the two atoms which form it, and secondarily on the nature of all other atoms that may simultaneously be linked to either. We shall here confine attention to the bond energy, D, which may be very simply defined as the energy required to break it.

In homologous series, the energies of atomisation show a nearly constant increment for every addition of the methylene group, —CH_2—, to the molecule. This is at once apparent from the data given in Table XIII.7, from which the energy increments between neighbouring pairs in different homologous series are as follows: methane and ethane, 277·3; ethylene and propylene, 276·0; acetylene and allylene, 278·8; methanol and ethanol, 278·0. All these increments lie within the narrow range 277·5 ± 1·5, and it is to be noted that the margin of ± 1·5 kilocalories is comparable with the thermal correction $\Sigma(H_T - H_0)$, and with the sum of experimental errors. Care must therefore be exercised before deciding whether the difference between these increments is real. This additivity of the heats of atomisation of homologous compounds reflects one of the earliest generalisations of thermochemistry, which is the additivity of their heats of combustion. Thomsen found that, with each addition of a methylene group to a molecule in a homologous series, the heat of combustion at 291°K increased by 158·59 ± 0·20 kilocalories. As far as one may estimate the thermal correction, which requires a knowledge of the specific heat of the methylene group, the constancy of this increment allows us to write

$$D_{C-C} + 2D_{C-H} = 276 \cdot 13 \text{ kilocals}$$

where D stands for the energy of dissociation.

Let us analyse the data of Table XIII.7, on the assumption that, when we consider two neighbouring members in a homologous series, the various bond energies are constant. The first two entries then enable us to write:

$$\Delta E(CH_4) = 4D_{C-H}$$

$$\Delta E(CH_3-CH_3) = 6D_{C-H} + D_{C-C}$$

from which D_{C-H} is found to be 98·6 and D_{C-C} is 80·0. Proceeding with the heats of combustion of a few more of the lower paraffins, we find the best average values to be 98·7 and 79·3, respectively. To test the trustworthiness of the basic assumption, we calculate the energy of atomisation of *neo*-pentane, and find it to be in very satisfactory agreement with experiment. Let us next consider acetylene and allylene, assuming that the single C—C link and the three C—H links of the methyl group in the latter have the same energies as in ethane, but keeping an open mind on the C—H and C≡C links in acetylene. We have

$$\Delta E(CH{\equiv}CH) = 2D_{C-H} + D_{C{\equiv}C}$$

and

$$\Delta E(CH{\equiv}C{-}CH_3) = D_{C-H} + D_{C{\equiv}C} + D_{C-C} + 3D'_{C-H}$$

The last two dissociation energies are known, and we can solve for the others, obtaining 96·3 for D_{C-H} and 196·7 for $D_{C{\equiv}C}$. The energy of the carbon-carbon bond in the benzene ring is similarly found, by comparing the energies of atomisation of benzene and mesitylene, using the paraffinic constants for the methyl groups. Some bond energies found in this way are given in Table XIII.8. The dissociation energies of the bonds between the oxygen atom and the monovalent elements given in Table XIII.8 are simply one-half of the energies of atomisation of the symmetrical triatomic molecules. Similarly, the bond energy of As—H is one-third of the energy of atomisation of arsine, and that of As—As one-sixth of the energy of atomisation of the tetrahedral molecule As_4. The only datum used in estimating D for the univalent oxygen-oxygen bond has been the heat of formation of hydrogen peroxide; and it has been assumed that the energy of each O—H bond in this molecule is the same as in water.

We note in the first place that when the same two atoms are united by different valency bindings, the bond energy increases in the same direction as the valency. For the carbon-carbon bonds, we have

$$D_{C-C} : D_{C=C} : D_{C{\equiv}C} :: 1 : 1{\cdot}77 : 2{\cdot}48$$

This is noticeable also in the carbon-oxygen bond, which increases from a value of 79·6 in the monohydric alcohols and ethers to 168·7 in the aldehydes and ketones. A more careful analysis than we have attempted shows that the C—O bonds in the ethers and alcohols are different from each other, and that the C=O bonds in the aldehydes

Table XIII.8 *Bond energies, in kilocalories per mole, and bond lengths in Ångstrom units.*

Bond	Molecule	Length	Energy	Bond	Molecule	Length	Energy
C—H	Paraffins	1·095	98·7	C≡N	HCN, $(CN)_2$	1·158	207·9
C—H	Olefins	1·07	99·4	O—H	Water	0·958	109·5
C—H	Acetylenes, HCN, $CHCl_3$	1·064	96·3	O—H	Alcohols	0·96	104·7
				O—O	H_2O_2	1·48	33·3
C—H	Benzene	1·084	100·7				
C—F	CH_3F	1·381	116·3	O—F	F_2O	1·42	45·0
C—Cl	Alkyl chlorides	1·767	76·0	O—Cl	Cl_2O	1·70	48·9
C—Cl	CCl_4 and $CHCl_3$	1·767	75·8	S—H	H_2S	1·346	86·8
C—Cl	$COCl_2$	—	74·4	S=O	SO_2	1·432	125·9
C—Br	Alkyl bromides	1·94	63·3	S—Cl	S_2Cl_2	1·99	71·0
C—I	Alkyl iodides	2·14	47·2	S—S	S_2Cl_2	2·04	69·0
C—C	Paraffins $(CN)_2$	1·54	79·3	N—H	NH_3, amines	1·008	92·0
C—C	R · CHO and R_1R_2CO	1·516	83·8	N—N	N_2O_4	1·46	42·5
C=C	Benzene ring	1·397	116·4	N=O	Nitroparaffins	1·22	103·9
C=C	Olefins	1·337	140·5	N=O	NO	1·151	149·4
C≡C	Acetylenes	1·204	196·7	As—H	AsH_3	1·519	47·5
C—O	Alcohols, ethers	1·43	79·6	As—Cl	$AsCl_3$	2·161	60·3
C=O	R · CHO and R_1R_2CO	1·23	168·7	As—Br	$AsBr_3$	2·33	51·8
C=O	Carbon dioxide	1·160	191·0	As—I	AsI_3	2·54	33·1
C≡O	Carbon monoxide	1·128	255·8	As—As	As_4	2·43	15·1
C—N	Amines, nitroparaffins	1·472	65·9				

and ketones are also different from each other. With this increase in valency and bond strength, there is found, as a rule, a diminution in the interatomic distance. Such, however, is not always true. Thus, the carbon-oxygen distance in carbon monoxide is barely 1 per cent less than that in carbon dioxide, but the dissociation energy of the bond is almost 65 kilocalories greater.

While the additivity rule gives a logical basis for the analysis of energies of atomisation, it ignores mechanism. Thus, for example, the value of 218·8 kilocals for the reaction $H_2O \rightarrow 2H + O$ cited in Table XIII.6 ignores the fact that the dissociation may proceed in two stages: $H_2O \rightarrow H + OH$, followed by $OH \rightarrow O + H$. Bonhoeffer and Reichardt (1928) observed the spectrum of the hydroxyl radical in steam heated to 1 800°K, and from the temperature variation of the intensity of absorption estimated the value of 115 kilocal as the energy increase in the first dissociation. It follows that the dissociation energy of the hydroxyl radical is 104 kilocal. Later work on the absorption spectra of free radicals has shown this effect to be a general one. Thus, although in the following changes a single C—H bond is broken $(CH_4 \rightarrow CH_3 + H; \; CH_3 \rightarrow CH_2 + H; \; CH_2 \rightarrow CH + H)$ the energy necessary to break it is different in each case.

Discussion of bond energies

The basis of any discussion of bond energies must be the law of their additivity in aliphatic homologous series, a law which, with very few exceptions, is obeyed within the limits which can be ascribed to their experimental accuracy. The object of the discussion is to seek to discover why this law, when applied with the aliphatic constants to aromatic and inorganic molecules, gives such misleading results. One of the main guides in the discussion must be the recognition that chemical bonds vary widely in character from the homopolar bond in hydrogen to the ionic bond in the potassium chloride.

Let us consider the double bond between carbon and oxygen as an example. The data on the aldehydes and ketones give us $D_{C=O} = 168 \cdot 7$ kilocal, whereas in carbon dioxide, in which the bond is also indubitably double, we find $D_{C=O} = 191 \cdot 0$. The explanation offered by wave mechanics has already been given in Chapter IV, where we saw that, even for the simplest molecule, no single wave function, however complicated, can be constructed so as to incorporate all its properties. In a diatomic molecule the total wave function is a superposition of at least three wave functions, each of which concurrently and in varying degrees contributes to the total effect:

$$\psi = a\psi_{AB} + b\psi_{A^+B^-} + c\psi_{A^-B^+}$$

It is the relative magnitudes of the coefficients a, b and c which determine to what extent the bond in a molecule is covalent or ionic. When b and c are equal the bond, though containing ionic components, is said to be wholly covalent. As Pauling, Mulliken, Wheland and others have shown, the contribution to the binding energy which arises from the covalent component is approximately additive. Departures from additivity in bond energies must be attributed to the existence of polar components in the wave function. Thus, for example, in the carbon dioxide molecule, it is insufficient to construct a wave function based on the conventional and completely symmetrical arrangement of its 16 valency electrons. We must include functions constructed for at least two other electronic arrangements in which one oxygen atom has

363

a formal charge of unity. The three structures which suffice are

$$\overset{+}{O}\equiv C\overset{-}{-}O \qquad O=C=O \qquad \overset{-}{O}-C\equiv \overset{+}{O}$$

$$:\overset{..}{O}\overset{..}{:}\,C\overset{..}{:}\,\overset{..}{O}: \qquad \overset{..}{O}:\,:C\,:\,:\overset{..}{O} \qquad :\overset{..}{O}:C\overset{..}{:}\,\overset{..}{O}:$$

| I | II | III |

The solution of Schrödinger's equation now yields a minimum energy of the molecule which is less than that of structure II alone. The actual molecule is then said to have been stabilised by the resonance between the various structures. Because the purely covalent bonds in structure II already owe their existence to resonance attending the 'swopping' or 'trading' of indistinguishable electrons, the effect here considered is usually referred to as an additional ionic resonance.

Perhaps the best-known example of resonance in organic chemistry is that of the benzene molecule. When we compute the energy required to break up the benzene molecule into free atoms, using aliphatic constants for the bond energies, we arrive at 1251·6 kilocal per mole which is the sum of 6 energies of the C—H link, and three each of the C—C link as in ethane and the C=C link as in ethylene. The observed energy of atomisation is 1302·4. We may thus say that resonance between the various electronic structures which are possible for benzene has stabilised the molecule by 50·8 kilocals. This estimate is probably excessive, because we have ignored the fact that the carbon-carbon distance in the benzene ring is 0·15 Å shorter than in ethane and 0·01 Å longer than in ethylene. On using appropriate force constants, the revised resonance energy is reduced to 26·2 kilocals. This figure, though still to be corrected for residual energies, lies near to 36 kilocals which has long been regarded as the experimental resonance energy of the benzene molecule.

Electronegativity

In an attempt to bring coherence to the diversified experimental data on bond energies of inorganic compounds and of aliphatic and aromatic compounds, Pauling (1932) resolves the total bond energy into that due to normal covalency, assumed to be additive, and an extra energy due to ionic resonance. We begin by considering the conversion of a diatomic molecule into its elements, also in the diatomic state;

$$AB \rightleftarrows \tfrac{1}{2}A_2 + \tfrac{1}{2}B_2$$

The increase in energy attending the reaction in the ideal gas phase at the absolute zero of temperature is given in terms of the various dissociation energies by equation XIII.19, which in this instance takes the form

$$\Delta \varepsilon = D_{AB} - \tfrac{1}{2}(D_{AA} + D_{BB}) \qquad \text{XIII.36}$$

Normal covalency is ascribed to any heteronuclear molecule AB when $\Delta \varepsilon$ is zero. The criterion of normal behaviour here adopted is the same as the criterion of normal behaviour in solutions as treated by van Laar (equation XI.25). Experiment shows that $\Delta \varepsilon$ runs parallel with the dipole moment, μ. Pauling has defined the term electronegativity, x, of an atom as a measure of its power to attract electrons to itself, *within a molecule*. It differs from, but runs parallel with, the electron affinity of the free atom, and is thus positive for chlorine and negative for potassium. Consistent with general electrostatic principles and with the approximate additivity of experimental bond lengths in covalent compounds, he has shown that the energy $\Delta \varepsilon$ of equation XIII.36 (or that obtained by replacing the arithmetic mean of D_{AA} and D_{BB} by the geometric mean $(D_{AA}D_{BB})^{1/2}$ is proportional to the square of the difference between the x values of the two atoms:

$$\Delta \varepsilon = K(x_A - x_B)^2 \qquad \text{XIII.37}$$

By arbitrarily ascribing a value of $x = 0$ for the combined hydrogen atom, K can be found, and the relative values of x for other atoms determined. Some of these are given in Table XIII.9. Converting from electron volts to kilocalories, and using the geometric rather than the arithmetic mean of the dissociation energies of homonuclear molecules, the dissociation energies of heteronuclear diatomic molecules formed from them are given by the equation

$$D_{AB}(\text{kilocal/mole}) = (D_{AA}D_{BB})^{1/2} + 23 \cdot 03(x_A - x_B)^2 \qquad \text{XIII.38}$$

An alternative means of constructing an electronegativity scale has been proposed by R. S. Mulliken (1934). If it is assumed that the energies liberated when the molecules A^+B^- and A^-B^+ are formed from the neutral atoms A and B are identical, it follows that the electronegativity x of a combined atom is directly proportional to the sum

365

of its first ionisation potential and its electron affinity. Numerically the two schemes furnish nearly the same scale.

Table XIII.9 *Electronegativities, x, of combined atoms, such that* $(x_A - x_B)^2$ *is in electron-volts*

Combined atom	x	Combined atom	x
F	1·9	Si	−0·3
O	1·4	Be	−0·6
N	0·9	Al	−0·6
Cl	0·9	Mg	−0·9
Br	0·7	Li	−1·1
C	0·4	Ca	−1·1
S	0·4	Sr	−1·1
I	0·3	Na	−1·2
H	0	Ba	−1·2
P	0	K	−1·3
B	−0·1	Rb	−1·3
As	−0·1	Cs	−1·4

Equilibria in solutions

The study of equilibria in solution provides a rich variety of chemical types, of methods of investigation, and of ways in which the results have been expressed. Small energy changes, of the order of magnitude of 100 calories, usually attend simple configurational equilibria, such as the *cis-trans* conversion of *o*-chlorphenol,

cis form   *trans* form

which has been examined by the methods of infra-red spectroscopy (M. M. Davies, 1938) in carbon tetrachloride solution. Examples of equilibria associated with greater energy changes are given in Table XIII.10. The equilibrium constants from which these data have been calculated were determined, for the most part, by direct chemical analysis. Colour, viscosity, optical rotation, electrical conductivity,

366

freezing point depression, extinction coefficient, and any other physicochemical property which can be calibrated against the composition of the solution may also be used for the measurement of the equilibrium constant. The calibration, which is of the utmost importance, is seldom simple, for it must provide us with the exact concentration of one component in the presence of varying amounts of another.

Table XIII.10 *Certain chemical equilibria in non-aqueous solvents at 25°C*

Reference	Reaction	Solvent	ΔH^0 (kilocal/ mole)	ΔS^0 (cal/mole-deg)
1	$CH_3Cl + I^- \rightleftarrows CH_3I + Cl^-$	$(CH_3)_2CO$	1·44	−11·71
2	$(C_2H_5)_3SBr \rightleftarrows (C_2H_5)_2S$ $+ C_2H_5Br$	$C_6H_5CH_2OH$	7·7	+20·8
3	$(C_6H_5)_3C - C(C_6H_5)_3$ $\rightleftarrows 2C(C_6H_5)_3$	$CHCl_3, CS_2, C_6H_6$	11·6	23·4
4	$C_6H_5N(CH_3)_3I$ $\rightleftarrows C_6H_5N(CH_3)_2 + CH_3I$	$C_6H_5NO_2$	15·0	36·9

1. Farhat–Aziz and Moelwyn–Hughes (1959) 3. Ziegler (1934)
2. Corran (1927) 4. Essex and Gelormini (1920)

Equilibria in solution, unlike gaseous equilibria, are rarely complicated by adsorption on the surface of the vessel. The most frequent complication is reaction of one of the solutes with the solvent.

The condition of equilibrium, in liquid solutions, as in other homogeneous systems, is equality of the chemical potentials of the reactants and the resultants:

$$\sum v_i G_i(\text{reactants}) = \sum v_i G_j(\text{resultants}) \qquad \text{VI.39}$$

and the problem is to find the correct connexion between the chemical potential of each component of the solution and its concentration. The basic form usually assumed, by analogy with the law for ideal mixed gases, is

$$G_i = G_i^0 + RT \ln [\text{concentration}] \qquad \text{VI.52}$$

367

where the concentrations may be expressed as c moles per litre c solution or as molar fraction, x, or volume fraction, θ, or molality m, as defined in Chapter XI. Applied to the general equilibriur $bB + cC \rightleftarrows lL$, the basic forms of the equilibrium constants are:

$$K_c = \frac{c_L^l}{c_B^b \cdot c_C^c} \qquad \Delta G_c^0 = -RT \ln K_c \qquad \text{XIII.3}$$

$$K_x = \frac{x_L^l}{x_B^b \cdot x_C^c} \qquad \Delta G_x^0 = -RT \ln K_x \qquad \text{XIII.4}$$

$$K_\theta = \frac{\theta_L^l}{\theta_B^b \cdot \theta_C^c} \qquad \Delta G_\theta^0 = -RT \ln K_\theta \qquad \text{XIII.4}$$

$$K_m = \frac{m_L^l}{m_B^b \cdot m_C^c} \qquad \Delta G_m^0 = -RT \ln K_m \qquad \text{XIII.4}$$

These forms of the equilibrium law are naturally related to on another. In terms of the numbers, N_i, of gram-moles of component in a total volume V of solution, and of the partial molar volume, V_i of that component, its concentration, in moles per litre of solution is clearly

$$c_i = 1\,000 N_i / V \qquad \text{XIII.4}$$

Its molar fraction is

$$x_i = N_i / \Sigma N_i \qquad \text{XIII.4}$$

and its volume fraction is

$$\theta_i = N_i V_i / V = x_i V_i / \overline{V} \qquad \text{XIII.4}$$

where $\overline{V}$ is the volume of one mole of solution. Finally, the molality i

$$m_i = \frac{1\,000 N_i}{M_s N_s} \qquad \text{XIII.4}$$

where M_s is the molar weight of the solvent. It follows that

$$\frac{K_c}{K_x} = \left(\frac{\overline{V}}{1\,000}\right)^{b+c-l} \qquad \text{XIII.4}$$

$$\frac{K_\theta}{K_x} = \frac{V_L^l}{V_B^b V_C^c} (\overline{V})^{b+c-l} \qquad \text{XIII.48}$$

and

$$\frac{K_m}{K_c} = \left(\rho\frac{N_s M_s}{\Sigma N_i M_i}\right)^{b+c-l} \qquad \text{XIII.49}$$

where ρ is the density of the solution, and the subscript s denotes the solvent. We note, from equation XIII.48, that K_θ and K_x are identical in isomegethic equilibria, and that the term within the brackets in equation XIII.49 is very nearly ρ for dilute solutions.

The equilibrium established between liquid acetic acid and ethyl alcohol on the one hand and liquid ethyl acetate and water on the other hand,

$$CH_3COOH + C_2H_5OH \rightleftarrows CH_3COOC_2H_5 + H_2O$$

has been the subject of some classical researches by Berthelot and Pean de St Gilles (1862) and van't Hoff (1877). The stoichiometric integer $(b+c-l)$ in this case is zero, so that

$$K_c = K_x = K_m \qquad \text{XIII.50}$$

where, to evaluate the constant in terms of molalities any of four components may be regarded as the solvent. If the original system examined contains no ester or water, but is made up of 1 gram-mole of acid and y gram-moles of alcohol, the equilibrium constant becomes

$$K = \frac{[\text{Ester}] \times [\text{Water}]}{[\text{Acid}] \times [\text{Alcohol}]} = \frac{x^2}{(1-x)(y-x)} \qquad \text{XIII.51}$$

where x is the number of gram-moles of ester or of water present after the attainment of equilibrium. In Table XIII.11 are shown the values of x determined experimentally by Berthelot and St Gilles and those calculated by van't Hoff using $K = 4$. Within the errors of the experiments, K, in terms of concentrations or of molar fractions, is seen to be a true constant for all compositions. The sum of the molar free energies of acid and alcohol exceeds the sum of the molar free energies of ester and water by $RT \ln 4 = 777$ calories. The attainment of equilibrium is hastened, but the system itself is made more complicated, by the addition of hydrogen chloride. With little of this catalyst present, later investigators have confirmed the original value. With large amounts of hydrogen chloride, however, the apparent constant increases to about 8, in such a way as to suggest that the active mass of the water is reduced by the formation of the compound HCl,

369

Table XIII.11 *The esterification equilibrium at 282°K* (*equation* 84)

Initial number of moles of acetic acid	Initial number, y, of moles of ethyl alcohol	Equilibrium number, x, of moles of ester or of water		
		observed	calculated	Δ
1	0·05	0·05	0·049	+0·001
1	0·18	0·171	0·171	0·000
1	0·33	0·293	0·301	−0·008
1	0·50	0·414	0·423	−0·009
1	1·00	0·667	0·667	0·000
1	2·00	0·858	0·850	+0·008
1	8·00	0·966	0·970	−0·004

$2H_2O$ or of a set of compounds with this mean composition. (McC. Lewis, 1923; Mellor, 1904.)

The application of equations XIII.39, 40 and 41 to the colorimetric data of Cundall (1891) on the dissociation of dinitrogen tetroxide

$$N_2O_4 \rightleftarrows 2NO_2$$

shows that, if we take the experimental invariance of K as a criterion, there is little to choose between the various formulations (Table XIII.12), all of which are very good first approximations to the actual behaviour of equilibrated reactions in solution.

Table XIII.12

$$N_2O_4 \rightleftarrows 2NO_2 \text{ in } CHCl_3 \text{ at } 273 \cdot 16°K; K = [NO_2]^2/[N_2O_4]$$

Volume fraction of N_2O_4	$10^4 \times$ volume fraction of NO_2	Molar volume, $\bar{V}$, of solution in ccs	$K_c \times 10^5$ moles per litre	$K_x \times 10^7$	$K_n \times 10^7$
0	—	78·21	—	—	—
0·015	0·386	77·90	0·64	5·02	0·99
0·025	0·394	77·70	0·40	3·12	0·62
0·05	0·697	77·28	0·63	4·86	0·97
0·1	1·18	76·19	0·90	6·85	1·39
0·2	1·86	74·27	1·12	8·33	1·74
0·4	2·68	70·74	1·16	8·19	1·79
0·7	3·54	65·98	1·16	7·66	1·79
1·0	4·68	61·84	1·42	8·76	2·19

The relationship between equilibria in solution and in the crystalline phase; the van't Hoff–Dimroth law

When the chemical potential of each component in solution can be expressed as

$$G = G^0 + RT \ln c \qquad \text{VI.52}$$

we obtain equations XIII.39. Now suppose that equation VI.52 holds up to the saturation point, at which solid separates from the solution. The chemical potential of the solute is then equal to that of the crystal,

$$G^{cr} = G^0 + RT \ln s$$

where s is the saturation concentration. On eliminating G^0, we have

$$G = G^{cr} + RT \ln(c/s) \qquad \text{XIII.52}$$

Application to the equilibrium $bB + cC \rightleftarrows lL$ now gives us

$$K = \frac{(c_L/s_L)^l}{(c_B/s_B)^b (c_C/s_C)^c} \qquad \text{XIII.53}$$

and

$$-\Delta G^{cr} = bG_B^{cr} + cG_C^{cr} - lG_L^{cr} = RT \ln K = RT \ln K_c - RT \ln \frac{s_L^l}{s_B^b \, s_C^c}$$

We may eliminate $RT \ln K_c$ by means of equation XIII.39, and obtain

$$\Delta G^{cr} = \Delta G_c^0 + RT \ln \frac{s_L^l}{s_B^b \, s_C^c} \qquad \text{XIII.54}$$

which provides a means of obtaining the standard change in free energy attending a reaction in the solid phase, such as that between calcite and aragonite or between urea and ammonium cyanate. By means of the Kelvin–Helmholtz equation, we have also

$$\Delta H_{cr}^0 = \Delta H_c^0 - \sum \Delta H_{\text{dissolution}}^0 \qquad \text{XIII.55}$$

where the last term is the algebraic sum (reckoning products as positive) of the heats absorbed during the dissolution of the crystalline solutes.

Since ΔG^{cr} depends only on the properties of the crystals, the equilibrium constant in the form of equation XIII.53 must be independent of the solvent. The conclusion is due to van't Hoff, (1898) and has been tested by Dimroth (1910), who measured the equilibrium

371

constants and the solubilities of the isomeric forms of 1-phenyl-5 aminotriazole carboxylic acid esters in various solvents. In isomeri equilibria, $b = 1$, $c = 0$ and $l = 1$. His results (Table XIII.13) show that while K_c varies by a factor of 68, from solvent to solvent, K in terms c the solubilities varies only by a factor of 1·2.

Table XIII.13   *A test of the van't Hoff–Dimroth relation*

Solvent	Methyl ester			Ethyl ester		
	c_B/c_L	s_B/s_L	$\dfrac{c_B/s_B}{c_L/s_L}$	c_B/c_L	s_B/s_L	$\dfrac{c_B/s_B}{c_L/s_L}$
$(C_2H_5)_2O$	21·7	53·0	0·40	20·7	8·4	2·4
C_2H_5OH	2·3	7·0	0·33	4·56	2·1	2·3
$C_6H_5CH_3$	1·8	4·3	0·33	1·53	0·74	2·1
C_6H_6	1·02	3·2	0·32	1·20	0·60	2·4
$C_6H_5NO_2$	0·80	2·2	0·36	0·85	0·33	2·6
$CHCl_3$	0·32	1·1	0·32	0·32	0·19	1·7

The relationship between equilibria in solution and in the gaseous phase

When the chemical potential of each component in the vapour phase varies linearly with respect to the logarithm of its partial pressure the equilibrium in the ideal gaseous state is given by the equations

$$K_p = \frac{p_L^l}{p_B^b \, p_C^c} \qquad \Delta G_g^0 = -RT \ln K_p \qquad \text{XIII.56}$$

If the solution is ideal, that is, if each component obeys Raoult's law it follows that equation XIII.40 holds for the equilibrium in solution Moreover, on comparing equations XIII.40 and XIII.56, we see that

$$\frac{K_p}{K_x} = \frac{(p_L/x_L)^l}{(p_B/x_B)^b (p_C/x_C)^c} = \frac{(p_L^0)^l}{(p_B^0)^b (p_C^0)^c} \qquad \text{XIII.57}$$

in which p^0 stands for the saturation vapour pressure of the pure liquid. Equation XIII.57 is analogous to equation XIII.53. It is also evident that

$$\Delta H_p^0 = \Delta H_x^0 + \sum L_{vap} \qquad \text{XIII.58}$$

where the last term is the algebraic sum of the heats of vaporisation of the pure liquid components, These relationships have been verified by Blair and Yost (1933) for the equilibria $X_2 + Y_2 \rightleftarrows 2XY$, where X and Y are different halogens.

By comparing equations XIII.39 and XIII.56, we have

$$\frac{K_p}{K_c} = \frac{(p_L/c_L)^l}{(p_B/c_B)^b (p_C/c_C)^c} = \frac{r_L^l}{r_B^b \, r_C^c} \qquad \text{XIII.59}$$

where r is Henry's constant, and is to be discussed in Chapter XIV. In terms of the standard changes in free energy, we have

$$\Delta G_p^0 = \Delta G_c^0 - \sum RT \ln r_i \qquad \text{XIII.60}$$

The relation between the changes in heat content is consequently

$$\cdot \; \Delta H_p^0 = \Delta H_c^0 + \sum \Delta H_{\text{escape}} \qquad \text{XIII.61}$$

Thus the increase in heat content attending the reaction in the gaseous phase is equal to the increase in heat content attending the reaction in solution, plus the algebraic sum of the increases in heat content attending the escape of each component from a solution in which its concentration is unity to the gas phase in which its pressure is unity. The result is analogous to equation XIII.58.

ΔH_p^0 for the decomposition of ethane, $C_2H_6 \rightleftarrows C_2H_4 + H_2$ is 32 000 cal, and $\Sigma \Delta H_{\text{escape}}$ for the three solutes from a variety of solvents is only about 1 400 cal (Benford and Wasserman, 1939), so that the solvents have little effect on the equilibrium position. On the other hand, in the decomposition of ethylene iodide, $C_2H_4I_2 \rightleftarrows C_2H_4 + I_2$, ΔH_p^0 is 23 300 cal (Mooney and Ludlam, 1929), and ΔH_c^0 in carbon tetrachloride solution is about 11 300 cal (Polissar, 1930). The difference of some 10 000 cal between the heat effects in the two phases arises chiefly from the high value of the heat of escape of iodine from the solvent, and exerts, of course, a pronounced influence on the position of equilibrium.

Discussion

It will be appreciated that the foregoing passages throw little light on the real nature of equilibria in solution. What has been done is to discuss some accurate data and to formulate them in a way consistent with thermodynamic convention. In the last instances cited, for example, the question arises as to why the heat of escape of iodine should be so much greater than that of the hydrocarbons. To such a query no general answer can be given. We have seen in Chapter XI that in homogeneous systems of two components a reasonable account can be given of their behaviour when the interchange energy is less than $2kT$. Most systems of physicochemical and biological interest however readily change, with a change of composition, from homogeneity to heterogeneity, and reveal that solute-solvent interactions often exceed this amount. The problem is acute in aqueous solutions. We shall see in the next chapter that such an ostensibly simple process as the dissolution of methane in water is in fact extremely complicated, with a greater heat effect than one would expect, and a temperature coefficient of the heat of dissolution which is difficult to explain.

What happens, one may ask, to the molecule that dissolves, or, perhaps more pertinently, to the solvent molecules that surround it? Are their motions altered from those which they normally execute? Is the structure of the solvent modified? Can it be that those solvent molecules which surround a solute molecule, and so often form crystalline solvates with it, resemble surface molecules of the pure liquid more than its molecules in the bulk phase? To these queries also there is no ready answer, though the problem may be formulated and discussed. Let the partition function of a molecule of type i dissolved in a volume, V, of solution be

$$f_i = (2\pi m_i kT)^{3/2} Ve/h^3 N_i \cdot f_{rot} \cdot f_{vibr} f_{elect} \exp(-u_i/kT)$$

where the components of the partition function and the average potential energy, u_i, have already been defined. An assumption often made, i.e. that most of the components of f_i are the same for the gas as for the dissolved molecule, can no longer be regarded as sound. The translational component, for example, must be altered in some way so as to account for the fact that the heat capacity of monatomic liquids is nearer $3R$ than $\frac{3}{2}R$. The rotational component, on similar evidence, must be modified to allow for the fact that, for example, the chloroform molecule rotates freely around its three axes in the gas, but only around one axis in solution. Infra-red and ultra-violet spectroscopy make it clear that the internal molecular vibrations are sometimes modified by the presence of solvent molecules. Only in a few cases is the electrical component of the partition function different in the two phases. There remains the term u_i, which is zero in the gaseous

374

system, but may be very great in solution. $RT \ln K$ for a reaction in solution contains the algebraic sum of the u_i terms for reactants and resultant, and though the sum Σu_i may be small, explaining homogeneity and endowing the system with a seeming simplicity, the individual u_i terms can be large, as we know them to be in solutions of electrolytes. Each u_i is, principally, the product of c_i, the coordination number, and ϕ_i, the interaction energy of a solute molecule with a solvent molecule, and each ϕ_i, in turn, varies inversely as some integral power of the equilibrium distance, a_i, between solute and solvent molecules. If the negative component of ϕ_i is the dominant one, and is due to an electrostatic interaction, a relatively simple account of the solvent effect on chemical equilibria can be given. We shall discuss two sets of data to which this concept has been quantitatively applied.

Ionic association

More recent work than that mentioned in Chapter XII on this topic has brought considerable simplification to it, due mainly to very precise conductimetric measurements.

The equilibrium constant governing the association of univalent ions:

$$A^+ + B^- \rightleftarrows A^+B^-$$

when extrapolated to infinite dilution is given in terms of concentrations, c, by the equation

$$K_A = C_{A^+B^-}/C_{A^+}C_{B^-}$$

Denison and Ramsey (1955) and Fuoss and Kraus (1957) have independently argued that K_A must be given, to a first approximation, by the expression:

$$K_A = K_A^0 \cdot \exp\{\varepsilon^2/(DakT)\} \qquad \text{XIII.62}$$

when ε is the protonic charge, and a is the distance apart of the two charges in the ion-pair. K_A^0 is a constant which is discussed later.

The fraction of the solute which is unassociated may be determined from the electrical conductivity of the solution, and the logarithm of the association constant derived therefrom may be plotted as a function of $1/D$. If a is a true constant, the plot should be linear, since

$$\log_{10} K_A = \log_{10} K_A^0 + \frac{\varepsilon^2}{2.303 akT} \cdot \frac{1}{D} \qquad \text{XIII.62a}$$

375

or

$$\log_{10}K_A = \log_{10}K_A^0 + B/D \qquad\qquad \text{XIII.62b}$$

where B is an isothermal constant, whose value depends on the nature of the solute but not on that of the solvent. When applied to a temperature of $298 \cdot 16°K$, we have

$$\log_{10}K_A = \log_{10}K_A^0 + 243/(\mathring{a}D) \qquad\qquad \text{XIII.62c}$$

where $\mathring{a}$ is the value of a expressed in Ångström units. A typical graph, due to Inami, Bodenseh and Ramsey (1955), is reproduced in Fig. XIII.2. Further data summarised in the form of equation XIII.62b, are given in Table XIII.14. They differ from one another in their accuracy,

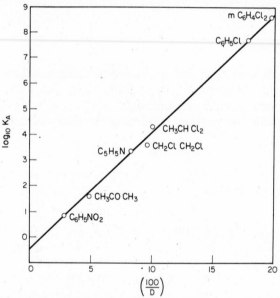

Fig. XIII.2 *Association constants of tetrabutylammoniumpicrate at 25°C* (after Inami, Bodenseh and Ramsey)

and in the ranges of dielectric constants covered. The data for silver nitrate refer to solutions in water, methanol and ethanol: those for tetrabutylammonium picrate to pure solvents; and those for tetra-*iso*amylammonium nitrate to dioxane-water mixtures of different compositions, with dielectric constants varying from 2 to 80.

Ramsey finds that, whereas this linear relationship holds for a given solute in a variety of pure solvents, points fall off the straight line when they refer to solvents, such as ethylene dichloride, which exist in two forms of differing polarity. To explain the divergence, he suggests that the effective dielectric constant for such solvents is greater than the macroscopic value. Subject to this limitation, equation XIII.62b appears to be obeyed with considerable accuracy, yielding reasonable values for the separation of the charges in the various ion pairs (column 4 of Table XIII.14).

Table XIII.14 *Temperature* $= 25°C$. $\log_{10} K_A(\text{litres/mole}) = \log_{10} K_A^0 + B/D = \log_{10} K_A^0 + \varepsilon^2/(2 \cdot 303 \, DakT)$

Electrolyte	$\log_{10}K_A^0$	B	$a[\text{Å}]$		
			From B	From K_A^0	Mean
$AgNO_3$	$\bar{2}{,}802$	88·5	2·75	3·06	2·91±0·16
$(C_4H_9)_4NBr$	$\bar{1}{·}041$	56·4	4·31	3·68	4·00±0·31
$(C_4H_9)_4NI$	$\bar{1}{.}892$	43·9	5·55	7·06	6·31±0·76
$(C_4H_9)_4NClO_4$	$\bar{1}{·}755$	50·2	4·85	6·37	5·61±0·76
$(C_4H_9)_4NPic$	$\bar{1}{·}543$	46·0	5·29	5·41	5·35±0·06
$(isoC_5H_{11})_4N \cdot NO_3$	$\bar{1}{·}549$	41·7	5·83	5·43	5·63±0·20

A simple statistical theory of ion association has been given in the following way (Moelwyn-Hughes, 1963). If ions repel one another with a force varying as the inverse $(s+1)$th. power of their distance, a, apart, the energy of interaction of a pair of univalent ions with charges of opposite signs in a medium of dielectric constant, D, is

$$\phi = \frac{A}{a^s} - \frac{\varepsilon^2}{Da} \qquad \text{XIII.63}$$

The interaction energy has the following minimum value when $a = a_e$:

$$\phi_e = -\frac{\varepsilon^2}{Da_e}\left(1 - \frac{1}{s}\right) \qquad \text{XIII.64}$$

By expanding $\phi - \phi_e$ as a power series in $a - a_e$, it can be shown that small displacements from the equilibrium separation are attended by a

N

harmonic vibration of frequency

$$v_e = \frac{\varepsilon}{2\pi a_e} \left[\frac{s-1}{m^* D a_e} \right]^{1/2}$$

where m^* is the reduced mass of the pair. In deriving the partition functions for the ions, it is assumed that their internal motions are the same in the free and associated states, so that only the translational components of their total partition functions need be considered. In terms of the masses, m_+ and m_-, of the ions, whether free or solvated, of their numbers, N_+ and N_-, in a total volume V and of their average potential energies, u_+ and u_-, these are:

$$f_+ = \frac{(2\pi m_+ kT)^{3/2} Ve}{h^3 N_+} \cdot e^{-u_+/kT}$$

and

$$f_- = \frac{(2\pi m_- kT)^{3/2} Ve}{h^3 N_-} \cdot e^{-u_-/kT}$$

The motions of the ion pair can be resolved into (1) translation throughout the total volume V, (2) rotation of the pair, with moment of inertia $I = m^* a_e^2$, about its centre of gravity, and (3) vibration along the line of centres. The magnitude of the vibration frequency v_e is such that hv_e is ordinarily much less than kT, so that the classical partition function may be used for this motion. The total partition function of the pair thus becomes

$$f_+ = \frac{[2\pi(m_+ + m_-)kT]^{3/2} Ve}{h^3 N_+} \cdot \frac{8\pi^2 IkT}{h^2} \cdot \frac{kT}{hv_e} \cdot e^{-u_+-/kT}$$

The condition of equilibrium is

$$\mu_+ + \mu_- = \mu_{+-}$$

where the chemical potential of each species is given by the equation

$$\mu_i = -kT \left[\ln f_i + \frac{d \ln f_i}{d \ln N_i} \right]_{T,V} \qquad \text{VI.59}$$

It follows that

$$K_A = \frac{n_{+-}}{n_+ n_-} = 4\pi a_e^3 \left[\frac{2\pi D a_e kT}{(s-1)\varepsilon^2} \right]^{1/2} \cdot \exp\left\{ -\frac{u_{+-} - u_+ - u_-}{kT} \right\} \qquad \text{XIII.65}$$

According to equation XIII.64, the algebraic sum of the potential energies appearing in the exponent is $(\varepsilon^2/Da_e)(s-1)/s$. On converting the units of K_A from ccs per molecule to litres per gram-mole, the association constant becomes

$$K_A = \frac{N_0}{1\,000}4\pi a_e^3\left[\frac{2\pi Da_e kT}{(s-1)\varepsilon^2}\right]^{1/2} \cdot \exp\left\{\frac{\varepsilon^2}{Da_e kT}\left(\frac{s-1}{s}\right)\right\} \qquad \text{XIII.66}$$

When applied to data at $298 \cdot 16°K$, the equation may be cast in the form

$$\log_{10}\frac{K_A}{D^{1/2}} = \bar{4} \cdot 905 + \log_{10}\left[\frac{\mathring{a}_e^{7/2}}{(s-1)^{1/2}}\right] + 243\left(\frac{s-1}{s\mathring{a}_e}\right) \cdot \frac{1}{D}$$

which allows an evaluation of a_e and s. The latter ranges from 5 for silver nitrate to 50 for tetra-*iso*amylammonium nitrate. In this treatment, no appeal has been made to the concept of ionic radius. The term a_e is the average distance apart of the charges in the ion pair when in its state of lowest potential energy. The root-mean-square displacement about the average separation is given by the equation

$$\frac{\bar{x}}{a_e} = \left[\frac{Da_e kT}{(s-1)\varepsilon^2}\right]^{1/2}$$

If $\log_{10}K_A$, rather than $\log_{10}(K_A/D^{1/2})$ is plotted against $1/D$, a constant gradient is not obtained since

$$\frac{d\log_{10}K_A}{d(1/D)} = \frac{1}{2 \cdot 303}\left[\frac{\varepsilon^2}{a_e kT}\left(\frac{s-1}{s}\right) - \frac{D}{2}\right]$$

which increases as $1/D$ increases. It is in this direction that deviations from linearity have been observed by Bodenseh and Ramsey.

Dimerisation in solution; the hydrogen bridge

Polar molecules tend to form double molecules, or dimers, in solution, particularly in solvents of low dielectric constant, and when the solute contains the group $-OH$ or $>NH$. Relatively weak coupling takes place between molecules of the aryl halides in carbon tetrachloride solution, and the increase in heat content attending the break-down of the double molecule $(RX)_2 \rightleftharpoons 2RX$ has been found by Sakurada (1935) to lie between 1 000 and 1 700 calories. By indirect means the increase in heat content associated with the breakdown of double molecules of the normal alcohols in normal hydrocarbons, $(ROH)_2 \rightleftarrows 2ROH$, has also been estimated (von Elbe (1934)). The most thoroughly investigated dimerisation equilibrium in solution is that between molecules of the carboxylic acids, with which we shall now deal.

The pressure of a system of molecules which associate is less than that of a system of free molecules, and the difference affords a measure of the degree of association, from the temperature variation of which the change in heat content is readily calculated. Let us consider the dissociation of a dimer of a carboxylic acid,

$$(RCOOH)_2 \rightleftarrows 2RCOOH$$

Experiments with acetic acid vapour $(R = CH_3)$ show that at about 400°K, $\Delta H_p = 14\cdot32\pm0\cdot29$ kilocalories (Nernst, 1918). For formic acid $(R = H)$, it is found that $\Delta H_p = 14\cdot125$. (Coolidge, 1928.) The bonds that are broken during the dissociation of a double molecule of a carboxylic acid are weaker than most covalent bonds, and are due to a pair of interactions of the hydroxyl group in one molecule with the carbonyl group in the other. The juxtaposition of the two molecules places each hydrogen atom in between two oxygen atoms, forming a novel kind of bond which Latimer and Rodebush (1920) appropriately termed a hydrogen bridge. Their deduction regarding the structure of the dimer has been amply confirmed by the method of electron diffraction, (Pauling and Brockway, 1934) according to which the double molecule of formic acid is planar, and the distance, r_{00}, between the oxygen atoms lies between 2·55 and 2·85 Å (see Fig. XIII.3).

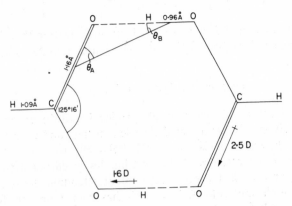

Fig. XIII.3   *The formic acid dimer*

To obtain the increase in internal energy attending the rupture of a single hydrogen bridge in the gas phase, we must subtract RT from the value of ΔH_p, and divide the result by 2. Then ΔE for breaking a single hydrogen bridge in the gaseous phase at 400°K is seen to be 6.76 ± 0.15. It is a matter of interest to compare this result with the electrostatic attraction of the two dipoles at the absolute zero of temperature. (Moelwyn-Hughes, 1938). Denoting the $C\!\!=\!\!O$ bond of one molecule by A and the $O\!\!-\!\!H$ bond of the second molecule by B, and accepting the usual values for the bond lengths ($l_A = 1.16$, $l_B = 0.96$Å), dipole moments ($\mu_A = 2.5$, $\mu_B = 1.6$ D), and $O\!\!-\!\!C\!\!-\!\!O$ valency angle (125°16′), we can show that, polarisation effects being neglected, the distance (r_{AB}) of the lines joining the centres of the attracting dipoles, and the angles (θ_A and θ_B) which they make with it, have the following values:

r_{oo}(Å)	2.85	2.55
r_{AB}(Å)	2.68_7	2.39_3
θ_A	51° 35′	50° 26′
θ_B	11° 3′	12° 26′
U (cal/g-mol.)	$-4\,310$	$-6\,570$

The last row gives the contribution of the dipole-dipole interaction to the energy of formation of the single bond, according to the equation

$$U = -2N_0\mu_A\mu_B \cos\theta_A \cos\theta_B / r^3(1 - l^2/r^2)$$

We have seen, however, that, if Mie's potential applies, the minimum energy of the pair of molecules must be corrected by a factor of $1 - (m/n)$, where, in the present example, $m = 3$. If we assume that $n = 9$, it follows that the estimated energy of rupture of a single hydrogen bridge at $T = 0$ is 2.87 or 4.38 kilocalories per mole. The latter estimate requires ΔC_V to have an average value of 5.95 cal/mole-degree, which is reasonable. We may conclude that the energy required to break a single hydrogen bridge in the gaseous phase is, in cal per mole, $4\,380 + 3RT$.

If the force of attraction, though not necessarily that of repulsion, between the two molecules is electrostatic, then the standard increase in free energy ΔG_c^0, attending the dissociation of the dimer in dilute solution, is given either by the expression

$$\Delta G_c^0 = \Delta G_g^0/D \qquad\qquad \text{XIII.67}$$

or by the expression

$$\Delta G_c^0 = \Delta G_g^0 (D+2)/3D \qquad \text{XIII.68}$$

where the subscript g refers to the vapour phase, and D is the dielectric constant. By applying the Kelvin–Helmholtz equation, the increase in heat content is

$$\Delta H_c^0 = [(1-LT)/D]\Delta H_g^0 \qquad \text{XIII.69}$$

or

$$\Delta H_c^0 = \{[D+2(1-LT)]/3D\}\Delta H_g^0 \qquad \text{XIII.70}$$

where L is Abegg's constant (see equation XII.40). The first of these relations is shown in Fig. XIII.4 (Davies, Jones, Patnaik and Moelwyn-Hughes, 1951), in which the line is a theoretical one, and the points are experimental values determined as explained in Chapter XIV. These results show that such information as we have on the influence of the solvent on the dimerisation of monocarboxylic acids is not inconsistent with electrostatic principles, as far as these can at present be applied to the complicated system of solutions of polar molecules.

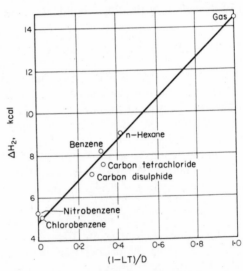

Fig. XIII.4 *Heats of dissociation of dimeric acetic acid in various media*

Complex formation in solution

Addition compounds formed from neutral, unionised molecules in solution now appear, despite the scepticism that has long existed about them, to be the rule rather than the exception. They are generally formed from polar molecules, and are most stable in inert solvents, as one would expect if their existence is due to the attraction of the two dipoles. The well-known coloured complexes often formed from nitro-compounds and hydrocarbons probably have a similar origin. They are less stable than the dipole-dipole complexes, and not yet so fully understood. The presence of the complex in solution is sometimes attended by the appearance of as many as four new Raman frequencies which are not present in the solutions of either reactant. This is the case, for example, in the complex formed from hydrogen bromide and diethyl ether (Briegleb and Lauppe, 1935). When one of the molecules forming the complex is initially non-polar, it is found from polarisation measurements that in the complex formed it has lost its symmetry (Ulich, 1931).

Generally, when a complex is formed between two solutes, its presence is betrayed by the departure of the properties of the solution from those which we expect if the solutes do not interact. By ascribing the difference between the observed property of the solution and that anticipated from the addition of its separate solutes, A and B, to a complex AB, equilibrium constants may be derived, as instanced in dealing with the Dolezalek–Schulze hypothesis (equation XI.53). Some results thus derived at $298 \cdot 16°K$ are summarised in Table XIII.15.

It is a matter of interest to attempt to compute the stability of intermolecular complexes in terms of intermolecular forces. If, for example, the force attracting two molecules in a solvent of dielectric constant D is due to the electrostatic interaction of two dipoles, of moments μ_A and μ_B, we may, for a linear arrangement, express the total interaction energy as follows:

$$\phi = Aa^{-9} - Ba^{-3} \qquad \text{XIII.71}$$

Here A is a repulsion constant, and a is the distance apart of the dipoles. We may adopt, for the attraction constant, the expression

$$B = 2\mu_A\mu_B \left(\frac{D+2}{3D}\right) \qquad \text{XIII.72}$$

The distance, a_0, apart of the dipoles in their most stable state, and

Table XIII.15 *Complex formation in solution* $(AB \rightleftarrows A+B : K = a_A a_B / a_{AB})$

A and B	Solvent	ΔH^0 (kilocals/g-mole)	ΔS^0 (calories/g-mole-degree)	Method
$1:3:5\text{-}(NO_2)_3C_6H_3 + C_6H_5N(CH_3)_2$	$CHCl_3$	4·9	10·6	Photometric
$1:3:5\text{-}(NO_2)_3C_6H_3 + p\text{-}CH_3C_6H_4N(CH_3)_2$	$CHCl_3$	2·1	9·5	Ebullioscopic
$o\text{-}ClC_6H_4OH + p\text{-}CH_3C_6H_4NH_2$	C_6H_6	3·5	5·05	Cryoscopic
$p\text{-}ClC_6H_4OH + p\text{-}CH_3C_6H_4NH_2$	C_6H_6	4·2	5·25	
$p\text{-}ClC_6H_4OH + C_5H_5N$	C_6H_6	6·8	13·9	
$CHCl_3 + (CH_3)_2CO$	Pure liquids	4·1	12·4	Vapour pressure
$CHCl_3 + (C_2H_5)_2O$	Pure liquids	6·0	3·0	Calorimetric
$C_{10}H_8 + 1:3:5\text{-}(NO_2)_3C_6H_2OH$	CCl_4	0·7	5·7	Spectrometric
$C_{10}H_8 + 1:3:5\text{-}(NO_2)_3C_6H_3$	CCl_4	2·7	5·5	
$C_{10}H_8 + m\text{-}(NO_2)_2C_6H_4$	CCl_4	1·5	7·4	

the energy, ϕ_0, of the pair in that state are found, from the equilibrium condition, $d\phi/da = 0$, to be given by the relations

$$a_0^6 = 3A/B$$

and

$$-\phi_0 = \frac{2B}{3a_0^3}$$

whence, by elimination, the repulsion constant becomes

$$A = \frac{4}{27} \frac{B^3}{\phi_0^2} \qquad \text{XIII.73}$$

On applying these formulae to the interaction of pyridine ($\mu = 2\cdot16 \times 10^{-18}$ e.s.u.) and p-chlorophenol ($\mu = 2\cdot25 \times 10^{-18}$) in benzene solution, for which $(D+2)/3D$ is 0·6464, we find that B is $6\cdot28 \times 10^{-36}$ erg-cm³. From the cryoscopic work of Madgin and his collaborators (Table XIII.15), $-\phi_0$ in the case of this complex is seen to be $4\cdot7 \times 10^{-13}$ erg/pair. Hence, the repulsion constant becomes $A = 1\cdot66 \times 10^{-82}$ erg-cm⁹. This estimate from freezing-point data in solution is in close proximity to the value $(3\cdot5 \times 10^{-82})$ found by

384

Lennard-Jones (1924) for the repulsion constant between two neon atoms from the virial coefficients of the gas.

We can now use this value of A to determine the properties of other complexes of the same type, in which the chief source of repulsion arises from the electronic octets in the carbon and nitrogen atoms, such, for example, as that formed between pyridine and methyl iodide ($\mu = 1.41 \times 10^{-18}$) in the same solvent. B now becomes 3.95×10^{-36}, and $a_0 = 2.24 \times 10^{-8}$ cm, while $-\phi_0 = 3\,385$ cal/mole, and the intermolecular frequency of vibration,

$$v_0 = \frac{3}{2\pi a_0} \sqrt{\frac{3|-\phi_0|}{m^*}} \qquad \text{XIII.74}$$

is 1.96×10^{12} sec^{-1}.

Equilibria in terms of activities

When none of the theoretical equations XIII.39 to XIII.42 reproduces the facts, the results of experiment can be formalised in the equation

$$K_a = \frac{a_L^l}{a_B^b\, a_c^c}; \qquad \Delta G_a^0 = -RT \ln K_a \qquad \text{XIII.75}$$

where the activity, a, for each component is so chosen as to make the equation fit the facts and to reduce to the conventional concentrations, c or m, at infinite dilution or to the molar fraction, x, under ideal conditions. The corresponding activity coefficients have already been discussed in some detail in Chapter XI, and we shall content ourselves here with two instances only.

(1) Burnham and Madgin (1937) have employed the freezing point method to determine the activities of various organic bases and benzene derivatives in benzene solution. By combining the information with the freezing points of solutions containing both solutes, they have evaluated the equilibrium constant governing the formation of the complex, $A + B \rightleftarrows AB$.

$$K_a = \frac{a_{AB}}{a_A a_B} = \frac{m_{AB}}{m_A m_B} \frac{\gamma_{AB}}{\gamma_A \gamma_B} = K_m \frac{\gamma_{AB}}{\gamma_A \gamma_B}$$

They find that, with a change of about 100 in the molar ratio m_A/m_B, the equilibrium constant in terms of concentrations alters by a factor of 2, but in terms of activities is virtually constant.

N*

385

(2) Farhat-Aziz and Moelwyn-Hughes (1959) have measured the equilibrium constant for the displacement reaction

$$CH_3Cl + I^- \rightleftarrows CH_3I + Cl^-$$

in acetone solution:

$$K = \frac{a_{CH_3I} a_{Cl^-}}{a_{CH_3Cl} a_{I^-}} = \frac{c_{CH_3I} c_{Cl^-}}{c_{CH_3Cl} c_{I^-}} \times \frac{\gamma_{CH_3I} \gamma_{Cl^-}}{\gamma_{CH_3Cl} \gamma_{I^-}}$$

At the concentrations employed, the activity coefficients of the molecules are both unity and those of the ions equal, which accounts for the fact that the K obtained by them in terms of concentrations is constant. We note, *en passant*, from Table XIII.10, that the entropy of the chloride ion in this solvent is less than that of the iodide ion by about 12 cal/mole-degree, as it is in aqueous solution.

Certain hypothetical equilibria

We shall require for later reference statistical expressions for equilibria which have the common property that the integer l is unity. Except when $a + b + c + \cdots = 1$, which clearly corresponds to intramolecular changes, these reactions are all association reactions, wherein molecules of type $A, B, C, \ldots$ coalesce to form a complex molecule of type $ABC \ldots$. All the hypothetical molecules are considered to be non-degenerate ($g = 1$) and to occupy the ground electronic state. We shall consider the equilibria to be established at a constant total volume.

(1) *Equilibria of type $A \rightleftarrows X$.* Suppose that the molecule A is converted by acquisition of energy ε_0 into a molecule X, the process being either an isomerisation or an activation, according as A changes or retains its original molecule structure. To express the equilibrium constant, which in this case is dimensionless, we require only the ratio of the partition functions for the two species. In general, all the partition functions, with the exception of the translational function, are altered during the change. When only the vibrational degrees of freedom are excited, we may, as an approximation, consider all the other factors in the total partition functions of A and X to be identical; hence

$$K = \frac{n_X}{n_A} = \frac{q_X}{q_A} = \frac{\prod_1^i (1 - e^{-h\nu_i(X)/kT})^{-1}}{\prod_1^i (1 - e^{-h\nu_i(A)/kT})^{-1}} e^{-\varepsilon_0/kT}$$

Now the acquisition of vibrational energy generally loosens at least one bond. Let us denote the frequency of this weak bond in the molecule X by v_x so that

$$K = \frac{(1-e^{-hv_x/kT})^{-1} \prod_{1}^{i-1} (1-e^{-hv(X)/kT})^{-1}}{\prod_{1}^{i} (1-e^{-hv(A)/kT})^{-1}} e^{-\varepsilon_0/kT}$$

Since, however, for small values of hv_x/kT, we have the approximate relation $(1-e^{-hv_x/kT})^{-1} \doteqdot (kT/hv_x)$, the equilibrium constant becomes

$$K = \frac{kT}{hv_x} \frac{\prod_{i}^{i-1} (1-e^{-hv(X)/kT})^{-1}}{\prod_{1}^{i} (1-e^{-hv(A)/kT})^{-1}} e^{-\varepsilon_0/kT}$$

A further simplification is possible if we are prepared to regard all the frequencies in the molecule X as identical with those of the original molecule A, except the one for the excited bond, which has the value v_x in X and v_a in A. Under these conditions, we have the very simple equation

$$K = \frac{n_X}{n_A} = \frac{kT}{hv_x}(1-e^{-hv_a/kT}) e^{-\varepsilon_0/kT} \qquad \text{XIII.76}$$

Finally, if the ground state vibration frequency, v_a, of the bond which is excited is very high,

$$K = \frac{kT}{hv_x} e^{-\varepsilon_0/kT} \qquad \text{XIII.77}$$

The assumptions leading to this equation have been carefully pointed out, and must not be overlooked.

(2) *Equilibria of type* $A + B \rightleftarrows AB$. The equilibrium established between free atoms of type A and B and the stable diatomic molecule AB is governed by the relation

$$K = \frac{n_{AB}}{n_A n_B} = \frac{q_{AB}}{q_A q_B} e^{-\varepsilon_0/kT}$$

$$= \frac{\dfrac{\{2\pi(m_A+m_B)kT\}^{3/2}}{h^3} \cdot \dfrac{8\pi^2 I_{AB}kT}{h^2} (1-e^{-hv_{AB}/kT})^{-1}}{\dfrac{(2\pi m_A kT)^{3/2}}{h^3} \dfrac{(2\pi m_B kT)^{3/2}}{h^3}} e^{-\varepsilon_0/kT}$$

387

provided A and B are dissimilar and provided the vibrations executed by the molecule are simple harmonic. Rearranging the terms, and noting that

$$I_{AB} = \frac{m_A m_B}{m_A + m_B} r_{AB}^2 = \mu_{AB} r_{AB}^2$$

we have

$$K = h r_{AB}^2 \sqrt{\left(\frac{8\pi}{kT\mu_{AB}}\right)} (1 - e^{-h\nu_{AB}/kT})^{-1} e^{-\varepsilon_0/kT}$$

When $h\nu \gg kT$, the equation reduces to

$$K = h r_{AB}^2 \sqrt{\left(\frac{8\pi}{kT\mu_{AB}}\right)} e^{-\varepsilon_0/kT}$$

and when $h\nu \ll kT$, we have

$$K = \frac{r_{AB}^2}{\nu_{AB}} \sqrt{\left(\frac{8\pi kT}{\mu_{AB}}\right)} e^{-\varepsilon_0/kT} \qquad \text{XIII.78}$$

If the restoring force constant is weak, the frequency, ν_{AB}, is $\bar{u}/2a$, where $\bar{u}$ is the average velocity (equation II.6) and a is the amplitude. When ε_0 is zero, we then have

$$K = 8\pi r_{AB}^2 a$$

3. *Equilibria of the type* $A + BC \rightleftarrows ABC$. Let us consider the equilibrium established between free atoms A and diatomic molecules BC on the one hand, and linear triatomic molecules ABC on the other hand, such as might hold for the chemical reaction between atoms of bromine and molecules of nitric oxide:

$$Br + NO \rightleftarrows BrNO.$$

Making the usual assumption of harmonic vibrations and rigid rotations we obtain the equilibrium constant:

$$K = \frac{n_{ABC}}{n_A n_{BC}} = \frac{q_{ABC}}{q_A q_{BC}} e^{-\varepsilon_0/kT}$$

$$= \frac{\dfrac{[2\pi(m_A + m_B + m_C)kT]^{3/2}}{h^3} \dfrac{8\pi^2 I_{ABC}kT}{\sigma_{ABC}h^2} \prod\limits_{i=1}^{4} (1 - e^{-h\nu_i/kT})^{-1}}{\dfrac{[2\pi m_A kT]^{3/2}}{h^3} \dfrac{[2\pi(m_B + m_C)kT]^{3/2}}{h^3} \dfrac{8\pi^2 I_{BC}kT}{\sigma_{BC}h^2} (1 - e^{-h\nu_{BC}/kT})^{-1}} e^{-\varepsilon_0/kT}$$

which, after cancelling and rearranging, becomes

$$K = \frac{h^3}{(2\pi kT)^{3/2}}\left[\frac{m_A+m_B+m_C}{m_A(m_B+m_C)}\right]^{3/2}\frac{I_{ABC}}{I_{BC}}\frac{\sigma_{BC}}{\sigma_{ABC}}\frac{\prod_{i=1}^{4}(1-e^{-hv_i/kT})^{-1}}{(1-e^{-hv_{BC}/kT})^{-1}}e^{-\varepsilon_0/kT}$$

Of the four vibrations executed by the molecule ABC, let us suppose that one of them, say the transverse motion, has a low frequency, v_t, in which case we may write $(1-e^{-hv_t/kT})^{-1} = kT/hv_t$. Of the other motions, the bending frequency v_ϕ is doubly degenerate, since the molecule can bend equally in two planes at right angles to each other, and the symmetrical frequency v_s is single. Hence

$$K = \frac{[ABC]}{[A][BC]} = \frac{1}{v_t}\left(\frac{h}{2\pi}\right)^2\left(\frac{2\pi}{kT}\right)^{1/2}\left[\frac{m_A+m_B+m_C}{m_A(m_B+m_C)}\right]^{3/2}\frac{I_{ABC}}{I_{BC}}\frac{\sigma_{BC}}{\sigma_{ABC}}$$

$$\times\frac{(1-e^{-hv_s/kT})^{-1}(1-e^{-hv_\phi/kT})^{-2}}{(1-e^{-hv_{BC}/kT})^{-1}}e^{-\varepsilon_0/kT} \qquad \text{XIII.80}$$

Reference to Fig. XIII.1 enables us to write

$$\varepsilon_0 + \tfrac{1}{2}hv_{BC} = \varepsilon_s + \tfrac{1}{2}h(v_s + 2v_\phi) \qquad \text{XIII.81}$$

Hence, denoting $h/2kT$ by β.

$$K = \frac{1}{4v_t}\left(\frac{h}{2\pi}\right)^2\left(\frac{2\pi}{kT}\right)^{1/2}\left[\frac{m_A+m_B+m_C}{m_A(m_B+m_C)}\right]^{3/2}\frac{I_{ABC}}{I_{BC}}\frac{\sigma_{BC}}{\sigma_{ABC}}$$

$$\times\frac{\sinh\beta v_{BC}}{\sinh\beta v_s \sinh^2\beta v_\phi}e^{-\varepsilon_s/kT} \qquad \text{XIII.82}$$

Since the molar increase in total energy at temperature T is given by $\Delta E_T = N_0kT^2(d\ln K/dT)_V$, we have

$$\frac{(\Delta E)_T}{N_0} = \varepsilon_s - \tfrac{1}{2}kT + \tfrac{1}{2}h(v_s\coth\beta v_s + 2v_\phi\coth\beta v_\phi - v_{BC}\coth\beta v_{BC})$$

When one of the vibration frequencies of the complex has an imaginary value v_i, which may be written as iv_x where v_x is real,

$$K = \frac{h^3}{(8\pi kT)^{3/2}}\cdot\left[\frac{m_A+m_B+m_C}{m_A(m_B+m_C)}\right]^{3/2}\frac{I_{ABC}}{I_{AB}}\frac{\sigma_{BC}}{\sigma_{ABC}}$$

$$\times\frac{\sinh\beta v_{Bc}}{\sinh\beta v_s \sinh^2\beta v_\phi\, i\sin\beta v_x}\cdot e^{-\varepsilon_s/kT}$$

and consequently

$$\frac{(\Delta E)_T}{N_0} = \varepsilon_s - \tfrac{3}{2}kT + \tfrac{1}{2}h(v_s \coth \beta v_s + 2v_\phi \coth \beta v_\phi$$

$$+ v_x \cot \beta v_x - v_{BC} \coth \beta v_{BC}) \qquad \text{XIII.83}$$

It is to be noted that the relevant functions of βv_x are now the sine and cotangent, rather than the hyperbolic sine (sinh) and the hyperbolic contangent (coth). These theoretical expressions of the mass-action constants governing hypothetical equilibria in which atoms and molecules coalesce to form complexes are useful in the statistical treatment of chemical kinetics (Chapter XV).

XIV Equilibria in heterogeneous systems

It would have been impossible to travel so far along the road of physical chemistry without encountering heterogeneous phenomena such as photoelectricity, sublimation, fusion, vaporisation, dissolution and surface tension. We shall in this chapter consider further examples of systems containing more than one phase, so as to outline the main feature of simple phase changes, chemical equilibria in heterogeneous systems, hydrate formation, electromotive force and adsorption.

Phase relations in systems of one component

According to the phase rule (equation VI.41) the number, f, of degrees of freedom in a system of one component is $3-p$, where p is the number of phases. In a one-component system consisting of a single phase, therefore, there are 2 degrees of freedom, or 2 independent variables. These may be any 2 from the variables pressure, temperature and volume, as we have seen in studying the pure gaseous, liquid and solid phases. In a one-component system consisting of two phases, there is only one degree of freedom. If, for example, the system consists of a liquid phase L and a vapour phase G, we may alter the temperature at will; in doing so, the system automatically adjusts its pressure, for there can be only one equilibrium pressure corresponding to any given temperature. In a one-component system with three phases, there is no degree of freedom, i.e. we can alter neither temperature nor pressure without causing one phase to disappear. A typical pressure-temperature diagram for such a system is shown in Fig. XIV.1, which is illustrative only and not drawn to scale. The areas labelled S, L and G, which denote the range of existence of the pure phases, are bounded by the axes and by the sublimation curve, ON, the fusion curve, NB, and the vaporisation curve, NA, which ends at the critical point. The point c represents a gaseous system at a definite temperature and pressure. As this system is bivariant, we may alter the temperature and the pressure independently. Increasing the pressure at constant temperature brings the system to the point a,

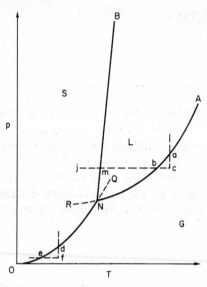

Fig. XIV.1 *Pressure temperature diagram of a one-component system*

at which the liquid phase appears. A further increase in P at constant T merely compresses the liquid and brings about no further phase changes. Starting again from the point c, we may decrease the temperature at constant pressure, when liquid now appears at the point b. A further decrease in T at constant P merely cools the liquid, until the point m is reached when the phase change liquid-to-solid takes place. Further reduction of T at constant P merely cools the solid. When the line jc is drawn so as to meet the ordinate at $P = 760$ mm, the points m and b are termed the melting and boiling points. Their relation to the triple point, N, and the critical point, A, is at once clear from the diagram. Beginning at a point f, the temperature of which is below that of the triple point, the phase change vapour-to-solid takes place at the points d or e, depending on whether we have increased P at constant T or decreased T at constant P. Points which lie on the curves represent univariant systems, in which two phases coexist at equilibrium. If we require to maintain two phases in such systems, there is only one independent variable available. Thus, for example, if we wish to alter the state of the system represented by point b, while retaining both liquid and vapour, we may vary T, but in doing so P automatically varies. The triple point N

392

represents an invariant system, in which solid, liquid and vapour coexist at equilibrium. If we increase T at constant P, the whole system passes into the vapour phase. If we increase P at constant T, the whole system passes into the solid phase. If we increase the pressure only, while letting the temperature look after itself, only the vapour phase disappears, and we trace the fusion curve NB, which shows how the melting point is increased by an increase in pressure. The gradient of this curve may be used to calculate the increase in volume which attends fusion (equation VI.30). For gallium and water, the NB curve tilts to the left, because the volumes of these anomalous solids are greater than those of the liquids. The short curves NQ and NR represent the metastable equilibria of the vapour phase with the superheated solid and the subcooled liquid respectively.

Systems of two components

According to the phase rule, f is now $4-p$. To indicate the range of existence of a two-component system in a single phase, we must know how three independent variables are related to one another, and for this purpose a solid model must be constructed. If, however, we confine attention to isothermal studies ($T = $ constant) or to condensed systems in which P is constant, f becomes $3-p$, and a complete survey of any single phase ($p = 1$) can be given in terms of two independent variables. Two-dimensional graphs will suffice to represent their behaviour. This is the course adopted here. From sets of such isothermal or isobaric diagrams for any given two-component system, solid models may readily be constructed.

Two-component systems with a vapour phase and one solid phase: solid solutions

When solid borneol ($C_{10}H_{17}OH$; $T_m = 476°K$) and camphor ($C_{10}H_{16}O$; $T_m = 448°K$) are mixed in varying proportions at any fixed temperature below the lower melting-point, the equilibrium pressure of the system is found to vary linearly with respect to the composition (Vanstone, 1910). We have the isothermal

$$P = p_B + p_C = p_B^0 x_B + p_C^0(1-x_B) = p_C^0 + (p_B^0 - p_C^0)x_B \qquad \text{XI.2}$$

where x_B is the molar fraction of borneol in the solid phase, and the p^0 terms are the vapour pressures of the pure solids. This system is

393

clearly that of an ideal solid solution. There is no evidence of association or of complex formation in the solid phase, or for the existence of more than one solid phase. Since $f = 3 - p$ for this isothermal
two-component system, we have $f = 2$ in the homogeneous vapour or
solid phase, and $f = 1$ for the heterogeneous system. The two regions
of existence of the homogeneous phases are separated by the line
corresponding to the equation written above.

If we keep the pressure rather than the temperature constant, we
again have $f = 3 - p$. Hence, in a two-component system examined at
atmospheric pressure, there are two independent variables available
in the homogeneous phases ($p = 1$), but only one degree of freedom
for the system which contains both phases ($p = 2$). The temperature-
composition curve must therefore be continuous, as is found, for
example, in the mercuric bromide-mercuric iodide system.

On plotting the melting points of the solids as a function of their
molar fractions in the solid phase, and the freezing points of the liquids
as a function of their molar fractions in the liquid phase, we obtain
two somewhat similar curves (Fig. XIV.2), which touch at the minimum point. Again there is only one solid phase and one liquid phase.

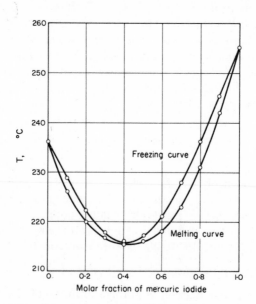

Fig. XIV.2   *Solidus and liquidus curves of the* $HgBr_2$-HgI_2 *systems*

Pairs of chemically similar compounds, like p-dichlorobenzene and p-iodochlorobenzene, often behave in this way. The compositions of the melts and the solids are different at all temperatures, except the minimum. The melt is always richer than the solid in that component which lowers the freezing point (Konowaloff's law).

In the β-naphthol-naphthalene system, the freezing points of solutions of all composition lie between those of the pure components, and in the d-carvoxime-l-carvoxime system, the freezing point-composition curve passes through a maximum at a temperature which is about 20° higher than that of either pure component. These systems, taken in conjunction with those of the $HgBr_2$-HgI_2 type, represent normal behaviour and positive and negative deviations from it, exactly as in the vapour-liquid systems discussed in Chapter XI. Only when the temperature-composition curve has neither a maximum nor passes through a minimum, can the components of the system be completely separated by fractional crystallisation.

Condensed two-component systems with solid phases; eutectic mixtures

We here consider condensed two-component systems in which the solids are not mutually soluble. The three phases possible are solid I, solid II and the liquid phase. Since $f = 3 - p$, the phase diagram must contain an invariant point, corresponding to the coexistence of the three phases. Fig. XIV.3 shows the melting and freezing points of the silver nitrate-water system as a function of the molar fraction of salt at atmospheric pressure. Point O is the freezing point of water, and point M the melting point of the rhombic modification of silver nitrate. The curve OE shows how the freezing point of water is lowered by addition of silver nitrate; the curve ME shows the effect of water on freezing point of silver nitrate. These curves intersect at the eutectic point, E, which corresponds to a temperature of $-7.3°C$, and to a molar fraction of 0.08468 of salt. The ratio of the number of moles of water to that of salt at the eutectic point is thus 10.81, which does not correspond to the composition of any simple compound. The solid which appears at the eutectic, as viewed under the microscope, is simply a mixture and not a solid solution. The eutectic point in a condensed two-component system containing water is often referred to as the cryohydric point. On cooling an unsaturated solution with a lower molar fraction than 0.08468 of salt, the first solid to appear is ice, when we cross the line OE. Further cooling results in the deposition

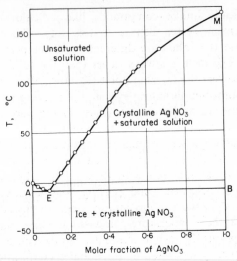

Fig. XIV.3   *The silver nitrate-water system*

of crystalline salt. The area OAE represents ice plus saturated solution. On cooling a solution which is richer in salt than is the eutectic mixture, the first solid to appear is silver nitrate. The area MEB represents the range of existence of the heterogeneous system consisting of solid salt and saturated solution. Further cooling results in the deposition of ice. The position of the horizontal line AB shows that it is impossible for ice to be at equilibrium with crystalline silver nitrate at any temperature above -7.4, or for an aqueous solution of silver nitrate to be at equilibrium with ice or the crystalline salt at any temperature below -7.4. Because of the great difference between the melting points of ice and salts, cryoscopic curves are usually highly asymmetric. When, however, the two components are fairly similar chemically, and do not differ greatly in melting points, the eutectic curve may be nearly symmetrical. Such is the case with the system p-toluidine ($T_m = 316.5°K$) and o-nitrophenol ($T_m = 317.3°K$).

Condensed two-component systems with compound formation; the congruent melting point

Departures from normal eutectic behaviour in two-component systems provide evidence for the existence and composition of inter-

396

molecular compounds. Such a departure is observed, for example, in the system composed of phenol and p-toluidine (Fig. XIV.4), in which two eutectic points E_1 and E_2 appear, as well as a maximum point, M, at which the liquid freezes into a solid of the same composition, which is that of molar fraction one-half. The complete diagram can obviously be regarded as two halves; the one on the left representing the normal eutectic behaviour of solid A and compound AB, and that on the

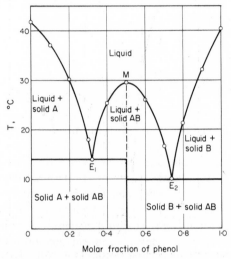

Fig. XIV.4 *Setting of the p-toluidine-phenol system*

right of compound AB and component B. The division is not hypothetical, for the compound AB can be readily prepared by mixing A and B in equimolar proportions, heating to facilitate the chemical change, which always goes more smoothly in the liquid than in the solid phase, and cooling. The two halves of the curve can thus be separately investigated. It is important to realise that AB is a definite chemical compound, with properties differing from those of a mechanical mixture of A and B in equimolar proportions.

A similar analysis of the system ammonia plus water reveals three eutectic and two congruent melting points, M_1 and M_2, which indicate the formation of the crystalline compounds H_2O,NH_3 and $H_2O,2NH_3$ (Fig. XIV.5). The first of these we would now write in the ionic form $(NH_4^+)(OH)^-$, just as we write $Na^+(OH)^-$ for crystalline sodium hydroxide. The second crystal, if entirely ionic, is clearly $(NH_4^+)_2O^{--}$, by analogy with $(Na^+)_2O^{--}$.

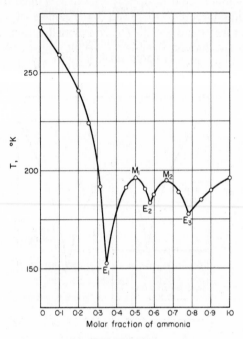

Fig. XIV.5 *Freezing-point-composition plot of the system* H_2O *and* NH_3

Two-component systems with a vapour phase and two liquid phases

These systems have $4-p$ degrees of freedom. If, for example, we wish to specify the exact state of the system while in the homogeneous vapour phase ($p = 1$), we must specify the temperature, T, pressure, P, and composition, which may provisionally be denoted by c_2, the concentration of that component which is present in the smaller amount. Clearly, while the system is entirely in the vapour phase, these three parameters can be varied at will. To specify the exact state of the system when the vapour phase and one homogeneous liquid phase are present ($p = 2$), two independent variables suffice. We may illustrate this fact by reference to the methyl halides in water. These systems obey Henry's law (1803), according to which the partial pressure of a gas in equilibrium with its solution in a liquid is

398

proportional to its concentration in solution:

$$p_2 = Kc_2 \qquad \qquad \text{XIV.1}$$

where the proportionality constant, K, depends on the temperature and on the nature of the solute and solvent, but in most of the systems examined is independent of the composition of the solution, and of the pressure. If the gas over the solution obeys the ideal gas laws, the ratio of the concentration in the two phases is clearly

$$s = \frac{c_S}{c_G} = \frac{kT}{K} \qquad \qquad \text{XIV.2}$$

This ratio is known as Ostwald's absorption coefficient. Valentiner (1927) and Lannung (1930) find that the logarithm of Henry's constant varies with respect to temperature according to the equation

$$\log (p_2/c_2) = a - b \log T - c/T \qquad \qquad \text{XIV.3}$$

where a, b and c are specific constants. It is immaterial which of the variables p_2, c_2 or T we regard as independent; provided two of them are specified, the third is known, i.e. it is a dependent variable. When, at a given constant temperature, the pressure p_2 is increased to p_2^0, which lies very near to the vapour pressure of the pure liquid halide at that temperature, a second homogeneous liquid phase appears. This second liquid phase is a dilute solution of water in the liquid halide, but we shall here regard it as the pure liquid halide, obeying the vapour pressure law

$$\log p_2^0 = a^0 - b^0 \log T - c^0/T \qquad \qquad \text{VIII.10}$$

The maximum concentration of halide in solution, found by substituting p_2^0 for p, is consequently given by the equation

$$\log c_2^0 = (a^0 - a) - (b^0 - b) \log T - (c^0 - c)/T \qquad \qquad \text{XIV.4}$$

Here c_2^0 is the concentration of solute in an aqueous solution which is at equilibrium with the liquid halide. The system contains three phases in all, and is therefore univariant; either T or c_2^0 can be varied independently, but not both. The pressure-temperature curve for such a system is shown by the upper curve in Fig. XIV.6. When $P = 3\ 640$ mm and $T = 293 \cdot 55°K$, a solid phase appears, which is a crystalline hydrate of methyl chloride. There are now 4 phases present, namely, vapour, liquid solution of methyl chloride in water, liquid solution of water in methyl chloride, and crystalline hydrate. The point therefore

399

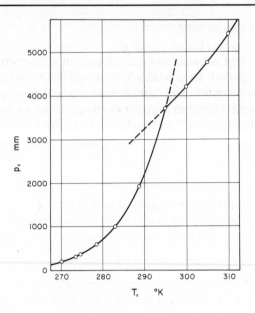

Fig. XIV.6 *Quadruple point of methyl chloride hydrate*

corresponds to an invariant system, and we cannot alter the temperature, pressure or composition of the system at this point without causing one phase to disappear. The point of intersection of the curves is referred to as the quadruple point. The lower curve is the equilibrium pressure-temperature relationship of the univariant system containing vapour, liquid solution of methyl chloride in water and crystalline hydrate.

Adopting as the constants in equation XIV.4 those values which refer to systems at a total pressure of one atmosphere, the solubility of liquid methyl iodide, expressed in moles per litre of solution, is found to be given by the equation

$$\log c_2^0 = -110.78 + 37.621 \log T \times 4\,823/T \qquad \text{XIV.5}$$

which indicates a minimum solubility of 0.0973 mole per litre at 295.2°K. This well-known effect has been observed for numerous liquids in water, (Rex, 1906; Winkler, 1906), and particularly for alkyl halides (van Arkel and Vles, 1936) and hydrocarbons (Bohon and Claussen, 1951).

400

Two-component systems with a vapour phase and two solid phases

When the lower curve of Fig. xiv.6 is followed further than is shown in the diagram, a second invariant point is reached, at which ice appears. At this point, the phases consist of vapour, liquid solution of solute in water, crystalline hydrate and ice. Such a point is shown in Fig. xiv.7, which refers to the water-chlorine system, and has been

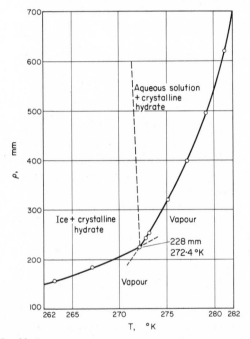

Fig. xiv.7   *The chlorine-water system*

drawn from the data of Roozeboom (1884). The upper curve shows the equilibrium pressure-temperature relationship of the system consisting of the three phases, vapour, aqueous solution and crystalline hydrate. It is reproduced by the equation

$$\log p(\text{mm}) = 16 \cdot 5755 - (3884 \pm 208)/T$$

Without going through all the details of the argument in terms of chemical potentials, we may accept the increase in heat content

401

derivable from this equation as relating to the change:

$$Cl_2, mH_2O(cr) \rightarrow mH_2O(liq) + Cl_2(gas); \quad \Delta H_x = 17\,760 \pm 950 \text{ cal}$$

where m is the unknown number of molecules of water in the hydrate. The lower curve in Fig. XIV.7 reproduces the equilibrium pressure-temperature of the system consisting of the phases vapour, ice and crystalline hydrate, and corresponds to the equation

$$\log p(\text{mm}) = 7 \cdot 5005 - (1395 \pm 101)/T$$

Again omitting the details, we may show that the change concerned is simply

$$Cl_2, mH_2(cr) \rightarrow mH_2O(cr) + Cl_2(gas); \quad \Delta H_y = 11\,370 \pm 460$$

On subtracting, we see that

$$\Delta H_x - \Delta H_y = mL \qquad\qquad \text{XIV.6}$$

where L is the latent heat of fusion of one mole of ice. Accepting the value which holds at its melting-point, which is $1\,435 \cdot 7$ cal, we conclude that $m = 7 \cdot 92 \pm 0 \cdot 98$. This example illustrates one of the many ingenious methods developed by de Forcrand to determine the composition of hydrates of this kind.

Roozeboom found the density of the crystalline hydrate at 0°C to be $1 \cdot 229 \pm 0 \cdot 009$ g/cc. From the known densities of liquid chlorine and water, we thus have the volume change:

$$Cl_2(liq) \quad + \quad 8H_2O(liq) \quad \rightarrow \quad Cl_2, 8H_2O(cr)$$

$$48 \cdot 26 \qquad\quad 8 \times 18 \cdot 018 \qquad\qquad 175 \cdot 0 \pm 1 \cdot 2 : \Delta V = -17 \cdot 2 \pm 1 \cdot 2$$

This observed shrinkage is somewhat surprising. Moreover, the density of the liquid system containing chlorine and water in a molar ratio of 1 to 8 is only $1 \cdot 024$, so that the solution expands on being formed;

$$Cl_2(liq) + 8H_2O(liq) \rightarrow Cl_2, 8H_2O(aq); \quad \Delta V = +17 \cdot 6$$

The actual shrinkage on making the crystalline hydrate from a liquid mixture of the same composition is thus about 35 cm³.

The structure of gas hydrates

A review by Schröder (1927) covers the work done upon gas hydrates during a century from the time of their discovery by Davy, and includes the classical contributions of Faraday, Roozeboom, Tammann, Villard and de Forcrand. Latterly, the gas hydrates have been studied by Claussen (1951) who interprets his results on the principle of the molecular model, and by von Stackelberg (1949), who has examined them by the scattering of X-rays and by other methods. From their conclusions, which differ in detail but are in the main mutually confirmatory, it appears that the solute (*Hydratbildner*) occupies holes in a tetrahedral ice structure, each hole being surrounded by a number, c, of H_2O molecules, each of which retains its own coordination number of 4. This interesting and unpredictable conclusion is difficult to visualise without seeing the models. The hydrate formed from solutes with a coordination number of 20 may be considered as an example. The model (Fig. XIV.8) shows how the 20 molecules of

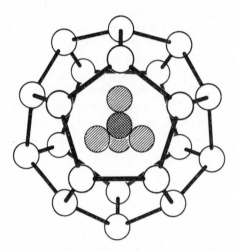

Fig. XIV.8   *Crystalline* CH_3Cl, $8H_2O$. *Coordination number 20*

H_2O arrange themselves around the solute, each being directly linked to 4 other H_2O molecules, of which 3 are in the coordination shell, and the fourth outside it. Without greatly straining the distances or angles which characterise pure ice, the figure formed is a regular dodecahedron, the surface of which consists of equal plane pentagons. von Stackelberg has further shown that the gas hydrates can probably be classified into groups, with formulae M, $6H_2O$, M, $8H_2O$ and M, $17H_2O$, and values of ΔH_x of 15 000, 19 000 and 31 500 cal respectively.

This classification of the gas hydrates seems to be supported by an independent classification based on the magnitude of heats of escape of the solute from solution (Glew and Moelwyn-Hughes, 1956).

Four items call for brief comment. (1) In computing the lattice energy of hydrates formed in this way, the interaction of a shell molecule with the solute must be regarded as additional to, and not as replacing, its other interactions. (2) The 28 water molecules forming the shell in compounds of the formula M, $17H_2O$ make 4 equal hexagons and 12 equal pentagons. Proceeding to still larger lacunae, we have a plausible structure for the surface of ice, without, as it were, any loose ends. (3) In the smaller crystals, some of the water molecules in the coordination shell are attached to 3, and others to 2, water molecules in the shell. Inspection of the models up to $c = 12$ makes it clear that the number of water-water interactions in the shell is $\frac{3}{2}(c-2)$. (4) The integral stoichiometric ratio in the formula representing the crystalline hydrate may involve large numbers. According to Pauling and Marsh (1952) the X-ray evidence on the crystalline hydrate of chlorine indicates the unit cell to be a body-centred cubic, the centre and eight corners of which are occupied by regular dodecahedra of water molecules. Each dodecahedron contains a molecule of chlorine at its centre, as in Fig. xiv.8, and is symmetrically surrounded by twelve tetrakai-decahedra, as shown in Figs. xiv.9 and xiv.10. The stoichiometric formula of the hydrate on this basis is $6Cl_2,46H_2O$, or $Cl_2, 7\frac{2}{3}H_2O$.

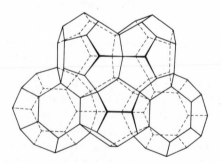

Fig. xiv.9 *Dodecahedron of oxygen atoms surrounded by four out of a total of twelve tetrakai-decahedra* (after Pauling and Marsh)

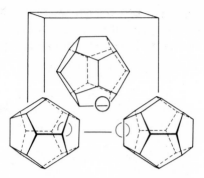

Fig. XIV.10 *Dodecahedra of oxygen at two corners and a body centre of unit cell, with three additional oxygen atoms (circles) needed to complete the structure*

The decomposition of calcium carbonate

The familiar chemical reaction by means of which quick-lime is made by heating lime in a kiln,

$$CaCO_3(\text{crystal}) \rightleftarrows CaO(\text{crystal}) + CO_2(\text{gas})$$

is a simple and carefully investigated example of a heterogeneous equilibrium, which we shall study by applying the general conditions that the chemical potential of each species which exists in the gas phase must equal its chemical potential in the crystal, and that in the homogeneous gas phase, the sum of the chemical potentials of reactants equals the sum of the chemical potentials of the resultants. For the reaction in the homogeneous gas phase,

$$CaCO_3(\text{gas}) \rightleftarrows CaO(\text{gas}) + CO_2(\text{gas})$$

we obtain, by writing $\mu = \mu^0 + kT \ln p$ for each species, the equilibrium constant

$$K = p_{CaO}\, p_{CO_2}/p_{CaCO_3} = \exp[-(\mu^0_{CaO} + \mu^0_{CO_2} - \mu^0_{CaCO_3})/kT]$$

where μ^0 is the chemical potential of the component at unit pressure and at temperature T. Experiment shows that the gas phase contains only subanalytical amounts of the vapours of calcium oxide and calcium carbonate, so that the total pressure of the system is effectively the pressure of carbon dioxide gas:

$$P = p_{CaCO_3} + p_{CaO} + p_{CO_2} \doteqdot p_{CO_2}$$

405

We shall next assume that the extremely small pressures exerted by the vapour of CaO and $CaCO_3$ are the equilibrium vapour pressures of the pure solids at temperature T. The equilibrium constant thus becomes

$$K = (p^0_{CaO}/p^0_{CaCO_3})P$$

Finally, since there is no solid carbon dioxide present at all the temperatures at which the system has been studied, the heterogeneous equilibria reduce to two, governed by the equalities

$$\mu^0(CaCO_3, \text{gas}) + kT \ln p^0_{CaCO_3} = \mu^{cr}_{CaCO_3}$$

and

$$\mu^0(CaO, \text{gas}) + kT \ln p^0_{CaO} = \mu^{cr}_{CaO}$$

Hence, on eliminating the p^0 terms, we obtain, for the total pressure of the system, the expression

$$P = \exp\{-[\mu^0_{CO_2, \text{gas}} + \mu^{cr}_{CaO} - \mu^{cr}_{CaCO_3}]/kT\} \qquad \text{XIV.7}$$

On taking logarithms, and converting to molar notations, we have, at any temperature,

$$\Delta G^0 = G^0_{CO_2} + G_{CaO} - G_{CaCO_3} = -RT \ln P \qquad \text{XIV.8}$$

In order to construct the expression for ΔG^0, we begin with the concordant thermochemical data obtained by Berthelot, by Thomsen and by de Forcrand at room temperatures, combined with the accurate values of specific heats of the three reactants at various temperatures, and with some experimental decomposition pressures, such as that of one atmosphere at $T = 1171°K$. This procedure leads to the following expression (Bäckström 1925) for the decomposition pressure as a function of temperature:

$$\log_{10} P(\text{mm}) = 7{\cdot}162 + 1{\cdot}6797 \log_{10} T - 1{\cdot}5048 \times 10^{-3} T$$
$$+ 0{\cdot}1503 \times 10^{-6} T^2 - 9212{\cdot}4/T$$

It follows that, at $298{\cdot}16°K$,

$$\Delta G^0 = -RT \ln P(\text{atm.}) = 31\,258$$

$$\Delta H = RT^2 \frac{d \ln P}{dT} = 42\,600$$

and

$$\Delta S^0 = (\Delta H - \Delta G^0)/T = 38 \cdot 05$$

where the energies are in calories per gram-mole. We note that the equilibrium pressure of the system at this temperature is $1 \cdot 175 \times 10^{-23}$ atm. It is because this is much lower than the pressure of atmospheric carbon dioxide that limestone is stable under ordinary conditions. By combining these results with the standard entropies of the two solids, Bäckström evaluated the standard entropy of gaseous carbon dioxide:

$$\Delta S^0 = S_{CaO} + S^0_{CO_2} - S_{CaCO_3}$$
$$38 \cdot 05 = 9 \cdot 50 + S^0_{CO_2} - 22 \cdot 3$$

Thus $S^0_{CO_2}$ is $50 \cdot 85$ calories per mole-degree at one atmosphere and at $298 \cdot 16°K$, in good agreement with values found spectroscopically.

It is of interest to note the following constants for the crystalline reaction under standard conditions:

$$CaCO_3(\text{aragonite}) \rightleftarrows CaCO_3(\text{calcite})$$

$\Delta H = 30$ calories per mole; $\Delta S^0 = 0 \cdot 74$ calories per mole-degree; $\Delta G^0 = -190$ cals/mole; $\Delta V^0 = -2 \cdot 75$ cc/mole. Hence, under ordinary conditions, calcite is the stable form of crystalline calcium carbonate, into which aragonite must be changing, though how slowly is not known. At high pressures, as Bäckström points out, aragonite may be the stable form.

From the point of view of the phase rule, the present system is one of two components, which are usually taken as CaO and CO_2. The composition of the solid phases is completely determined when the amounts of both these components are known, for the excess of one over the other represents the amount of crystalline $CaCO_3$. When the three phases, solid CaO, solid $CaCO_3$ and gaseous CO_2 are all present the system is univariant.

The decomposition of crystalline ammonium hydrogen sulphide

Isambert (1881) measured the pressures exerted by the products of decomposition of solid NH_4HS in a 'Torricellian vacuum' at various temperatures with the results given in Table XIV.1. The condition of equilibrium is

$$G(NH_4HS, cr) = G^0_{NH_3} + RT \ln p_{NH_3} + G^0_{H_2S} + RT \ln p_{H_2S}$$

Table XIV.1 *Decomposition pressures of crystalline ammonium hydrogen sulphide*

$T°K$	P(mm)	$-\Delta G^0$(cals/mole)	
		obs.	calc.
227·4	132	4 616	4 605
288·2	259	5 569	5 615
298·3	501	6 545	6 545
308·8	919	7 521	7 525
317·6	1 560	8 373	8 335

provided the ideal gas laws hold. The total pressure of the system is

$$P = p_{NH_4HS} + p_{NH_3} + p_{H_2S}$$

If there are no undecomposed molecules of the salt in the vapour phase, and provided ammonia and hydrogen sulphide are not added (except in equimolar amounts), the partial pressure of each vapour is one-half the total pressure, so that

$$-\Delta G^0 = G_{cr} - G^0_{NH_3} - G^0_{H_2S} = 2RT \ln (P/2) \qquad \text{XIV.9}$$

These standard free energies vary almost linearly with respect to temperature, according to the equation

$$\Delta G^0 = 21,075 - 92·6T$$

The standard increase in entropy attending the conversion of crystalline NH_4HS into its gaseous products is thus 92·6. If the reference state of each vapour were 1 atmosphere, ΔS^0 would be less by $2R \ln 760$, and would be then 66·24 cal/mole-degree. From the standpoint of the phase rule, the system hitherto examined is a system of one component in two phases; it is therefore univariant. If, however, ammonia and hydrogen sulphide gases are added in any proportion other than the equimolar proportion, the system contains two components, and gains a second degree of freedom. The pressure of such a system, for example, is not determined by temperature only, but depends also on the composition of the vapour phase. Let us examine this point more closely.

408

The equilibrium law (equation XIV.9) in its general form is $-\Delta G^0 = RT \ln (p_1 p_2)$, where ΔG^0 depends on temperature and specific properties of the reactants but is independent of pressure. At a constant temperature, therefore, the product of the partial pressures, $p_1 p_2$, is constant, or, if we wish to deal with concentrations, c, the product $c_1 c_2$ must be constant. Let us consider one litre of the gaseous phase, so that the concentrations, c_1 of ammonia and c_2 of hydrogen sulphide, are the numbers of moles of each in the vapour phase. Without the addition of either gas, each value is c_0, say. Let us now add c moles of ammonia gas. The instantaneous concentrations, before chemical reaction has occurred, are $c_1 = c_0 + c$ and $c_2 = c_0$. The system in this state, however, is unstable and adjusts itself to a stable state by forming s moles of crystalline salt. The equilibrium concentrations are then

$$c_1 = c_0 + c - s \quad \text{and} \quad c_2 = c_0 - s$$

The equilibrium pressure of the system is clearly

$$P = RT(c_1 + c_2) = RT[2(c_0 - s) + c]$$

But, according to the equilibrium law

$$(c_0 + c - s)(c_0 - s) = c_0^2$$

On eliminating s, we find the total pressure of the system to be

$$P = 2RTc_0 \sqrt{\left(1 + \frac{c^2}{4c_0^2}\right)}$$

But $2RTc_0$ is P^0, the total pressure of the system when both vapours originate solely from the decomposition of the pure crystal, and RTc is the instantaneous additional partial pressure p of the gaseous component which was added. Hence

$$P = P^0 \sqrt{\left[1 + \left(\frac{p}{P^0}\right)^2\right]} \qquad \text{XIV.10}$$

It follows that, if $p \gg P^0$, the equilibrium pressure of the system is very nearly p, the additional pressure of the added gas. If we add either component at an additional pressure equal to P^0, the resulting equilibrium pressure is not $2P^0$, as it would be in the absence of the heterogeneous equilibrium, but $P^0 \sqrt{2}$.

o

The distribution of a solute between two immiscible solvents, with partial dimerisation in one solvent

Let us denote the solute by HA. With water as one of the solvents, we have the distribution equilibrium

$$HA(\text{water}) \rightleftarrows HA(\text{second solvent})$$

which gives us

$$K_1 = [HA]_S/[HA]_W$$

The dissociation of the dimers

$$(HA)_2 \text{ (second solvent)} \rightleftarrows 2\,HA(\text{second solvent})$$

gives us

$$K_2 = [HA]_S^2/[(HA)_2]_S$$

Now let the total formal concentration of solute, reckoned as moles of monomer per litre, whether partially dimerised or not, be c. Then, since all the solute in the water layer is regarded as monomeric,

$$c_W = [HA]_W$$

The total formal concentration in the second solvent is clearly

$$c_S = [HA]_S + 2[(HA)_2]_S$$

On dividing this equation by its predecessor and eliminating the term $[HA]_S$, we obtain the following result:

$$\frac{c_S}{c_W} = K_1 + \left(\frac{2K_1^2}{K_2}\right)c_W \qquad \text{XIV.11}$$

By plotting the formal distribution ratio, c_S/c_W against the concentration, c_W, in the aqueous layer, we should obtain a linear relationship, the intercept giving us K_1, while K_2 is determinable from the gradient, $2K_1^2/K_2$. The distribution of polar solutes, such as ammonia, amines and carboxylic acids, between water and relatively immiscible solvents have been found to conform to this equation, at aqueous concentrations not exceeding one mole per litre. Nernst's data on the distribution of benzoic acid between water and benzene at 20°C, analysed in this way (see Fig. XIV.11), yield $K_1 = 1\cdot80$, and $K_2 = 5\cdot70 \times 10^{-3}$ gram-mole/litre. From the variation of K_1 and K_2 with respect to temperature, the standard increases in entropy and heat

410

content can be measured for the transfer of single molecules from one solvent to another and for the dimerisation. The dependence of ΔH_2 on the dielectric constant of the solvent has already been discussed in Chapter XIII.

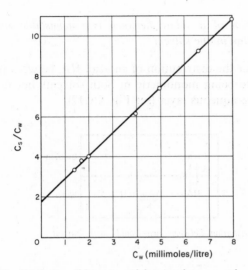

Fig. XIV.11   *The distribution of benzoic acid between benzene and water*

When there is no dimerisation, K_2 is infinite, and equation XIV.11 becomes

$$\frac{c_S}{c_W} = K_1 \qquad \text{XIV.12}$$

which is the simple distribution law of Berthelot and Jungfleisch (1891), usually attributed to Nernst (1897). When there is extensive dimerisation K_2 is small, and equation XIV.11 reduces to

$$\frac{\sqrt{c_S}}{c_W} = K_1 \sqrt{\frac{2}{K_2}} = K \qquad \text{XIV.13}$$

This form of the distribution law is due to Nernst, and is seen to be based on the assumption that there are no single molecules in the non-aqueous solvent. This assumption we now know to be false. If the monomer in the aqueous layer is ionised to a fraction α, the correct form of the distribution law is then (M. Davies, P. Jones, Patnaik and

411

Moelwyn-Hughes, 1951):

$$\frac{c_S}{c_W(1-\alpha)} = K_1 + \left(\frac{2K_1^2}{K_2}\right) c_W(1-\alpha) \qquad \text{XIV.14}$$

The distribution of a solute between two immiscible solvents, with partial ionisation in one solvent

Let us consider the distribution of an acid, HA, between benzene and water, its state being monomeric in both solvents but ionised to an extent α in the aqueous layer (see Fig. XIV.12).

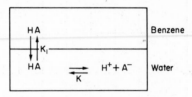

Fig. XIV.12 *Distribution between two liquids with partial ionisation in one*

In the notation of the previous section, the equilibrium between monomeric molecules of the solute in the two layers may be expressed as follows:

$$K_1 = \frac{[HA]_S}{[HA]_W} = \frac{c_S}{c_W(1-\alpha)}$$

so that

$$\alpha = 1 - \frac{c_S}{K_1 c_W}$$

The ionisation equilibrium in the aqueous medium is represented as

$$K_2 = \frac{[H^+]_W[A^-]_W}{[HA]_W} = \frac{c_W^2 \alpha^2}{(c_S/K_1)}$$

so that

$$\alpha = \sqrt{\left(\frac{K_2}{K_1}\right)\frac{\sqrt{c_S}}{c_W}}$$

412

On eliminating α from these equations, and rearranging, we obtain the relation:

$$\frac{\sqrt{c_S}}{c_W} = \sqrt{\left(\frac{K_1}{K_2}\right)\left(1 - \frac{1}{K_1}\frac{c_S}{c_W}\right)}$$

XIV.15

The linear relationship between $\sqrt{(c_S)}/c_W$ and c_S/c_W is shown in Fig. XIV.13 which has been drawn from the data of Rothmund and Drucker (1903) on the distribution of picric acid between water and benzene

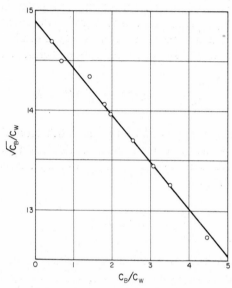

Fig. XIV.13 *The distribution of picric acid between benzene and water at 18°C*

at 18°C. The concentration unit is the gram mole per litre. The intercept yields a value of 14·895 for $(K_1/K_2)^{1/2}$ and the gradient a value of 2·132 for $(K_1 K_2)^{1/2}$. Hence $K_1 = 31·76$, and $K_2 = 0·143$. The investigators themselves have analysed the results using the same hypotheses but a different method of computation. The mean of 9 out of the 10 values given by them for K_2 is 0·146. The aqueous concentrations ranged from 2·08 to 33·42 millimoles per litre, and the corresponding values of the degree of ionisation range from 0·985 to 0·837. Rothmund and Drucker confirmed these estimates by conductimetric and cryoscopic experiments.

413

If van't Hoff's laws are inapplicable, we may add the correction term $kT \ln \gamma$ to his expression for the chemical potential, obtaining, for the solute in the benzene layer:

$$\mu_B = \mu_B^0 + kT \ln c_B \gamma$$

and for the solute in the aqueous layer,

$$\mu_W = \mu_+^0 + kT \ln c_+ \gamma_+ + \mu_-^0 + kT \ln c_- \gamma_-$$

The latter expression is the sum of the chemical potentials of the ions in the aqueous layer, and is, of course, equal to the chemical potential of the un-ionised acid in the same layer. At equilibrium, μ_B and μ_W are equal, so that, writing c_i for the concentration of either ion,

$$\frac{c_B \gamma}{c_i^2 \gamma_+ \gamma_-} = e^{-(\mu_B^0 - \mu_+^0 - \mu_-^0)/kT} = K$$

If we now assume that γ is unity, i.e. that van't Hoff's law holds in the layer in which the solute is the more soluble, and that there are no un-ionised molecules in the aqueous layer, we may clearly write c_W for c_i, and obtain the result

$$\frac{\sqrt{c_B}}{c_W} = \text{constant} \times (\gamma_+ \gamma_-)^{1/2}$$

Since the activity coefficients of the two ions are so defined as to be unity at infinite dilution, the value of $(\sqrt{c_B})/c_W$ extrapolated to zero concentration gives us the numerical value of the constant, from which values of the mean activity coefficient may be obtained for real concentrations. In this way, G. N. Lewis and M. Randall (1923) find the constant to be 15·4, and $(\gamma_+ \gamma_-)^{1/2}$ to vary from 0·97 to 0·82. The assumption that there are no un-ionised molecules of picric acid in water is, however, as unwarrantable as if one were to deny the existence of un-ionised molecules of phenol in water. The distinction between the two acids is one of degree only, and we must regard picric acid as we regard other strong acids, such as nitric and iodic acids. In other words, the interpretation of the results given by the investigators themselves is to be preferred on general grounds to that which invites us to ignore the existence of un-ionised molecules of acid in water and to fasten on to the ions properties which they do not possess.

414

The distribution of a solute between the gaseous phase and a solvent in which it is partially ionised and partially dimerised

Ammonia in water is the best example to discuss under this heading (Fig. XIV.14). If p denotes the partial pressure of ammonia over an aqueous solution, and c_W denotes the total formal concentration of ammonia (of all kinds) in the water, then the ratio p/c_W is found to

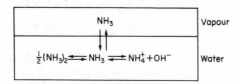

Fig. XIV.14 *The distribution of ammonia between water and the gaseous phase*

vary, i.e. Henry's law is not obeyed. Independent conductivity measurements tell us what fraction, α, of the solute is ionised; and we next inquire whether $p/c_W(1-\alpha)$ is constant. Experiment shows that it varies less than the previous quantity, but is by no means constant (Scheffer and de Wijs, 1925). At $298 \cdot 16°K$, it is found that

$$\frac{p\text{(mm)}}{c_W(1-\alpha)} = 12 \cdot 9[1 + 0 \cdot 046\, c_W(1-\alpha)]$$

or, if we use the ideal gas laws,

$$\frac{c_g}{c_W(1-\alpha)} = \frac{12 \cdot 9}{RT}[1 + 0 \cdot 046\, c_W(1-\alpha)] \qquad \text{XIV.16}$$

The distribution law in this form is obeyed up to concentrations of $1 \cdot 6$ moles per litre. On comparing with the theoretical relation

$$\frac{c_g}{c_W(1-\alpha)} = K_1 + \frac{2K_1^2}{K_2}\, c_W(1-\alpha) \qquad \text{XIV.17}$$

we find that K_1 is $6 \cdot 94 \times 10^{-7}$ and K_2 is $3 \cdot 02 \times 10^{-5}$ gram-moles/litre. Clearly the dimerisation constant, at any concentration, lies near to the ionisation constant K_i (Table XII.2), which suggests that the two processes may be closely related to each other and that one of the ions, instead of being completely hydrated, is directly attached to one

415

molecule of ammonia. The conventional way of writing the equilibria

$$NH_3 + H_2O \rightleftarrows NH_4^+ + OH^-; \quad K_i,$$

$$NH_3 + NH_3 \rightleftarrows (NH_3)_2; \quad K_2$$

should, therefore, be replaced by the equations

$$NH_3 + nH_2O \rightleftarrows NH_4^+, mH_2O + OH^-, (n-m-1)H_2O \quad K_i,$$

$$NH_3 + NH_3 + (n-1)H_2O \rightleftarrows NH_4^+, (m-1)H_2O, NH_3$$
$$+ OH^-, (n-m-1)H_2O; \quad K_2$$

Both ionisation and dimerisation can then be regarded as proton transfers, the proton being provided by a water molecule in the first case and by an ammonia molecule in the second. In strong aqueous ammonia, we would expect the hydroxyl and the ammonium ions to contain ammonia of solvation as well as water of solvation. Such complex ions as we are here discussing are best known in ammoniacal solutions of salts, such as those of copper, in which the stable cation is $[Cu(NH_3)_4]^{++}$.

Heterogeneous equilibria involving metals and electrolytes; the galvanic cell

A simple galvanic cell may be formed by the appropriate arrangement of a rod of metallic zinc, dipping in an aqueous solution of one of its salts (say zinc sulphate), and a rod of metallic copper, dipping in an aqueous solution of one of its salts (say cupric sulphate). If the two solutions are connected by means of any conducting solution, and the two metals by means of any conducting wire (see Fig. XIV.15), a current is found to flow through the system, attended by either the dissolution of some zinc and the deposition of some copper, or by the dissolution of some copper and the deposition of some zinc. When the circuit is completed in this haphazard fashion, the current quickly diminishes and the electrode solutions irreversibly mix. If, however, the electromotive force responsible for the current is opposed by an external electromotive force, the flow of electricity can be stopped. The magnitude of this external e.m.f. is the e.m.f. of the cell, which can now be made to work reversibly. When the applied e.m.f. slightly exceeds that of the cell, the current flows and chemical change occurs in a given direction; when the applied e.m.f. is made slightly smaller

416

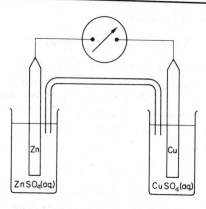

Fig. XIV.15   *The principle of the construction of a simple galvanic cell*

than that of the cell, the current flows and chemical change occurs in the opposite direction. If this slight reversal on either side of the balance point of the potentiometer bridge could be made any number of times without causing any change in the cell, the conditions would be precisely those required in a reversible process, like the melting or boiling of a pure compound without chemical decomposition, at a constant pressure. In practice, however, the conditions are not quite ideal, because the solutes in the two principal components of the cell diffuse irreversibly, into the liquid used as a bridge, or, if no bridge is used, into each other. It is known from independent experiments that the rate of diffusion in aqueous solution is slow in comparison with the time required to obtain reproducible measurements of the electromotive force. When the bridge consists of a concentrated aqueous solution of a salt which, while not reacting chemically with either solution, has an anion in common with both, the computation of the junction potential is simplified. It is advantageous in choosing a bridge electrolyte, to select a salt like potassium chloride or ammonium nitrate, the aqueous ions of which have nearly the same mobility. In the cell under consideration, we can dispense with a junction liquid, and fill the connecting tube with the solution of the same composition as one of the electrode compartments. The cell is qualitatively described by the symbols:

$$Zn \mid ZnSO_4(aq) \vdots CuSO_4(aq) \mid Cu$$

or, since the anion plays no role,

$$\text{Zn} \mid \text{Zn}^{++}(\text{aq}) \vdots \text{Cu}^{++}(\text{aq}) \mid \text{Cu}$$

A complete specification of the cell includes its temperature, the external pressure and the composition of the two solutions. The chemical change attending the passage of positive electricity, through the cell, from left to right, is determined as follows. In the left compartment, metallic zinc is converted into dissolved ions – a change which can be represented as:

$$\text{Zn} \rightarrow \text{Zn}^{++} + 2\ominus$$

where the symbol $\ominus$ stands for an electron. In the right compartment, positive electricity is transported in the same direction by the process:

$$\text{Cu}^{++} + 2\ominus \rightarrow \text{Cu}$$

On adding, the net chemical change is

$$\text{Zn} + \text{Cu}^{++} \rightarrow \text{Zn}^{++} + \text{Cu} \qquad \text{xiv.18}$$

In words, when two faradays of positive electricity are passed through the cell, from left to right, one gram-atom of metallic zinc and one gram-ion of ionic copper in solution of some arbitrary concentration are converted into one gram-atom of metallic copper and one gram-ion of ionic zinc at another arbitrary concentration. We now apply the law

$$\sum \mu_i = \sum \mu \qquad \text{vi.39}$$

to determine the equilibria involved between reactants and resultants in all the homogeneous phases, and the law

$$\mu_i(\text{phase A}) = \mu_i(\text{phase B}) \qquad \text{vi.40}$$

to determine all the heterogeneous equilibria established in the cell, and, omitting the detailed steps, obtain the fundamental equation of reversible galvanic cells:

$$\sum \mu = -z\varepsilon E \qquad \text{xiv.19}$$

The term on the left represents the increase in free energy of the system when z units of positive electricity are carried through the cell from left to right, corresponding, in this example, to the chemical change $\text{Zn} + \text{Cu}^{++} \rightarrow \text{Zn}^{++} + \text{Cu}$. The term on the right represents the electrical work which must be performed by external agency in driving z

units of positive electricity from right to left above the water line, and this also is the gain in free energy of the system. The notation adopted in molar units is

$$\Delta G = -zE\mathfrak{F} \qquad \text{XIV.20}$$

It is to be observed that no superscript is needed.

The electrochemical determination of thermal equilibria

The special forms assumed by these basic equations when each of the cell reactants is in its reference state are

$$\sum \mu^0 = -z\varepsilon E^0 \quad \text{and} \quad \Delta G^0 = -z\mathfrak{F}E^0 \qquad \text{XIV.21}$$

The particular value, E^0, of the electromotive force of the cell when each of its reactants is in its reference state is termed the standard e.m.f. of the cell. We have seen that

$$\sum \mu^0 = -kT \ln K \quad \text{or} \quad \Delta G^0 = -RT \ln K \qquad \text{XIII.16}$$

Hence

$$E^0 = \frac{kT}{z\varepsilon} \ln K \quad \text{or} \quad E^0 = \frac{RT}{z\mathfrak{F}} \ln K \qquad \text{XIV.22}$$

The measurement of the standard electromotive force of a cell thus yields immediately the value of the equilibrium constant for the reaction occurring in it. By combining equations XIV.19 and XIV.21, we obtain the following general expression for the e.m.f. of a reversible cell:

$$E = E^0 - \frac{1}{z\varepsilon} \sum (\mu - \mu^0) \qquad \text{XIV.23}$$

As an example, we shall describe the electrometric evaluation of the equilibrium constant for the gaseous reaction:

$$H_2 + Cl_2 \rightleftarrows 2HCl$$

which can be made to take place in the cell

$$H_2(gas) \mid HCl(aqueous) \mid Cl_2(gas)$$

using inert electrodes of platinum or of a platinum-iridium alloy. When two units of positive electricity are passed through the cell from left to right, the electrode processes are, respectively, $H_2 \rightarrow 2H^+ + 2\ominus$ on the

419

left, and $Cl_2 \rightarrow 2Cl^- - 2\ominus$ on the right, which add up to the chemical reaction $H_2(gas) + Cl_2(gas) \rightarrow 2HCl(aqueous)$. The aqueous hydrogen chloride, however, is in equilibrium with gaseous hydrogen chloride above the solution; its chemical potential must therefore be the same in the two phases. The external electrical work done on the system is consequently a direct measure of the gain in free energy attending the gaseous reaction. We may regard each gas as obeying the ideal laws, and thus use the familiar expression

$$\mu_i = \mu_i^0 + kT \ln p_i$$

to express the chemical potential of each. Equation XIV.23 now becomes

$$E = E^0 - \frac{1}{z\varepsilon}\sum(\mu - \mu^0)$$

$$= \frac{kT}{z\varepsilon}\ln K - \frac{kT}{z\varepsilon}\ln\left(\frac{p_{HCl}^2}{p_{H_2} \cdot p_{Cl_2}}\right)$$

With $z = 2$ and $T = 303\cdot1°K$, this equation can be written in the form:

$$\log_{10}K = 33\cdot3E(\text{volts}) + \log_{10}\left(\frac{p_{HCl}^2}{p_{H_2} \cdot p_{Cl_2}}\right) \qquad \text{XIV.24}$$

Values of $\log_{10} K$ thus calculated by Bodenstein and Geiger (1904) from the electromotive data of Dolezalek (1898) are seen, from Table XIV.2, to be sensibly constant during a thousand-fold change in the partial pressure of hydrogen chloride.

Table XIV.2 *Equilibrium constants for the gaseous reaction* $H_2 + Cl_2 \rightleftarrows 2HCl$ *from electromotive force data at* $303\cdot1°K$

p_{HCl} (mm)	$p_{H_2} = p_{Cl_2}$ (mm)	E(volts)	$\log_{10} K$
0·24	750	1·190	32·58
0·69	750	1·147	32·25
134	621	1·005	32·26
189	566	0·999	32·36
313	442	0·981	32·41
337	415	0·974	32·33
			Av. = 32·37

The variation of electromotive force with respect to temperature

On applying the Kelvin-Helmholtz operation to equation XIV.20 we obtain the Gibbs-Helmholtz equation

$$\Delta H = -zE\mathfrak{F} + z\mathfrak{F}T\left(\frac{dE}{dT}\right)_P \qquad \text{XIV.25}$$

Hence the temperature coefficient of the electromotive force may be at once determined when E at a given temperature and the absorption, ΔH, of heat are known. This relation has usually been verified by measuring $(dE/dT)_P$ directly, and by comparing the computed increase in heat content with that measured calorimetrically. Some typical results are given in Table XIV.3, the first three entries of which refer to a temperature of 273·1°K, and the remaining values to 298·1°K.

Table XIV.3 *Application of the Gibbs-Helmholtz relation to certain reversible cell reaction* (*energies in kilocal per gram-mole*)

Cell and reaction	E(volts)	$(dE/dT)_P \times 10^4$ (volt/degree)	$zE\mathfrak{F}$	$zT\mathfrak{F}\left(\frac{dE}{dT}\right)_P$	ΔH (calc.)	ΔH (obs.)
Ag, AgCl, ZnCl$_2$, 50H$_2$O, Zn 2Ag + ZnCl$_2$ → 2AgCl + Zn	1·0171	−2·1	46·89	−2·65	−49·54	−49·08
Ag, AgBr, ZnBr$_2$, 25H$_2$O, Zn 2Ag + ZnBr$_2$ → AgCl + Zn	0·84095	−1·06	38·77	−1·34	−40·11	−39·94
Zn, ZnSO$_4$molten, CuSO$_4$molten, Cu Zn + CuSO$_4$ → Cu + ZnSO$_4$	1·0934	−4·3	50·40	−5·52	−55·92	−55·20
Pb, PbCl$_2$, HCl$_{aq}$, AgCl, Ag Pb + 2AgCl → PbCl$_2$ + 2Ag	0·4900	−1·86	22·61	−2·56	−25·17	−24·17
Pb, PbI$_2$, KI$_{aq}$, AgI, Ag Pb + 2AgI → PbI$_2$ + 2Ag	0·2135	−1·73	9·85	−2·38	−12·23	−12·20
Ag, AgCl, HCl$_{aq}$, Hg$_2$Cl$_2$, Hg Ag + (1/2)Hg$_2$Cl$_2$ → AgCl + Hg	0·0455	+3·38	1·05	+2·33	+1·28	+1·90

Standard electrode potentials

It is clear from equation XIV.22 that the electromotive force of a complete cell can be regarded as the algebraic sum of the potential differences between each electrode and the solution with which it is in equilibrium. Although single electrodes are not encountered in practice, it is convenient to treat them as separate entities. Let us, therefore, consider the half-element represented by the scheme:

$$Ag(metal) \,\big|\, Ag^+(aqueous) + NO_3^-(aqueous)$$

$$\psi_m \qquad\qquad \psi_s$$

where ψ denotes the electric potential.

Atoms of silver in the metal are at equilibrium with electrons and silver ions in the metal, and the latter must also be in equilibrium with silver ions in solution. At a constant temperature and pressure, we thus have:

$$\mu(Ag \text{ metal}) = \mu(Ag^+ \text{ in the metal}) + \mu(\text{electrons in the metal})$$

and

$$\mu(Ag^+ \text{ in the metal}) = \mu(Ag^+ \text{ in solution})$$

The chemical potential of the ions in solution may be resolved into components arising from their internal energy, their electrostatic energy, and the energy due to thermal motion as modified by the presence of other ions. Then

$$\mu(Ag^+ \text{ in solution}) = \mu^0(Ag^+ \text{ in solution}) + \psi_s\varepsilon + kT \ln a_{Ag^+}$$

The chemical potential of the electrons in the metal may, as usual, be expressed as the sum

$$\mu(\text{electrons in metal}) = \mu^0(\text{electrons}) - \psi_m\varepsilon$$

On adding and rearranging, we find

$$(\psi_m - \psi_s)\varepsilon = \sum\mu^0 + kT \ln a_{Ag^+} \qquad\qquad \text{XIV.26}$$

where

$$\sum\mu^0 = \mu^0(Ag^+ \text{ in solution}) + \mu^0(\text{electrons}) - \mu(\text{metal})$$

corresponding to the standard increase in chemical potential attending the change

$$Ag(metal) \rightarrow Ag^+(\text{ions in solution}) + \ominus(\text{reference state}) \quad \text{XIV.27}$$

which occurs when one protonic charge is passed from the metal to the solution. The potential, E, of a single electrode is conventionally taken as a measure of the natural tendency of positive electricity to flow from it to the solution, that is

$$E = \psi_m - \psi_s \qquad\qquad \text{XIV.28}$$

Equation XIV.26, therefore, becomes

$$E\varepsilon = \sum\mu^0 + kT\ln a_{Ag^+} \qquad \text{XIV.29}$$

The standard electrode potential is defined as the value of E when the activity, a, reckoned on a molality basis, is unity, i.e.

$$E^0\varepsilon = \sum\mu^0 \qquad \text{XIV.30}$$

Then

$$E = E^0 + (kT/\varepsilon)\ln a_{Ag^+}$$

or, generally, for an ion of valency, z,

$$E = E^0 + (kT/z\varepsilon)\ln a \qquad \text{XIV.31}$$

Table XIV.4 *Relative electrode potentials in aqueous solutions at 298·1°K and 1 atmosphere*

Electrode	Reaction	Potential (volts)
$H_2(g)$, H^+	$\frac{1}{2}H_2 \to H^+ + \ominus$	0
Li, Li^+	$Li \to Li^+ + \ominus$	$-3\cdot024$
Na, Na^+	$Na \to Na^+ + \ominus$	$-2\cdot7139$
K, K^+	$K \to K^+ + \ominus$	$-2\cdot9239$
Rb, Rb^+	$Rb \to Rb^+ + \ominus$	$-2\cdot924$
Cs, Cs^+	$Cs \to Cs^+ + \ominus$	$-3\cdot02$
Cu, Cu^{++}	$Cu \to Cu^{++} + 2\ominus$	$+0\cdot339$
Ag, Ag^+	$Ag \to Ag^+ + \ominus$	$+0\cdot7995$
Zn, Zn^{++}	$Zn \to Zn^{++} + 2\ominus$	$-0\cdot7611$
Cd, Cd^{++}	$Cd \to Cd^{++} + 2\ominus$	$-0\cdot4019$
Hg, Hg^{++}	$Hg \to \frac{1}{2}Hg^{++} + \ominus$	$+0\cdot7986$
Tl, Tl^+	$Tl \to Tl^+ + \ominus$	$-0\cdot3385$
Sn, Sn^{++}	$Sn \to Sn^{++} + 2\ominus$	$-0\cdot140$
Pb, Pb^{++}	$Pb \to Pb^{++} + 2\ominus$	$-0\cdot126$
Fe, Fe^{++}	$Fe \to Fe^{++} + 2\ominus$	$-0\cdot441$
Co, Co^{++}	$Co \to Co^{++} + 2\ominus$	$-0\cdot283$
Ni, Ni^{++}	$Ni \to Ni^{++} + 2\ominus$	$-0\cdot236$
$Cl_2(g)$, Cl^-	$Cl^- \to \frac{1}{2}Cl_2(g) + \ominus$	$+1\cdot3585$
$Br_2(l)$, Br^-	$Br^- \to \frac{1}{2}Br_2(l) + \ominus$	$+1\cdot066$
$I_2(cr)$, I^-	$I^- \to \frac{1}{2}I_2(cr) + \ominus$	$+0\cdot5345$
Ag, AgCl(cr), Cl^-	$Ag + Cl^- \to AgCl(cr) + \ominus$	$+0\cdot2225$
Ag, AgBr(cr) Br^-	$Ag + Br^- \to AgBr(cr) + \ominus$	$+0\cdot0711$
Ag, AgI(cr), I^-	$Ag + I^- \to AgI(cr) + \ominus$	$-0\cdot1522$
Hg, Hg_2Cl_2(cr), Cl^-	$Hg + Cl^- \to \frac{1}{2}Hg_2Cl_2(cr) + \ominus$	$+0\cdot2681$
Hg, Hg_2SO_4(cr), SO_4^{--}	$2Hg + SO_4^{--} \to Hg_2SO_4(cr) + 2\ominus$	$+0\cdot6141$

Because all the terms in $\Sigma\mu^0$ are not known, it is not possible to evaluate the standard potential of any element absolutely. We are content with comparative values, based on the convention that the standard potential of the hydrogen electrode is zero at all temperatures. Some accepted values are given in Table XIV.4. E^0 as defined here is a measure of the tendency of the electrode to emit positive ions into solution. The high negative electrode potentials of the alkali metals confirm the violence of their interaction with aqueous solutions. If we were to join the standard lithium half-element on the left with the standard hydrogen half-element on the right, positive electricity would flow from right to left in the metals, and from left to right in the cell, i.e. $\varepsilon \rightarrow$ Li. Iron, for example, displaces cobalt, and cobalt displaces nickel. At 298.1°K, kT/ε is $1.3803 \times 10^{-16} \times 298.16/4.802 \times 10^{-10}$ e.s.u. Since one e.s.u. of potential is 299.79 volts, and $\ln x$ is $2.3026 \log_{10} x$, we have at this temperature,

$$E(\text{volts}) = E^0 + \frac{0.05916}{z} \log_{10} a \qquad \text{XIV.32}$$

Concentration cells

Let us consider a galvanic cell formed from two half-elements which differ only in the concentrations of the ion with respect to which the electrodes are reversible, such as $Ag(cr) \vdots AgNO_3(aq., 0.1 \text{ molar}) \vdots AgNO_3(aq., 0.01 \text{ molar}) \vdots Ag(cr)$. According to equation XIV.31, the e.m.f. of the cell, assuming the liquid junction potential to be eliminated, is simply

$$E = E_1 - E_2 = \frac{kT}{z\varepsilon} \ln \frac{a_1}{a_2}$$

where the a's are the activities of the silver ion in the two half-elements. We can resolve E into components ascribable to the concentrations, c, and the activity coefficients, γ, thus

$$E = \frac{kT}{z\varepsilon} \ln \frac{c_1}{c_2} + \frac{kT}{z\varepsilon} \ln \frac{\gamma_1}{\gamma_2} \qquad \text{XIV.33}$$

We shall see (Table XIV.5) that the first component is the dominant one. The e.m.f. depends principally on the ratio of the ionic concentrations and only to a secondary extent on their absolute values. For that reason, cells of this type are referred to as concentration cells.

Ignoring the second term, and inserting appropriate numerical constants, we see that

$$E_{298 \cdot 16}(\text{millivolts}) = \frac{59 \cdot 16}{z} \log_{10} \frac{c_1}{c_2} \qquad \text{XIV.34}$$

According to this equation, the cell described above should have the same e.m.f. as one in which the compartments contained 0·001 and 0·0001 moles per litre. Experiments show that this is not quite true; and the second term in equation XIV.33 is one way of recording the difference. The greater the difference between the concentrations in the two compartments, the greater is the e.m.f. of the cell. This fact makes equation XIV.33 a very useful one in many ways. Suppose, for example, we have in one compartment 0·1 mole of $AgNO_3$ per litre, and in the other a very small concentration of silver ions, as in an argenti-cyanide solution. The cell would give a high e.m.f., and would enable the small concentration to be measured exactly. Solubilities of sparingly soluble salts can thus be accurately measured electro-metrically. Suppose, in the second place, that we worked with two electrodes which are reversible with respect to hydrogen ions, and that one half-element contained 0·01 molar HCl and the other 0·01 molar NaOH. On account of the very low concentration of hydrogen ion in the alkaline solution, the cell gives a large e.m.f., and since the concentration of hydroxyl ion is effectively 0·01, the ionic product of water can be accurately measured. Finally, let the concentration cell contain solutions of known concentrations of a salt of an unknown valency type. Equation XIV.34 allows us to evaluate z. In this way, the electrovalency of the mercurous ion was shown to be 2.

The negative of the decadic logarithm of the hydrogen ion concentration (in moles per litre of solution) is defined as the pH of the solution (Sörensen). From equation XIV.34, we thus have

$$E_{298 \cdot 16}(\text{millivolts}) = 59 \cdot 16(\text{pH}_2 - \text{pH}_1)$$

The electrometric determination of activity coefficients

Let us consider the cell

$$\text{Ag} \mid \text{AgCl, KCl}(c_1) \mid \text{K}_x\text{Hg} \mid \text{KCl}(c_2), \text{AgCl} \mid \text{Ag}$$

which is seen to consist of two silver electrodes, each dipping into a solution of potassium chloride which is saturated with silver chloride.

The two half-elements are joined by an amalgam of potassium. By again applying equations VI.39 and VI.40 to all the homogeneous and heterogeneous equilibria in the system, the electromotive force of the cell is found to be

$$E = E_1 - E_2$$
$$= \mu(KCl, c_1) - \mu(KCl, c_2)$$

or, if we write

$$\mu(KCl) = \mu^0(KCl) + kT \ln a_{KCl}$$

$$E = \frac{kT}{\varepsilon} \ln \left(\frac{a_1}{a_2}\right) \qquad \qquad \text{XIV.35}$$

where a_{KCl} is the activity of the dissolved salt and a is the mean ionic activity of its constituents. This rather elaborate experimental arrangement thus leads to a very simple expression for the electromotive force which, at a given temperature, depends solely on the activities, or corrected concentrations, of the salt in the two compartments. The explanation may be found by examining in detail the steps attending the passage of positive electricity through the cell from left to right. The first step is the conversion of metallic silver in cell 1 into silver ions in this cell:

$$Ag(1) \rightarrow Ag^+(1) + \ominus$$

As the solution is already saturated with silver chloride, the new silver ions brought to it combine with chlorine ions, and crystalline silver chloride is precipitated:

$$Ag^+(1) + Cl^-(1) \rightarrow AgCl(1)$$

This step leaves the solution with extra positive ions, K^+, which carry the current by being converted into ions in the amalgam:

$$K^+(1) \rightarrow K^+(amalgam)$$

Other potassium ions are ejected from the amalgam into cell 2:

$$K^+(amalgam) \rightarrow K^+(2)$$

These new entrants stand in need of partners, the only means of providing which is for crystalline silver chloride to dissolve:

$$AgCl(2) \rightarrow Ag^+(2) + Cl^-(2)$$

The final step in the passage of electricity is the discharging and deposition of the resulting silver ions on to the right-hand electrode:

$$\ominus + Ag^+(2) \to Ag(2)$$

On adding the equations, the total physicochemical change attending the passage of one unit of positive electricity through the two opposing cells is found to be

$$Ag(1) + Cl^-(1) + K^+(1) + AgCl(2) \to Ag(2) + Cl^-(2) + K^+(2) + AgCl(1)$$

which represents the removal of one atom of silver and one ion of each type in solution from cell 1 to cell 2, and the removal of one ion of each type in the solid from the second cell to the first. The states of the two solids are independent of the cells which they occupy, so that the free energy expended is that required to transfer one dissolved ion of each type from cell 1 to cell 2, though, in fact, no salt has passed the boundary. For this reason, this type of cell is referred to as a concentration cell without transference. It provides, in principle, a direct means of measuring the relative activities of electrolytes. Technical difficulties with fluid amalgams are, however, so great, that the electrometric measurement of salt activities is usually made in cells with transference, such as the following:

$$Ag \,|\, AgCl, HCl(c_1) \vdots HCl(c_2), AgCl \,|\, Ag$$

The electromotive force of such a cell, if the liquid-liquid junction could be eliminated, would be $(kT/\varepsilon) \ln (a_1/a_2)$ where a now stands for the activity of the dissolved hydrogen chloride.

It can readily be shown that the potential difference at the junction in this cell is

$$E_J = \frac{kT}{\varepsilon} \left(\frac{u-v}{u+v} \right) \ln \frac{a_1}{a_2} \qquad \text{XIV.36}$$

where u and v are, respectively, the mobilities of the cation and the anion. Addition gives us, for the total e.m.f. of the cell:

$$E = \frac{kT}{\varepsilon} \left(\frac{2u}{u+v} \right) \ln \frac{a_1}{a_2}$$

$$= \frac{kT}{\varepsilon} 2t_+ \ln \frac{a_1}{a_2} \qquad \text{XIV.37}$$

where t_+ is the transport number of the cation. On inserting numerical

427

values appropriate to a temperature of 298·1°K, and on making use of the definition of the activity coefficient, γ, we have

$$E(\text{volts}) = 0\cdot1184t_+ \log\frac{c_1}{c_2} + 0\cdot1184t_+ \log\frac{\gamma_1}{\gamma_2} \qquad \text{XIV.38}$$

The experimental values of McInnes (1939) for the cationic transport number and the electromotive force of this cell, when c_1 is kept constant at 0·1 mole per litre, are shown in columns 2 and 3 of Table XIV.5. The fourth column gives the ideal electromotive force which such a cell would have if the activity coefficients were unity, as calculated by the equation which heads the column. It is from the difference (column 5) between the observed and the ideal potentials that the activity coefficients are derived. On plotting the values of $\log_{10}(\gamma_2/\gamma_1)$ obtained from these differences against the square-root of the variable concentration, c_2, it is found that at low concentrations,

$$\log_{10}(\gamma_2/\gamma_1) = 0\cdot0835 - 0\cdot3175\sqrt{c_2} \qquad \text{XIV.39}$$

Table XIV.5 *Mean ionic activity coefficients of hydrogen chloride in water at 298·1°K, from potentials of the cell*

Ag|AgCl, HCl($c_1 = 0\cdot1$ molar, constant)| HCl(c_2, variable), AgCl|Ag

c_2 (moles/litre)	t_+	E(observed)	$\frac{kT}{\varepsilon}t_+ \ln\frac{c_1}{c_2}$	Difference	$\log_{10}(\gamma_2/\gamma_1)$	γ_2
			(Millivots)			
0	—	—	—	—	0·0835	1·0000
0·0034468	0·8234	136·264	142·57	6·31	0·06473	0·9577
0·0052590	0·8239	118·815	124·77	5·96	0·06109	0·9497
0·010017	0·8251	92·529	97·63	5·10	0·05220	0·9305
0·010029	0·8251	92·480	97·57	5·09	0·05210	0·9303
0·019914	0·8266	64·730	68·58	3·85	0·03934	0·9033
0·020037	0·8266	64·464	68·34	3·88	0·03965	0·9038
0·020132	0·8266	64·282	68·13	3·85	0·03934	0·8826
0·040492	0·8286	36·214	38·51	2·30	0·02345	0·8708
0·059826	0·8297	20·600	21·92	1·32	0·01344	0·8509
0·078076	0·8306	9·948	10·57	0·62	0·00630$_5$	0·8371
0·100000	0·8314	0	0	0	0	0·8250

Now by definition, when c_2 is zero, γ_2 is unity; hence $\log_{10} \gamma_1 = -0.0835$, and consequently $\gamma_1 = 0.825$. The evaluation of the activity coefficients at the various concentrations, c_2, is now simple:

$$\log_{10} \gamma_2 = -0.3175\sqrt{c_2} \qquad \text{XIV.40}$$

The results are given in the last column of Table XIV.5.

The vapour pressure of spherical particles

The general condition of equilibrium (equation VI.44) in a system which is free from gravitational and electrical forces, and which is maintained at a constant temperature, T, and a constant total pressure, P, is

$$dG_{T,P} = \sum \mu_i \, dN_i + \sum \gamma \, dO = 0$$

where the first summation is to be taken over all the components in all the phases, and the second summation over all the interfaces. Let us apply this condition to a system containing one component in two phases, for example, the vapour phase, which may be denoted by the subscript G, and the liquid or solid phase, which may be denoted by the subscript L.

There is now only one interface, so that

$$dG_{T,P} = \mu_G \, dN_G + \mu_L \, dN_L + \gamma \, dO = 0$$

In closed systems, such as are usually studied, the total number of molecules is kept constant, so that $dN_G + dN_L = 0$. Hence

$$\mu_G = \mu_L + \gamma \left(\frac{dO}{dN_L} \right)_{T,P} \qquad \text{XIV.41}$$

Let us now suppose that the vapour phase is continuous, and that the liquid phase is uniformly dispersed into M identical spheres, of radius r each. The total area, O, of the interface, and the total volume of the (dispersed) liquid phase are consequently

$$O = M \cdot 4\pi r^2; \qquad N_L v_L = M(4/3)\pi r^3 \qquad \text{XIV.42}$$

where v_L is the molecular volume of the liquid. This we shall take as being the same in the spheres as in an undispersed sample of the liquid

429

at the same temperature and pressure. The general relationship between the total interfacial area, O, and the total number, N_L, of molecules in the dispersed phase is thus

$$O = 3N_L v_L/r \qquad \text{XIV.43}$$

It is to be observed that N_L and r are independent variables, i.e. the interfacial area can be altered by changing the number of liquid molecules in the system, without changing the radius of the spheres; it can also be altered by changing the radius without changing the number of molecules in the liquid phase. Hence

$$dO = \left(\frac{\partial O}{\partial N_L}\right)_r dN_L + \left(\frac{\partial O}{\partial r}\right)_{N_L} dr$$

and

$$\frac{dO}{dN_L} = \left(\frac{\partial O}{\partial N_L}\right)_r + \left(\frac{\partial O}{\partial r}\right)_{N_L} \frac{dr}{dN_L}$$

On using equation XIV.43, we have

$$\frac{dO}{dN_L} = \frac{3v_L}{r} - \frac{3N_L v_L}{r^2} \frac{dr}{dN_L}$$

By means of equation XIV.42, we have $dN_L/dr = (M/v_L)4\pi r^2 = 3N_L/r$. Hence

$$\frac{dO}{dN_L} = \frac{3v_L}{r} - \frac{v_L}{r} = \frac{2v_L}{r} \qquad \text{XIV.44}$$

It follows that

$$\mu_G = \mu_L + 2\gamma v_L/r \qquad \text{XIV.45}$$

When the vapour is sufficiently dilute to justify our adopting the ideal gas laws, we have

$$\mu_G = \mu_L + kT \ln (p/p^0) \qquad \text{XI.3}$$

where p^0 is the ordinary saturation pressure of the liquid. Hence

$$kT \ln (p/p^0) = 2\gamma v_L/r$$

or

$$p/p^0 = e^{2\gamma v_L/rkT} \qquad \text{XIV.46}$$

430

The equilibrium pressure of the system, i.e. the vapour pressure of the spherical particles, thus decreases as their radii are increased, and becomes equal to the ordinary saturation pressure when the radius of curvature is infinite, i.e. when the interface is planar. Table XIV.6 shows to what extent the vapour pressure of liquid droplets, of radius 100 Å, exceeds that of the bulk liquid. The hazards attending work with toxic liquids are thus greatly enhanced when they are present in the form of small drops.

Table XIV.6 *The vapour pressure of liquid spheres of radius 10^{-6} cm at 298·1°K*

Liquid	γ(dynes/cm)	$v_L \times 10^{23}$(cc/molecule)	p/p^0
Hg	460·6	2.44478	1·735
H_2O	69·85	2·9801	1·108
CCl_4	25·02	16·013	1·216

In the derivation given here, it was necessary to assume that all the spherical droplets had identical radii, and exerted no influence on one another, except the indirect one via the vapour phase. Neither nature nor artifice produces a uniform dispersion; real dispersed systems contain particles of various sizes. Since the vapour pressure of small spheres is greater than that of large ones, the latter grow at the expense of the former. The gravitational field, here omitted, also plays its part, and the problem becomes a complicated one.

The derivation given here applies to a single sphere at equilibrium with its own vapour; and it is in this form that Kelvin's law (1881) has been experimentally verified.

Bubbles in a liquid

Let us now regard the liquid phase as the continuous one, and the vapour phase as being uniformly dispersed in it, in the form of spherical bubbles. On retracing the argument, we find that, if equilibrium is to be established at a constant total pressure,

$$kT \ln (p/p^0) = -2\gamma v_L/r \qquad \text{XIV.47}$$

In this case, the pressure within the cavity is less than the saturation

431

pressure over the plane surface of the liquid and the bubble, being in-trinsically unstable, tends to collapse. If it survives its ascent through the liquid, and its arrival at the surface is aided by a capillary of suitable bore, it will retain the lower half of its form. (Döring, 1937.) The energy required to form a spherical cavity of radius r in a liquid of surface tension γ, is $4\pi r^2 \gamma$, which should equal the heat of vapori-sation. The concentration of holes in a liquid should consequently decrease as the temperature is raised, in accordance with the observed decrease in its density. Statistical theories of liquids as solutions of holes in matter have been developed for holes of uniform size (Fürth, 1941) and for holes of varying sizes (Altar, Eyring, 1936).

The solubility of finely divided solids

The condition of equilibrium between saturated vapour and spherical droplets of liquid, given by equation XIV.45, may be directly applied to the equilibrium between saturated solution and spherical crystals of solid. We then have

$$\mu_{sat.\,soln.} = \mu_{cr.} + 2\gamma c_{cr.}/r \qquad \text{XIV.48}$$

But, in dilute solutions, without dissociation or polymerisation, we have

$$\mu_{sat.\,soln.} = \mu^0 + kT\ln s \qquad \text{XIV.49}$$

where s is the saturation concentration of solid, and μ^0 is the chemical potential of the solute in a solution of unit concentration. Then

$$kT\ln s = (\mu_{cr.} - \mu^0) + 2\gamma v_{cr.}/r \qquad \text{XIV.50}$$

The term in the brackets may be eliminated by using s_∞, the saturation solubility for crystals of infinite radius. Then

$$kT\ln (s/s_\infty) = 2\gamma v_{cr.}/r \qquad \text{XIV.51}$$

The more finely divided the solid, the greater is its solubility. The result which is the analogue of Kelvin's law (equation XIV.47) has been experimentally verified (Hulett, 1901), and used to measure the inter-facial tension between a crystal and its solvent.

Thermodynamic approach to the study of interfaces

The Gibbs free energy of a system containing N_1 molecules of the first type and N_2 molecules of the second type and a single interface

432

of area O is

$$G_{T,P} = N_1\mu_1 + N_2\mu_2 + \gamma O$$

Consequently

$$dG_{T,P} = N_1\,d\mu_1 + \mu_1\,dN_1 + N_2\,d\mu_2 + \mu_2\,dN_2 + \gamma\,dO + O\,d\gamma$$

But we have seen that

$$dG_{T,P} = \mu_1\,dN_1 + \mu_2\,dN_2 + \gamma\,dO \qquad\qquad \text{VI.44}$$

It follows that

$$N_1\,d\mu_1 + N_2\,d\mu_2 + O\,d\gamma = 0$$

or

$$d\gamma = -\Gamma_1\,d\mu_1 - \Gamma_2\,d\mu_2 \qquad\qquad \text{XIV.52}$$

where each Γ is a surface concentration, in molecules per cm^2. More strictly, it is, in the condensed system which we have in mind, the difference between the total number of molecules of a particular kind in the system and the number of molecules of that kind in the bulk phase, divided by the area, 0. In a dilute solution of species 2 in species 1, Γ_1 can be taken as zero, and we have left

$$d\gamma = -\Gamma_2\,d\mu_2$$

If, in the bulk phase, we adopt van't Hoff's equation

$$\mu_2 = \mu_2^0 + kT\ln n_2$$

it follows that

$$\Gamma_2 = -\frac{n_2}{kT}\frac{d\gamma}{dn_2} \qquad\qquad \text{XIV.53}$$

which is the adsorption isotherm of Gibbs, first verified experimentally by McC. Lewis and Donnan (1910). Nonylic acid, though but slightly soluble in water, dissolves sufficiently to allow a direct measurement of the rate of decrease of the surface tension of the solution with respect to its concentration, n_2. The number, Γ_2, of molecules of the acid per unit area of interface was measured by passing through the solution a stream of air bubbles, of known radius, r, at a sufficiently slow rate to allow equilibrium to be established at the interface before the bubbles escape from the solution. If N bubbles have passed during the experiment, the total surface area is $N(4\pi r^2)$. If

433

the initial concentration of the solution is n_2^0 molecules/cm^3, and its final concentration is n_2^∞, the decrease in the number of solute molecules in solution is $(n_2^0 - n_2^\infty)V$, where V is the volume of the solution, in cubic centimeters. The excess surface concentration is thus $(n_2^0 - n_2^\infty)V/N(4\pi r^2)$ minus n_2^∞. Within the limits of experimental error, both sides of equation XIV.53 were found to be equal. The numerical value of Γ_2 for nonylic acid at the water-air interface was found to be $4\cdot55 \times 10^{14}$ molecules/cm^2; hence, $1/\Gamma_2$ is 22×10^{-16} cm^2 per molecule. If the interface resembles in density the pure acid in its condensed state, for which the number of molecules per cm^3 is $n_L = 3\cdot35 \times 10^{21}$, the thickness, λ, of the film is $\Gamma_2/n_L = 13\cdot8 \times 10^{-8}$ cm, which lies near to the height of an unbranched chain of ten carbon atoms as estimated from the carbon-carbon internuclear distance, provided the atomic chain stands as erect as the tetrahedral valency angle permits. These early experiments show that, provided the interface consists chiefly of molecules of the relatively insoluble substrate, the thickness of the interface is the maximum length of the flexible substrate molecule – a conclusion which has since been confirmed by direct X-ray examination of the interface, and by other methods now to be described.

The direct experimental investigation of monolayers

Traube (1891) found that, with dilute aqueous solutions, the difference between the surface tension of pure water and that of the solution is proportional to the concentration, n_2, of solute in the aqueous phase:

$$\prod = \gamma^0 - \gamma = Kn_2 \qquad \text{XIV.54}$$

Here K is an empirical constant which is positive when the solute is not ionised, and negative when it is an electrolyte. With non-electrolytes, therefore, $\prod$ is a positive quantity, denoting the lateral pressure exerted by the film against a barrier which has the film on one side and a clean-water surface on the other side. On combining with equation XIV.53, it follows that, for dilute aqueous solutions of non-electrolytes,

$$\Gamma_2 = \prod/kT \qquad \text{XIV.55}$$

We shall denote a surface concentration henceforth by the symbol

n_σ rather than Γ. We thus have

$$\prod = n_\sigma kT \qquad \text{XIV.56}$$

which is the two-dimensional analogue of the ideal gas laws, $P = nkT$. We may also denote the average area per molecule by o; then

$$\prod o = kT \qquad \text{XIV.57}$$

corresponding to the gas equation $Pv = kT$. This interpretation of Traube's work on the surface tension of aqueous solutions was given by Langmuir (1917) in a publication which also described a simple film balance by which the surface pressure of films of insoluble substances can be measured directly. His film balance has been modified by later workers, and can be made sensitive to less than 0·01 dyne per centimetre. One form is shown in Fig. XIV.16.

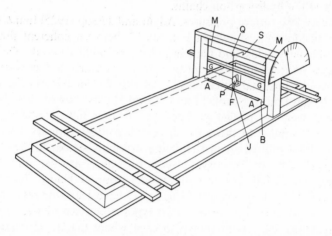

Fig. XIV.16 *The Langmuir trough* (after Adam, *The Physics and Chemistry of Surfaces*, 3rd edition, Oxford, 1941)

The liquid, often called the substrate, is contained in a long, shallow trough. On the flat tops of the sides slide 'barriers', usually of glass coated with paraffin wax: these control the area of the film-covered surface and are also used for sweeping the surface free from contamination before putting on the film. A light float AA divides the film-covered from a clean surface, the surface pressure Π, i.e. the force on the float per unit length, being measured by a torsion balance. Flexible threads close the gaps between the ends of the float and the

435

sides of the trough thus preventing leakage of the film, and permitting sufficient free movement to allow accurate measurement of the surface pressure.

Substances whose molecules contain long aliphatic chains, or other insoluble hydrocarbon in quantity, and at least one polar or water-soluble group, preferably at the end of the molecule, form films one molecule thick, often called 'monolayers'. These are most frequently coherent, liquids or solids in two dimensions, and in many cases the molecules are very closely packed with the long hydrocarbon chains perpendicular to the surface. Such films have given a great deal of information on the dimensions of organic molecules, which has been confirmed and extended by later X-ray diffraction measurements. The coherent films are held together by the lateral attraction between the film molecules, which increases with increasing length of the hydrocarbon chains.

At very low surface pressures, Adam and Jessop (1925) found transition phenomena, shown in Fig. XIV.17, between coherent films of insoluble fatty acids, and films in a state resembling two-dimensional gases or dilute solutions, approaching at extremely low pressures to the two-dimensional equation of state (XIV.55) for adsorbed films of soluble substances. Schofield and Rideal (1925) showed that the departures from the perfect gas state, in adsorbed films of soluble fatty acids, are similar to those for three-dimensional vapours, curves in which ΠO is plotted against Π_s being strikingly similar to the $PV - P$ curves of Amagat. The curves inset in Fig. XIV.17 are also similar, but correspond to temperatures of vapours near, or below, the critical point: and the $\Pi - O$ curves of Fig. XIV.17 have a striking resemblance to the $P - V$ curves for gases. Two types of surface phase, coherent and gaseous, have been shown to exist where the $\Pi - O$ curves are horizontal, just as liquid and vapour are both present when the $P - V$ curves are horizontal.

A wealth of fascinating information on monolayers and many other surface phenomena is to be found in monographs by Rideal (1930) and Adam (1941).

When derivatives of long chained saturated hydrocarbons form stable films on water, the polar groups, —COOH, —CONH$_2$, —COCH$_3$, form the bottom layer of the interface. Such an oriented array of polar molecules constitutes an electrical double layer, across which there exists an electrostatic potential, which has been directly measured (Frumkin, 1925; Shulman and Rideal, 1931).

436

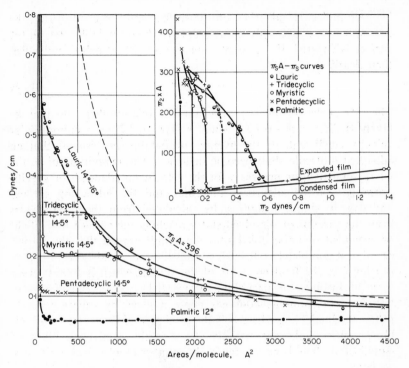

Fig. XIV.17 *Surfaces pressures of fatty acids as a function of the molecular areas* (after Adam, *Physical Chemistry*, Oxford, 1956)

A general equation of state for monolayers has been derived on statistical grounds by J. S. Mitchell (1935). When the dipolar axes are normal to the surface, the equation can be compared with experiment, yielding values of the dielectric constant of the film. This proves to be always lower than that of the bulk liquid or solid.

The kinetic treatment of interfaces: Langmuir's adsorption isotherm

Langmuir regarded the surface of a solid as providing N_s sites on which molecules from more attenuated, homogeneous phases may alight and adhere. In terms of intermolecular force theory, these sites are identified as positions of minimum energy which occur at regular intervals over the whole surface, reflecting, as it were, the internal regularity of the solid. When equilibrium has been established between molecules adsorbed on the surface and those still free in the homogeneous phase, only a fraction, θ, of the occupiable sites on the surface is covered. If N_a denotes the number of adsorbed molecules, then clearly

$$N_a = \theta N_s \qquad \qquad \text{XIV.58}$$

The rate of desorption is proportional to this number, and may be taken as $\theta N_s v \exp(-\psi/kT)$, where $v \exp(-\psi/kT)$ is a unimolecular velocity coefficient, or the average probability per second that an adsorbed molecule shall become detached. The magnitude of ψ, the energy of activation necessary for the detachment, depends on specific properties of the adsorbed molecules and the adsorbing surface, and can, in simple instances, be calculated from them. Molecules from the gaseous or dissolved states reaching the surface may alight on occupied or unoccupied sites. Langmuir argued that the former are almost completely reflected, so that the rate of adsorption is proportional to the fraction, $1-\theta$, of the surface which is free. If every molecule hitting a free part of the surface sticks to it, the rate of adsorption from the homogeneous gas phase is given by equation II.9 as $pO(1-\theta)/(2\pi mkT)^{1/2}$, where O is the total area of the surface, and p is the pressure of the gas, assumed to obey the ideal laws. Since, at equilibrium, there is no change in the number of adsorbed molecules, we have

$$dN_a/dt = pO(1-\theta)/(2\pi mkT)^{1/2} - N_s v \theta e^{-\psi/kT} = 0$$

or

$$\theta = \frac{p}{(N_s/O)(2\pi mkT)^{1/2} \, v e^{-\psi/kT} + p} \qquad \qquad \text{XIV.59}$$

which is Langmuir's adsorption isotherm. The number of molecules adsorbed per unit area of surface under equilibrium conditions is, therefore,

$$\frac{N_a}{O} = \frac{(N_s/O)p}{(N_s/O)(2\pi mkT)^{1/2} \, v e^{-\psi/kT} + p} \qquad \qquad \text{XIV.60}$$

At a constant temperature, the number of molecules adsorbed is proportional to the pressure, when the pressure is low, and is independent of the pressure when the pressure is high; the limiting value of N_a is N_s, i.e. the most that the crystal can do is to adsorb one molecule on each site. At a constant pressure, the extent of adsorption on a given surface decreases as the temperature is raised. These are the principal facts of the adsorption of gases and vapours by solids, as found, for example, when helium, argon, nitrogen, carbon monoxide, oxygen, carbon dioxide, ammonia, methane and ethylene are adsorbed by charcoal.

Let us apply equation XIV.60 to the data of Peters and Weil (1930) on the adsorption of krypton on the surface of a charcoal after prolonged heating at 400°C in a high vacuum (Table XIV.7). The values in

Table XIV.7 *The adsorption of krypton by charcoal at 193·5°K*

x = Amount of gas adsorbed, by 1 gram of C, expressed in cc of gas at 273·1°K and 1 atm	p (mm Hg)	$(N_a/O) \times 10^{-13}$ (molecules/cm²)
5·98	2·45	2·30
7·76	3·5	3·00
10·10	5·2	3·90
12·35	7·2	4·77
16·45	11·2	6·35
18·05	12·8	6·97
19·72	14·6	7·62
21·10	16·1	8·15

the last column have been obtained on the assumption that the specimen of charcoal employed exposed an area of 700 square metres per gram, which is probably an upper limit. The results are shown in the upper curve of Fig. XIV.18, which has the typical shape of normal adsorption. A better test of the theory is to invert equation XIV.60, writing

$$\frac{O}{N_a} = \frac{O}{N_s} + (2\pi mkT)^{1/2} \, ve^{-\psi/kT} \left(\frac{1}{p}\right) \qquad \text{XIV.61}$$

On plotting the area per adsorbed molecule against the reciprocal of the pressure, we then obtain, from the intercept, the area per site. From the coefficient of $(1/p)$ at two temperatures, we find $v = 1·08 \times 10^{10}$ sec^{-1}, and $\psi = 2\,230$ cals/mole. Later work has concentrated on the simpler surfaces presented by ionic crystals. It is in such systems that Langmuir's hypothesis of a unimolecular film has been most directly confirmed. De Boer (1932), for example, found that the maximum amount of iodine adsorbed by the surface of barium chloride crystals

439

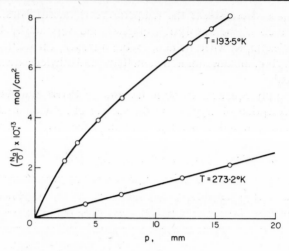

Fig. xiv.18   *The adsorption of krypton by charcoal*

corresponded to a film which was one atom thick, so that the iodine molecules lie flat on the surface, each presumably anchored on two sites. p-nitrophenol, on the other hand, seemed to occupy only one-half of the sites, i.e. the maximum number of molecules adsorbed was the same as the maximum number of iodine molecules. In this instance, the molecule may again be doubly anchored, through the two oxygen atoms of the nitro group.

Multi-layer adsorption

Fig. xiv.19, drawn from the data of Brunauer and Emmett, resembles a Langmuir isotherm at low pressures, but as the pressure is increased, the curve does not become horizontal, but passes through a point of inflexion, at which d^2V/dp^2 is zero. From the amount of gas adsorbed at 800 mm, it is found that two atoms of gas have been adsorbed on each site. Adsorbed films can, therefore, be more than one molecule thick. A theory of adsorption leading to the formation of many layers, and finally to a liquid film, was advanced by Baly (1937), and has been improved by Brunauer, Emmett and Teller (1938) who find, for example, that nitrogen adsorbed on an iron surface is 6 molecules thick.

440

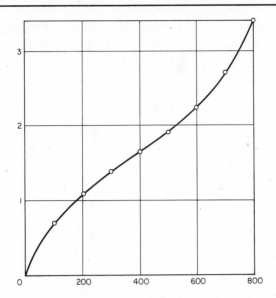

Fig. XIV.19 *The adsorption of argon on crystalline potassium chloride at 90°K* (data of Brunauer and Emmett). *Ordinate: ces. of gas, measured at S.T.P., adsorbed by 197 grams of salt; Abscissa: pressure of the system, in mm Hg*

The simultaneous adsorption of two substrates

When a surface has established adsorption equilibrium with two different substrates, we have, instead of equation XIV.59, the following simultaneous equations in terms of the concentrations, n, the number of sites per unit area, n_s, and the specific constants v and k:

$$\theta_1 n_s v_1 = n_1 k_1 (1 - \theta_1 - \theta_2)$$

and

$$\theta_2 n_s v_2 = n_2 k_2 (1 - \theta_1 - \theta_2) \qquad \text{XIV.62}$$

from which the fractions of the surface sites which are occupied are

$$\theta_1 = \frac{n_1 k_1}{n_1 k_1 + n_0 v_1 + n_2 k_2 (v_1/v_2)}$$

and

$$\theta_2 = \frac{n_2 k_2}{n_2 k_2 + n_0 v_2 + n_1 k_1 (v_2/v_1)} \qquad \text{XIV.63}$$

P

441

Conditions can thus arise in which the fraction of the surface which is covered by one type of molecule is nearly inversely proportional to the concentration of the other type of molecule. The surface concentrations are

$$n_1^\sigma = n_s \theta_1; \qquad n_2^\sigma = n_s \theta_2.$$

These relationships have contributed greatly to our understanding of enzyme action and heterogeneous catalysis, which are dealt with in the next chapter.

XV Chemical kinetics

In the practice of chemistry it is essential to know how far a given reaction will go. This, as we have seen, thermodynamics can tell us. What it cannot tell us is how fast it will go, and this, to the chemist, is of equal importance. Chemical kinetics deals with the rates of chemical changes and physicochemical processes, such as diffusion, dissolution and vaporisation. Expressions representing the rate of chemical change as a function of the concentration of reactants are seldom simple, but when based on sound data, lead to equations which reduce, as time is made infinite, to the equilibrium laws of thermodynamics. Chemical kinetics is therefore wider than thermodynamics, and, in fact, the whole of physical chemistry can be described in its terms. The formal incorporation of time as a variable in chemical systems has not yet been completed, and chemical kinetics, in the meantime, continues to develop as a science in its own rights. Its basic laws are few.

(1) Provided the temperature and pressure of the system, the extent of surface and the rate of absorption of radiation are constant, the instantaneous rate, dx/dt, of a chemical reaction is proportional to the product of the concentrations of the reactants raised to a small integral or fractional power, which experiment shows to be usually 1, 2 or $\frac{3}{2}$. When the surface of the vessel or of particles contained or formed in it has no influence on the rate, the reaction is said to be homogeneous. When radiation affects the rate, the reaction is said to be photochemical. These generalities apply to unitary steps, whose synchronisation determines the net rate of reaction.

(2) In a sequence of unitary processes, as found, for example, in the spontaneous disintegration of radioactive compounds, the net rate of reaction is that of the step with the lowest rate constant. This principle applies only when the rate constants differ in order of magnitude.

(3) Unstable intermediaries, usually atoms, free radicals or ions, may appear in small concentrations during the course of reaction. Their initial and final concentrations are zero, but, unless they accumulate in the system, they soon attain a maximum concentration

which thereafter diminishes. Hydrogen atoms, for example, in the reaction between H_2 and Br_2 are initially present in negligible amounts; during the course of reaction, their concentration, a, increases to a steady value, governed by the rates of the various chemical changes taking place; finally, their concentration is zero. During the steady, or stationary, state, $da/dt = 0$.

Chemists are concerned with the rate constants, k_n of chemical change, i.e. with the number, n_P, of molecules of product appearing in unit time and unit volume when the concentrations of each reactant is unity:

$$\frac{dn_P}{dt} = k_n n_A^\lambda n_B^\mu n_C^\nu \qquad \text{xv.1}$$

The integers or fractions λ, μ, ν are the orders of reaction with respect to the reactants A, B and C, respectively, and the net order of reaction is their sum. There are many methods for determining these integers and the velocity constant k_n. The most reliable are those derived from direct chemical analysis of the reacting system at various times. If, however, any physicochemical property of one or more of the reactants or resultants is found to be proportional to the concentration, or can be empirically related to it, its measurement suffices. In gases, for example, pressure and thermal conductivity may be used; in solutions, viscosity, optical density, rotatory power, refractive index and electrical conductivity.

Unimolecular reactions

Let the initial concentration of reactant be a gram-moles per litre, and its concentration after a time t be $a-x$. Then if the rate of change is simply proportional to the concentration, we have

$$-\frac{d(a-x)}{dt} = \frac{dx}{dt} = k_1(a-x) \qquad \text{xv.2}$$

where k_1 is the unimolecular, or first-order constant. Integration gives us the familiar equation

$$k_1 = \frac{1}{t} \ln \frac{a}{a-x} \qquad \text{xv.3}$$

The best method of determining k_1 is to plot the logarithm of $(a-x)$

against the time. On rewriting equation xv.3 in the following way

$$\frac{x}{a} = 1 - e^{-k_1 t} \qquad \text{xv.4}$$

we see that the reaction is complete after an infinite lapse of time. The time, $t_{1/2}$, necessary for the reaction to go half way is seen to be $k_1/\ln 2$, which is independent of the initial concentration. Most radioactive disintegrations obey this law, as do many reactions in solution, such as $CCl_3COOH \rightarrow HCCl_3 + CO_2$, the rate of which has been measured by analysing the amount of acid remaining and the amount of carbon dioxide formed. The unimolecular reaction which has been most carefully studied in the gaseous phase is the decomposition of dinitrogen pentoxide, which, despite an apparent kinetic simplicity, is represented stoichiometrically as follows; $N_2O_5 \rightarrow O_2 + 2N_2O_4 \rightleftarrows 4NO_2$ (Daniels, 1921). The fact that one of the products of decomposition becomes partly dissociated offers no real difficulty, because the rate of dissociation of N_2O_4 is known to be rapid (Richards and Reid, 1933). According to the second general principle enunciated above the rate-determining step is the first one. The real difficulty in understanding the mechanism of this reaction arises from the fact that, at pressures below about 0·01 mm, k_1 falls below the constant value which prevails at higher pressures. This phenomenon, originally observed in the much more complicated pyrolysis of propionaldehyde (Hinshelwood and Thompson, 1926), is fairly general in those gas reactions which appear to be unimolecular.

During the racemisation of optically active compounds, such as the substituted biphenyls, and during the mutarotation of the reducing sugars, the unimolecular change in the forward direction is opposed by a change of the same kinetic order in the reverse direction, so that, denoting the initial concentrations of the two forms by a and b, we have the kinetic scheme

$$A \underset{k_2}{\overset{k_1}{\rightleftarrows}} B$$

$$(a-x) \qquad (b+x)$$

and the differential equation

$$dx/dt = k_1(a-x) - k_2(b+x) \qquad \text{xv.5}$$

which gives on integration

$$x = \left(\frac{k_1 a - k_2 b}{k_1 + k_2}\right)[1 - e^{-(k_1 + k_2)t}] \qquad \text{xv.6}$$

When t becomes infinite, x_∞ is seen to equal the term in the first bracket; hence, on rearranging, we find

$$\frac{b+x_\infty}{a-x_\infty} = \frac{k_1}{k_2} = K \qquad \text{XV.7}$$

which is the kinetic derivation of the equilibrium constant, K.

The mutarotation of aluminium benzoylcamphor in carbon tetrachloride solution consists of two consecutive unimolecular reactions, following the course

$$A \xrightarrow{k_1} B \xrightarrow{k_2} C$$
$$(a-x-y) \quad x \quad y$$

The differential equations now are $-d(a-x-y) = k_1(a-x-y)$ and $-dx/dt = k_2 x - k_1(a-x-y)$, which give, on integration:

$$x = a\left(\frac{k_1}{k_2-k_1}\right)(e^{-k_1 t} - e^{-k_2 t}) \qquad \text{XV.8}$$

and

$$y = a\left[1 - \left(\frac{k_2}{k_2-k_1}\right)e^{-k_1 t} + \left(\frac{k_1}{k_2-k_1}\right)e^{-k_2 t}\right] \qquad \text{XV.9}$$

When the concentration, x, of the intermediate B has reached a stationary value, $dx/dt = 0$. On differentiating equation xv.8, we see that, under stationary conditions $k_1 e^{-k_1 t} = k_2 e^{-k_2 t}$, and therefore $x = a(k_1/k_2)e^{-k_1 t}$. The expression for the concentration of the final product C reduces, when $k_1 \gg k_2$, to $y = a(1-e^{-k_2 t})$, and when $k_2 \gg k_1$ to $y = a(1-e^{-k_1 t})$, which illustrates the second general principle enunciated earlier.

Bimolecular reactions

Interaction between molecules, as distinct from the decomposition of molecules, requires that they should meet, and since the frequency with which they meet must be proportional to the product of their concentrations, it is not difficult to understand the preponderance of bimolecular reactions among all chemical changes. We now have the scheme

$$A + B \rightarrow P$$
$$(a-x) \quad (b-x) \quad x$$

the differential equation

$$dx/dt = k_2(a-x)(b-x) \qquad \text{xv.10}$$

and the integrated equation

$$k_2 = \frac{1}{t(a-b)} \ln \frac{b(a-x)}{a(b-x)} \qquad \text{xv.11}$$

where k_2 is the bimolecular constant. It has the dimensions of time $\times$ (concentration)$^{-1}$, and may be expressed in the units of cc. per molecule-second or of litres per mole-second. It is best found by plotting the logarithm of $(a-x)/(b-x)$ against time. Equation xv.11 can be written as follows:

$$\frac{x}{a} = \frac{1-e^{+k_2 t(a-b)}}{1-(a/b)e^{+k_2 t(a-b)}} \qquad \text{xv.12}$$

As t becomes infinite, x_∞ becomes a or b, whichever is the less. When the difference between the initial concentrations is small, we may expand the exponential terms, obtaining

$$\frac{x}{a} = \frac{k_2 tb}{1+k_2 ta}$$

and when the difference is vanishingly small, $a = b$, and therefore

$$k_2 = \frac{1}{ta} \frac{x}{a-x} \qquad \text{xv.13}$$

which is the expression for the bimolecular constant when the initial concentrations of reactants are equal. It is usually derived by integration of the equation $dx/dt = k_2(a-x)^2$. The half life is now inversely proportional to the initial concentration, since $t_{1/2} = 1/k_2 a$. One of the many methods for determining the kinetic order of reaction makes use of the dependence of the half-life on the initial concentration.

The velocity of the saponification of esters in aqueous solution obeys these equations accurately, provided the inorganic reactant is recognised as the hydroxyl ion; $R.COOR' + OH^- \rightarrow R.COO^- + R'OH$. The work of Warder (1881), Reicher (1885) and Arrhenius (1887) on the saponification of esters by the bases $NaOH, Ba(OH)_2$ and NH_4OH showed that, if a stoichiometric second order constant k_2' is calculated in terms of molar concentrations, by means of the equation $-d[\text{ester}]/dt = k_2' [\text{ester}] [\text{total base}]$, its value with $Ba(OH)_2$

447

is twice that found with NaOH. Moreover, the value of k_2' found with ammonia is not only less by several powers of 10, but, instead of being constant, decreases rapidly with the course of reaction. Arrhenius argued that the ratio of 2 could be explained if NaOH and $Ba(OH)_2$ were regarded as being completely ionised in solution, and that the curious k_2' found with ammonia could be explained if this compound were regarded as only slightly ionised. His conclusion has been vindicated. The inadequacy of a stoichiometric second-order rate equation to account for these kinetic facts led him to an important conception – that of ionisation in solution. Stoichiometric second-order rate 'constants' have with one exception (Hughes, Ingold and Parker, 1960), not since been used.

Neither in the gas phase nor in solution are bimolecular reactions free from complications. The bimolecular reactions between oppositely charged ions in the gas phase, for example, and between certain molecules in solution, are opposed by unimolecular processes. We shall here consider one complication only, i.e. the occurrence of a bimolecular opposition reaction to a bimolecular forward reaction:

$$A \ + \ B \ \underset{k_4}{\overset{k_2}{\rightleftarrows}} C + D$$

$$(a-x) \quad (b-x) \quad x \quad x$$

where

$$dx/dt = k_2(a-x)(b-x) - k_4 x^2 \qquad \text{xv.14}$$

which gives on integration

$$x = \frac{ab}{1-K} \{\alpha + \beta \coth[(k_2 - k_4)\beta t]\}^{-1}$$

We have

$$K = k_4/k_2$$

$$\alpha = (a+b)/2(1-K),$$

and

$$\beta = [(a-b)^2 + 4Kab]^{1/2}/2(1-K) \qquad \text{xv.15}$$

This equation holds for the reaction between hydrogen and iodine in the gaseous phase (Bodenstein, 1894), but, because the products C and D are now identical ($H_2 + I_2 \rightleftarrows 2HI$), k_4 must be replaced by $4k_4$. It holds also for the reactions $CH_3X + Y^- \rightleftarrows CH_3Y + X^-$ in solution.

Termolecular reactions

There are very few reactions of the third kinetic order in solution or in the gas phase. They all belong to the generic scheme $A + 2B \rightarrow products$, which suggests that the rate-determining step may be a reaction between A and B_2. The combination of atoms to form diatomic molecules belong to this category. When two atoms combine to form a molecule, the process is endothermic, and cannot occur except in the presence of a third particle, sometimes referred to as a chaperon, whose role is to stabilise the union by depriving it of its excess energy. The termolecular velocity constants for the atomic reactions $A + A + M \rightarrow A_2 + M$ are generally in agreement with the frequency of ternary collisions, as estimated by equation II.14 (Steiner, 1935).

The equation of Arrhenius; the apparent energy of activation

Equation XV.7 is a particular case of a generalisation, according to which the equilibrium constant, K, of a chemical reaction is the ratio of the velocity constants for the direction and reverse reactions; $K = k_1/k_2$. We can therefore write

$$\Delta E = RT^2\left(\frac{d \ln K}{dT}\right) = RT^2\left(\frac{d \ln k_1}{dT}\right) - RT^2\left(\frac{d \ln k_2}{dT}\right) = E_j - E_i$$

$$\text{XV.16}$$

where E_j is the sum of the energies of the products, and E_i the sum of the energies of the reactants. On adding and subtracting an arbitrary energy E_c, we have

$$RT^2\left(\frac{d \ln k_1}{dT}\right) - RT^2\left(\frac{d \ln k_2}{dT}\right) = (E_c - E_i) - (E_c - E_j) = E_1 - E_2$$

The form of this equation suggests that the equations

$$E_1 = RT^2\left(\frac{d \ln k_1}{dT}\right) \quad \text{and} \quad E_2 = RT^2\left(\frac{d \ln k_2}{dT}\right) \qquad \text{XV.17}$$

may hold separately for the direct and reverse reactions, and that E_c is no longer arbitrary but specific. As velocity constants increase with a rise in temperature, E_1 and E_2, whose relationship to the other energies is shown in Fig. XV.1, must be positive. We may therefore

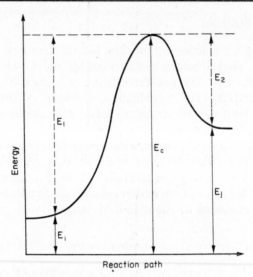

Fig. xv.1 *The relationship between initial energy E_i, final energy, E_j, and critical energy, E_c*

define an energy, E_A, by the equation

$$E_A = RT^2\left(\frac{d \ln k}{dT}\right) = -R\left[\frac{d \ln k}{d(1/T)}\right]$$ xv.18

E_A, known as the apparent, or Arrhenius, energy of activation, being a kinetic analogue of ΔE in van't Hoff's isochore (equation xiii.13) denotes the difference between the average energy of those molecules that react and the average energy of all the molecules. Its value for a given reaction can be found by plotting $\ln k$ against $1/T$, or analytically from velocity constants at two temperatures, T and T':

$$E_A = \frac{RTT'}{T'-T}\ln\left(\frac{k'}{k}\right)$$

If E_A should prove to be, as Arrhenius assumed, independent of T, equation xv.18 can be integrated to give $\ln k = -(E_A/RT)+a$ *constant*. Denoting the constant by $\ln A$, we have

$$k = A \cdot e^{-E_A/RT}$$ xv.19

This equation has the same form as many other physicochemical equations such, for example, as that relating the saturation pressure of a liquid to the temperature; and the meaning underlying it is the

450

same in all cases. In vaporisation, the concentration of molecules in the vapour phase is proportional to the fractional number of molecules in the liquid phase which have sufficient energy, L, to escape from it. Similarly, in chemical reactions, the concentration of molecules that react is proportional to the concentration of molecules which have acquired an energy E_A over and above the average energy of all the molecules. This is the basic idea of the Arrhenius hypothesis (1889); only activated molecules react.

It is intrinsically unlikely that E_A for any reaction should be independent of the temperature. In fact, even the data used by Arrhenius to test his hypothesis sufficed to show that such is not the case. Trautz (1909) improved the theory by admitting the possibility of a difference, ΔC, between the heat capacity of the active molecules and that of the normal reactants. Then

$$E_A = E_0 + \int_0^T \Delta C \, dT$$

and, if ΔC is independent of T, $E_A = E_0 + \Delta CT$. Integration of equation xv.18 now gives us $\ln k = -(E_0/RT) + (\Delta C/R) \ln T + a$ constant, or, denoting the constant by $\ln B$,

$$k = B \cdot T^{\Delta C/R} \cdot e^{-E_0/RT} \qquad \text{xv.20}$$

Few reactions have been examined with sufficient accuracy in the gas phase to allow the term ΔC to be evaluated. Though possibly a small quantity, the rate constants for many gas reactions are such that they cannot be explained without attributing real values to ΔC. Several reactions in solution, on the other hand, provide data of sufficient accuracy to ascribe to ΔC precise values. It is found to be always negative, indicating that the heat capacity of activated molecules in solution is less than that of the normal solutes.

The collision theory

If, as suggested by Trautz (1916) and McC. Lewis (1918) the essential condition for the occurrence of bimolecular reactions is that the reacting molecules, A and B, should collide with a critical energy of at least E, the number of molecules reacting per cc. per second should, according to equation ii.13 be:

$$\frac{dn}{dt} = n_A n_B (r_A + r_B)^2 \left[8\pi kT \left(\frac{1}{m_A} + \frac{1}{m_B} \right) \right]^{1/2} e^{-E/kT} \qquad \text{xv.21}$$

451

The bimolecular velocity constant, expressed in litres/mole-second, is

$$k_2 = \frac{1}{c_A c_B} \frac{dc}{dt} = \frac{N_0}{1\ 000} \frac{1}{n_A n_B} \frac{dn}{dt} \qquad \text{xv.22}$$

In these units, therefore,

$$k_2 = \frac{N_0}{1\ 000}(r_A + r_B)^2 \left[8\pi kT \left(\frac{1}{m_A} + \frac{1}{m_B}\right) \right]^{1/2} e^{-E/kT} = Z_0 e^{-E/kT}$$

$$\text{xv.23}$$

where Z_0 is the standard collision frequency. Because the effects of large radii and large masses in this equation are roughly compensating, Z_0 is numerically not very sensitive to the nature of the colliding molecules, and is an approximate constant. According to equation xv.18, $E_A = E + \frac{1}{2}kT$, and the pre-exponential term A of equation xv.19 becomes $Z_0 e^{1/2}$. Experimental values, for some representative reactions in solution and in the gas phase are given in Table xv.1. That there is reasonable agreement with the equation of Trautz and Lewis is evident. If, for example, in the first reaction cited, we use spectroscopically determined values for the radii, we calculate a velocity

Table xv.1 *Kinetic constants for certain bimolecular reactions;* $k_2 = A \cdot e^{-E_A/kT}$

Reference Reaction	Medium	$A \times 10^{-10}$ (lit/mole-sec)	E_A (cal/mole)	k_2 (at 298·16°K)
1 $H + HBr \rightarrow H_2 + Br$	gas	1·35	1 090	$2·14 \times 10^{+9}$
2 $CO_2 + OH^- \rightarrow HCO_3^-$	H_2O	1·50	9 060	$3·41 \times 10^{+3}$
3 $2NOBr \rightarrow 2NO + Br_2$	gas	4·15	13 880	$2·74 \times 10^0$
4 $CH_3Cl + I^- \rightarrow CH_3I + Cl^-$	$(CH_3)_2CO$	2·14	17 950	$1·48 \times 10^{-3}$
5 $XCl + I^- \rightarrow XI + Cl^-$	$C_2H_4(OH)_2$	3·50	28 000	$1·03 \times 10^{-10}$
6 $2HI \rightarrow H_2 + I_2$	gas	9·17	44 450	$2·30 \times 10^{-22}$

1. Bach, Bonhoeffer and Moelwyn-Hughes (1934).
2. Brinkman, Margaria and Roughton (1933)
3. Trautz and Dalal (1918)
4. Farhataziz and Moelwyn-Hughes (1959).
5. Baker and Nathan (1936). XCl stands for $1:3:5\ Cl(NO_2)_2C_6H_3$
6. Bodenstein (1889).

constant which is about four times that found. The result can be interpreted as indicating a collision efficiency of 0·25. The significant observation to be drawn from Table xv.1 is that, although the velocity constants differ by a factor of 10^{31}, the term A does not alter beyond a factor of 7. There thus seems little doubt of the fundamental soundness of the theory of Trautz and Lewis. That it requires extension and modification, and that there are many instances of its apparent inapplicability are also not to be disputed.

Bimolecular reactions which have velocity constants conforming to equation xv.23 are said to proceed with normal velocities. A statistical survey (Moelwyn-Hughes, 1933) of the A terms relating to some 200 bimolecular reactions, of which only 4 per cent were gas reactions, revealed that the largest group of reactions was that whose A values agreed with this simple collision theory. Reactions with A values greater than Z_0 were fewer than those whose A values were less than Z_0. To account for the relatively fast reactions is not difficult, because equation xv.23 is limited to activation energies expressible in two quadratic terms only, whereas, if $2s$ quadratic terms are necessary, the simple exponential term of Boltzmann must be replaced by the more general one of Berthoud (1911), giving for the bimolecular constant the approximate expression

$$k_2 = Z_0 e^{-E/kT} \frac{(E/kT)^{s-1}}{(s-1)!} \qquad \text{xv.24}$$

The relationship between the true and apparent energies of activation is seen to be

$$E = E_A + (s - \tfrac{3}{2})RT \qquad \text{xv.25}$$

A comparative study of the hydrogen ion-catalysed hydrolysis of disaccharides, trisaccharides and glykosides made it clear that s would have to be about 45 – a result since confirmed by the experimental value of $-90\,\text{cal/mole-deg}$ for dE_A/dT. To account for the relatively slow reactions, it has been suggested that the colliding molecules, though possessing sufficient energy to react, may have to be (1) in an appropriate phase of internal motion (factor p), (2) suitably oriented (factor o), and (3) able to overcome a blockage or steric hindrance due to the presence of interfering groups (factor s). The standard collision frequency Z_0 would then have to be multiplied by the product pos. In the bimolecular reaction between acraldehyde and *cyclo*pentadiene in benzene solution and in the gas phase, the factor *pos* is about 10^{-5}, due mainly, it is thought, to a stringent orientational necessity (Wassermann, 1936).

We shall next discuss in some detail a few representative reactions, some of which have been measured in the gas phase only, some in the gas phase and in solution, and others in solution only.

The reaction between bromine and hydrogen in the gaseous phase

When hydrogen and bromine are mixed at relatively high temperatures, hydrogen bromide is formed, according to the simple stoichiometric equation $H_2 + Br_2 \rightarrow 2HBr$. The rate of reaction, however, unlike that between hydrogen and iodine, is found to obey the following unusual kinetic law: (Bodenstein and Lind, 1907):

$$\frac{d[HBr]}{dt} = \frac{k_0[H_2][Br]^{1/2}}{m + \dfrac{[HBr]}{[Br_2]}} \qquad \text{xv.26}$$

where k_0 and m are empirical constants. The form of the integrated equation depends on whether $[H_2]$ is equal to, greater than, or less than $[Br_2]$, and is complicated. The interpretation of the mechanism was given simultaneously by Christiansen, Herzfeld and Polanyi (1919) in terms of the following sequence of reactions:

(1) $\qquad\qquad Br_2 \rightarrow 2Br$

(2) $\qquad\qquad Br + H_2 \rightarrow HBr + H$

(3) $\qquad\qquad H + Br_2 \rightarrow HBr + Br$

(4) $\qquad\qquad H + HBr \rightarrow H_2 + Br$

(6) $\qquad\qquad 2Br \rightarrow Br_2$

Reaction (4) is the reverse of reaction (2), and reaction (6) is the reverse of reaction (1). The reverse of reaction (3) is omitted because it is highly endothermic, and therefore unlikely to proceed with a significant velocity. The numeral 5 is not used here, as it will be when we discuss the photochemical reaction. We may evaluate the stationary concentrations of the free atoms from the equations:

$$\frac{d[Br]}{dt} = 2k_1[Br_2] - k_2[Br][H_2] + k_3[H][Br_2] + k_4[H][HBr] - 2k_6[Br]^2$$

$$= 0 \qquad\qquad \text{xv.27}$$

$$\frac{d[H]}{dt} = k_2[Br][H_2] - k_3[H][Br_2] - k_4[H][HBr] = 0 \qquad \text{xv.28}$$

By subtraction, we see that

$$[Br] = (k_1/k_6)^{1/2}[Br_2]^{1/2}$$

which is the kinetic expression for the equilibrium between bromine molecules and atoms. From equation xv.28, we have

$$[H] = \frac{k_2[H_2][Br]}{k_3[Br_2] + k_4[HBr]} \qquad \text{xv.29}$$

The rate of formation of hydrogen bromide is

$$\frac{d[HBr]}{dt} = k_2[H_2][Br] + k_3[Br_2][H] - k_4[HBr][H]$$

which, on substituting the expressions for the stationary atomic concentrations, becomes

$$\frac{d[HBr]}{dt} = 2k_2\left(\frac{k_1}{k_6}\right)^{1/2}\frac{k_3}{k_4}\frac{[H_2][Br_2]^{1/2}}{(k_3/k_4) + [HBr]/[Br_2]} \qquad \text{xv.30}$$

The empirical constants of equation xv.26 have thus the following meaning:

$$m = k_3/k_4 \qquad \text{xv.31}$$

and

$$k_0 = 2k_2\left(\frac{k_1}{k_6}\right)^{1/2}\frac{k_3}{k_4} \qquad \text{xv.32}$$

The bimolecular constant governing the rate of the second step is

$$k_2 = k_0/2mK^{1/2}$$

where K is the dissociation constant of bromine, and is known with considerable accuracy. Bodenstein and Lind found m to be 10, and independent of temperature. It follows that the energy of activation for reaction 2 is

$$E_2 = E_{obs} - \tfrac{1}{2}\Delta E \qquad \text{xv.33}$$

where $E_{obs} = RT^2(d \ln k_0/dT)$. Figure xv.2 shows the results of Bodenstein and Lind, obtained by the method of chemical analysis, and those of later workers obtained spectrophotometrically. E_2 is found to be $17\,740 \pm 500$ cal, and

$$k_2 = 6.92 \times 10^{10} \cdot e^{-17\,740/RT} \qquad \text{xv.34}$$

455

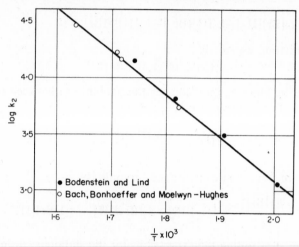

Fig. xv.2 *Experimental determination of the energy of activation for the reaction between bromine atoms and hydrogen molecules*
● Bodenstein and Lind, *Z. physikal. Chem.*, 57, 168 (1907)
○ Bach, Bonhoeffer and Moelwyn-Hughes, *Z. physikal. Chem.*, B27, 71 (1934)

A comparison with equation xv.23, using the spectroscopic value of $r_A + r_B$ (1·88 Å) shows that the efficiency of activating collisions is 0·23. In the much faster reaction $Cl + H_2 \rightarrow ClH + H$, which has been measured over a temperature range of 700° (Rideal and Steiner, 1939; Ashmore and Chanmugan, 1953), a comparable efficiency (0·37) is found. In the reaction when the bromine atom reacts with the deuterium molecule, it is found that

$$k_2 = 8·34 \times 10^{10} . e^{-19\,870/RT} \qquad \text{xv.35}$$

indicating an energy of activation greater by 2 130 than that for the $Br - H_2$ reaction. The difference is due mainly to the difference in the residual energies of the molecules. If we assume that the total energy of the reactive complex is the same for the $H_2 - Br$ and the $D_2 - Br$ systems, we have the simple scheme shown in Fig. xv.3. The spectroscopic value of the difference in residual energies is $\frac{1}{2}h\nu(H_2) - \frac{1}{2}h\nu(D_2)$ $= 6\,285 - 4\,458 = 1\,827$ cal. Both these reactions have recently been studied in the temperature range 1 300–1 700°K (D. Britton and R. M. Cole, 1961).

The equilibrium constant for the system $Br + H_2 \rightleftarrows BrH + H$ can

456

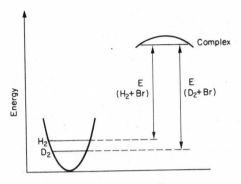

Fig. xv.3   *Schematic representation of the isotope effect*

be readily calculated from spectroscopic constants. On combining it with the kinetic equation for the forward reaction, we obtain for the bimolecular constant of the reverse reaction the data cited in the first entry of Table xv.1. This reaction is seen to be a very rapid one. When the reactants are at molar concentrations, which is what the chemist usually uses, the half-life is less than 5×10^{-10} sec.

The decomposition of dinitrogen pentoxide in the gaseous phase and in solution

This classical example of a first-order homogeneous reaction (Daniels and Johnston, 1921) has been carefully investigated under a wide variety of conditions, using chemical analysis as well as the increase in pressure and colour which attend the decomposition. The results were first interpreted on a molecular basis and later in terms of free radicals.

The scheme, according to the molecular interpretation, consists of three steps:

$$N_2O_5 + N_2O_5 \underset{k_4}{\overset{k_2}{\rightleftharpoons}} N_2O_5 + N_2O_5 \overset{k_3}{\rightarrow} \text{Products}$$

$$n \qquad n \qquad n \qquad a$$

Normal molecules are activated in binary collisions, attaining a stationary concentration, a. The fate of the activated molecules is either to loose their energy in binary collisions or to break down spontaneously into products. Under stationary conditions

$$da/dt = k_2 n^2 - k_4 na - k_3 a = 0$$

457

Then

$$a = \frac{k_2 n^2}{k_4 n + k_3} \qquad \text{xv.36}$$

If there were no chemical reaction, k_3 would be zero, and

$$\frac{a}{n} = \frac{k_2}{k_4} = K \qquad \text{xv.37}$$

which is a kinetic formulation of Boltzmann's law. The rate of reaction is

$$-\frac{dn}{dt} = k_3 a = \frac{k_3 k_2 n^2}{k_4 n + k_3} \qquad \text{xv.38}$$

This simple hypothesis can explain Hinshelwood and Thompson's observation that the apparent order of a gas reaction can be 1 at high pressures and 2 at low pressures. The equation for the observed velocity constant.

$$k_1 = -\frac{1}{n}\frac{dn}{dt} = \frac{k_3 k_2 n}{k_4 n + k_3} \qquad \text{xv.39}$$

reduces at high pressures, to

$$k_1 = k_3\frac{k_2}{k_4} = k_3 K \qquad \text{xv.40}$$

The Boltzmann distribution law is here maintained, and the rate of reaction is governed by the spontaneous decomposition of the activated molecules. At low pressures, however, we have

$$-\frac{dn}{dt} = k_2 n^2 \qquad \text{xv.41}$$

showing that the rate of reaction is now the rate at which molecules are activated (Trautz, 1916; McC. Lewis, 1918; Lindemann, 1922). Equation xv.39 can be written in the form

$$\frac{1}{k_1} = \frac{k_4}{k_3 k_2} + \frac{1}{k_2}\frac{1}{n} \qquad \text{xv.42}$$

from which k_2 and k_4/k_3 may be determined. The data of Schumacher and Sprenger (1930) at 35°C, analysed in this way, yield the values $k_2 = 2\cdot11 \times 10^1$ litres/mole-sec, and $k_4/k_2 = 1\cdot37 \times 10^5$ litres/mole. The first of these constants can be examined in the light of equations xv.24 and xv.25, accepting the experimental value of $E_A = 24\,710$ cal at 305·6°K. In order to account for the rate constant, it is necessary to take s as 19, so that $E = E_A + (35/2)RT = 36\,420$. The unimolecular constants observed by various workers can be summarised empirically as follows:

$$\log_{10}k_1(\text{sec}^{-1}) = 66\cdot7661 - 18\cdot0533\log_{10}T - 7\,920\cdot87/T \quad \text{xv.43}$$

according to which $E = E_A + 18\cdot0533\,RT = 36\,238$, in close agreement with the value found by the first method. If deactivations occur at every collision between normal and active molecules, k_4 may be identified with Z_0, and k_3 becomes $7\cdot74 \times 10^5$. The average life time of the activated molecules is $1/k_3 = 1\cdot29 \times 10^{-6}$ sec.

The reaction proceeds in chloroform solution at a rate which is only 11 per cent higher than the rate of the gas reaction, while E_A is lower by only 260 cal (Lueck, 1922). Numerous other solvents, including bromine, dinitrogen tetroxide and nitromethane have no sensible effect on the rate or energy of activation (Eyring and Daniels, 1930).

The free radical mechanism, formulated for gas reactions in general by Rice and Herzfeld (1934), has been applied by Ogg (1947) to this reaction. With but a slight modification, it can be represented by the sequence:

$$\underset{n}{N_2O_5} + \underset{n}{N_2O_5} \rightarrow \underset{n}{N_2O_5} + \underset{a}{NO_3} + \underset{b}{NO_2} \quad k_1$$

$$\underset{a}{NO_3} + \underset{b}{NO_2} + \underset{n}{N_2O_5} \rightarrow \underset{n}{N_2O_5} + \underset{n}{N_2O_5} \quad k_2$$

$$\underset{a}{NO_3} + \underset{b}{NO_2} \rightarrow \underset{b}{NO_2} + O_2 + \underset{c}{NO} \quad k_3$$

$$\underset{c}{NO} + \underset{n}{N_2O_5} \rightarrow \underset{b}{3NO_2} \quad k_4$$

The first step is now taken to be the dissociation of one molecule of reactant into NO_3 and NO_2 in a binary collision. The second step is the reverse of this reaction. Nitric oxide is assumed to be formed in the third step and destroyed in the last step. The stationary

459

concentrations are obtained in the usual way:

$$da/dt = k_1 n^2 - k_2 nab - k_3 ab = 0 \quad \therefore \quad ab = k_1 n^2/(k_2 n + k_3)$$

$$dc/dt = k_3 ab - k_4 cn = 0 \quad \quad \therefore \quad c = k_3 ab/k_4 n$$

The rate of reaction is

$$db/dt = k_1 n^2 - k_2 nab + 3k_4 cn$$

After eliminating ab and c, and noting that the rate of production of NO_2 is twice as great as the rate of disappearance of N_2O_5, we obtain the rate equation

$$-\frac{dn}{dt} = \frac{2k_1 k_3 n^2}{k_2 n + k_3} \qquad \text{xv.44}$$

which, like that derived on the molecular basis (equation xv.38) is in a form to account for kinetics of the first, second and intermediate orders.

In deciding which of the two interpretations is the right one, we must note in the first place that the molecular mechanism is the simpler one and is self-consistent. Without supplementary evidence, it would, indeed, be difficult to justify its rejection. Such supplementary evidence, nevertheless, is provided by absorption spectra, which prove that the radical NO_3 does in fact exist in the reacting system. Moreover, reaction 4 has been separately examined, and the relative slowness of reaction 3 established by using the isotopes N^{13} and N^{15} (J. H. Smith and Daniels, 1947). The free radical mechanism thus wins the day, not only in this instance but in most other apparently unimolecular reactions in gaseous systems. Many methods are available for the detection of transient intermediaries. Their identification, by means of the mass spectrometer, for example, guides and limits the choice of reaction mechanism which, without collateral evidence, could be misleading.

It remains to point out that, since the rate of reaction is unaffected in numerous solvents, such bimolecular processes as those represented by steps 3 and 4, and consequently the standard collision frequency, Z_0, are also unaffected by the solvents. This is the conclusion reached by all the experimentalists who have measured the velocity of bimolecular reactions in the gas phase and in solution (Hinshelwood and Moelwyn-Hughes, 1931; Arnold and Kistiakowsky, 1933; Farkas and Garbatsky, 1933; Wassermann, 1936).

Reactions between ions in solution

In aqueous and ethanolic solutions, the conversion of ammonium cyanate into urea $[NH_4CNO \rightleftharpoons CO(NH_2)_2]$ is found to be a bimolecular reaction, opposed by a unimolecular reaction. That the rate of the forward change is proportional to the product of the concentrations of the ammonium and cyanate ions has been demonstrated by addition of other ammonium salts and other cyanates; the real reaction is thus $NH_4^+ + CNO^- \rightleftharpoons CO(NH_2)_2$ (J. Walker and Hambly, 1889; Doyle, 1922; Miss C. C. Miller, 1934; Svirbely and Warner, 1935). At low ionic strength, j, the effect of added electrolytes on the bimolecular constant, k_2, is such that $\ln k_2$ decreases linearly with respect to $j^{1/2}$. The rate of reaction between the bromocetate and thiosulphate ions in water $[CH_2Br \cdot COO^- + S_2O_3^{--} \rightarrow CH_2(S_2O_3) \cdot COO^{--} + Br^-]$ is increased by the addition of strong electrolytes, in such a way that $\ln k_2$ increases linearly with respect to $j^{1/2}$, the limiting gradient being -2 times that found in the ammonium cyanate reaction at the same temperature and in the same solvent (Krapiwin, 1913; Kappanna and Patwardhan, 1933; Fräulein von Kiss and Vass, 1934; La Mer and Kamner, 1935; C. W. Davies and I. W. Williams, 1958). To explain such observations, Brönsted and Bjerrum (1922) independently suggested that when ions A and B react, they first form a complex ion, C, with which they establish equilibrium: $A + B \rightleftharpoons C$. In terms of activities, a, concentrations, c, and activity coefficients, γ, we then have, at a constant temperature and pressure, $K = a_C/a_A a_B = (c_C/c_A c_B)(\gamma_C/\gamma_A \gamma_B)$. The concentration of the complex ion is thus $c_C = K c_A c_B(\gamma_A \gamma_B/\gamma_C)$, and to this the rate of reaction is assumed to be proportional:

$$-\frac{dc_C}{dt} = \frac{dc_P}{dt} = k c_C = kK c_A c_B \frac{\gamma_A \gamma_B}{\gamma_C} \qquad \text{xv.45}$$

The bimolecular velocity constant now becomes

$$k_2 = \frac{1}{c_A c_B} \cdot \frac{dc_P}{dt} = kK \frac{\gamma_A \gamma_B}{\gamma_C} \qquad \text{xv.46}$$

But the ionic activity coefficient in dilute solution is so defined that it is unity at infinite dilution. If, therefore, we denote by k_2^0 the value of the bimolecular constant found by extrapolating to infinite dilution, we may write

$$k_2 = k_2^0 \left(\frac{\gamma_A \gamma_B}{\gamma_C} \right) \qquad \text{xv.47}$$

According to equations XII.67 and XII.61, however, $\ln \gamma_i = -\alpha z_i^2 j^{1/2}$, where z_i is the electrovalency, and $\alpha = (\varepsilon^2/2DkT)(8\pi N_0\varepsilon^2/1\,000DkT)^{1/2}$. Since $z_C = z_A + z_B$, it follows that

$$\ln(k_2/k_2^0) = 2\alpha z_A z_B j^{1/2} \qquad \text{XV.48}$$

or

$$\log_{10}(k_2/k_2^0) = \frac{\varepsilon^2}{2\cdot303DkT}\left(\frac{8\pi N_0\varepsilon^2}{1\,000DkT}\right)^{1/2} z_A z_B j^{1/2} \qquad \text{XV.49}$$

If, therefore, $\log_{10}k_2$ is plotted against $j^{1/2}$, the gradient should be zero when either z_A or z_B is zero; otherwise, it should be an integral multiple, positive or negative, of 2α. It happens that 2α for water at 25°C is 1·018, so that, in this solvent at this temperature, we have, approximately

$$\log_{10}(k_2/k_2^0) = z_A z_B j^{1/2} \qquad \text{XV.50}$$

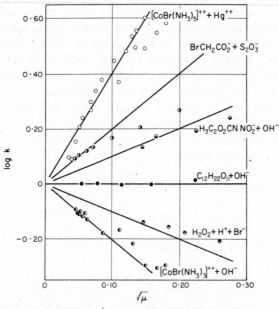

Fig. xv.4 *Livingston's diagram illustrating the effect of ionic strength on the velocity constants of certain ionic reactions in water at 25°C. In our notation, the ordinate would be marked $\log_{10}(k_2/k_2^0)$, and the abscissa $j^{1/2}$. The organic reactant in the case of a zero electrolyte effect is ethyl acetate, and not a disaccharide; and the data refer to 19·4°C.*

The data available on ionic reactions in 1930, plotted in this way by Livingston (Fig. xv.4), clearly illustrates the near relationship between the prediction of the Brönsted–Bjerrum treatment and the facts. When z_A is known, z_B can be determined from the magnitude and sign of the electrolyte effect. In this way, the nitration of benzene sulphonates ($z_A = -1$) was shown to be due to the ion NO_2^+ (G. Williams, 1944).

It is not necessary, as Christiansen (1924) showed, to use thermodynamics. The facts can be understood on the simple assumption that ions react when they meet while possessing an energy not less than E, of which one part, E_n, is of unpredictable origin, and another part, E_e, is due to electrostatic forces. The energy of interaction of two ions when they are infinitely far apart, as they are in solutions at infinite dilution, is zero. The interaction energy when they are at a distance r apart in a solution of ionic strength j is essentially $(z_A z_B \varepsilon^2 / Dr)$ $(1 - \kappa r)$, where κ is related to j by equation xii.61. Improvements on this simple treatment suggested by the use of equation xii.59 cannot be quantitatively formulated without assuming sphericity, or some other geometrical simplicity to the ions and the reactive complex. Ignoring them, we have

$$k_2 = Z \cdot \exp(-E_n/kT) \cdot \exp[-(z_A z_B \varepsilon^2 / DrkT)(1 - \kappa r)] \quad \text{xv.51}$$

from which a number of consequences emerge.

(1) Denoting by k_2^0 the velocity constant when κ is zero, we have

$$k_2 = k_2^0 \cdot \exp[(z_A z_B \varepsilon^2 / DkT)\kappa], \quad \text{xv.52}$$

which is another way of expressing the Brönsted–Bjerrum relationship. It satisfactorily accounts for the effects of charge product, dielectric constant and ionic strength under isothermal conditions, without requiring a knowledge of the critical interionic distance, r.

(2) At zero ionic strength,

$$k_2^0 = Z_0 \cdot \exp(-E_n/kT) \cdot \exp(-z_A z_B \varepsilon^2 / DrkT) \quad \text{xv.53}$$

If, for a given reaction at a constant temperature, the dielectric constant is altered by the addition of a second miscible solvent, we have a means of evaluating r, since, as Scatchard (1932) indicated,

$$\left[\frac{d \ln k_2^0}{d(1/D)} \right]_T = -\frac{z_A z_B \varepsilon^2}{rkT} \quad \text{xv.54}$$

(3) The apparent energy of activation becomes

$$E_A = E_n + \tfrac{1}{2}RT + \frac{N_0 z_A z_B \varepsilon^2}{Dr}(1 - LT)(1 - \tfrac{3}{2}\kappa r) \qquad \text{xv.55}$$

Thus for a given reaction at a constant temperature, E_A may increase or decrease with respect to the ionic strength, depending on the sign of $(1 - LT)$, where $L = -(d \ln D/dT)_P$, as used in Chapter XII. Observed changes in E_A for certain reactions in aqueous solution are compared in Table xv.2 with those calculated by means of this equation.

(4) By eliminating the unknown energy term, E_n, from equations xv.53 and xv.55, we find that

$$k_2^0 = Z_0 \,.\, \exp(-z_A z_B \varepsilon^2 L/kDr) \,.\, \exp(-E_A/RT) \qquad \text{xv.56}$$

so that the first empirical constant of the equation of Arrhenius (equation xv.19) becomes

$$A^0 = Z_0 \,.\, \exp(-z_A z_B \varepsilon^2 L/kDr) \qquad \text{xv.57}$$

which, with reasonable values of r, can account for ratios A^0/Z_0 ranging from 10^8 to 10^{-8} (Moelwyn-Hughes, 1936). If, in a pair of reactions, we assume both r and Z_0 to be the same, we may evaluate both from the experimental A^0 terms. For example, from the following data:

$$NH^+ + CNO^- ; \quad z_A z_B = -1; \quad A^0 = 3 \cdot 14 \times 10^{13} \text{ (litres/mole-sec)}$$

$$BrAc^- + S_2O_3^{--} ; \quad z_A z_B = +2; \quad A^0 = 1 \cdot 36 \times 10^9 \text{ (litres/mole-sec)}$$

We find $r = 2 \cdot 94 \times 10^{-8}$ cm, and $Z_0 = 1 \cdot 10 \times 10^{12}$ litres/mole-sec.

(5) If Z_0 and E_n are the same for a pair of reactions such as

$$CH_2Br \,.\, COO^- + S_2O_3^{--} \rightarrow CH_2(S_2O_3^-) \,.\, COO^- + Br^-$$

and

$$CH_2Br \,.\, COOCH_3 + S_2O_3^{--} \rightarrow CH_2(S_2O_3^-) \,.\, COOCH_3 + Br^-$$

we can write

$$\ln_e \left[\frac{k_2^0(\text{ion-ester})}{k_2^0(\text{ion-ion})} \right] = \frac{z_A z_B \varepsilon^2}{DrkT} \qquad \text{xv.58}$$

Table xv.2 *Observed and calculated changes in E_A with respect to j in aqueous solution*

Reaction	Reference	$z_A z_B$	T	B	j	E_A (observed)	Difference in E_A	
							Observed	Calculated
$NH_4^+ + CNO^-$	a	-1	313·2	1 103	0	$(24\,455 \pm 8)$		
					0·05	24 200		
					0·20	23 970	-230	-246
$NH_4^+ + CNO^-$	b	-1	323·1	1 187	0	$(23\,580)$		
					0·0376	23 240	-340	-230
$BrAc^- + S_2O_3^{--}$	c	$+2$	285·6	631	0	$(15\,799 \pm 31)$		
					0·008	15 881		
					0·020	16 009	$+128$	$+66$
$BrY^{--} + OH^-$	d	$+2$	288·1	662	0	$(12\,361 \pm 14)$		
					0·0023	12 439		
					0·0086	12 470	$+31$	$+59$

a. Doyle, (1922); Moelwyn-Hughes (1932).
b. Svirbely and Warner, (1935).
c. La Mer and Kamner, (1935).
d. La Mer and Amis, (1938); Panepinto and Kilpatrick, (1937): The complex ions are the tetra-halogeno-phenolsulphonephthaleins, or halogenophenol blues.

From the limiting value of the ratio of the velocity constants found by La Mer (1932), r in this instance is found to be 3·52 Å.

(6) Without making any assumption concerning Z_0, but by taking r to be the same for a pair of reactions of this kind, we have, from equation xv.55,

$$E_A^0(\text{ion-ion}) - E_A^0(\text{ion-molecule}) = (1 - LT)\frac{z_A z_B \varepsilon^2}{Dr} \qquad \text{xv.59}$$

which affords another means of finding r. For the two reactions

$$CH_2Br.COO^- + S_2O_3^{--} \rightarrow CH_2(S_2O_3).COO^- + Br^-$$

and

$$CH_2Br.COO^- + MgS_2O_3 \rightarrow CH_2(S_2O_3^-).COO^- + MgBr^-$$

$E_A^0(\text{ion-ion})$ is known to be 15 710 cals, from the numerous sets of data already cited. From results to be described below, $E_A^0(\text{ion-molecule})$ is 16 415 cal. Hence, in water at 25°C, the difference is -705 ± 90 cal, from which r is found to be 4·56 Å. It is not the numerical reasonableness of this result that is important, but the fact that the treatment has led to an understanding of the effect of electrical fields on the rate of substitution at the saturated carbon atom, for the reactions concerned, although described as those between ions, are, in fact, reactions between the ion $S_2O_3^-$ and the polar bond C—Br, breaking in the presence and in the absence of a second strong electrostatic field. The effect of substituents on the rate of chemical change is one of the most assiduously studied subjects in modern chemistry, comprising, in this country, most of the publications listed under the somewhat misleading title of 'physical organic chemistry'. Altering the charge of one of the reactants from zero to -2ε here results in the unexpected but explicable phenomenon of a decrease in the velocity constant and in the apparent energy of activation.

The study of ionic reactions, as that of electrical conductivity, is incomplete unless account is taken of the role of ion-pairs. Sodium bromacetate reacts more rapidly with calcium and barium thiosulphate than with sodium and potassium thiosulphate at the same ionic strength. A similar effect, noted by Holmberg (1912) in the reaction between the hydroxyl and dibrom–malonate ions, has sometimes been referred to as cationic catalysis, since the divalent cations appear to have a positive catalytic effect. Now the presence of sulphate ions depresses the rate of reaction between the hydroxyl and the brompentammine-cobaltic ion. These observations have been given a quantitative explanation by C. W. Davies (1949, 1958) in terms of ion-pairs, having reactivities which may exceed or be less than that of the unassociated ions. The ion-pairs to be reckoned with in the bromacetate–thiosulphate reaction in the presence of divalent cations of metal M are MS_2O_3 and $MBrAc^+$, whose dissociation constants are

$$K_1 = [M^{++}][S_2O_3^{--}]\gamma_2^2/[MS_2O_3] \qquad \text{xv.60}$$

and

$$K_2 = [M^{++}][BrAc^-]\gamma_2/[MBrAc^-] \qquad \text{xv.61}$$

where the subscript to the activity coefficient, γ, denotes electrovalency. If both these ion pairs, as well as the free thiosulphate ion, react with the bromacetate ion, the instantaneous rate of reaction is governed by the specific and simultaneous breakdown of three Brönsted complexes, according to the equation

$$-\frac{d[S_2O_3]}{dt} = k_2^0[S_2O_3^{--}][BrAc^-]\left(\frac{\gamma_1\gamma_2}{\gamma_3}\right)$$

$$+ k_3^0[MS_2O_3][BrAc^-]\left(\frac{\gamma_0\gamma_1}{\gamma_1}\right) + k_4^0[S_2O_3^{--}][MBrAc^-]\frac{\gamma_2\gamma_1}{\gamma_1}$$

$$\text{xv.62}$$

which, since γ_0 is unity, can be rewritten in the form

$$-\frac{1}{[S_2O_3^{--}][BrAc^-]} \cdot \frac{d[S_2O_3^{--}]}{dt} = k_2$$

$$= k_2^0\left[\frac{\gamma_1\gamma_2}{\gamma_3} + \frac{1}{k_2^0}\left(\frac{k_3^0}{K_1} + \frac{k_4^0}{K_2}\right)[M^{++}]\gamma_2^2\right] \qquad \text{xv.63}$$

From conductivity data on solutions of the separate salts, Davies and Monk (1963) have obtained accurate values for K_1 and K_2 which, combined with kinetic data and activity coefficients derived from solubilities, allow the evaluation of the bimolecular constants k_2^0, k_3^0 and k_4^0. From this intricate equation, k_4^0 is found to be insignificant, and k_2^0 and k_3^0 are found to be true constants. This means that, when quantitative allowance is made for the part played by ion pairs, the reaction between the bromacetate and the thiosulphate ions shows a positive electrolyte effect in accordance with the Brönsted–Bjerrum theory, and that the reaction between the bromacetate ion and the uncharged ion pair shows no electrolyte effect, which also agrees with the theory. Davies, having successfully explained the depressing influence of divalent anions on the rate of the reaction between the hydroxyl ion and the brompentammine–cobaltic ion in the same way, concludes that the varied salt effects predicted by Brönsted's theory are strictly obeyed when quantitative allowance, based on extra-kinetic data, is made for the incidence of ion-association. Olson and Simonson (1949), discussing Livingston's diagram, along with some supplementary data of their own on two of the reactions, conclude that 'for reactions between ions of the same charge . . . the rate is not dependent upon the ionic strength'. The kinetic data on which they drew this false conclusion had not at that time been adequately supplemented by independent estimates of activity coefficients.

Comment

The three reactions here considered have, despite their differences, one feature in common. None is, from the point of view of mechanism, as simple as the stoichiometric equation suggests. In each case, the rate-determining step is controlled by the concentration of intermediate substances – atoms in the hydrogen-bromine reaction, free radicals in the decomposition of dinitrogen pentoxide, and various complex ions in the bromacetate–thiosulphate reaction. The absolute magnitude of the bimolecular velocity coefficients in all these systems can be interpreted in terms of the classical kinetic theory.

Catalysed reactions

1. *General.* A substance which hastens a chemical reaction while retaining its identity is termed a catalyst. It may perform its work in many ways; for example, by initiating a chain mechanism or by lengthening previously established chains, by increasing the concentration of molecules of one reactant in the locality of another, or by lowering the energy of activation. The two most general laws of catalysis are that the instantaneous velocity of chemical change is proportional to the concentration of catalyst and that the energy of activation of the catalysed reaction is less than that of the uncatalysed reaction. If an uncatalysed chemical reaction $A \rightarrow P$ is accompanied by the catalysed reactions $A + B \rightarrow P + B$ and $A + D \rightarrow P + D$, the instantaneous velocity of chemical change is

$$-dc_A/dt = k_0 c_A + k_B c_A c_B + k_D c_A c_D$$

where the c terms are concentrations, k_0 is a first order constant, and k_B and k_D are the catalytic coefficients, which are seen to be second order constants. Since $k_1 = -(1/c_A)(dc_A/dt)$, we have

$$k_1 = k_0 + k_B c_B + k_D c_D$$

or more generally

$$k_1 = k_0 + \sum k_i c_i \qquad \text{xv.64}$$

The second general law of catalysis, i.e. the lowering of the apparent energy of activation, is exemplified by the data summarised in Table xv.3.

2. *Catalysis in non-polar solvents.* In carbon tetrachloride solution, beryllium benzoylcamphor mutarotates according to the law of opposing unimolecular reactions (equation xv.6) with an apparent energy of activation of 26 500 cal (Lowry and Traill, 1931). The reaction is powerfully catalysed by a variety of polar molecules, including pyridine, p-cresol and ethanol. The observed first order constant is found to be given in terms of the concentration, c_c, of catalyst, by the simplest form of equation xv.64:

$$k = k_0 + k_c c_c \qquad \text{xv.65}$$

where k_c, the catalytic coefficient, varies little from one catalyst to another. The apparent energy of activation of the catalysed reaction is approximately 18 600 cal. The data conform to equation xv.23 (Traill, 1932). In the same solvent the picryl ether of benzophenone undergoes the Beckmann rearrangement

$$
\begin{array}{ccc}
C_6H_5-C-C_6H_5 & & C_6H_5-C-O-C_6H_5(NO_2)_3 \\
\parallel & \rightarrow & \parallel \\
N-O-C_6H_2(NO_2)_3 & & C_6H_5-N
\end{array}
$$

unimolecularly, with $E_A = 27\,900$ cal (Chapman, 1936). Equation xv.65 again holds, and k_c, determined by the gradients shown in Fig. xv.5, increases as the dipole moment of the catalyst increases. E_A found for the various catalytic coefficients is about 23 600 cal, and equation xv.23 is obeyed. Chapman has shown that non-polar molecules also may act as catalysts, provided the internally compensating dipoles which they contain are sufficiently far apart not to cancel out each other's external fields. Thus *trans*-dichlorethylene has no catalytic efficiency, but p-dichlor-benzene is effective. E_A for the

469

Table xv.3

Reaction	Catalyst	E_A
The decomposition of hydrogen peroxide in aqueous solution	None	18 000
	Iodide ion	13 500
	Colloidal platinum	11 700
	Liver catalase	5 500
The decomposition of acetone-dicarboxylic acid in aqueous solution	None	23 200
	Aniline	13 900
The hydrolysis of sucrose in aqueous solution	Hydrogen ion	25 560
	Saccharase	8 700
The hydrolysis of casein in aqueous solution	Hydrochloric acid	20 600
	Trypsin-kinase	14 400
The decomposition of triethylsulphonium bromide in acetone solution	None	33 500
	4 per cent water	30 700
The decomposition of trinitrobenzoic acid in nitrobenzene solution	None	35 000
	Adventitious impurity, probably water	21 700
The decomposition of trichloracetic acid	Water (solvent)	37 050
	Aniline (solvent)	28 350
The Beckmann rearrangement of the picryl ether of benzophenone oxime in carbon tetrachloride solution	None	30 250
	Nitromethane	23 800
The decomposition of ethylene iodide in the gas phase and in carbon tetrachloride solution	None	37 000
	Iodine (atomic)	12 500
The decomposition of diethylether in the gas phase	None	53 500
	Iodine (molecular)	34 300

uncatalysed unimolecular decomposition of ethylene di-iodide $(C_2H_4I_2 \rightarrow C_2H_4 + I_2)$ is 37 500 cal, but for the reaction catalysed by the iodine atom $(C_2H_4I_2 + I \rightarrow C_2H_4 + I_2 + I)$ E_A is 12 500 cal in the gas phase (Kistiakowsky, 1935) and in carbon tetrachloride solution (Polissar, 1930). Here again, equation xv.23 is valid.

470

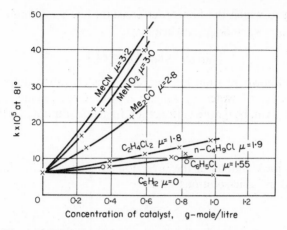

Fig. xv.5 *The catalysis of the Beckmann change by a variety of solutes* (after A. W. Chapman, 1934)

3. *Catalysis in aqueous solution.* As even pure water contains hydrogen ions and hydroxyl ions, any solute decomposing in it is liable to two catalytic influences, and equation xv.64 becomes

$$k_1 = k_0 + k_H c_H + k_{OH} c_{OH} \qquad \text{xv.66}$$

where c_H and c_{OH} stand for the concentrations of hydrogen ion and hydroxyl ions respectively, and k_H and k_{OH} are the corresponding catalytic coefficients, k_0 is usually referred to as the water constant. We shall denote it henceforth by the symbol k_W. By adding to the solution a highly ionised acid whose anion has no catalytic effect, we may suppress the concentration of hydroxyl ions to such an extent that the last component in the rate equation can be ignored. Then

$$k_1 = k_W + k_H c_H \qquad \text{xv.67}$$

Similarly, by adding a highly ionised base whose cation has no catalytic effect, we may suppress the second term in equation xv.66 to negligible proportions, obtaining conditions for which

$$k_1 = k_W + k_{OH} c_{OH} \qquad \text{xv.68}$$

The two catalytic coefficients can, as a rule, be readily measured in this way. Since $K_W = c_H c_{OH}$, equation xv.66 may be written as follows,

$$k_1 = k_W + k_H c_H + k_{OH} K_W / c_H$$

471

according to which the first order constant has a minimum value of $k_W + 2k_H c_H = k_W + 2k_{OH} c_{OH}$ when

$$c_H/c_{OH} = k_{OH}/k_H = c_H^2/K_W \qquad \text{xv.69}$$

This well-known relationship enabled Wijs (1893) to determine the ionic product of water by kinetic means. Occasionally, the water constant k_W can be ignored altogether. In acidic solution, we then have

$$k_1 = k_H c_H \qquad \text{xv.70}$$

as found, for example, in the inversion of cane sugar in dilute solutions; and in basic solutions we have

$$k_1 = k_{OH} c_{OH} \qquad \text{xv.71}$$

as found, for example, in the decomposition of diacetone alcohol.

When weak acids or bases are used as the source of the catalyst, the solution contains undissociated molecules which, in addition to the hydrogen and hydroxyl ions, may catalyse the reaction. Thus, for example, in the catalytic hydrolysis of certain esters and in the catalytic enolisation of various ketones, the rate constant in the presence of a weak acid HA may be expressed as follows:

$$k_1 = -(1/c)(dc/dt) = k_W + k_H c_H + k_{OH} c_{OH} + k_{HA} c_{HA} + k_A c_A$$

where A represents the anion. It is impossible to say in advance which reactions are catalysed only by hydrogen ions and which are catalysed by acids in the general sense used by Lowry and Brönsted, according to whom an acid is any compound which can dissociate to yield a hydrogen ion. Brönsted (1928) found that the catalytic coefficient is related as follows to the dissociation constant of the acid:

$$k_A = aK_A^\alpha \qquad \text{xv.72}$$

a and α are specific isothermal constants for the system. A corresponding relation

$$k_B = bK_A^{-\beta} \qquad \text{xv.73}$$

holds for basic catalysis, where K_A is the dissociation constant of the acid from which the base is formed. This empirical relation is illustrated logarithmically in Fig. xv.6 where n is an integer. To translate these relationships into the realm of energy we must assume, though without direct experimental support, that a and α in acid catalysis, and

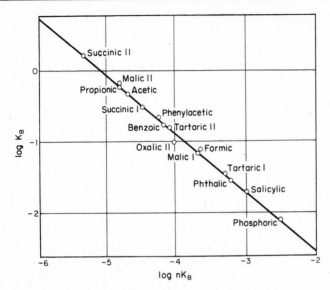

Fig. xv.6 *The general basic catalysis of the nitramide decomposition*

b and β in basic catalysis, are independent of temperature. Then

$$E_A = E_a + \alpha H_A \qquad \text{xv.74}$$

and

$$E_B = E_b - \beta H_A \qquad \text{xv.75}$$

where E_A, E_B stand for the Arrhenius energies of activation of the catalysed reactions, H for the increase in heat content attending the ionisation of the acid, and E_a, E_b are generic constants. On applying relation xv.74 to catalysis by hydrogen ion, for which H_A is obviously zero, we see that E_a is in fact E_H, so that

$$E_A = E_H + \alpha H_A \qquad \text{xv.76}$$

In words, the energy of activation for a reaction catalysed by an undissociated acid exceeds the energy of activation of the same re-action catalysed by hydrogen ion by an amount which is proportional to the energy of dissociation of the acid. This fact is one for which Horiuti and Polanyi (1935) have offered an interpretation in terms of the general theory of the forces holding the proton to the water mole-cule and to other bases. On applying relation xv.75 to catalysis by water molecules, for which H_A is again obviously zero, we see that

Q

473

$E_b = E_W$, so that

$$E_B = E_W - \beta H_A \qquad \text{xv.77}$$

On combining equation xv.76 as applied to catalysis by hydrogen ion and water molecules, with equation xv.77 as applied to catalysis by hydroxyl ion and water molecules, we have the evident result:

$$\frac{E_H - E_{OH}}{H_W} = \beta - \alpha \qquad \text{xv.78}$$

Experiment shows that the ratio on the left is 0·45 for a number of reactions; hence, very roughly,

$$(\beta - \alpha) \sim \tfrac{1}{2} \qquad \text{xv.79}$$

which agrees with the general observation that β is greater than α. Two cases of interest arise. When $\alpha = \tfrac{1}{2}$, $\beta = 1$; that is, $E_{OH} = E_b - H_W$. Applied to Pedersen's data (1934) on enolisation, this leads to a value of almost zero for the reaction as catalysed by hydroxyl ions. Secondly, when $\beta = \tfrac{1}{2}$, $\alpha = 0$; that is, there is no acid catalysis. We may therefore predict that β is not far off 0·5 for reactions which, like the catalytic hydrolysis of trichloracetic esters, are insensitive to hydrogen ions.

In the mutarotation of glucose, the ratio of the catalytic coefficients, k_D/k_H, using D_3O^+ and H_3O^+ at 25°C is 0·64, and $E_A(H) - E_A(D)$ is $-1\,250$ cal (Moelwyn-Hughes, 1934). The isotope effect in this reaction, as in most others which show general acid-base catalysis, is thus in the same direction as in gas reactions, and finds its principal explanation in the difference between the residual energies. In the hydrolysis of sucrose, on the other hand, k_D/k_H is 1·76 and $E_A(H) - E_A(D)$ is $+1\,450$ cal (Moelwyn-Hughes and Bonhoeffer, 1934). Similar ratios of catalytic coefficients and similar differences in the apparent energies of activation have been found for other reactions, such as the hydrolysis of ethyl orthoformate (Brescia and La Mer, 1940). The heavy isotope of hydrogen can thus be used to distinguish between the two types of acid catalysis (Bonhoeffer, 1934; Wynne-Jones, 1935). In the following familiar scheme for the catalysed hydrolysis of a substrate, S,

$$S + H^+ \underset{k_1}{\overset{k_2}{\rightleftarrows}} SH^+ \overset{k_3}{\to} P + H^+$$

the general expression for the catalytic coefficient, k, becomes

$$k = \frac{k_2 k_3}{k_1 + k_3} \qquad \text{xv.80}$$

which reduces to k_2 when $k_3 \gg k_1$, as in mutarotations and other proton-transfer reactions, and to $k_3(k_2/k_1)$ when $k_1 \ll k_3$ as in hydrolysis.

4. *Catalysis by hydrogen ion.* Hydrogen ion is the arch catalyst, and at least one instance of its behaviour must be examined in detail. We shall select for discussion the catalysed decomposition of ethyl diazoacetate in aqueous hydrochloric acid, which is conventionally written as follows:

$$N_2CH \cdot COOEt + H_2O \xrightarrow{H+} HOCH_2 \cdot COOEt + N_2$$

The first order constant, k_1, was found by Fraenkel (1907) to be proportional to the concentration, c_H, of hydrogen ion (equation xv.70), but to decrease, in ester-rich solutions, during a given run, due to the consumption of hydrogen ion in the substitution reaction

$$N_2CH \cdot COOEt + H^+ + X^- \rightarrow XCH_2 \cdot COOEt + N_2$$

A monometric examination of the reaction over a catalyst concentration range of 7×10^{-5} to 3×10^{-2} molar and a temperature range of 0 to 65°C (Moelwyn-Hughes and Johnson, 1941) confirmed these findings in the main, but led to the following empirical expression for the first order constant:

$$k_1 = k_0 + k_2 c_H + k_3 c_H^2 \qquad \text{xv.81}$$

The water constant, k_0, is too small to be measured with accuracy, and may probably be assumed to be zero, leaving

$$k_1 = k_2 c_H + k_3 c_H^2 \qquad \text{xv.82}$$

A thermometric evaluation of the velocity constant at 0°C has further extended our information in the catalyst concentration range of 0·25 to 2·50 molar (Albery and Bell, 1961). Moelwyn-Hughes and Johnson estimating the concentration of ethylmonochloracetate from the magnitude of the drifts in k_1, found it to vary from 5·5 to 20 per cent of the initial acid concentration. Albery and Bell have obtained by analysis the more reliable estimates of from 6·0 to 7·5 per cent, and have offered the following explanation of equation xv.82.

475

Hydrogen ion unites with the ethyl diazoacetate molecule, instantaneously forming a complex, with which it is in sustained equilibrium:

$$\overset{-}{N}{=}\overset{+}{N}{-}CH.COOEt + H^+ \rightleftarrows N{\equiv}\overset{+}{N}{-}CH_2.COOEt \qquad K = c_c/c_E c_H$$
$$c_E c_H c_C$$

The concentration of the complex is thus

$$c_C = K c_E c_H \qquad\qquad \text{xv.83}$$

assuming the activity coefficients of the ions to be identical, and that of the ester to be unity. There follow two rate-determining steps when the complex reacts simultaneously with a water molecule and with the anion of the acid:

$$N{\equiv}\overset{+}{N}{-}CH_2COOEt + H_2O \rightarrow N_2CH_2OH.COOEt + H^+ \qquad k_2'$$

$$N{\equiv}\overset{+}{N}{-}CH_2COOEt + X^- \rightarrow N_2 + CH_2X.COOEt \qquad k_3'$$

The net rate of reaction is thus

$$-\frac{dc_E}{dt} = k_2' c_C + k_3' c_C c_X$$
$$= k_2' K c_E c_H + k_3' K c_E c_H c_X$$
$$= k_2 c_E c_H + k_3 c_E c_H c_X$$

Electrical neutrality demands that the concentration of hydrogen ion at any time is equal to that of the anion, X^-. Hence, since

$$k_1 = -(1/c_E)(dc_E/dt)$$
$$k_1 = k_2 c + k_3 c^2 \qquad\qquad \text{xv.82}$$

Another mechanism, often advanced, is that the rate-determining step is the spontaneous break-down of the complex into N_2 and the substituted carbonium ion $\overset{+}{C}H_2.COOEt$, which then reacts rapidly with water and the anion. If this mechanism held, the relative amounts of ethyl gloccolate and the ethyl ester of the monosubstituted acetic acid would depend solely on the concentration of the catalyst, which is contrary to what Albery and Bell find. At the same concentration of acid, the net rate of decomposition is not the same with hydrochloric as it is with perchloric acid.

5. *Surface catalysis.* The key to the kinetics of catalysis by surfaces – a subject of great industrial importance – is provided by Langmuir's

476

theory, which, applied to the adsorption of one substrate (solute or gaseous) on a surface in the presence of a second substrate has already been formulated (equation XIV.63). We shall here first consider the simplest type of surface catalysis, which is found when only one type of substrate is adsorbed, and the rate of reaction is proportional to the extent of adsorption.

When the concentration of substrate molecules is n_S, and the number of sites per unit area of surface is n_0, we obtain, by the method previously used, the following expression for the fraction of the total number of surface sites which are occupied

$$\theta_S = \frac{k_S n_S}{n_0 v_S + k_S n_S} \qquad \text{XV.84}$$

Here $k_S = (kT/2\pi m_S)^{1/2} \cdot \exp(-E_2/kT)$, where E_2 denotes any energy which may be necessary before a molecule arriving at a site can occupy it, and v_S, the probability per second that an adsorbed molecule shall undergo chemical change is $v_S^0 \cdot \exp(-E_1/kT)$, where E_1 is the energy required by an adsorbed molecule before it can decompose. The rate of chemical change in a system exposing a surface area 0 cm^2 is thus

$$-\frac{dN_S}{dt} = 0 n_0 v_S \frac{k_S n_S}{n_0 v + k_S n_S}$$

Writing $V\, dn_S$ for dN_S, where V is the volume of the system, we have

$$-\frac{dn_S}{dt} = \frac{0 n_0 v_S}{V} \cdot \frac{k_S n_S}{n_0 v_S + k_S n_S} = r \qquad \text{XV.85}$$

At low concentrations of substrate, the reaction is seen to be one of the first order, since

$$-\frac{dn_S}{dt} = \frac{0 k_S}{V} \cdot n_S \qquad \text{XV.86}$$

and at high concentrations of substrate, the reaction is seen to be one of zero order, since

$$-\frac{dn_S}{dt} = \frac{0 n_0 v_S}{V} = R \qquad \text{XV.87}$$

The ratio of the rate of reaction generally to the limiting rate, R, is evidently

$$\frac{r}{R} = \frac{n_S}{(n_0 v_S/k_S) + n_S} \qquad \text{xv.88}$$

which has the form, established by Michaelis and Menten (1913), of the most widely applicable equation in enzyme kinetics. The bracketed term is known as the Michaelis constant: it is the value of n_s when $r/R = \frac{1}{2}$. The change in apparent kinetic order from 1 to zero as the concentration increases resembles the change from 2 to 1 later found for gas reactions. When the catalytic surface is provided by spherical particles of concentration n_E and radius r_E, the total catalytic surface in the system is $4\pi r_E^2 n_E V$, and the number of substrate molecules decomposing per unit volume per unit time is, according to equation xv.86.

$$-\frac{dn_S}{dt} = n_E n_S r_E^2 \sqrt{\frac{8\pi kT}{m_S}} \; e^{-E_2/RT}$$

But the second-order catalytic coefficient under the conditions imagined is defined by the equation $-(dn_S/dt) = (N_0/1\,000)\,k_2 n_E n_S$. Hence, in litres per mole-second,

$$k_2 = \frac{N_0 r_E^2}{1\,000} \sqrt{\left(\frac{8\pi kT}{m_S}\right)} \; e^{-E_2/RT} \qquad \text{xv.89}$$

Applied to the case of benzoylarginine ($m_S = 278/N_0$), hydrolysed by trypsin ($r_E = 2 \cdot 62 \times 10^{-7}$ cm), we obtain the theoretical formula

$$k_2 = 11 \cdot 4 \times 10^{10} \times \sqrt{T} \times e^{-E_2/RT}$$

The experimental results may be summarised in the form:

$$k_2 = 9 \cdot 2 \times 10^{10} \times \sqrt{T} \times e^{-E/RT}$$

where $E_2 = 15\,000$ cal (Butler, 1941). The catalytic effects of sucrase (Moelwyn-Hughes, 1929), catalase (Haldane, 1931), carbonic-anhydrase (Roughton, 1934) and choline-esterase (Easson and Stedman, 1936) have been examined in the same way. Equation xv.89 is recognised as a special case of equation xv.23.

When two kinds of substrates are adsorbed, we solve two simultaneous equations of the Langmuir type, obtaining

$$\theta_S = \frac{k_S n_S}{n_0 v_S + k_S n_S + k_I (v_S/v_I) n_I} \qquad \text{xv.90}$$

where the subscript I refers to the second substrate. Inhibition of surface-catalysed reactions is explained by the fact that inhibitors are more firmly adsorbed than the reacting substrate. If the inhibitor is a product of the reaction, we can replace n_I by $(n_S^0 - n_S)$, where n_S^0 is the initial concentration of substrate. Then

$$-\frac{dn_S}{dt} = \frac{O n_0 v_S}{V} \cdot \frac{k_S n_S}{n_0 v_S + k_S n_S + k_I (v_S/v_I)(n_S^0 - n_S)} \qquad \text{xv.91}$$

Now n_S may be written as $(a - x)$ and $(n_S^0 - n_S)$ as x, where a is the initial concentration of substrate, and x the decrease in its value at time, t. Then since k_S and k_I can be taken as commensurate, while $v_I \ll v_S$, the equation approximates to

$$\frac{dx}{dt} = k\left(\frac{a-x}{x}\right)$$

Under these conditions, the instantaneous velocity of reaction is proportional to the concentration of substrate still unreacted and inversely proportional to the concentration of products. Integration gives the equation

$$kt = a \ln\left(\frac{a}{a-x}\right) - x$$

Hence, during the early stages of the reaction

$$x = (2akt)^{1/2} \qquad \text{xv.92}$$

Since k is proportional, through O, to the concentration of enzyme, we see that the extent of chemical change is proportional to the square root of the product of the enzyme concentration and the time. This is the well known law of Schütz (1900) which has been extensively verified by Armstrong, Euler, Northrop, Waldschmidt–Leitz and Willstatter in the peptic, tryptic and pancreatic digestion of peptides and proteins and in the enzymic hydrolysis of carbohydrates and fats. The inhibitive effect of oxygen on the rate of decomposition of nitric oxide and nitrous oxide in the presence of platinum (Hinshelwood, 1926) can be explained in terms of equation xv.92, with pressures replacing concentrations.

Langmuir has considered catalysis by surfaces, extended and dispersed, between molecules of different kinds, when only the reacting molecules, and not the products of reaction, are adsorbed. Even under these limited conditions, there is scope for a wide variety of kinetic behaviour. If, for example, the rate of reaction depends on collisions of molecules of type 2 in solution or in the gas phase with adsorbed molecules of type 1, the rate becomes proportional to $n_2\theta_1$. Equally possible is the complementary mechanism which makes the rate proportional to $n_1\theta_2$. If the reaction depends on the simultaneous occupancy of neighbouring sites by the different molecules, the rate becomes proportional to $\theta_1\theta_2$. In this case, the velocity of reaction may be proportional to the product of the concentrations n_1n_2 in the continuous phase, or proportional to n_1 and independent of n_2, or to n_2 and independent of n_1. Moreover, when the extent of adsorption is proportional to the square root of the gas pressure, the adsorbed state is an atomic one, as, for example, in the reactions between oxygen and ethylene (Twigg, 1936) and between oxygen and hydrogen (Hinshelwood, Moelwyn-Hughes, and Rolfe, 1933) in the presence of metallic silver.

Processes controlled by diffusion

If diffusion is the slowest step in a sequence of steps, the rate at which molecules diffuse towards a surface of other molecules may determine the net rate of reaction. Fick's first law

$$\frac{dN}{dt} = -DO\frac{\partial n}{\partial R} \qquad \text{xv.93}$$

applied to spherical diffusion, when $O = 4\pi R^2$, leads directly to the second law

$$\frac{d(Rn)}{dt} = D\frac{\partial^2(Rn)}{\partial R^2} \qquad \text{xv.94}$$

D is the coefficient of diffusion, and n the molecular concentration at a distance R from the origin. A solution of sufficient mathematical validity for us is

$$n = A + \frac{B}{R} \qquad \text{xv.95}$$

where A and B are constants, to be determined by boundary conditions.

Let us first consider the rate of escape of molecules by evaporation from a spherical particle of radius r. When $R = r$, $n = n^0$, the saturation concentration of the vapour, and when R is infinite, n is zero.

Then

$$n = n^0 \frac{r}{R} \qquad \text{xv.96}$$

From Fick's first law, with $O = 4\pi R^2$, we see that the number of molecules escaping per second is

$$\frac{dN}{dt} = 4\pi n^0 Dr \qquad \text{xv.97}$$

The rate of loss of weight of the particle is

$$-\frac{dW}{dt} = m\frac{dN}{dt} = 4\pi m n^0 Dr \qquad \text{xv.98}$$

This equation has been used to measure the coefficient of diffusion of iodine (Langmuir, 1918) and the saturation vapour pressure of numerous solids and liquids (Bradley, 1949). If the concentration of molecules in the solid or liquid sphere be denoted by n_L, the number of molecules in it is $N_L = \frac{4}{3}\pi r^3 n_L$, so that $dN_L/dr = 4\pi r^2 n_L$. The rate of diminution of the radius of the particle is

$$-\frac{dr}{dt} = -\frac{dr}{dN_L} \cdot \frac{dN_L}{dt} = \frac{D}{r} \frac{n^0}{n_L}$$

The life time of the sphere is thus found to be

$$t = \int_0^t dt = -\frac{1}{D}\frac{n_L}{n^0}\int_r^0 r\, dr = \frac{r^2}{2D}\frac{n_L}{n^0} \qquad \text{xv.99}$$

The rate of diminution of the area is similarly found:

$$\frac{dO}{dt} = \frac{dO}{dr} \cdot \frac{dr}{dt} = -8\pi D(n^0/n_L),$$

from which it follows that the surface area of a spherical droplet diminishes linearly with respect to the time (Topley and Whytlaw–Gray, 1927):

$$O_t = O_0 - 8\pi D(n^0/n_L)t \qquad \text{xv.100}$$

Let us next consider diffusion to a spherical surface at which the molecules are changed or destroyed. When R, of equation xv.96, is infinite, n is n^0, the bulk concentration; and when $R = r$, n is zero.

We now have

$$n = n^0 \left(1 - \frac{r}{R}\right) \qquad \text{xv.101}$$

and therefore

$$\frac{dN}{dt} = -4\pi D n^0 r$$

The number of molecules diffusing per second from the surface of a sphere of radius r under those conditions is thus negative, and $-dN/dt$ is consequently the number of molecules which, by the process of diffusion, reach this surface in unit time. This we may regard as the number of collisions made per second by molecules of type A with one molecule of type B, provided r is now identified with the sum of the radii, $r_A + r_B$, and D, to be denoted by D_A, is the coefficient of diffusion of molecules of type A. The total number of collisions made per unit volume per unit time, would, on this reckoning be $4\pi D_A(r_A + r_B)n_A n_B$. Had we argued the other way round, we would have found a similar expression, but with D_B instead of D_A. The mean frequency of collisions is therefore taken as

$$Z = 2\pi(D_A + D_B)(r_A + r_B)n_A n_B \qquad \text{xv.102}$$

On using the Stokes–Einstein equation (II.28), we obtain Smoluchowski's result (1918)

$$Z = \frac{kT}{3\eta} \frac{(r_A + r_B)^2}{r_A r_B} n_A n_B \qquad \text{xv.103}$$

which, for collisions between identical spheres, yields the equation

$$Z = \frac{4kT}{3\eta} n^2 \qquad \text{xv.104}$$

If, therefore, change takes place simply when particles meet, the bimolecular velocity constant is

$$k_2 = \tfrac{4}{3}(kT/\eta) \qquad \text{xv.105}$$

Such is the case with the coagulation of gold sol in water (Zsigmondy, 1918; Wiegner and Tuorila, 1926) and aerial dispersions of various solids (Whytlaw–Gray, 1932). Quantitative agreement with Smoluchowski's equation is found for particles with radii ranging from 37 to 970 Å.

482

Fluorescence and the quenching of resonance radiation, in gases and in solutions, are other phenomena to which equation xv.102 applies. The simplest instance to examine is that where molecules of type A become electronically excited by the absorption of mono-chromatic radiation, and thereafter either emit radiation spon-taneously or are deprived of their excitation energy by radiationless transfers during collisions with molecules of type B:

$$A + h\nu \rightarrow A^x \quad : k_0$$
$$A^x \quad \rightarrow A \quad : k_1$$
$$A^x + B \rightarrow A + B : k_2$$

The stationary concentration, e, of excited molecules is given by $de/dt = k_0 n_A - k_1 e - k_2 e n_B = 0$. The rate of emission of light is $k_1 n_e$, and the intensity of the emitted light is $h\nu k_1 n_e$, or

$$I = \frac{h\nu k_0 k_1 n_A}{k_1 + k_2 n_B} \qquad \text{xv.106}$$

The ratio of the intensity, I^0, of light emitted in the absence of the quenching ($n_B = 0$) to that in its presence is then

$$\frac{I_0}{I} = 1 + \frac{k_2}{k_1} n_B \qquad \text{xv.107}$$

from which k_2/k_1 may be derived. Einstein has shown how k_1 can be found from the coefficient of absorption. For the excited mercury atom ($6^3 P_1$), for example, k_1 is 9.1×10^{-6} sec^{-1}. With H_2 as quencher, equation xv.107 accounts quantitatively for the experimental value of k_2, indicating that de-excitation occurs at every binary encounter. With N_2, CO, CO_2 and H_2O, the observed values of k_2 are lower than those estimated from equation II.13, so that there is a slight inefficiency of de-excitation during collision. The helium atom is wholly ineffective (Stern and Volmer, 1919). Most anions quench the fluorescence of the quinine ion in water, the order of diminishing effectiveness being $I^- > CNS^- > Br^- > Cl^- > NO_3^- > F^-$ (Wawi-low, 1929). The proportionality between k_2 and T/η required by Smoluchowski's theory has been experimentally confirmed for this system in water over a temperature range of 79°.

Semenoff (1929) has shown that the rate of decrease in the concentration, n, of molecules in a cylinder of diameter, d, is

$$-dn/dt = \frac{12D}{d^2} n \qquad \text{xv.108}$$

when every molecule reaching the surface of the cylinder by diffusion is destroyed.

Chain reactions

The second and third steps in the hydrogen-bromine reaction ($Br + H_2 \rightarrow HBr + H$ and $H + Br_2 \rightarrow HBr + Br$) each account for the formation of one molecule of product. In the second step, however, an atom of bromine is destroyed and an atom of hydrogen generated, while in the third step an atom of hydrogen is destroyed and an atom of bromine formed. Such a sequence is typical of chain reactions, where, as a rule, there are two chain carriers, like the free atoms in this reaction, which are alternately formed and removed in those steps which produce the product. The inherently unstable intermediaries may diffuse to the wall of the reaction vessel, where they are destroyed, or may react rapidly with adventitious impurities. Sensitivity to the nature and extent of the surface and to the presence of impurities is a distinctive feature of chain reactions. Another distinguishing characteristic is, in general, a complicated expression for the net rate of reaction. Bodenstein (1913) applied these ideas to the photochemical reaction between hydrogen and chlorine. A simple but widely applicable formulation of chain reactions has been given as follows by Christiansen and Kramers (1923).

Active molecules of reactant are assumed to reach a stationary concentration, a, according to the equation

$$da/dt = k_2 n^2 - k_3 a - k_4 na + \alpha k_6 nb = 0$$

The first three terms have the same meaning as in the molecular treatment of the decomposition of dinitrogen pentoxide. The fourth term allows for the formation of active molecules of reactants by collisions between normal molecules and active molecules of products, whose stationary concentration, b, is given by the equation

$$db/dt = k_3 a - k_6 nb = 0$$

The important factor α is included in the equation because not all the collisions between normal molecules and active products which succeed in deactivation are successful in generating active molecules of reactants. After eliminating the product $k_6 b$ from these equations, and noting that the rate of chemical change is $k_3 a$, we find, for the instantaneous velocity of reaction

$$-\frac{dn}{dt} = \frac{k_2 n^2}{(k_4/k_3)n + (1-\alpha)} \qquad \text{xv.109}$$

When α is zero, we recover equation xv.38, derived for thermal reactions. When α is unity, the reaction becomes one of the first order at all concentrations. If the first term in the denominator were negligible compared with the second term, we would have second-order kinetics, since

$$-\frac{dn}{dt} = k_2 n^2 \left(\frac{1}{1-\alpha}\right) \qquad \text{xv.110}$$

Thus, for each activating collision between normal molecules, a number $1/(1-\alpha)$ of molecules undergo chemical change. When α is less than, but very near to unity, this number, known as the chain length, can be very large. Bäckström (1931) found it to be 5×10^4 for the oxidation of the sulphite ion in water. Finally, when α exceeds unity, a collision resulting in the destruction of one chain carrier results in the appearance of more than one chain carrier of the other kind. Unless further destructive changes occur within the system, the concentration of chain carriers increases indefinitely, and the rate becomes infinite, or explosive, when $\alpha = 1 + (k_4/k_3)n$. The chains in such cases are said to branch.

Lower explosion limits

When oxygen is mixed with oxidisable gases or vapours, reaction takes place at a measurable rate provided the total pressure is either below a certain limit, P_1, or above another limit, P_2. At intermediate pressures, the reactions get out of hand, and the mixtures explode. We shall give here with an elementary theory of the conditions governing the lower explosion limit.

We shall suppose that the rate at which chain carriers are produced and destroyed is given by the equation $da/dt = k_0 + k_1 a - k_2 a$, which gives on integration

$$a = \frac{k_0}{k_1 - k_2} [e^{(k_1 - k_2)t} - 1].$$

When more chain carriers are destroyed than are formed per second, $(k_2 > k_1)$, there results an exponential, or first-order, decrease of the concentration of a with respect to time. When $k_2 < k_1$, a increases exponentially with respect to time, and the rate of reaction, which is proportional to a, correspondingly increases. The change from a quiet and measurable reaction rate to a violent and uncontrollable reaction rate corresponds to the condition $k_1 = k_2$. Now the rate at which chain carriers are generated under branching chains conditions is $(da/dt)_1 = Z_0 n_A a\beta[n_B/(n_A + n_B)] + Z_0 n_B a\beta[n_A/(n_A + n_B)]$, where $Z_0 na$ is the total number of collisions made per unit volume and unit time between normal reactants and chain carriers, the molar fractions represent the probability that collisions of the carriers with one type of reactant will be accompanied or followed by collisions with the other type of reactant, and β denotes the remaining probability that the collisions result in branching. Then $k_1 = 2Z_0\beta[n_A n_B/(n_A + n_B)]$. If the only mechanism which results in the destruction of chain carriers at low pressures is their diffusion to, and destruction at, the walls of the vessel, we have, for a cylindrical reactor, Semenoff's equation $(da/dt)_2 = -(12D/d^2)a$, or $k_2 = 12D/d^2$. The lower explosion limit is thus given by the equation

$$\frac{Z_0\beta d^2}{6D}\left(\frac{n_A n_B}{n_A + n_B}\right) = 1 \qquad \text{xv.111}$$

By extending the Stefan–Maxwell theory of diffusion in binary gas mixtures to ternary systems, it can be shown that, approximately,

$$Z_0/D = 2\pi\sigma^4(n_A + n_B + n_M) \qquad \text{xv.112}$$

where σ is a mean molecular 'diameter' and n_M is the concentration of the third component. On using the ideal gas laws ($p_i = n_i kT$), the conditions governing the lower explosion limit are seen to be

$$\frac{\beta\pi\sigma^4 d^2}{3(kT)^2}p_A p_B\left(1 + \frac{p_M}{p_A + p_B}\right) = 1 \qquad \text{xv.113}$$

which has been verified in all particulars for the oxidation of phosphorus (Chariton and Walta, 1926), phosphine (Dalton and Hinshelwood, 1930) and hydrogen (Hinshelwood and Moelwyn-Hughes, 1932). The factor β in the last reaction is found to be 2.5×10^{-3}.

486

Photochemical reactions

When a system of diatomic molecules is irradiated with light of frequency v, the molecules dissociate into atoms, provided the quantum hv is not less than the energy of dissociation, D. The threshold frequency, below which light is ineffective, is given by the equation $hv = D$. For each quantum of light, of wave length less than $4\,040\,\text{Å}$, absorbed by hydrogen iodide, two molecules decompose. This quantum efficiency of 2, which holds over a temperature range from 300 to 448°K and over a pressure range from 0·0075 to 2 660 mm (Warburg, 1918; Bonhoeffer and Farkas, 1928) has been explained by supposing, with Einstein, that in the primary act of photolysis, one molecule is decomposed for each quantum of light absorbed. The atoms so formed then undergo two rapid changes according to the scheme

$$HI + hv \rightarrow H + I \qquad \text{primary photochemical change}$$

$$\left.\begin{array}{l} H + HI \rightarrow H_2 + I \\ I + I + M \rightarrow I_2 + M \end{array}\right\} \quad \text{secondary dark reactions}$$

$$\overline{2HI + hv \rightarrow H_2 + I_2} \qquad \text{total reaction.}$$

The rate of reaction in this case is thus the rate of absorption of radiation. In the reaction between hydrogen and bromine, there is a similar photochemical production of halogen atoms, but this is supplemented by their thermal generation, according to the scheme already described, which must now be amended to read as follows:

$$
\begin{array}{llll}
(1) & Br_2 + M \rightarrow 2Br + M & ; k_1 & , \\
(2) & Br + H_2 \rightarrow HBr + H & ; k_2 & , \\
(3) & H + Br_2 \rightarrow HBr + Br & ; k_3 & , \\
(4) & H + HBr \rightarrow H_2 + Br & ; k_4 & , \\
(5) & Br + \text{wall} \rightarrow \tfrac{1}{2}Br_2 & ; k_5 & , \\
(6) & Br + Br + M \rightarrow Br_2 + M & ; k_6 & , \\
(7) & Br_2 + hv \rightarrow 2Br & ; k_7 = I.
\end{array}
$$

Steps 2, 3 and 4 are as in the earlier treatment. Steps 1 and 6 take cognisance of the established mechanisms governing the thermal dissociation of diatomic molecules and the recombination of atoms. The additional steps 5 and 7 are self-explanatory, as is the fact that k_7 must be proportional to the intensity of light. On applying the stationary state hypothesis, we now find the rate equation

$$\frac{d[\text{HBr}]}{dt} = \frac{2k_2[\text{H}_2]}{1 + \frac{k_4}{k_3}\frac{[\text{HBr}]}{[\text{Br}_2]}} \cdot \frac{\sqrt{(8k_6[M][\text{Br}_2]\{2k_1[M]+I\}+k_5^2)} - k_5}{4k_6[M]} \qquad \text{xv.114}$$

For experiments carried out at pressures sufficiently great to allow the wall effect to be ignored, we evidently have (using equation xv.30)

$$\frac{\text{rate of photochemical reaction}}{\text{rate of thermal reaction}} = \sqrt{\left(\frac{2k_1[M]+I}{2k_1[M]}\right)} \qquad \text{xv.115}$$

from which k_1 may be determined. Its value is found to agree with that computed from the equilibrium constant governing the dissociation of bromine into atoms (Bodenstein and Cramer, 1916) and the rate of combination of bromine atoms (Steiner, 1936). Because any kind of atom or molecule serves almost equally well as the third body in the recombination of bromine atoms, the term $k_1[M]$ may be taken as a constant, proportional to k_1 $(p_{\text{H}_2}+p_{\text{Br}_2}+p_{\text{HBr}})$. Jost and Jung's analysis indicates that k_5 is proportional to $1/(p_{\text{H}_2}+5p_{\text{Br}_2}+3p_{\text{HBr}})$, as one would expect if the rate of destruction of bromine atoms due to step 5 is governed by diffusion.

The statistical formulation of kinetic equations

In terms of the partition functions, f_i, and the concentration terms, $q_i = n_i f_i/e$, the equilibrium constant governing the formation of a complex $ABC\ldots$ from the reactants $A, B, C\ldots$ is given, for dilute solutions and gaseous systems by the equation

$$K = \frac{n_{ABC\ldots}}{n_A \cdot n_B \cdot n_C \ldots} = \frac{q_{ABC\ldots}}{q_A \cdot q_B \cdot q_C \ldots} \cdot e^{-E_0/kT} \qquad \text{xv.116}$$

where E_0 is the total energy of the complex less the sum of the total energies of the reactants at the absolute zero of temperature. If the complex can, in addition to reverting to its progenitors, decompose into products, P, at a rate insufficient to upset the equilibrium, the rate of production of products is

$$\frac{dn_P}{dt} = v_x n_{ABC\ldots} = v_x K n_A n_B n_C \ldots$$

where v_x is the probability per second that the complex shall decompose. The velocity constant is therefore

$$k_n = \frac{1}{n_A n_B n_C \ldots} \cdot \frac{dn_P}{dt} = v_x K = \frac{q_{ABC\ldots}}{q_A q_B q_C \ldots} \cdot e^{-E_0/kT} v_x \quad \text{XV.117}$$

In an isomeric equilibrium $A \rightleftarrows X$, where v_A is large and v_x small, and E_0 is confined to one bond, we have (equation XIII.76)

$$K = \frac{n_x}{n_A} = \frac{kT}{hv_x}(1 - e^{-hv_A/kT})e^{-E_0/kT} \quad \text{XV.118}$$

which has been amply verified for stable equilibria. These are distinguished from the kinetic equilibria with which we are here concerned in that v_x is real for stable equilibria, but imaginary for the critically activated complexes occurring in kinetic equilibria. Nevertheless, since the unimolecular constant, k_1, is Kv_x, it is real, and is

$$k_1 = \frac{kT}{h}(1 - e^{-hv_A/kT}) \cdot e^{-E_0/kT} \quad \text{XV.119}$$

This equation was first derived, in another way, by Herzfeld (1919). If the bond to be broken is very stable in the ground state, we have the approximation

$$k_1 = (kT/h)e^{-E_0/kT} \quad \text{XV.120}$$

It follows that $E_A = E_0 + kT$, and therefore

$$k_1 = (kTe/h)e^{-E_A/kT} \quad \text{XV.121}$$

The constant A, of the Arrhenius equation, should accordingly be kTe/h. Its value at 285°K is $1·61 \times 10^{13}\text{sec}^{-1}$ and at 760°K is $4·30 \times 10^{13}$. While these estimates compare favourably with the empirical constants of Table XV.4, it must not be overlooked that observed unimolecular constants are, as in the N_2O_5 case, frequently composite.

In Chapter XIII there was derived the statistical expression XIII.82 for the equilibrium established between atom A and molecule BC on the one hand, and the linear triatomic molecule ABC on the other hand, when one of the internal vibration frequencies of the complex molecule has a small value, v_t. An equation of the same form can be applied to the equilibrium between the reactants A and BC and a critically activated complex, ABC, provided v_t is now recognised as an

Table xv.4 *Arrhenius constants for certain reactions of the first kinetic order*

No.	Reaction	A (sec^{-1})	E_A (cal/g-mol)	Average Temperature (°K)
1	$Cl.COO.CCl_3 \rightarrow 2COCl_2$	$1\cdot4 \times 10^{13}$	14 500	285
2	$N_2O_5 \rightarrow N_2O_4 + \tfrac{1}{2}O_2$	$4\cdot57 \times 10^{13}$	24 710	306
3	$CH_3ONO \rightarrow CH_3O + NO$	$1\cdot8 \times 10^{13}$	36 400	488
4	$C_2H_5Br \rightarrow C_2H_4 + HBr$	$9\cdot1 \times 10^{13}$	52 000	666
5	$(CH_3)_2O \rightarrow CH_4 + HCHO$	$2\cdot4 \times 10^{13}$	58 500	760

1. Ramsperger and Waddington, (1933).
2. Daniels and Johnston, (1928).
3. Steacie and Katz, (1937).
4. Goldberg and Daniels, (1957).
5. Hinshelwood and Askey, (1927).

imaginary frequency. On multiplying the equilibrium constant K of equation xiii.82 by v_t, the following equation is obtained for the bimolecular velocity constant (Pelzer and Wigner, 1932; Farkas and Wigner, 1936)

$$k_2 = \frac{1}{4}\left(\frac{h}{2\pi}\right)^2\left(\frac{2\pi}{kT}\right)^{1/2}\left[\frac{m_A+m_B+m_C}{m_A(m_B+m_C)}\right]^{3/2}\frac{I_{ABC}}{I_{AB}}\frac{\sigma_{BC}}{\sigma_{ABC}}$$

$$\times \frac{\sinh \beta v_{BC}}{\sinh \beta v_s \sinh^2 \beta v_\phi}e^{-E_s/kT} \qquad \text{xv.122}$$

Here $\beta = h/2kT$, and E_s is the difference between the energy of the critical complex and the sum of the energies of the reactants, all in vibrationless states. From the general definition of the apparent energy of activation, we see that

$$E_s = E_A + \tfrac{1}{2}kT + \tfrac{1}{2}hv_{BC}\coth \beta v_{BC} - \sum_{}^{3}\tfrac{1}{2}hv_i \coth \beta v_i \qquad \text{xv.123}$$

When applied to the reaction between Br and H_2 at 555°K, we have, in calories, for the first three terms, the experimental values

$$17\ 740 + 552 + 6\ 285 = 24\ 577,$$

so that

$$E_s = 24\ 577 - \sum_{}^{3}\tfrac{1}{2}hv_i \coth \beta v_i$$

To evaluate the last three terms requires a more detailed knowledge of the internal motions of the reactive complex than is possible to arrive at, although praiseworthy attempts have been made for this system and, earlier, for the ortho-para conversion of hydrogen (Farkas and Wigner, 1936). If the treatment is simplified on the assumption that the internal vibrations in the reactive complex are all classical, E_s becomes 21 265 cals. This we accept as an experimental datum. It remains to calculate E_s theoretically.

The quantal evaluation of the energy of activation

London (1929), extending the Heitler–London treatment of the covalent bond in diatomic systems to systems containing three atoms, showed that the energy of the linear arrangement is given by the expression

$$E = A + B + C + \{\tfrac{1}{2}[(\alpha - \beta)^2 + (\beta - \gamma)^2 + (\alpha - \gamma)^2]\}^{1/2} \qquad \text{xv.124}$$

where A, B and C are Coulombic components, and α, β and γ the resonance or exchange components. Eyring and Polanyi (1931) argued that the sums $A + \alpha$, $B + \beta$ and $C + \gamma$ are the experimental potential energies of the diatomic systems. This eliminates much guess-work and simplifies the computation, leaving open only one adjustable parameter, which is the ratio of A to $A + \alpha$, about which there is no general agreement or absolute guide. Values used range from 0·03 to 0·20. Taking the ratio as 0·14, equation xv.124 becomes

$$E = 0\cdot 14[(A + \alpha) + (B + \beta) + (C + \gamma)] + 0\cdot 61\{[(A + \alpha) - (B + \beta)]^2$$
$$+ [(B + \beta) - (C + \gamma)]^2 + [(A + \alpha) - (C + \gamma)]^2\}^{1/2} \qquad \text{xv.125}$$

Applied to the reaction between the bromine atom and the hydrogen molecule, $Br + H-H \rightarrow Br-H + H$, we have the initial, critical and final linear arrangements shown in Fig. xv.8 and the following expressions, adopting Morse functions:

$$(A + \alpha) = D_{H_2}^e[1 - e^{-a_{H_2}[r_1 - r_0(H_2)]}]^2,$$
$$(B + \beta) = D_{HBr}^e[1 - e^{-a_{HBr}[r_2 - r_0(HBr)]}]^2, \qquad \text{xv.126}$$
$$(C + \gamma) = D_{HBr}^e[1 - e^{-a_{HBr}[r_2 + r_1 - r_0(HBr)]}]^2,$$

where D^e is the experimental energy of dissociation (D) plus the residual energy ($\tfrac{1}{2}hv_0$). By combining equations xv.125 and xv.126, we

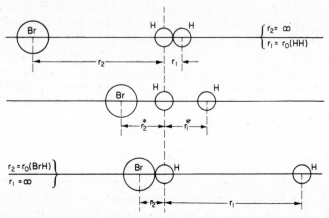

Fig. xv.7 *Initial, critical and final internuclear distances in the reaction* $Br + H_2 \rightarrow BrH + H$

obtain an expression for the potential energy of the triatomic system in terms of two spatial coordinates, r_1 and r_2, and are enabled to draw the energy contour map shown in Fig. xv.8. The initial system

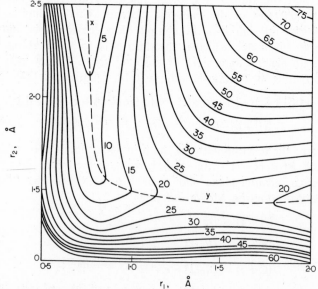

Fig. xv.8 *Potential energy diagram for the system* $Br \ldots H \ldots H$. *The contours are given in kilocalories/g. mol.*

492

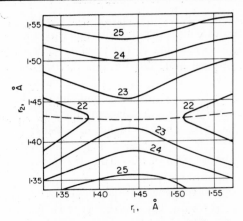

Fig. xv.9 *The energy of the* Br − H − H *system in the saddle region*

consists of a free bromine atom at an infinite distance away from a stable hydrogen molecule, and is represented by a point $[r_2 = \infty;\ r_1 = r_0(H_2);\ E = D^e_{H_2}]$ in the top left-hand corner. The final system corresponds to a free hydrogen atom, infinitely separated from a stable hydrogen bromide molecule, and is characterised by the point $[r_1 = \infty;\ r_2 = r_0(HBr);\ E = D^e_{HBr}]$. The passage of the system from its initial to its final state clearly corresponds to the occurrence of the chemical reaction Br + HH → BrH + H. The easiest of an infinite number of such passages is that traced by the broken line. If we imagine ourselves to take the place of the representative point of the reacting system, we can gain a clearer view of what happens. Starting at x, we climb a gentle ascent southwards in a valley flanked by mountains, those on our right being the steeper. Round about the position y there is a virtually horizontal walk, beyond which we descend into a second valley eastwards. The height of the pass is the energy of activation. The critically activated complex, represented by the point y, has certain definite probabilities of decomposing and of being formed in either of two ways: H + HBr ⇌ [H—H—Br] ⇌ H_2 + Br. From the magnified contour of the saddle region (Fig. xv.9), the complex is found to be characterised by $r_1^* = r_2^* = 1\cdot43\,\text{Å}$ and $E_s =$ 22 100 cal (Moelwyn-Hughes, 1935). The identity of r_1^* and r_2^* fits in with the hypothesis of D. S. Villars, (1930), according to which the energy of activation in reactions between diatomic molecules corresponds to the energy required to stretch the bond length of the smaller molecule so as to make it equal to that in the larger molecule. The

493

hypothesis accounts well for the energy of activation of the H_2—I_2 reaction, and the idea of having bonds of equal length has been applied to surface catalysis. Returning to the reaction between the bromine atom and the hydrogen molecule, we note that the theoretically calculated value of E_s (22,100) is in satisfactory agreement with the experimental value (21,265) given by equation xv.123. Moreover, the bimolecular constant is accurately reproduced by equation xv.122. A computed value of E_s which is higher by 3 000 cals. than the one given here has been found (Wheeler, Topley and Eyring, 1935) by adopting a Coulombic ratio of 0·20. Thus the method of calculating E_s is sensitive to the ratio adopted.

Calculations by Hirschfelder, Topley and Eyring (1936) on the kindred reaction $H + para\ H_2 \rightarrow ortho\ H_2 + H$ led to an energy contour differing from that shown in Figs. xv.8 and 9 by having a dip of depth 2 Kcals round the col at the point y. Recent work, however, by R. E. Weston (1959) and by F. T. Wall and R. N. Porter (1962) makes it clear that the contour for the $H_2 - H$ reaction resembles that given here for the $Br_2 - H$ reaction. There is no dip round the col, and therefore there is only one saddle point.

Appendices

Integrals of the type $\int e^{ax} x^n \, dx$

The first member may be integrated directly, giving

$$\int e^{ax} \, dx = \frac{e^{ax}}{a} + \text{constant } (C)$$

The second member is

$$\int e^{ax} x \, dx$$

Let

$$U = x, \quad \therefore \, dU = dx,$$

and

$$dV = e^{ax} \, dx, \quad \therefore V = \frac{e^{ax}}{a}$$

Now

$$\int U dV = UV - \int V dU \, ;$$

hence

$$\int e^{ax} x \, dx = e^{ax} \frac{x}{a} - \int \frac{e^{ax}}{a} \, dx = e^{ax} \frac{x}{a} - \frac{1}{a} \frac{e^{ax}}{a} + C$$

and therefore

$$\int e^{ax} x \, dx = \frac{e^{ax}}{a} \left(x - \frac{1}{a} \right) + C$$

The third member is

$$\int e^{ax} x^2 \, dx.$$

495

Let

$$U = x^2, \quad \therefore dU = 2x \, dx$$

and

$$dV = e^{ax} \, dx, \quad \therefore V = \frac{e^{ax}}{a}$$

hence

$$\int e^{ax} x^2 \, dx = \frac{x^2}{a} e^{ax} - 2 \int \frac{e^{ax}}{a} x \, dx$$

$$= \frac{2e^{ax}}{a^3} \left[\frac{(ax)^2}{2} - ax + 1 \right] + C$$

Generally,

$$\int e^{ax} x^n \, dx = \frac{e^{ax} n!}{a^{n+1}} \left[\frac{(ax)^n}{n!} - \frac{(ax)^{n-1}}{n-1!} + \frac{(ax)^{n-2}}{(n-2)!} - \cdots \frac{(ax)^{n-r}}{(n-r)!} \cdots + 1 \right] + C,$$

which holds for positive and negative values of a. Thus:

$$\int e^{-ax} x^n \, dx = \frac{-e^{ax} n!}{a^{n+1}} \left[\frac{(ax)^n}{n!} + \frac{(ax)^{n-1}}{(n-1)!} + \cdots + 1 \right] + C$$

The first member, integrated symmetrically from -1 to $+1$, gives us

$$\int_{-1}^{+1} e^{ax} \, dx = \left[\frac{e^{ax}}{a} \right]_{-1}^{+1} = \frac{1}{a}(e^{+a} - e^{-a}) = \frac{2}{a} \sinh a$$

The second member, integrated within the same limits, is

$$\int_{-1}^{+1} e^{ax} x \, dx = \left[\frac{e^{ax}}{a} \left(x - \frac{1}{a} \right) \right]_{-1}^{+1} = \frac{e^{+a}}{a} \left(1 - \frac{1}{a} \right) - \frac{e^{-a}}{a} \left(-1 - \frac{1}{a} \right)$$

$$= \frac{1}{a}(e^{+a} + e^{-a}) - \frac{1}{a^2}(e^{+a} - e^{-a})$$

$$= \frac{2}{a} \cosh a - \frac{2}{a^2} \sinh a$$

496

The ratio of the second integral to the first is

$$\coth a - \frac{1}{a}$$

which is known as Langerin's function.
Note that

$$\int_0^\infty e^{-ax} x^n \, dx = \frac{n!}{a^{n+1}}$$

APPENDIX 2

Integrals of the type $\displaystyle\int_0^\infty e^{-ax^2} x^n \, dx$

These integrals, which occur more frequently in physicochemical problems, may all be related to the first two members

$$\int_0^\infty e^{-ax^2} \, dx \qquad\qquad \text{A2.1}$$

and

$$\int_0^\infty e^{-ax^2} x \, dx \qquad\qquad \text{A2.2}$$

The latter may be evaluated first. Let

$$\eta = x^2$$

then

$$d\eta = 2x \, dx$$

and

$$\int_0^\infty e^{-ax^2} x \, dx = \frac{1}{2} \int_0^\infty e^{-a\eta} \, d\eta = \frac{1}{2} \left[\frac{e^{-a\eta}}{-a} \right]_0^\infty = \frac{1}{2a}$$

as found in the foregoing section. To integrate equation A2.1, first consider the integral

$$\int_0^\infty \int_0^\infty e^{-a(x^2 + y^2)} \, dx \, dy$$

Let

$$r^2 = x^2 + y^2$$

then

$$r \, dr \, d\theta = dx \, dy$$

and

$$\int_0^\infty \int_0^\infty e^{-a(x^2+y^2)} \, dx \, dy = \int_0^{\pi/2} \int_0^\infty e^{-ar^2} r \, dr \, d\theta = \frac{\pi}{2} \int_0^\infty e^{-ar^2} r \, dr$$

Substitute

$$z = r^2$$

so that

$$dz = 2r \, dr$$

and

$$\int_0^\infty e^{-ar^2} r \, dr = \frac{1}{2} \int_0^\infty e^{-az} \, dz = \frac{1}{2a}$$

Hence

$$\int_0^\infty \int_0^\infty e^{-a(x^2+y^2)} \, dx \, dy = \frac{\pi}{4a}$$

No restriction has been placed on the relative contributions of x^2 and y^2 to r^2; hence this relation is true in general, and in particular when $x = y$, i.e., when

$$\int_0^\infty \int_0^\infty e^{-a(x^2+y^2)} \, dx \, dy = \left[\int_0^\infty e^{-ax^2} \, dx \right]^2 = \left[\int_0^\infty e^{-ay^2} \, dy \right]^2$$

Consequently

$$\int_0^\infty e^{-ax^2} \, dx = \int_0^\infty e^{-ay^2} \, dy = \frac{1}{2} \sqrt{\frac{\pi}{a}}$$

Integrals of the same form are readily obtained for values of n greater than 1 or 2, by successively differentiating the lower integrals. The results may be summarised as follows:

498

n	Integral	n	Integral
0	$\int_0^\infty e^{-ax^2}\,dx = \frac{1}{2}\sqrt{\frac{\pi}{a}}$	1	$\int_0^\infty e^{-ax^2}x\,dx = \frac{1}{2a}$
2	$\int_0^\infty e^{-ax^2}x^2\,dx = \frac{1}{4}\sqrt{\frac{\pi}{a^3}}$	3	$\int_0^\infty e^{-ax^2}x^3\,dx = \frac{1}{2a^2}$
4	$\int_0^\infty e^{-ax^2}x^4\,dx = \frac{3}{8}\sqrt{\frac{\pi}{a^5}}$	5	$\int_0^\infty e^{-ax^2}x^5\,dx = \frac{1}{a^3}$
$\vdots$	$\vdots$	$\vdots$	$\vdots$
Even	$\int_0^\infty e^{-ax^2}x^n dx = 1.3.5\ldots(n-1)\dfrac{(\pi a)^{\frac{1}{2}}}{(2a)^{\frac{1}{2}n+1}}$	Odd	$\int_0^\infty e^{-ax^2}x^n\,dx = \dfrac{[\frac{1}{2}(n-1)]!}{2a^{\frac{1}{2}(n+1)}}$

Note that, when n is even, $\int_{-\infty}^{\infty} = 2\int_0^\infty$, and that when n is odd $\int_{-\infty}^{\infty} = 0$

APPENDIX 3

To integrate the expression

$$\iiint_{-\infty}^{\infty} e^{-\varepsilon/kT}\,dp_x\,dp_y\,dp_z$$

when $\varepsilon = (1/2m)(p_x^2 + p_y^2 + p_z^2)$, let us denote the sum of the squares of the momenta by R^2. Then

$$2m\varepsilon = p_x^2 + p_y^2 + p_z^2 = R^2$$

This is the equation of a sphere of radius R, and the rectangular volume element $dp_x dp_y dp_z$ in Cartesian coordinates may be replaced by the shell volume element $4\pi R^2 dR$ in polar coordinates:

$$dp_x\,dp_y\,dp_z = 4\pi R^2 dR$$

Now

$$R = (2m\varepsilon)^{1/2}$$

499

and
$$dR = (2m\varepsilon)^{-1/2}m\,d\varepsilon$$

The integral thus becomes
$$\int_0^\infty e^{-\varepsilon/kT}\,2\pi(2m)^{3/2}\varepsilon^{1/2}\,d\varepsilon$$

The limits of integration have been changed from zero to infinity, since we can never have a negative energy. The integral is now in a standard form
$$\int_0^\infty e^{-ax}\,x^n\,dx = n!/a^{n+1}$$

In this instance, $a = 1/kT$, $x = \varepsilon$, and $n = \frac{1}{2}$. Noting that $\frac{1}{2}! = \pi^{1/2}/2$
$$2\pi(2m)^{3/2}\int_0^\infty e^{-\varepsilon/kT}\varepsilon^{1/2}\,d\varepsilon = (2\pi mkT)^{3/2}$$

The distribution law now becomes
$$\frac{dN}{N} = \frac{e^{-\varepsilon/kT}\,dpx\,dpy\,dpz}{\displaystyle\int_{-\infty}^\infty e^{-\varepsilon/kT}\,dpx\,dpy\,dpz}$$

$$= \frac{e^{-\varepsilon/kT}2\pi(2m)^{3/2}\varepsilon^{1/2}\,d\varepsilon}{(2\pi mkT)^{3/2}}$$

$$= \frac{2\,e^{-\varepsilon/kT}\varepsilon^{1/2}\,d\varepsilon}{\pi^{1/2}(kT)^{3/2}} \qquad \text{II.35}$$

From equations II.35 and II.38,
$$\bar{\varepsilon} = \int_0^\infty \varepsilon\frac{dN}{N} = \frac{2}{\sqrt{\pi}}\frac{1}{(kT)^{3/2}}\int_0^\infty e^{-\varepsilon/kT}\varepsilon^{3/2}\,d\varepsilon$$

The constant a is again $1/kT$, but n is now 3/2, so that the integral here is
$$\frac{3\sqrt{\pi}}{4}\cdot(kT)^{5/2}$$

Hence
$$\bar{\varepsilon} = \tfrac{3}{2}kT \qquad \text{II.2}$$

From equations II.36 and II.38,
$$\bar{c} = \int_0^\infty c\frac{dN}{N} = \left(\frac{2}{\pi}\right)^{1/2}\left(\frac{m}{kT}\right)^{3/2}\int_0^\infty e^{-(mc^2/2kT)}c^3\,dc$$

When the integer n is odd, we have the general equation
$$\int_0^\infty e^{-ax^2}x^n\,dx = \frac{[(n-1)/2]!}{2a^{(n+1)/2}}$$

In this example, $n = 3$, and $a = m/2kT$. The integral is therefore $2(kT/m)^2$ and consequently

$$\bar{c} = (8kT/\pi m)^{1/2} \qquad \text{II.5}$$

which is the average velocity of an ideal gas molecule in space.

The average velocity in a given direction is obtained in the same way. Only the component of the kinetic energy in a given dimension need be considered, and the numerator in the expression

$$\bar{u} = \frac{\displaystyle\int_{0}^{\infty} e^{-\frac{1}{2}(mu^2/kT)} \cdot u \, du}{\displaystyle\int_{-\infty}^{\infty} e^{-\frac{1}{2}(mu^2/kT)} \, du}$$

must clearly be integrated from zero to infinity. Hence

$$\bar{u} = (kT/2\pi m)^{1/2} \qquad \text{II.6}$$

APPENDIX 4

Some useful expansions

When x^2 is less than unity, we have a number of useful expansions:

(1) *Binomial*

$$(1+x)^n = 1 + nx + \frac{n(n-1)}{2!} \cdot x^2 + \frac{n(n-1)(n-2)}{3!} \cdot x^3 + \cdots$$

$$(1-x)^n = 1 - nx + \frac{n(n-1)}{2!} \cdot x^2 - \frac{n(n-1)(n-2)}{3!} \cdot x^3 + \cdots$$

$$(1+x)^{-n} = 1 - nx + \frac{n(n+1)}{2!} \cdot x^2 - \frac{n(n+1)(n+2)}{3!} \cdot x^3 + \cdots$$

$$(1-x)^{-n} = 1 + nx + \frac{n(n+1)}{2!} \cdot x^2 + \frac{n(n+1)(n+2)}{3!} \cdot x^3 + \cdots$$

$$(1+x)^{-1} = 1 - x + x^2 - x^3 + \cdots$$

$$(1-x)^{-1} = 1 + x + x^2 + x^3 + \cdots$$

(2) *Logarithmic*

$$\ln(1+x) = x - \tfrac{1}{2}x^2 + \tfrac{1}{3}x^3 - \tfrac{1}{4}x^4 + \cdots$$

$$\ln(1-x) = -(x + \tfrac{1}{2}x^2 + \tfrac{1}{3}x^3 + \tfrac{1}{4}x^4 + \cdots)$$

$$\ln\frac{1+x}{1-x} = 2\left(x + \frac{x^3}{3} + \frac{x^5}{5} + \cdots\right)$$

(3) *Exponential*

$$e^x = 1+x+\frac{1}{2!}x^2+\frac{1}{3!}x^3+\cdots$$

$$e^{-x} = 1-x+\frac{1}{2!}x^2-\frac{1}{3!}x^3+\cdots$$

(4) *Trigonometric*

$$\sin x = x-\frac{x^3}{3!}+\frac{x^5}{5!}-\cdots$$

$$\cos x = 1-\frac{x^2}{2!}+\frac{x^4}{4!}-\cdots$$

$$\tan x = x+\frac{1}{3}x^3+\frac{2}{15}x^5+\cdots$$

$$\operatorname{cosec} x = \frac{1}{x}\left(1+\frac{1}{6}x^2+\frac{7}{360}x^4+\cdots\right)$$

$$\sec x = 1+\frac{1}{2}x^2+\frac{5}{24}x^4+\cdots$$

$$\cot x = \frac{1}{x}\left(1-\frac{1}{3}x^2-\frac{1}{45}x^4-\cdots\right)$$

(5) *Hyperbolic*

$$\sinh x = \frac{1}{2}(e^x-e^{-x}) = x+\frac{x^3}{3!}+\frac{x^5}{5!}+\cdots$$

$$\cosh x = \frac{1}{2}(e^x+e^{-x}) = 1+\frac{x^2}{2!}+\frac{x^4}{4!}+\cdots$$

$$\tanh x = x-\frac{1}{3}x^3+\frac{2}{15}x^5-\cdots$$

$$\operatorname{cosech} x = \frac{1}{x}\left(1-\frac{1}{6}x^2+\frac{7}{360}x^4-\cdots\right)$$

$$\operatorname{sech} x = 1-\frac{1}{2}x^2+\frac{5}{24}x^4-\cdots$$

$$\coth x = \frac{1}{x}\left(1+\frac{1}{3}x^2-\frac{1}{45}x^4+\cdots\right)$$

From the last approximation, Langevin's function for small values of x is

$$L(x) = \coth x - \frac{1}{x} = \frac{1}{3}x-\frac{1}{45}x^3+\cdots$$

502

APPENDIX 5

The expansion of the equations of Mie and Morse

We have the following form of the intermolecular energy equation:

$$\phi = \phi_e \frac{1}{(m-n)}\left[m\left(\frac{a_e}{a}\right)^n - n\left(\frac{a_e}{a}\right)^m\right] \qquad \text{VII.10}$$

The energy required to dissociate the stable pair is clearly

$$D_e = \phi_{a=\infty} - \phi_{a=a_e} = -\phi_e$$

and the excess energy at a separation a over that at the separation a_e, is consequently

$$w = \phi - \phi_e = \frac{D_e}{(n-m)}\left\{n\left[1-\left(\frac{a_e}{a}\right)^m\right] - m\left[1-\left(\frac{a_e}{a}\right)^n\right]\right\}$$

In order to see how this displacement energy, w, varies as the molecules are displaced slightly from their equilibrium position, let us substitute

$$x = \frac{a-a_e}{a_e}$$

so that

$$\frac{a_e}{a} = \frac{1}{1+x}$$

and

$$w = \frac{D_e}{n-m}\{n[1-(1+x)^{-m}] - m[1-(1+x)^{-n}]\}$$

On expanding the terms in the small brackets by means of the binomial theorem (Appendix 4), and ignoring powers of x greater than the second, we obtain the expression

$$w = \frac{1}{2}mnD_e x^2 = \frac{1}{2}\frac{mnD_e}{a_e^2}(a-a_e)^2$$

so that the displacement energy is proportional to the square of the displacement. The motion is thus a simple harmonic one, with frequency

$$v_e = \frac{1}{2\pi a_e}\sqrt{\left(\frac{mnD_e}{\mu}\right)} \qquad \text{VII.11}$$

The interatomic energy equation of Morse,

$$w = D_e[1-e^{-\kappa(a-a_e)}]^2 \qquad \text{IV.46}$$

503

gives, on expansion to the second term,

$$w = D_e \kappa^2 (a - a_e)^2 \qquad \text{IV.47}$$

If both equations were applicable to the same system, we would have

$$\kappa = \frac{1}{a_e} \sqrt{\left(\frac{mn}{2}\right)}$$

APPENDIX 6

Numerical values of important physicochemical constants

Property	Symbol	Magnitude
Velocity of light *in vacuo*	c	$2{\cdot}9979 \times 10^{10}$ cm sec^{-1}
Faraday constant	$\mathfrak{F}$	$9{\cdot}6493 \times 10^4$ coulombs/g-eq.
Electronic charge	ε	$4{\cdot}802 \times 10^{-10}$ e.s.u.
Avogadro number	N_0	$6{\cdot}024 \times 10^{23}$ molecules per mole
Gas constant	R	$8{\cdot}3144 \times 10^7$ ergs/deg-mole
Gas constant	R	$1{\cdot}9872$ cal/deg-mole
Gas constant	R	$0{\cdot}082054$ litre-atm/deg-mole
Boltzmann constant	k	$1{\cdot}3803 \times 10^{-16}$ erg/deg-molecule
Absolute temperature	T	$273{\cdot}16 + t°$(centigrade)
Gravitational constant	g	$980{\cdot}665$ cm/sec^2
Joule's constant	J	$4{\cdot}1840 \times 10^7$ ergs/defined cal.
Standard molar volume of gas	V^0	$2{\cdot}2415 \times 10^4$ cm^3/mole
Planck's constant	h	$6{\cdot}624 \times 10^{-27}$ erg-sec
Rest mass of proton	m_H	$1{\cdot}673 \times 10^{-24}$ g.
Rest mass of electron	m_e	$9{\cdot}109 \times 10^{-28}$ g.
Ratio of rest masses of proton and electron	m_H/m_e	$1{\cdot}837 \times 10^3$
Standard atmospheric pressure	P^0	$1{\cdot}0132 \times 10^6$ dynes/cm^2.

Conversion factors

1 volt-electron $\equiv 1{\cdot}6018 \times 10^{-12}$ ergs/molecule $\equiv 2{\cdot}3062 \times 10^4$ calories/mole. $h\omega c$ per molecule (ω in cm^{-1}) $\equiv 2{\cdot}8591\,\omega$ calories/mole.

Name index

R

505

Subject index